LECTURES ON THE THEORY OF FUNCTIONS OF A COMPLEX VARIABLE

GIOVANNI SANSONE - JOHAN GERRETSEN

LECTURES ON THE THEORY OF FUNCTIONS OF A COMPLEX VARIABLE

I. HOLOMORPHIC FUNCTIONS

1960

P. NOORDHOFF - GRONINGEN

PRINTED IN THE NETHERLANDS

PREFACE

Fourteen years ago the first undersigned published in the Italian language two volumes on the theory of the functions of a complex variable designed to provide a convenient account of various branches of this part of analysis. The gratifying reception of this work made a third edition necessary.

The second and younger undersigned thought it desirable to make this work accessible to English readers. A mere translation seemed inattractive. Consequently, he preferred preparing a new text based on the Italian edition. This afforded an opportunity to add some novelties to the proofs and to rearrange the material.

The idea underlying the work is the desire to present in a somewhat novel form matter of permanent value to the mathematical science. The greatest difficulty encountered in preparing a book of this kind is in the matter of selection of material and method. It is beyond dispute that much valuable material had to be excluded. The authors have endeavoured to present those parts of the theory which find their roots in the classical treatises and may be considered as indispensable to all who wish to penetrate into more special subjects. As regards the method it should be observed that a rigorous axiomatic foundation has not been attempted. More than once a call has been made on intuition in order to save space and to make the book accessible to the wide class of readers who are more interested in techniques than in logical foundations. The reader who is desirous to become acquainted with a systematic rigorous development may consult the book by W. J. Thron, *Introduction to the theory of functions of a complex variable.*

The work is rather self-contained, but a knowledge of elementary analysis is tacitly assumed.

This first volume is devoted to the study of holomorphic functions, i.e., functions which are differentiable at every point of an open set in the complex plane. These functions are often called analytic, but the authors prefer to use this name for functions obtained from holomorphic functions by analytic continuation and in general many valued. They will be considered in detail in a second volume in connection with the geometric aspect of the theory of functions. Most of the topics dealt with in this volume have little bearing on geometric considerations and, therefore, no attention has been given to conformal mapping.

The first chapter contains material of a preliminary and introductory character; it serves to recapitulate some fundamental notions and theorems which are of use to the material treated in the subsequent chapters.

The second chapter should be considered as the actual starting point. It deals for the greater part with Cauchy's famous integral theorem and a number of its corollaries. The proof of this theorem is based on Artin's Notre Dame Lectures while use has been made of the elementary topological notion of winding number. Thus the theorem appears in a rather general form which is very well suited to many applications. It has not been attempted to present it in its strongest known form. In fact, the assumptions underlying the statement and the proof can be weakened in various ways, but only in exceptional cases a form of the theorem is needed which is stronger than the one presented in this chapter. For the same reason also Jordan's curve theorem has not been proved, for in the applications only direct evident situations occur.

The development of the theory of singular points in the third chapter has also been inspired by Artin's lectures. This theory has attained a certain standard of clarity and elegance by avoiding the use of Laurent series. The main part of this chapter has been devoted to the theorem of residues and its many applications.

In the fourth chapter the classical theorems of Weierstrass and Mittag-Leffler come in for discussion. In this frame the gamma function finds its proper place. It may be that Mittag-Leffler's theorem in its special and general form is only of transitory importance, but it has marked the time in the development of modern analysis and it is well worth knowing.

This chapter also paves the way for one of the most famous classical applications of the general theory, viz. the elliptic functions dealt with in the fifth chapter. The group-theoretic aspect of this theory must be deferred to the second volume where it shows to full advantage in general considerations of geometric character.

The sixth chapter is devoted to another application of the general theory. It contains an introductory account of the important and extensive field of the integral functions, centering around the classical results of Borel and Poincaré.

In the seventh chapter a rather advanced subject has been introduced, viz. the Dirichlet series and the Laplace integral. A great amount of attention has been given to the Riemann zeta function and the prime number theorem. It is true that we are now in possession of an "elementary" proof of this famous theorem, but it is also true that the wonderful classical proof based on transcendental methods still deserves to be honoured.

The eighth chapter is concerned with the summability of power series outside the circle of convergence according to the method of Borel and its generalization by Mittag-Leffler. Further the Euler-Maclaurin sum formula has been brought forward and it concludes with an introduction to the theory of asymptotic expansions.

No attempt has been made at adding a bibliography. The reason is that this book is not intended as a monograph, but it ought to be considered a text-book for those who are interested in various advanced methods in analysis. An appalling number of books and articles dealing with the theory of functions of a complex variable is published every year and it did not seem to be in keeping with the purpose of this book to inform the reader of existing literature. Every mathematical library even of a modest size contains the more important text-books and the reader desirous to be acquainted with original papers should consult the "Mathematical Reviews" or the "Zentralblatt für Mathematik". Many papers and books of historical interest are referred to in the "Jahrbuch über die Fortschritte der Mathematik" and the German and French mathematical encyclopedias.

Neither have the authors attempted to determine where credit for any particular theorem or proof is due. They humbly confess that they owe almost all material to the study of many works whose object is more or less similar to this book. It was, however, their ambition to present some masterpieces of mathematical thinking and to make these accessible to a rather wide circle of interested readers in not too pedantic a way.

Florence (Italy) G. Sansone

Groningen (The Netherlands) J. Gerretsen

CONTENTS

CHAPTER 1. HOLOMORPHIC FUNCTIONS. POWER SERIES AS HOLOMORPHIC FUNCTIONS. ELEMENTARY FUNCTIONS.

1.1 The complex plane 1
1.2 Continuous functions 6
1.3 Holomorphic functions 10
1.4 Conjugate functions 12
1.5 Sequences of functions 14
1.6 Power series 17
1.7 The power series as a holomorphic function 23
1.8 The theorems of Picard and Abel 24
1.9 The A-summability of a series. Tauber's theorem 27
1.10 The exponential, circular and hyperbolic functions 29
1.11 The logarithm and the power 34
1.12 The inverse circular and hyperbolic functions 37

CHAPTER 2. CAUCHY'S INTEGRAL THEOREM AND ITS COROLLARIES. EXPANSION IN TAYLOR SERIES.

2.1 Chains and cycles 41
2.2 The connectivity of a region 44
2.3 The line integral of a complex function 45
2.4 Properties of the line integrals of complex functions 52
2.5 Cauchy's integral theorem 56
2.6 The fundamental theorem of algebra 62
2.7 Cauchy's integral formula 63
2.8 Formula for the derivative. Riemann's theorem 64
2.9 Differentiation inside the sign of integration 66
2.10 Morera's theorem 68
2.11 Zeros of a holomorphic function 69
2.12 The Cauchy-Liouville theorem 72
2.13 The maximum modulus theorem 73
2.14 Real parts of holomorphic functions 76
2.15 Representation of a holomorphic function by its real part . 77
2.16 The Taylor expansion 80
2.17 Some remarkable power series expansions 84
2.18 Cauchy's inequality. Parseval's identity 89
2.19 An extension of the Cauchy-Liouville theorem 91
2.20 Weierstrass's theorems about the limits of sequences of functions 93
2.21 Schwarz's lemma 98
2.22 Vitali's theorem 100
2.23 Laurent's expansion. The Fourier series 104

CHAPTER 3. REGULAR AND SINGULAR POINTS-RESIDUES-ZEROS.

3.1 Regular points 112
3.2 Isolated singularities 113
3.3 Residues 116
3.4 Rational functions 119
3.5 The theorem of residues 121
3.6 Evaluation of some integrals by means of the theorem of residues 122
3.7 Evaluation of the sum of certain series 139
3.8 The logarithmic derivative 145
3.9 Jensen's theorem. The Poisson-Jensen formula 151
3.10 Rouché's theorem 154
3.11 A theorem of Hurwitz 156
3.12 The mapping of a region 158
3.13 Generalization of Taylor's and Laurent's series 162
3.14 Legendre's polynomials 169

CHAPTER 4. WEIERSTRASS'S FACTORIZATION OF INTEGRAL FUNCTIONS. CAUCHY'S EXPANSION IN PARTIAL FRACTIONS. MITTAG-LEFFLER'S PROBLEM.

4.1 Infinite products 175
4.2 The factorization of integral functions 180
4.3 Primary factors of Weierstrass 181
4.4 Expansion of an integral function in an infinite product . . 183
4.5 Canonical products 185
4.6 The gamma function 188
4.7 The Eulerian integrals 195
4.8 The Gaussian psi function 204
4.9 Binet's function 211
4.10 Cauchy's method for the decomposition of meromorphic functions into partial fractions 217
4.11 Mittag-Leffler's theorem 221
4.12 The Weierstrass factorization of an integral function deduced from Mittag-Leffler's theorem 229
4.13 The general Mittag-Leffler problem 231

CHAPTER 5. ELLIPTIC FUNCTIONS.

5.1 Periodic functions 235
5.2 Elliptic functions 239
5.3 The pe function of Weierstrass 242
5.4 The differential equation of the pe function 246
5.5 Addition theorems 249
5.6 The sigma functions of Weierstrass 252
5.7 The bisection formula of the pe function 257
5.8 The theta functions of Jacobi 260
5.9 The expression for the theta functions as infinite products . 265
5.10 Jacobi's imaginary transformation 269
5.11 The logarithmic derivative of the theta functions 272
5.12 The pe function with real invariants 276

5.13 The periods represented as integrals 281
5.14 The Jacobian elliptic functions 286
5.15 Fourier expansions of the Jacobian functions 292
5.16 Addition theorems 296
5.17 Legendre's elliptic integral of the second kind 303

CHAPTER 6. INTEGRAL FUNCTIONS OF FINITE ORDER.

6.1 The genus of an integral function 308
6.2 The theorems of Laguerre 313
6.3 Poincaré's theorems 316
6.4 The order of an integral function 318
6.5 Integral functions with a finite number of zeros 323
6.6 The order of a function related to the coefficients of its Taylor expansion 324
6.7 Hadamard's first theorem 328
6.8 Hadamard's second theorem 330
6.9 Hadamard's factorization theorem 333
6.10 The Borel-Caratheodory theorem 335
6.11 Picard's theorem for integral functions of finite order 339
6.12 The theorem of Phragmén 342
6.13 Mittag-Leffler's function 345

CHAPTER 7. DIRICHLET SERIES. THE ZETA FUNCTION OF RIEMANN, THE LAPLACE INTEGRAL.

7.1 Dirichlet's series. Absolute convergence 350
7.2 Simple convergence 353
7.3 Formulas for the abscissa of convergence 356
7.4 The representation of a Dirichlet series by an infinite integral 360
7.5 The functional equation of the zeta function 364
7.6 Euler's infinite product 368
7.7 Some properties of the zeta function 370
7.8 The existence of zeros in the critical strip 374
7.9 The generalized zeta function 376
7.10 The representation of the generalized zeta function by a loop integral 380
7.11 Perron's formula 382
7.12 A formula of Hadamard 386
7.13 Representation of the sum of a Dirichlet series as a Laplace integral 387
7.14 The Laplace integral 390
7.15 Abscissa of convergence 393
7.16 Regularity 394
7.17 Some remarkable integrals of the Laplace type 396
7.18 The prime number theorem 399
7.19 The incomplete gamma functions 406
7.20 Representability of a function as a Laplace integral 412

CHAPTER 8. SUMMABILITY OF POWER SERIES OUTSIDE THE CIRCLE OF CONVERGENCE. SUM FORMULAS. ASYMPTOTIC SERIES.

8.1 The principal star of a function 419
8.2 Existence of barrier-points 421
8.3 The Borel summability of a power series 425
8.4 The Mittag-Leffler summability of a power series 431
8.5 Plana's sum formula 438
8.6 The Euler-Maclaurin sum formula 443
8.7 Stirling's series 447
8.8 The Bernoullian polynomials 449
8.9 The associate periodic functions 451
8.10 Asymptotic expansions 454
8.11 Asymptotic expansion of Laplace integrals 458
8.12 Illustrative examples 462
8.13 Rotation of the path of integration 469
8.14 The method of steepest descents 477

INDEX 483

CHAPTER 1

HOLOMORPHIC FUNCTIONS
POWER SERIES AS HOLOMORPHIC FUNCTIONS
ELEMENTARY FUNCTIONS

1.1 – The complex plane

1.1.1 – MODULUS AND ARGUMENT OF A COMPLEX NUMBER

A complex number z may be written in *algebraic form*

$$\boxed{z = x + iy,} \tag{1.1–1}$$

where x and y are real numbers and i denotes the imaginary unit, ($i^2 = -1$). Its geometrical representation in the *complex plane* is obtained by considering the point M, having rectangular coordinates x and y, (fig. 1.1–1). The correspondence between the complex numbers and the points of the complex plane is obviously one-to-one and we shall often indicate a point of the complex plane by the complex number which it represents.

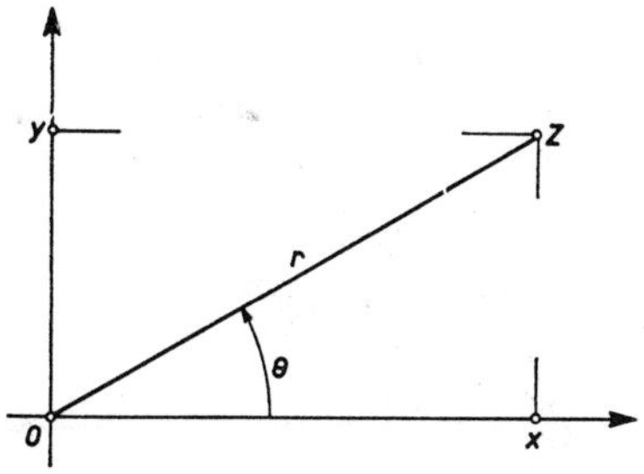

Fig. 1.1–1. Representation of a complex number

Introducing a system of polar coordinates (r, θ) whose pole is the origin of the rectangular system of axes and whose polar axis coincides with the positive x-axis, we may write

$$x = r \cos \theta, \qquad y = r \sin \theta \tag{1.1–2}$$

and the complex number appears in the so-called *polar form*

$$\boxed{z = r(\cos \theta + i \sin \theta),} \tag{1.1–3}$$

where

$$r = \sqrt{x^2 + y^2} \tag{1.1–4}$$

and, if $r \neq 0$,

$$\cos\theta = \frac{x}{r}, \qquad \sin\theta = \frac{y}{r}. \tag{1.1–5}$$

The non-negative number r is called the *modulus* $|z|$ of the complex number z and θ its *argument*, written Arg z. The square $|z|^2$ of the modulus of z is $x^2+y^2 = (x+iy)(x-iy) = z\bar{z}$, where $\bar{z} = x-iy$ denotes the *conjugate complex* value of z. The argument is determined up to a multiple of 2π, provided $z \neq 0$; the value of the argument which satisfies

$$-\pi < \theta \leqq \pi \tag{1.1–6}$$

is termed the *principal argument* arg z. The argument of the number zero cannot be defined unambiguously.–

Consider two complex numbers $z_1 = r_1(\cos\theta_1 + i\sin\theta_1)$ and $z_2 = r_2(\cos\theta_2 + i\sin\theta_2)$. Their product can be written in the form $r_1r_2\{\cos\theta_1\cos\theta_2 - \sin\theta_1\sin\theta_2)+i(\sin\theta_1\cos\theta_2 + \cos\theta_1\sin\theta_2)\}$ and by means of the well-known addition theorems of elementary trigonometry we can express the product z_1z_2 in the form $r_1r_2\{\cos(\theta_1+\theta_2)+ + i\sin(\theta_1+\theta_2)\}$, (fig. 1.1–2).

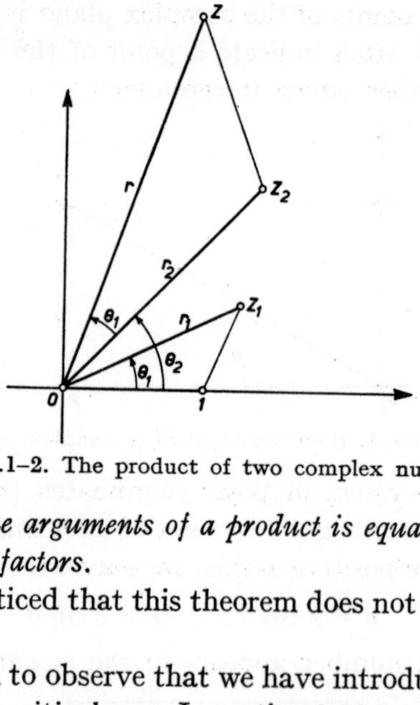

Fig. 1.1–2. The product of two complex numbers

Hence *one of the arguments of a product is equal to the sum of the arguments of the factors.*

It should be noticed that this theorem does not hold for principal arguments.–

Finally we wish to observe that we have introduced the notion of argument in an uncritical way. In section 1.10.7 we shall give a more satisfactory definition from the viewpoint of rigorous analysis.

1.1.2 – Fundamental properties of the moduli of complex numbers

We wish to mention the *triangle inequality*

$$\boxed{|a+b| \leqq |a|+|b|} \qquad (1.1\text{–}7)$$

which is of frequent use. This inequality is geometrically evident, (fig. 1.1–3). A formal proof runs as follows. First we observe that

$$\boxed{|ab| = |a||b|.} \qquad (1.1\text{–}8)$$

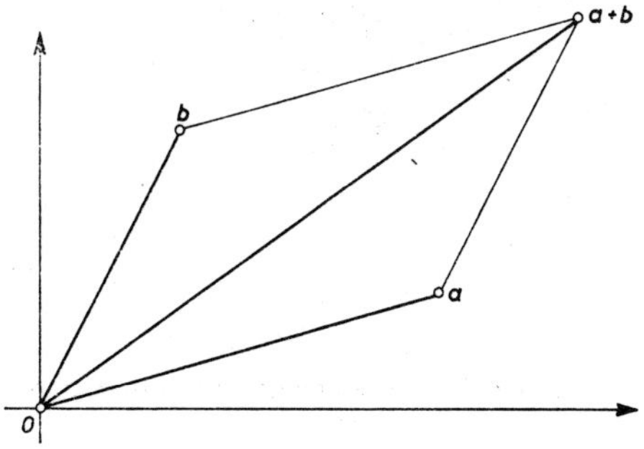

Fig. 1.1–3. The triangle inequality

This can be proved by writing the numbers in their polar form, but is also clear from $|ab|^2 = ab\overline{ab} = ab\bar{a}\bar{b} = a\bar{a}b\bar{b} = |a|^2|b|^2$.–

Now $|a+b|^2 = (a+b)(\bar{a}+\bar{b}) = a\bar{a}+b\bar{b}+(\bar{a}b+a\bar{b}) \leqq |a|^2+|b|^2+ +2|a||b| = (|a|+|b|)^2$, since $\bar{a}b+a\bar{b}$ is the real part of $2\bar{a}b$ and does not exceed $2|\bar{a}b| = 2|\bar{a}||b| = 2|a||b|$.

An easy consequence of (1.1–7) is

$$\boxed{|a-b| \geqq ||a|-|b||.} \qquad (1.1\text{–}9)$$

In fact, $|a| = |(a-b)+b| \leqq |a-b|+|b|$ and similarly $|b| \leqq |b-a|+|a| = |a-b|+|a|$.–

1.1.3 - Stereographic projection

In contradistinction to the conventions of projective geometry we shall extend the complex plane by only one ideal point at infinity which we shall denote by $z = \infty$, i.e., we shall consider the *extended* complex plane as a closed surface having a single point at infinity. This convention may be justified by considering a *stereographic projection* of the points of the complex plane upon a unit sphere whose centre is in the plane from the south pole of this sphere, the *complex sphere.*

We wish to give explicitely the formulas which link the coordinates x, y of a point M of the complex plane and the rectangular coordinates ξ, η, ζ of the image M' on the sphere, when the origin of these latter coordinates is the centre of the sphere, the axes ξ, η

coinciding respectively with the axes x, y in the plane. (fig. 1.1–4).

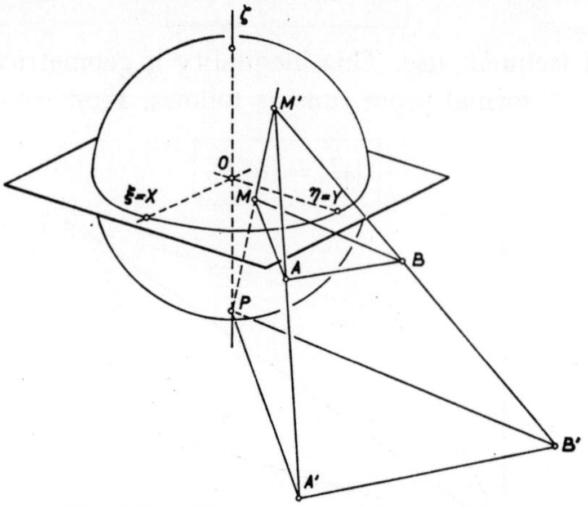

Fig. 1.1–4. The stereographic projection

Since the points M, M' and the pole $P(0, 0, -1)$ are collinear we must have

$$\frac{x}{\xi} = \frac{y}{\eta} = \frac{1}{1+\zeta}, \tag{1.1–10}$$

whence

$$x = \frac{\xi}{1+\zeta}, \quad y = \frac{\eta}{1+\zeta}, \tag{1.1–11}$$

and these equations express the coordinates x, y of the point M in terms of the coordinates ξ, η, ζ of the point M'. The value of the complex variable z at the point (ξ, η, ζ) is therefore given by

$$\boxed{z = \frac{\xi+i\eta}{1+\zeta}.} \tag{1.1–12}$$

The pole P $(\zeta = -1)$, where the images of all points at infinity of the plane $\zeta = 0$ are collected, corresponds to the value $z = \infty$, i.e., we identify all these infinite points.

Conversely, if the coordinates x and y of M are given we may evaluate the coordinates ξ, η, ζ of M', observing that

$$\xi^2+\eta^2+\zeta^2 = 1. \tag{1.1–13}$$

Hence, in view of (1.1–12),

$$(1+\zeta)(z+\bar{z}) = 2\xi, \qquad (1+\zeta)(z-\bar{z}) = 2i\eta$$

and, taking account of (1.1–13),

$$1+z\bar{z} = 1+\frac{\xi^2+\eta^2}{(1+\zeta)^2} = \frac{2}{1+\zeta},$$

whence

$$\boxed{\xi = \frac{z+\bar{z}}{1+z\bar{z}},\quad \eta = \frac{1}{i}\frac{z-\bar{z}}{1+z\bar{z}},\quad \zeta = \frac{1-z\bar{z}}{1+z\bar{z}}.} \tag{1.1–14}$$

This formula and (1.1–12) are the required formulas.

1.1.4 – Fundamental properties of the stereographic projection

By simple geometric arguments we may establish the following fundamental properties of the stereographic projection:

(i) *It preserves the angles,* that is, the angle between two curves on the sphere at a common point M' is equal to the angle between the corresponding curves at M. We express this by saying that the stereographic projection realises a *conformal mapping* of the sphere upon the plane. – The proof runs as follows, (fig. 1.1–4): Let the tangents at M' to the curves through this point cut the tangent plane to the sphere at P in A' and B'. Since the segments $A'M'$ and $A'P$ are equal as well as the segments $B'M'$ and $B'P$, the triangles $A'M'B'$ and $A'PB'$ are congruent. If, moreover, A, B denote the intersections of the considered tangents at M' with the plane $\zeta = 0$ (the complex plane), the triangles AMB and $A'M'B'$ are similar. The conclusion now follows at once.–

(ii) *To a circle or a straight line in the plane corresponds a circle on the sphere,* and conversely. – It is obvious that to a straight line in the plane corresponds a circle on the sphere through the pole P and conversely. Let us consider the case of a circle in the plane. If M is a point on this circle and M' the corresponding point on the sphere, there exists a second sphere through M' and this circle. Let N be another point on this circle and N' its image on the sphere. Then $PM \cdot PM' = PN \cdot PN' = 2$, but this means that N' is also a point of the intersection which is a circle. The converse may be proved in the same way.–

1.1.5 – The chordal distance

The euclidean distance of two points $z = a$ and $z = b$ in the complex plane is expressed by $|a-b|$. In this metric the ideal point $z = \infty$ plays an exceptional role. It is, however, possible to introduce a metric avoiding this trouble.

Let A and B denote the points in the z-plane characterized by

$z = a$, $z = b$ respectively, A' and B' being the corresponding points on the sphere, (fig. 1.1–5). The length of the segment $A'B'$ is called

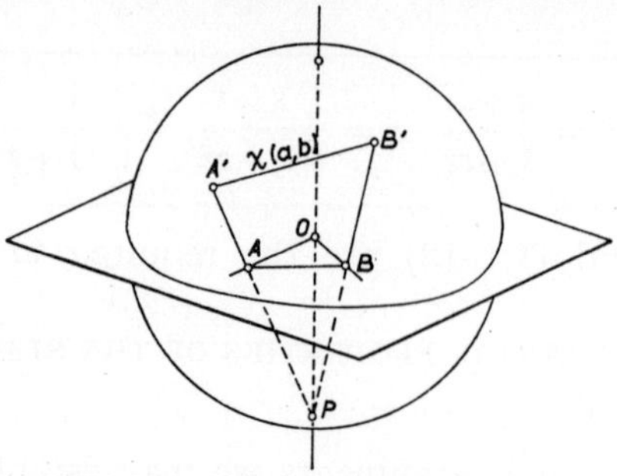

Fig. 1.1–5. The chordal distance

the *chordal distance* $\chi(a, b)$ of the points $z = a$ and $z = b$. Since $PA \cdot PA' = PB \cdot PB' = 2$ the triangles PAB and $PB'A'$ are similar. Hence

$$A'B' : AB = PA' : PB = PA \cdot PA' : PA \cdot PB = 2 : PA \cdot PB.$$

By the Pythagorean theorem we have $PA = \sqrt{1+a\bar{a}}$, $PB = \sqrt{1+b\bar{b}}$ and so

$$\boxed{\chi(a, b) = \frac{2|a-b|}{\sqrt{1+a\bar{a}}\sqrt{1+b\bar{b}}}.} \tag{1.1–15}$$

In particular

$$\chi(a, \infty) = \frac{2}{\sqrt{1+a\bar{a}}}.$$

It is easy to show that the chordal distance satisfies the following conditions:

(i) $\chi(a, b) = \chi(b, a)$.

(ii) $\chi(a, b) = 0$ if and only if $a = b$.

(iii) $\chi(a, b) + \chi(b, c) \geqq \chi(a, c)$.

(iv) $\chi(a, b) \leqq 2$.

In most cases we shall only deal with finite points. Then we can confine ourselves to the ordinary euclidean distance.

1.2 – **Continuous functions**

1.2.1 – Definitions

Let $\mathfrak{S}$ be a set of points in the extended complex plane which we shall individualize by means of the complex variable z. A *neighbourhood* of a point $z = z_0 \neq \infty$ in the complex plane consists of all points z such that $|z-z_0| < \delta$ where δ is a positive number. A neighbourhood of $z = \infty$ consists of all points z such that $|z| > \delta$. Applying the notion of chordal distance we may say that a neighbourhood of a point z_0 is the set of all points which satisfy $\chi(z, z_0) < \delta$. The case $z_0 = \infty$ need not be excluded.

A point z_0 is said to be an *accumulation point* of the set $\mathfrak{S}$ if every neighbourhood of z_0 contains a point of $\mathfrak{S}$ distinct from z_0. An accumulation point may or may not belong to $\mathfrak{S}$. If every accumulation point of a set $\mathfrak{S}$ belongs to the set we shall say that $\mathfrak{S}$ is *closed*.

Let $f(z)$ denote a complex function of z defined throughout $\mathfrak{S}$, that is, there is a rule f by means of which a complex number $f(z)$ is made to correspond to every point z of $\mathfrak{S}$. We agree that $f(\infty)$ means the same value as that of $f(1/z)$ for $z = 0$. We shall say that *the limit of $f(z)$, as z tends to an accumulation point z_0 of $\mathfrak{S}$, exists and is equal to the complex number a if, when any positive number ε is assigned, we can find a neighbourhood of z_0 such that for all points of $\mathfrak{S}$ belonging to the neighbourhood the inequality $|f(z)-a| < \varepsilon$ holds;* we shall write

$$\lim_{z \to z_0} f(z) = a. \tag{1.2–1}$$

Similarly we shall say that *the limit of $f(z)$ exists, as z tends to z_0 and is infinite if, when any positive number K is assigned, we can find a neighbourhood of z_0 such that for all points of $\mathfrak{S}$ belonging to the neighbourhood the inequality $|f(z)| > K$ holds;* we shall write

$$\lim_{z \to z_0} f(z) = \infty. \tag{1.2–2}$$

The function $f(z)$ is said to be *continuous* at $z = z_0$ when z_0 is an accumulation point of $\mathfrak{S}$ belonging to $\mathfrak{S}$ and, moreover, $f(z_0) = \lim_{z \to z_0} f(z)$. An alternative phrasing is: when any positive number ε is assigned we can find a neighbourhood of z_0 such that for all points of $\mathfrak{S}$ belonging to the neighbourhood the inequality $|f(z)-f(z_0)| < \varepsilon$ is valid. In particular, a function $f(z)$ is continuous at $z = \infty$ when $f(1/z)$ is continuous at $z = 0$.

In our definition it is tacitly assumed that $f(z_0)$ is a finite number. Sometimes, however, it is desirable to admit infinite values of $f(z)$. The exceptional role of the infinite value can be eliminated by introducing the notion of chordal continuity.

The function $f(z)$ is said to be *chordally continuous* at $z = z_0$ if to a given number $\varepsilon > 0$ corresponds a number $\delta > 0$ such that

$$\chi\{f(z), f(z_0)\} < \varepsilon$$

for all values of z belonging to $\mathfrak{S}$ and satisfying

$$\chi(z, z_0) < \delta.$$

It is easy to see that a function which is continuous at a given point is also chordally continuous there. But the converse is not always true. Thus, for instance, the function $1/z$ is chordally continuous at $z = 0$, but not continuous in the ordinary sense.

A function will be considered continuous at an *isolated* point of the set, that is a point of the set which is not an accumulation point. A function is said to be *continuous throughout a set* if it is continuous at every point of the set.

1.2.2 – Continuity of the principal argument

An illustrative example of a continuous function is provided by the principal argument of the variable z. This function turns out to be continuous at every (finite) point of the z-plane, except at the origin and at the points corresponding to negative real values of z. When we delete these points from the complex plane we shall say that we have cut the plane along the negative real axis. The remaining points are evidently characterized by

$$z+|z| \neq 0. \tag{1.2–3}$$

In fact, $z+|z| = 0$ means $x+iy+|z| = 0$, hence $y = 0$ and $x = -|z| \leqq 0$.

The set of all points satisfying (1.2–3) will be called the *principal region*, (fig. 1.2–1). Now we shall prove:

The principal argument of the variable z is continuous throughout the principal region.

First we take $z_0 = 1$. Let z be any point within a circle of radius

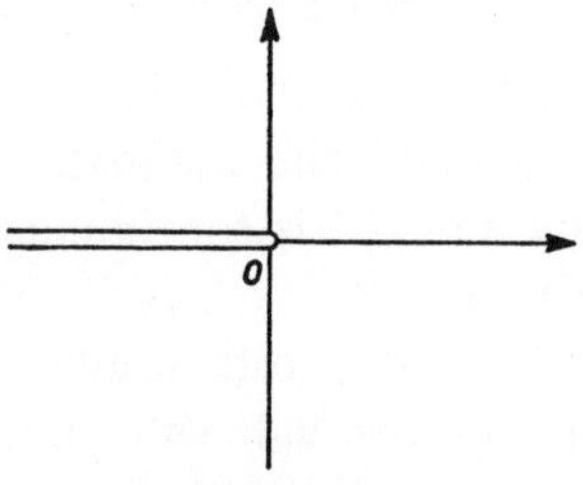

Fig. 1.2–1.
The principal region $z+|z| \neq 0$.

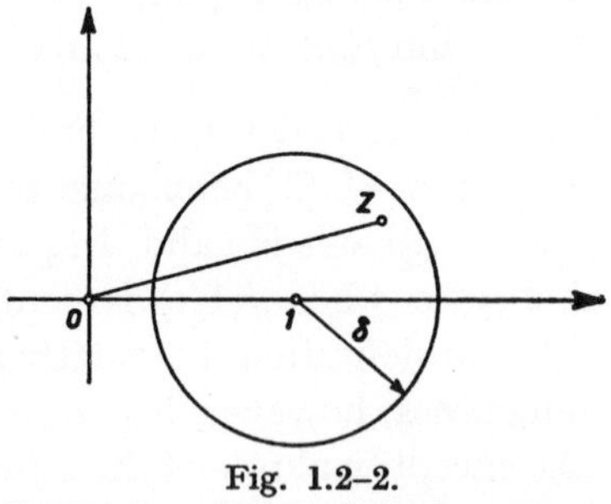

Fig. 1.2–2.
Continuity of the principal argument

$\delta < 1$ around $z = 1$, (fig. 1.2–2). If $\theta = \arg z$, then $r \cos \theta = x > 1-\delta > 0$. Hence $|\theta| < \frac{1}{2}\pi$. Moreover, $|y| < \delta$. Let ε be a given positive number. Now

$$|\arg z-0| = |\theta| \leqq \tan |\theta| = \frac{|y|}{x} < \frac{\delta}{1-\delta} < \varepsilon,$$

whenever $\delta < \varepsilon/(1+\varepsilon)$. Thus we see that $\arg z$ is continuous at $z = 1$.

Next consider an arbitrary point z_0 in the principal region. If δ is sufficiently small we have, on account of the result already obtained, that $|\arg z/z_0| < \pi - |\arg z_0|$, whenever $|z-z_0| < \delta$. Since $\arg z_0 + \arg z/z_0$ is one of the arguments of z and is numerically less than π, we have $\arg z = \arg z_0 + \arg z/z_0$, and letting $z \to z_0$ we find the desired result $\arg z \to \arg z_0$. It is plain that $\arg z$ cannot be continuous at a point of the negative real axis, for in a sufficiently small neighbourhood of such a point we have values of z whose arguments differ as little from π as desired, but also values of z whose arguments are nearly $-\pi$.–

1.2.3 – Uniform continuity

A set is said to be *bounded* if there exists a positive number k with the property that the inequality $|z| \leqq k$ is satisfied by each point of the set. Bolzano's theorem states that *a bounded set consisting of infinitely many points has at least one accumulation point.* We omit the proof.

The following theorem due to Cantor is of fundamental importance. *A function continuous in a closed and bounded set $\mathfrak{C}$ is uniformly continuous throughout the set.* In other words: if ε denotes a preassigned positive number we can find a number δ such that $|f(z)-f(z')| < \varepsilon$ provided $|z-z'| < \delta$ and z, z' in the set.

1.2.4 – Definitions. Statement of the Heine-Borel theorem

A point z_0 of a set $\mathfrak{S}$ is said to be an *interior point* of the set if there exists a neighbourhood of the point consisting entirely of points of $\mathfrak{S}$. An accumulation point which is not an interior point is called a *boundary point* of the set. A set all of whose points are interior points is called an *open* set. The *closure* $\overline{\mathfrak{S}}$ of a set $\mathfrak{S}$ is obtained by adding to it all its accumulation points. The closure of a set is closed.

Occasionally we shall use the following *Heine-Borel covering theorem:*

From a system of open sets whose sum contains a bounded and closed set $\mathfrak{C}$ we can select a finite system of open sets whose sum contains $\mathfrak{C}$.

A set is said to be *connected* if every pair of points can be joined by a polygonal arc which consists entirely of points of the set. An open and connected set is called a *region.*

1.2.5 – Statement of Jordan's theorem

The set of points

$$z = z(t) = x(t) + iy(t), \tag{1.2–5}$$

where $x(t)$, $y(t)$ are real continuous functions of the real variable t defined in the closed interval $0 \leqq t \leqq 1$ is called a *continuous curve.* A point z_0 is said to be a *multiple point* of the curve if the equation $z_0 = x(t)+iy(t)$ is satisfied by more than one value of t in the given interval. A *Jordan curve* is a continuous curve without multiple points. A *simple closed Jordan curve* or a *contour* is a continuous curve which has but one multiple point corresponding to the terminal values 0 and 1 of t.

A famous theorem of Jordan states: *a contour decomposes the plane into two separated regions, having the contour as a common boundary.* Every polygonial arc whose extremities belong to different regions necessarily meets the boundary. One of these regions is bounded and called the *interior* region, or the region *inside* the curve; the other is unbounded and is called the *exterior* region, or the region *outside* the curve. We take these intuitively rather obvious results for granted, for the proof is highly intricate. In the applications only those Jordan curves occur for which the statement is highly evident.

If t varies increasing from 0 to 1 the point moves along the contour in a certain sense; it moves in the opposite sense if t varies decreasing from 1 to 0. When the point moves in the counter-clockwise sense the internal region remains on the left, (fig. 1.2–3).

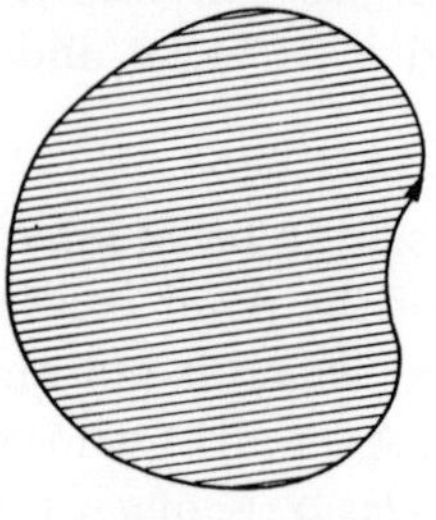

Fig. 1.2–3. Region inside a contour

1.3 – Holomorphic functions

1.3.1 – Necessary conditions for differentiability

Let the function $f(z)$ be defined in a set $\mathfrak{S}$ and let $z_0 \neq \infty$ be an interior point of $\mathfrak{S}$. If the modulus of h is sufficiently small, then z_0+h belongs to $\mathfrak{S}$. We shall say that the function $f(z)$ possesses a *derivative* at $z = z_0$, or that $f(z)$ is *differentiable* at $z = z_0$, if

$$\lim_{h\to 0} \frac{f(z_0+h)-f(z_0)}{h} \tag{1.3–1}$$

exists and has a finite value $f'(z_0)$. It is assumed that $f(z_0) \neq \infty$. Let us separate the real part from the imaginary by putting

$$z = x+iy, \qquad f(z) = u(x, y)+iv(x, y), \tag{1.3–2}$$

where $u(x, y)$ and $v(x, y)$ are real functions of the rectangular co-ordinates x, y of the point (x, y) which varies throughout the set $\mathfrak{S}$. If we put $z_0 = x_0+iy_0$ and consider only real increments $h = \Delta x$ then (1.3–1) becomes

$$\lim_{\Delta x\to 0} \left\{ \frac{u(x_0+\Delta x, y_0)-u(x_0, y_0)}{\Delta x} + i\,\frac{v(x_0+\Delta x, y_0)-v(x_0, y_0)}{\Delta y} \right\} \tag{1.3–3}$$

and it is easy to prove that $u(x, y)$, $v(x, y)$ possess partial derivatives with respect to x at the point (x_0, y_0). We obviously have

$$u_x(x_0, y_0)+iv_x(x_0, y_0) = f'(z_0). \tag{1.3–4}$$

Again, by considering purely imaginary increments $h = i\Delta y$, the expression (1.3–1) becomes

$$\lim_{\Delta y\to 0} \left\{ \frac{1}{i}\frac{u(x_0, y_0+\Delta y)-u(x_0, y_0)}{\Delta y} + \frac{v(x_0, y_0+\Delta y)-v(x_0, y_0)}{\Delta y} \right\}. \tag{1.3–5}$$

Hence $u(x, y)$ and $v(x, y)$ also possess partial derivatives with respect to y at the point (x_0, y_0), and we have

$$-iu_y(x_0, y_0)+v_y(v_0, y_0) = f'(z_0). \tag{1.3–6}$$

By comparing (1.3–4) and (1.3–6) we may infer: *A necessary condition that the derivative of $f(z) = u(x, y) + iv(x, y)$ should exist at the point $z_0 = x_0+iy_0$ is that at this point the Cauchy-Riemann equations*

$$\boxed{u_x = v_y, \qquad u_y = -v_x} \tag{1.3–7}$$

should be valid.

They are also called the *conditions of monogenity.*

1.3.2 – Sufficient conditions for differentiability

It should be reminded that the equations (1.3–7) express only a necessary condition for the existence of a derivative which is in general not sufficient, for we confined ourselves to the consideration of only real or pure imaginary increments h. We are, however, able to prove: *If $u(x, y)$ and $v(x, y)$ possess partial derivatives with respect to x and y in a neighbourhood of the internal point (x_0, y_0), being continuous at this point, and if there the equations* (1.3–7) *are satisfied, then $f(z)$ is differentiable at z_0.*

In fact, if we put $h = \Delta x+i\Delta y$, we have

$$\begin{aligned}\Delta u &= u(x_0+\Delta x,\, y_0+\Delta y)-u(x_0,\, y_0)\\ &= (u_x(x_0,\, y_0)+\alpha_1)\Delta x+(u_y(x_0,\, y_0)+\alpha_2)\Delta y,\\ \Delta v &= v(x_0+\Delta x,\, y_0+\Delta y)-v(x_0,\, y_0)\\ &= (v_x(x_0,\, y_0)+\beta_1)\Delta x+(v_y(x_0,\, y_0)+\beta_2)\Delta y.\end{aligned}$$

Hence, on account of (1.3–7),

$$\Delta u+i\Delta v = (u_x+iv_x)(\Delta x+i\Delta y)+(\alpha_1+i\beta_1)\Delta x+(\alpha_2+i\beta_2)\Delta y$$

or

$$\frac{f(z_0+h)-f(z_0)}{h}=\frac{\Delta u+i\Delta v}{\Delta x+i\Delta y}$$

$$=u_x+iv_x+(\alpha_1+i\beta_1)\frac{\Delta x}{\Delta x+i\Delta y}+(\alpha_2+i\beta_2)\frac{\Delta y}{\Delta x+i\Delta y}.$$

Since α_1, α_2, β_1, β_2 tend to zero as $\Delta x+i\Delta y$ tends to zero we have in view of $|\Delta x/(\Delta x+i\Delta y)| \leqq 1$, $|\Delta y/(\Delta x+i\Delta y)| \leqq 1$

$$\lim_{h\to 0}\frac{f(z_0+h)-f(z_0)}{h} = u_x(x_0,\, y_0)+iv_x(x_0,\, y_0),$$

which we desired to prove.

1.3.3 – Holomorphic functions

When a function $f(z)$ is defined throughout an *open* set $\mathfrak{A}$ which does not contain the point at infinity and possesses a derivative at every point of this set, it is called *holomorphic* in the set. The totality of derivatives constitute a new function $f'(z)$ or $df(z)/dz$, the *derivative* function, briefly the *derivative*.

Needless to say, the sum and the product of two holomorphic functions are again holomorphic. The same is true for the quotient, when we delete from the set those points for which the denominator vanishes. Finally if $g(z)$ is holomorphic in $\mathfrak{A}$ and $f(z)$ holomorphic in an open set which contains all values of $g(z)$ then also $f\{g(z)\}$ is holomorphic in $\mathfrak{A}$.

It is the purpose of the theory of functions of a complex variable to study the properties of holomorphic functions.

An example of a function which is not holomorphic is the function $|z|$. In general all functions of a complex variable which are not constant and take real values only, are not holomorphic, for the conditions of monogenity are not fulfilled.

1.4 – Conjugate functions

1.4.1 – Laplace's equation

In section 2.9.2 we shall prove that if a function $f(z) = u(x, y)+$ $+iv(x, y)$ is holomorphic in the set $\mathfrak{A}$ the functions $u(x, y)$ and $v(x, y)$

possess partial derivatives of all orders in $\mathfrak{A}$. Anticipating this result we deduce from (1.3–7)

$$u_{xx} = v_{xy}, \qquad u_{yy} = -v_{xy},$$

hence

$$u_{xx}+u_{yy} = 0 \tag{1.4–1}$$

and similarly

$$v_{xx}+v_{yy} = 0. \tag{1.4–2}$$

It appears that u and v are solutions of *Laplace's equation*

$$\boxed{\varphi_{xx}+\varphi_{yy} = 0.} \tag{1.4–3}$$

Every solution of (1.4–3) having continuous derivatives up to the second order at least is called a *harmonic function.*

Let $u(x, y)$ be a harmonic function in an open set $\mathfrak{S}$. If $v(x, y)$ is another harmonic function such that $f(z) = u(x, y)+iv(x, y)$ is holomorphic in the same set, then $v(x, y)$ is said to be a *conjugate* of $u(x, y)$ in the set. Thus we see that the study of holomorphic functions is closely associated with the study of pairs of conjugate solutions of Laplace's equation.

1.4.2 – Example of conjugate functions

It is not always possible to find a function $v(x, y)$ which is conjugate to $u(x, y)$ in the same set where $u(x, y)$ is harmonic. Consider, for instance, the function

$$\log \sqrt{x^2+y^2}. \tag{1.4–4}$$

It is easy to verify that this function is harmonic in the set which is obtained by deleting the point $z = 0$ from the z-plane. Since

$$\frac{\partial}{\partial x}\log \sqrt{x^2+y^2} = \frac{x}{x^2+y^2}, \qquad \frac{\partial}{\partial y}\log \sqrt{x^2+y^2} = \frac{y}{x^2+y^2},$$

a conjugate function must satisfy the equations

$$\frac{\partial v}{\partial y} = \frac{x}{x^2+y^2}, \qquad \frac{\partial v}{\partial x} = \frac{-y}{x^2+y^2},$$

or

$$dv = \frac{x\,dy-y\,dx}{x^2+y^2}. \tag{1.4–5}$$

Putting $x = r\cos\theta$, $y = r\sin\theta$, we find $dv = d\theta$. Hence, omitting an additive constant,

$$v = \arg z = \arg(x+iy). \tag{1.4–6}$$

But according to the theorem of section 1.2.2 this function is not continuous throughout the entire set considered above. In this case the statement would be true if the set were the principal region.

1.4.3 – Existence of a conjugate function

For many purposes the following theorem is useful:

Let $u(x, y)$ be harmonic in the interior of a circle. There exists a conjugate function $v(x, y)$ defined in the same set, this function being determined up to an additive constant.

Let (x_0, y_0) and (x, y) be two points inside the given circle. They can be connected by a broken line consisting of a horizontal and a vertical segment, (fig. 1.4–1).

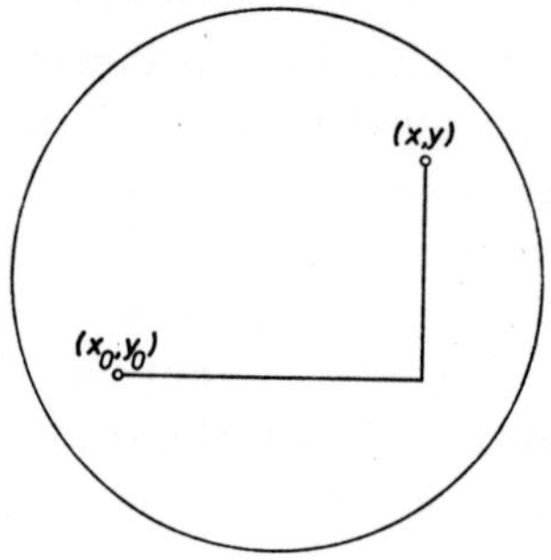

Fig. 1.4–1. Existence of a conjugate function

Now we put

$$v(x, y) = \int_{x_0}^{x} -u_y(x, y_0)dx + \int_{y_0}^{y} u_x(x, y)dy. \tag{1.4–7}$$

We immediately see that $v_y = u_x(x, y)$. Further

$$\begin{aligned} v_x &= -u_y(x, y_0) + \int_{y_0}^{y} u_{xx}(x, y)\, dy = -u_y(x, y_0) - \int_{y_0}^{y} u_{yy}(x, y)\, dy \\ &= -u_y(x, y_0) + u_y(x, y_0) - u_y(x, y) = -u_y(x, y). \end{aligned}$$

This proves the existence of a conjugate. Any other conjugate differs from it by a constant. In fact, the difference of two conjugates is again a conjugate corresponding to $u(x, y) = 0$. From $v_x = v_y = 0$ we deduce that v = constant.

1.5 – Sequences of functions

1.5.1 – Limit of a sequence of functions

Consider a *sequence* of functions

$$F_n(z), \quad n = 0, 1, 2, \ldots, \tag{1.5–1}$$

defined throughout a set $\mathfrak{S}$, i.e., to every number $n = 0, 1, 2, \ldots$ corresponds a function $F_n(z)$ on $\mathfrak{S}$.

We shall say that the sequence (1.5–1) is *convergent* at some point z of $\mathfrak{S}$ if

$$\lim_{n\to\infty} F_n(z) \tag{1.5–2}$$

exists and is finite. In the contrary case we say that the sequence is *divergent* at z.

The set of all points z at which the sequence is convergent is a subset $\mathfrak{T}$ of $\mathfrak{S}$ (which may be empty). The operation (1.5–2) defines a function $F(z)$ on $\mathfrak{T}$, the *limit of the sequence.*

An alternative phrasing is the following: Let z be a point of $\mathfrak{T}$. Given an positive number ε we can find a number n_0 such that

$$|F_n(z)-F(z)| < \varepsilon, \tag{1.5–3}$$

for all $n > n_0$. The smallest integer n_0 of this kind evidently depends on ε and might be considered as a measure of convergence. In general this measure of convergence varies with z in $\mathfrak{T}$. It may happen, however, that these measures are bounded in a certain subset $\mathfrak{U}$ of $\mathfrak{T}$, i.e., we can find a number n_0, depending only on ε, such that (1.5–3) is satisfied for all z in $\mathfrak{U}$. When this event occurs we say that the sequence (1.5–2) is *uniformly convergent* on $\mathfrak{U}$. The notion of uniform convergence is fundamental in the theory of functions.

1.5.2 – Continuity of the limit

We now make the assumption that the functions (1.5–1) are all (or from a certain index upwards) continuous at an accumulation point z_0 of a set $\mathfrak{S}$.

If the sequence is uniformly convergent on the set consisting of all points of $\mathfrak{S}$ which are in a certain neighbourhood of the accumulation point then the limit function is also continuous at this point.

Given $\varepsilon > 0$ we can find an integer n such that $|F_n(z)-F(z)| < \frac{1}{3}\varepsilon$ for all points of $\mathfrak{S}$ in the neighbourhood. Since $F_n(z)$ is continuous at z_0 we can find a number δ such that all points of $\mathfrak{S}$ satisfying $|z-z_0| < \delta$ are in the neighbourhood while $|F_n(z)-F_n(z_0)| < \frac{1}{3}\varepsilon$. For these values of z we have

$$|F(z)-F(z_0)| \leqq |F(z)-F_n(z)|+|F(z_0)-F_n(z_0)|+|F_n(z)-F_n(z_0)| < \varepsilon,$$

and the truth of the statement follows.

Without assuming the continuity of $F_n(z)$ at $z = z_0$ it is easy to prove the following theorem:

Let the sequence (1.5–1) *be uniformly convergent on $\mathfrak{S}$ to a function $F(z)$. Then, if z_0 is an accumulation point of $\mathfrak{S}$ and if* $\lim_{z\to z_0} F_n(z) = F_n$

exists from some n upwards, then also $\lim_{z\to z_0} F(z)$ *exists and is equal to* $\lim_{n\to\infty} F_n$, that is to say

$$\lim_{z\to z_0} \lim_{n\to\infty} F_n(z) = \lim_{n\to\infty} \lim_{z\to z_0} F_n(z) \tag{1.5–4}$$

1.5.3 – SERIES OF FUNCTIONS

Given a sequence

$$f_n(z), \qquad n = 0, 1, 2, \ldots \tag{1.5–4}$$

defined throughout a set $\mathfrak{S}$, we can construct another sequence of *partial sums*

$$F_n(z) = f_0(z)+f_1(z)+\ldots+f_n(z) = \sum_{\nu=0}^{n} f_\nu(z). \tag{1.5–5}$$

If the sequence (1.5–5) is convergent we shall say that the *infinite series*

$$f_0(z)+f_1(z)+\ldots = \sum_{\nu=0}^{\infty} f_\nu(z) \tag{1.5–6}$$

is *convergent* and possesses the *sum* $F(z) = \lim_{n\to\infty} F_n(z)$. The series is said to be uniformly convergent on a set when the sequence of the partial sums is uniformly convergent.

By virtue of the first theorem of the previous section the following statement is apparent:

If the sequence (1.5–4) *consists of functions which are continuous at an accumulation point* z_0 *of the set* $\mathfrak{S}$ *in which the functions are defined and if the series* (1.5–6) *is uniformly convergent on the set consisting of all points of* $\mathfrak{S}$ *which are included in a certain neighbourhood of* z_0, *then the sum is continuous at* z_0.

1.5.4 – TEST FOR UNIFORM CONVERGENCE

In many cases an alternative definition of uniform convergence is useful.

The sequence (1.5–1) *is then and only then uniformly convergent on a set when to a given number* $\varepsilon > 0$ *a number* n_0 *can be found such that*

$$|F_m(z)-F_n(z)| < \varepsilon \tag{1.5–7}$$

for all z *in the set, whenever* $m > n > n_0$.

The condition is necessary, for we can find a number n_0 such that $|F_m(z)-F(z)| < \frac{1}{2}\varepsilon$, $|F_n(z)-F(z)| < \frac{1}{2}\varepsilon$, hence (1.5–7) is satisfied for all z in the set, provided that $m > n > n_0$. Conversely, if the condition is satisfied then on account of the well-known Cauchy principle the sequence is convergent at every point of the set. Hence we may let $m \to \infty$ and find $|F(z)-F_n(z)| \leqq \varepsilon$ for every z in the set, provided that $n > n_0$.

On this theorem is based the *Weierstrass test* for uniform convergence of a series.

A series (1.5–5) *which can be dominated by a convergent series*

$$\gamma_0+\gamma_1+\ldots = \sum_{\nu=0}^{\infty} \gamma_\nu, \qquad (1.5\text{–}8)$$

i.e.,

$$|f_n(z)| \leqq \gamma_n, \qquad n = 0, 1, 2, \ldots,$$

throughout the set, is uniformly convergent.

In fact, assuming $m > n$

$$|F_m(z)-F_n(z)| = |f_m(z)+\ldots+f_{n+1}(z)| \leqq |f_m(z)|+\ldots+|f_n(z)|$$
$$\leqq \gamma_m+\ldots+\gamma_{n+1},$$

and on account of the convergence of the series the last sum can be made smaller than a given positive number ε, provided that n is large enough. This proves the assertion.

1.5.5 – Extension to an infinite integral

The previous considerations can be extended to the case of integrals. Let us assume that

$$\int_0^\infty f(t, z)\, dt \qquad (1.5\text{–}9)$$

has a meaning for all z in a certain set, the integrand being integrable in the sense of Riemann. It defines, therefore, a function $F(z)$. The integral (1.5–9) is called *uniformly convergent* on the set, if to a given positive number ε corresponds a number N such that

$$\left|\int_0^\omega f(t, z)\, dt - F(z)\right| < \varepsilon$$

for all z in the set, provided $\omega > N$. In particular we can prove:

If $|f(t, z)| \leqq f(t)$ *and if* $\int_0^\infty f(t)\, dt$ *is convergent, then the integral* (1.5–9) *is uniformly convergent.*

The arguments do not differ essentially from those used before.

1.6. – Power Series

1.6.1 – Convergence of power series

Very important series of functions are afforded by power series. A *power series* is an infinite series of the form

$$c_0+c_1z+c_2z^2+\ldots = \sum_{\nu=0}^{\infty} c_\nu z^\nu, \tag{1.6–1}$$

where $c_0, c_1, c_2, \ldots$ are constants. The functions of the sequence are here

$$f_n(z) = c_n z^n. \tag{1.5–4}$$

A power series is called *absolutely convergent* when the series of the moduli

$$\sum_{\nu=0}^{\infty} |c_\nu z^\nu| \tag{1.6–2}$$

is convergent. It is easy to see that an absolutely convergent series is convergent. The reverse need not be true.

There are power series which converge for every value of z, for instance the series

$$1+\frac{z}{1!}+\frac{z^2}{2!}+\ldots = \sum_{\nu=0}^{\infty} \frac{z^\nu}{\nu!}, \tag{1.6–3}$$

as we shall see in section 1.6.6. On the other hand there are series which converge only for $z = 0$. An example is

$$1+1!z+2!z^2+\ldots = \sum_{\nu=0}^{\infty} \nu!\, z^\nu. \tag{1.6–4}$$

Finally we may give an example of a series which is convergent for some values of z and divergent for other values. The simplest example is the geometric series

$$1+z+z^2+\ldots = \sum_{\nu=0}^{\infty} z^\nu. \tag{1.6–5}$$

1.6.2 – The circle of convergence

Assume that the series (1.6–1) is convergent for $z = z_0 \neq 0$. We shall prove that it is absolutely convergent for $|z| < |z_0|$. In fact, since the series $\sum_{\nu=0}^{\infty} c_\nu z_0^\nu$ is convergent we have

$$\lim_{n\to\infty} |c_n z_0^n| = 0 \tag{1.6–6}$$

as may be proved in the usual way. Hence all terms $|c_n z_0^n|$ are bounded, i.e., they remain below a fixed number M. If $|z| < |z_0|$ then

$$|c_n z^n| = |c_n z_0^n| \left|\frac{z}{z_0}\right|^n < M \left|\frac{z}{z_0}\right|^n, \tag{1.6–7}$$

and the series (1.6–2) turns out to be dominated by a convergent geometric series.

Next we assume that the series (1.6–1) is divergent for $z = z_0$. It is plain that it is also divergent for all $|z| > |z_0|$, when we take account of the previous statement.

These preliminaries enable us to prove:

For every power series (1.6–1) *there exists a number* R, $0 \leqq R \leqq \infty$ *such that the series is absolutely convergent for every* $|z| < R$, *whereas the series is divergent for* $|z| > R$.

Nothing is claimed about the convergence for $|z| = R$. Let R denote the least upper bound of all numbers $|z|$ for which the series is convergent. If $R = 0$ we have nothing to prove. Assume, therefore, $R > 0$. If z_1 is such that $|z_1| < R$ we can find, according to the definition of least upper bound, a number z_0 with $|z_1| < |z_0| < R$. The series, being convergent for $z = z_0$, turns out to be absolutely convergent for $z = z_1$. If $R < \infty$ and $|z_1| > R$ then the series is evidently divergent.

The set of all points with $|z| < R$ is the interior of a circle (when $0 < R < \infty$) or the entire z-plane (when $R = \infty$). In both cases it is a region, *the region of convergence of the series*. The number R is called the *radius of convergence*. In the event of a circle the boundary is the *circumference of convergence*; the term *circle of convergence* is used both for the region and for its boundary; which of the two is intended is usually clear from the context.

1.6.3 – Uniform convergence of power series

The series (1.6–1) *is uniformly convergent in every closed disc* $|z| \leqq \varrho < R$, where R is the radius of convergence. In fact, take z_0 such that $\varrho < |z_0| < R$. The assertion follows from

$$\left| \sum_{\nu=0}^{\infty} c_\nu z^\nu \right| \leqq \sum_{\nu=0}^{\infty} |c_\nu z_0^\nu| \tag{1.6–8}$$

on applying the Weierstrass test stated in section 1.5.4. As a direct consequence we have:

A power series represents a continuous function throughout its region of convergence.

In fact, given a point z_0 in the region of convergence, we can always find a closed disc which contains this point in its interior. Hence there exists a neighbourhood of the point consisting of points of the region on which the series is uniformly convergent. The statement now follows from the theorem of section 1.5.3.

From this theorem follows:

If

$$\sum_{\nu=0}^{\infty} c_\nu z^\nu = \sum_{\nu=0}^{\infty} d_\nu z^\nu$$

in a set of points which possesses $z = 0$ *as an accumulation point, then* $c_n = d_n$, $n = 0, 1, 2, \ldots$.

In fact, both series are continuous at $z = 0$. Hence $c_0 = d_0$. When $z \neq 0$ we have

$$\sum_{\nu=1}^{\infty} c_\nu z^{\nu-1} = \sum_{\nu=1}^{\infty} d_\nu z^{\nu-1},$$

and it follows that $c_1 = d_1$. Proceeding in this way the assertion follows.

1.6.4 – Limes superior and limes inferior

We proved the existence of a radius of convergence but we do not yet know how this radius may be found from the coefficients of the series. In this direction Cauchy has given a beautiful theorem which has later been rediscovered by Hadamard. Before stating this theorem we recall an important notion which is widely used in analysis.

Let $f(t)$ be a real function of a real variable t which can take arbitrarily large positive values. By $\bar{\lambda}_p$ we understand the least upper bound of all numbers $f(t)$ corresponding to $t > p$. Let $\bar{l}$ denote the greatest lower bound of all these numbers $\bar{\lambda}_p$. This uniquely defined number (which may also have the improper values $+\infty$ or $-\infty$) is called the *limes superior* of $f(t)$ as $t \to \infty$ written as

$$\bar{l} = \limsup_{t\to\infty} f(t). \tag{1.6–9}$$

It has the following properties. First let $\bar{l} < \infty$ and ε be a positive number. On account of the definition of greatest lower bound we can find a number p such that $\bar{\lambda}_p < \bar{l}+\varepsilon$. Since $f(t) \leqq \bar{\lambda}_p$, for all $t > p$ we have:

(i) If $\bar{l} < +\infty$, $\varepsilon > 0$ *there is a number* p *such that*

$$f(t) < \bar{l}+\varepsilon$$

provided that $t > p$.

Next we consider the case $\bar{l} > -\infty$. Given p, we can find a number $t > p$ such that $f(t) > \bar{\lambda}_p - \varepsilon$ and so $f(t) > \bar{l} - \varepsilon$. Hence:

(ii) *If* $\bar{l} > -\infty$ *there exists beyond every number* p *a number* t *such that*

$$f(t) > \bar{l} - \varepsilon.$$

In a similar way, by interchanging upper and lower bounds, we can define the *limes inferior* of $f(t)$ as $t \to \infty$,

$$\underline{l} = \liminf_{t\to\infty} f(t). \tag{1.6–10}$$

It is easy to prove that always $\underline{l} \leqq \bar{l}$. When $\underline{l} = \bar{l} = l$, then l is the limit of $f(t)$ as $t \to \infty$ in the ordinary sense.

When t takes only the values 0, 1, 2, . . ., it is customary to write f_n instead of $f(n)$.

1.6.5 – The Cauchy-Hadamard formula

The *Cauchy-Hadamard theorem* states:

The radius of convergence R of a power series (1.6–1) *is given by*

$$\boxed{\frac{1}{R} = \limsup_{n\to\infty} \sqrt[n]{|c_n|}.} \tag{1.6–11}$$

If $r < R$ the numbers $|c_n|r^n$ are bounded, i.e., we can find a constant A such that $|c_n|r^n < A$, or $\sqrt[n]{|c_n|} < (\sqrt[n]{A})/r$. Letting $n \to \infty$ we may infer that $\limsup \sqrt[n]{|c_n|} \leqq 1/r$. Since this is true for every $r < R$ we even have $\limsup \sqrt[n]{|c_n|} \leqq 1/R$.

If $r > R$ then $|c_n|r^n \geqq 1$ for infinitely many n and so $\sqrt[n]{|c_n|} \geqq 1/r$ for infinitely many n. This implies, however, $\limsup \sqrt[n]{|c_n|} \geqq 1/r$ and since this is true for all $r > R$ we also have $\limsup \sqrt[n]{|c_n|} \geqq 1/R$. This proves the assertion.

1.6.6 – The ratio formula

The following theorem is frequently used in the theory of series. Assuming that from a certain index upwards none of the coefficients of the series (1.6–1) vanish, *then the radius of convergence is given by*

$$\boxed{\frac{1}{R} = \lim_{n\to\infty} \frac{|c_{n+1}|}{|c_n|},} \tag{1.6–12}$$

provided that this limit exists.

It will be sufficient to prove $\limsup \sqrt[n]{|c_n|} \leqq \limsup |c_{n+1}/c_n|$, for in exactly the same way we also find $\liminf |c_{n+1}/c_n| \leqq \liminf \sqrt[n]{|c_n|}$. Let $l = \limsup |c_{n+1}/c_n|$. Obviously $l \geqq 0$.

If $l = \infty$ the assertion is trivial. Let ε denote a positive number. If m is sufficiently large we have for all $n \geqq m$ the inequality $|c_{n+1}/c_n| < l+\varepsilon$. Replacing n successively by $m, m+1, \ldots, n-1$ and multiplying corresponding members we find $|c_n/c_m| < (l+\varepsilon)^{n-m}$ or $|c_n| < A(l+\varepsilon)^n$ where $A = |c_m|(l+\varepsilon)^{-m}$. Thus we have $\sqrt[n]{|c_n|} < (l+\varepsilon)\sqrt[n]{A}$. Letting $n \to \infty$ we deduce $\limsup \sqrt[n]{|c_n|} \leqq l+\varepsilon$, and since ε is arbitrary we even have $\limsup \sqrt[n]{|c_n|} \leqq l$.

On applying this theorem we easily verify that the radius of convergence of the series (1.6–3) is ∞, that of (1.6–4) is 0, whereas the radius of convergence of (1.6–5) is unity.

1.6.7 – Extension of the definition of power series

We observe that the above considerations are also valid for power series of a more general type, viz.,

$$\sum_{\nu=0}^{\infty} c_\nu (z-a)^\nu, \tag{1.6–13}$$

where a is a fixed number. We have only to replace z by $z-a$. The point $z = a$ is the centre of the circle of convergence (when the radius is finite). The series

$$\sum_{\nu=0}^{\infty} c_\nu \left(\frac{1}{z}\right)^\nu \tag{1.6–14}$$

is convergent outside a circle around the origin of radius R, i.e., the circle of convergence surrounds the point $z = \infty$.

1.6.8 – Addition and multiplication of power series

Finally we wish to remark that the elementary operation of addition of two power series appears in the form

$$\boxed{\sum_{\nu=0}^{\infty} a_\nu z^\nu + \sum_{\nu=0}^{\infty} b_\nu z^\nu = \sum_{\nu=0}^{\infty} (a_\nu + b_\nu) z^\nu,} \tag{1.6–15}$$

provided that both series on the left are convergent. Assume now that $\sum_{\nu=0}^{\infty} a_\nu z^\nu$ and $\sum_{\nu=0}^{\infty} b_\nu z^\nu$ are convergent for $|z| < R$. Let ϱ denote a number such that $|z| \leqq \varrho < R$. We may write

$$\sum_{\nu=0}^{\infty} a_\nu z^\nu = P_n(z) + \varphi_n(z), \quad \sum_{\nu=0}^{\infty} b_\nu z^\nu = Q_n(z) + \psi_n(z) \tag{1.6–16}$$

where $P_n(z)$ and $Q_n(z)$ are polynomials consisting of the first $n+1$ terms of either series. Assuming n sufficiently large we have $|\varphi_n(z)| < \varepsilon$, $|\psi_n(z)| < \varepsilon$ for all $|z| \leqq \varrho$, because of the uniform convergence of the series. On the other hand the polynomials $P_n(z)$ and $Q_n(z)$ are bounded for $|z| \leqq \varrho$. Hence

$$\sum_{\nu=0}^{\infty} a_\nu z^\nu \cdot \sum_{\nu=0}^{\infty} b_\nu z^\nu = P_n(z) Q_n(z) + \chi_n(z) \tag{1.6–17}$$

and taking n sufficiently large we can make $|\chi_n(z)|$ as small as we wish. Thus we find Cauchy's rule for the multiplication of series

$$\boxed{\sum_{\nu=0}^{\infty} a_\nu z^\nu \cdot \sum_{\nu=0}^{\infty} b_\nu z^\nu = \sum_{\nu=0}^{\infty} c_\nu z^\nu, \quad c_n = a_0 b_n + a_1 b_{n-1} + \ldots + a_n b_0,} \qquad (1.6\text{–}18)$$

valid for all $|z| < R$.

1.7 – The power series as a holomorphic function

1.7.1 – The derivative of a power series

A power series (1.6–1) *and the series obtained from it by performing term-by-term differentiation*

$$c_1 + 2c_2 z + 3c_3 z^2 + \ldots = \sum_{\nu=1}^{\infty} \nu c_\nu z^{\nu-1} \qquad (1.7\text{–}1)$$

have the same radius of convergence.

The argument used in the proof of the theorem of section 1.6.6 shows that

$$\lim_{n\to\infty} \sqrt[n]{n} = \lim_{n\to\infty} \frac{n+1}{n} = 1. \qquad (1.7\text{–}2)$$

Hence

$$\limsup_{n\to\infty} \sqrt[n]{n|c_n|} = \limsup_{n\to\infty} \sqrt[n]{|c_n|}.$$

1.7.2 – The power series representing a holomorphic function

In the region of convergence the sum of the series (1.7–1) *represents the derivative of the sum $f(z)$ of the series* (1.6–2). In other words: *A power series is in its region of convergence a holomorphic function and possesses derivatives of all orders.*

Let $R > 0$ denote the radius of convergence (the case $R = 0$ is of no interest). Let $|z| < R$ and take a number ϱ such that $|z| < \varrho < R$. If h is a number such that also $|z+h| < \varrho$ we have

$$\frac{f(z+h)-f(z)}{h} = \sum_{\nu=1}^{\infty} c_\nu \{(z+h)^{\nu-1} + (z+h)^{\nu-2} z + \ldots + z^{\nu-1}\} \quad (1.7\text{–}3)$$

and is numerically less than $\sum_{\nu=1}^{\infty} \nu |c_\nu| \varrho^{\nu-1}$. Hence the series on the right, considered as a series of functions of h, is uniformly convergent for $|h| < \delta$, where δ is a suitably chosen small number. On account of the theorem of section 1.5.3 the function is continuous at $h = 0$. Letting $h \to 0$ we immediately find

$$\lim_{h\to 0} \frac{f(z+h)-f(z)}{h} = \sum_{\nu=1}^{\infty} \nu c_\nu z^{\nu-1}, \qquad (1.7\text{–}4)$$

the desired result.

1.7.3 – Integral functions

From the foregoing result it follows that *a power series represents a function which is holomorphic throughout the region of convergence.*

By an *integral function* we understand a function which is holomorphic throughout the entire z-plane. Hence:

A power series which is convergent throughout the entire plane represents an integral function.

1.8 – The theorems of Picard and Abel

1.8.1 – Picard's theorem

The following theorem is due to E. Picard.

Assume that the coefficients of the series (1.6–1) are real and satisfy the conditions

$$c_0 \geqq c_1 \geqq c_2 \geqq \ldots; \tag{i}$$

$$\lim_{n\to\infty} c_n = 0. \tag{ii}$$

Then the series converges at all points of the circumference $|z| = 1$, *save possibly at* $z = 1$, *and hence the radius of convergence is at least unity.*

Consider the sum

$$R_{n,p}(z) = \sum_{\nu=n+1}^{n+p} c_\nu z^\nu, \qquad p \geqq 1.$$

Obviously

$$(z-1)R_{n,p}(z) = -c_{n+1}z^{n+1} + \sum_{\nu=n+1}^{n+p-1} (c_\nu - c_{\nu+1})z^{\nu+1} + c_{n+p}z^{n+p+1}$$

and so

$$|z-1||R_{n,p}(z)| \leqq c_{n+1}|z|^{n+1} + \sum_{\nu=n+1}^{n+p-1} (c_\nu - c_{\nu+1})|z|^{\nu+1} + c_{n+p}|z|^{n+p+1},$$

since the differences between brackets are not negative. Taking $|z| = 1, z \neq 1$ we find

$$|R_{n,p}(z)| \leqq \frac{1}{|z-1|}\left(c_{n+1} + \sum_{\nu=n+1}^{n+p-1} (c_\nu - c_{\nu+1}) + c_{n+p}\right) = \frac{2c_{n+1}}{|z-1|},$$

c_{n+1} not being negative. Since this result holds for all $p \geqq 1$ we can let $p \to \infty$ and we find

$$|R_n(z)| = \left|\sum_{\nu=n+1}^{\infty} c_\nu z^\nu\right| \leqq \frac{2c_{n+1}}{|z-1|},$$

and on account of (ii) this tends to zero as $n \to \infty$.

Nothing is claimed about the convergence at $z = 1$. Thus for instance the series

$$\sum_{\nu=1}^{\infty} \frac{z^\nu}{\nu}$$

is divergent at $z = 1$, whereas the series

$$\sum_{\nu=1}^{\infty} \frac{z^\nu}{\nu^2}$$

is convergent at $z = 1$. Picard's theorem reduces to the well-known Leibniz theorem for alternating series by taking $z = -1$, i.e., *under the assumptions* (i) *and* (ii) *the series* $\sum_{\nu=0}^{\infty}(-1)^\nu c_\nu$ *is convergent.*

1.8.2 – Abel's theorem on power series

The following theorem, proved by N. H. Abel in the real case, deals with the continuity of the sum of a power series at a point of the circumference of convergence. This continuity must be understood in a somewhat restricted sense. It is sufficient to study the behaviour of the series (1.6–1) at $z = 1$, since the case $z = z_0$ can be reduced to this one by means of the substitution $z' = z/z_0$.

If the power series (1.6–1) *is convergent at* $z = 1$, *then*

$$\sum_{\nu=0}^{\infty} c_\nu z^\nu \to \sum_{\nu=0}^{\infty} c_\nu \tag{1.8–1}$$

as $z \to 1$, *provided that* z *ultimately remains in the area*

$$\frac{|1-z|}{1-|z|} \leqq k, \tag{1.8–2}$$

where k *is an arbitrary number greater than* 1.

The theorem gives only information beyond that what is given by the theorem of section 1.6.3. when the radius of convergence is exactly unity.

The proof is based on a device which is known as Abel's *method of summation by parts* (already used in the previous section). Consider two sequences of numbers $u_0, u_1, \ldots$ and $v_0, v_1, \ldots$. The sum

$$\sum_{\nu=n+1}^{n+p} u_\nu(v_\nu - v_{\nu-1}), \qquad n \geqq 0, \quad p \geqq 1$$

can be put in the form

$$\sum_{\nu=n+1}^{n+p} u_\nu v_\nu - \sum_{\nu=n+1}^{n+p} u_\nu v_{\nu-1} = u_{n+p} v_{n+p} - u_n v_n + \sum_{\nu=n}^{n+p-1} u_\nu v_\nu - \sum_{\nu=n+1}^{n+p} u_\nu v_{\nu-1}$$

$$= u_{n+p} v_{n+p} - u_n v_n + \sum_{\nu=n+1}^{n+p} u_{\nu-1} v_{\nu-1} - \sum_{\nu=n+1}^{n+p} u_\nu v_{\nu-1}.$$

Hence

$$\sum_{\nu=n+1}^{n+p} u_\nu(v_\nu - v_{\nu-1}) = u_{n+p} v_{n+p} - u_n v_n - \sum_{\nu=n+1}^{n+p} (u_\nu - u_{\nu-1}) v_{\nu-1}. \quad (1.8\text{–}3)$$

We apply this formula to the sum

$$R_{n,p}(z) = \sum_{\nu=n+1}^{n+p} c_\nu z^\nu, \qquad n \geqq 0, \quad p \geqq 1.$$

Put

$$u_n = z^n, \qquad v_n = \sum_{\nu=n+1}^{\infty} c_\nu .$$

Then

$$R_{n,p}(z) = -\sum_{\nu=n+1}^{n+p} u_\nu(v_\nu - v_{\nu-1}) = -v_{n+p} z^{n+p} + v_n z^n + \sum_{\nu=n+1}^{n+p} (z^\nu - z^{\nu-1}) v_{\nu-1}.$$

Now $v_n \to 0$ as $n \to \infty$. Assuming $|z| < 1$ and letting $p \to \infty$ we obtain

$$R_n(z) = \sum_{\nu=n+1}^{\infty} c_\nu z^\nu = v_n z^n - (1-z) \sum_{\nu=n+1}^{\infty} z^{\nu-1} v_{\nu-1}.$$

If $\varepsilon > 0$ is a given positive number we have for sufficiently large n

$$|R_n(z)| < \varepsilon\left(1 + |1-z| \sum_{\nu=1}^{\infty} |z|^{\nu-1}\right) = \varepsilon\left(1 + \frac{|1-z|}{1-|z|}\right) \leqq \varepsilon\,(1+k),$$

provided that (1.8–2) is satisfied. This inequality is also true for $z = 1$. Hence the series (1.6–1) is uniformly convergent in the point set characterized by (1.8–2) together with $|z| < 1$, this set being completed by $z = 1$. Since $z = 1$ is an accumulation point the assertion follows from the theorem of section 1.5.3.

1.8.3 – Sufficient condition for the validity of Abel's theorem

Consider the sector of a circle, (fig. 1.8–1), defined by

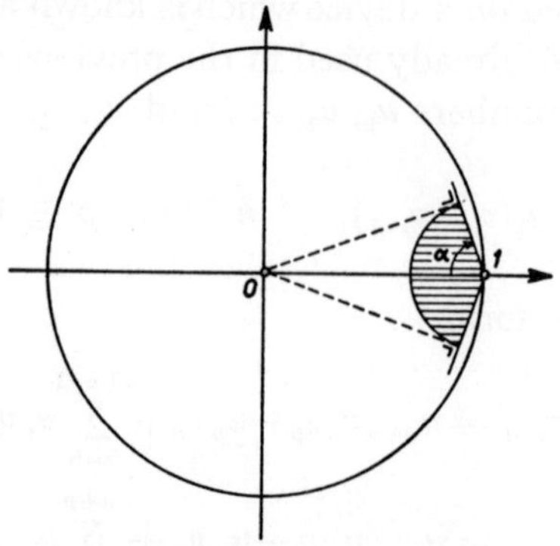

Fig. 1.8–1. Abel's theorem

$$\varrho = |1-z| \leqq \cos\alpha, \qquad |\arg(1-z)| \leqq \alpha < \tfrac{1}{2}\pi.$$

In this sector we have

$$1-z = \varrho(\cos\varphi + i\sin\varphi),$$

where $0 \leqq \varrho \leqq \cos\alpha$, $|\varphi| \leqq \alpha$. Hence

$$\begin{aligned}|z|^2 &= 1 - 2\varrho\cos\varphi + \varrho^2 \leqq 1 - 2\varrho\cos\alpha + \varrho^2 \leqq 1 - 2\varrho\cos\alpha + \varrho\cos\alpha \\ &= 1 - \varrho\cos\alpha \leqq 1 - \varrho\cos\alpha + \tfrac{1}{4}\varrho^2\cos^2\alpha,\end{aligned}$$

whence

$$|z| \leq 1 - \tfrac{1}{2}\varrho\cos\alpha,$$

and so, at each point of the sector, save $z = 1$,

$$\frac{|1-z|}{1-|z|} \leqq \frac{2}{\cos\alpha}.$$

Hence, Abel's theorem is certainly valid when $z \to 1$ remaining ultimately in this sector.

1.9 – The A-summability of a series. Tauber's theorem

1.9.1 – Definition of A-summability

If the series $\sum_{\nu=0}^{\infty} c_\nu$ is convergent then the radius of convergence of the corresponding power series (1.6–1) is at least unity. Abel's theorem asserts that

$$\sum_{\nu=0}^{\infty} c_\nu z^\nu \to \sum_{\nu=0}^{\infty} c_\nu, \tag{1.9–1}$$

as z tends to 1 along the real axis from the inside of the circle of convergence.

Now the interesting situation occurs that the limit on the left of (9.1–1) may exist without the series on the right being convergent. A classical example is provided by the geometric series

$$\sum_{\nu=0}^{\infty} (-z)^\nu = \frac{1}{1+z}, \qquad |z| < 1. \tag{1.9–2}$$

The sum tends to $\frac{1}{2}$ if $z \to 1$, but the series

$$\sum_{\nu=0}^{\infty} (-1)^\nu = 1-1+1-1+\ldots \tag{1.9–3}$$

is divergent. We can, however, extend the notion of summability by attributing a sum to a divergent series $\sum_{\nu=0}^{\infty} c_\nu$, being equal to the limit of the sum of a series (1.6–1), provided that this limit exists. When this event occurs we say that the series is *A-summable* and possesses an *Abel-sum*. Thus the series (1.9–2) is A-summable, its Abel-sum being $\frac{1}{2}$.

1.9.2 – TAUBER'S THEOREM

Abel's theorem asserts that the ordinary sum of a convergent series with constant terms coincides with the A-sum. We already pointed out that a series may be A-summable without being summable in the ordinary sense. If, however, we impose on the coefficients a restriction as to their order of magnitude we can obtain a sort of converse of Abel's theorem. Theorems of this type are called *tauberian* after A. Tauber, to whom is due a first theorem of this nature.

Let $f(z)$ denote the sum of a series (1.6–1) for $|z| < 1$ and assume that

$$f(z) \to s$$

as $z \to 1$ in the same fashion as described in Abel's theorem. If

$$\lim_{n\to\infty} nc_n = 0 \tag{1.9–4}$$

then the series

$$\sum_{\nu=0}^{\infty} c_\nu \tag{1.9–5}$$

is convergent and possesses the sum s.

Otherwise stated: If the series (1.9–5) is A-summable and if (1.9–4) is satisfied, then it is summable in the ordinary sense.

It suffices to show that

$$\sum_{\nu=0}^{\infty} c_\nu z^\nu - \sum_{\nu=0}^{n} c_\nu \to 0$$

as $n \to \infty$, where $n = [1/(1-|z|)]$ denotes the largest integer that does not exceed $1/(1-|z|)$. That is, we have to show

$$\sum_{\nu=n+1}^{\infty} c_\nu z^\nu - \sum_{\nu=0}^{n} c_\nu (1-z^\nu) \to 0$$

as $n \to \infty$. Put

$$S_1 = \sum_{\nu=n+1}^{\infty} c_\nu z^\nu, \qquad S_2 = \sum_{\nu=0}^{n} c_\nu (1-z^\nu).$$

If ε is a given positive number then $|nc_n| < \varepsilon$ for all sufficiently large values of n, i.e., for z sufficiently near to 1. Hence, assuming $0 < |z| < 1$,

$$|S_1| = \left| \sum_{\nu=n+1}^{\infty} \nu c_\nu \frac{z^\nu}{\nu} \right| < \frac{\varepsilon}{n+1} \sum_{\nu=n+1}^{\infty} |z|^\nu < \frac{\varepsilon}{(n+1)(1-|z|)} < \varepsilon,$$

whenever n is large enough.

In order to be able to prove that also S_2 tends to zero as $z \to 1$ we need the following lemma

If $b_n \to 0$ as $n \to \infty$ than also $\dfrac{b_0+\ldots+b_n}{n+1} \to 0$. In fact, we can find a number m such that $|b_n| < \varepsilon$ for all $n > m$. Hence

$$\frac{|b_0+\ldots+b_n|}{n+1} \leqq \frac{|b_0+\ldots+b_m|}{n+1} + \frac{|b_{m+1}+\ldots+b_n|}{n+1}$$

$$\leqq \frac{|b_0+\ldots+b_m|}{n+1} + \frac{(n-m)}{n+1}\varepsilon < 2\varepsilon$$

for sufficiently large values of n.

Now we observe that

$$|1-z^n| = |(1-z)(1+z+\ldots+z^{n-1})| \leqq |1-z|n.$$

If (1.8–2) is satisfied we have

$$|S_2| \leqq \sum_{\nu=0}^{n} |\nu c_\nu(1-z)| \leqq k(1-|z|) \sum_{\nu=0}^{n} \nu|c_\nu| \leqq \frac{k}{n} \sum_{\nu=0}^{n} \nu|c_\nu|.$$

On applying the lemma, taking account of (1.9–4), the proof is now easily completed.

1.10 – The exponential, circular and hyperbolic functions

1.10.1 – The exponential function

One of the most fundamental properties of the real exponential function e^x is expressed by the fact that the function is reproduced by differentiation. Now we shall try to find a holomorphic function of exactly the same nature. We shall seek it among the power series and assume that the power series (1.6–1) is a function having the desired property. Since this series must coincide with the series (1.7–1) in its region of convergence, the coefficients must satisfy the following recurrent relations

$$c_{n+1} = (n+1)c_n, \qquad n = 0, 1, 2, \ldots.$$

Hence

$$c_n = \frac{c_0}{n!}.$$

We may impose the additional condition that the function takes the value 1 for $z = 0$, like in the real case. Then $c_0 = 1$. But we already know (1.6.6) that the series

$$\boxed{\exp z = \sum_{\nu=0}^{\infty} \frac{z^\nu}{\nu!}} \tag{1.10–1}$$

represents an integral function (1.7.3) called the *exponential function* and the above considerations lead to the conclusion that it is the only power series satisfying the conditions

$$\exp 0 = 1$$

and

$$\boxed{\exp' z = \exp z.} \tag{1.10–2}$$

In section 2.16.1 we shall prove that there is no other holomorphic function satisfying the same conditions.

1.10.2 – Functional equation of the exponential function

Applying Cauchy's multiplication rule (1.6–18) we readily obtain the functional equation of the exponential function

$$\boxed{\exp(z+a) = \exp z \cdot \exp a.} \tag{1.10–3}$$

In particular,

$$\exp z \cdot \exp(-z) = \exp 0 = 1. \tag{1.10–4}$$

Hence:

The exponential function has no zeros.

We recall that by a *zero* of a function is understood a value of z for which the function takes the value 0.

1.10.3 – Euler's formulas

Taking account of (1.10–3) we evidently have

$$\exp z = \exp(x+iy) = \exp x \cdot \exp iy = \exp x \ (c(y)+is(y))$$

where $c(y)$ and $s(y)$ are real functions depending on y only. Taking the derivative we find

$$\exp' z = \frac{\exp x}{i} (c'(y)+i s'(y))$$

where the dots on the right denote differentiation with respect to y. Hence

$$c'(y) = -s(y), \qquad s'(y) = c(y).$$

Since $c(0) = 1$, $s(0) = 0$, the solutions are

$$c(y) = \cos y, \qquad s(y) = \sin y.$$

Hence the exponential function takes the canonical form

$$\boxed{\exp z = \exp x \cdot (\cos y + i \sin y).} \tag{1.10–5}$$

From (1.10–4) we deduce *Euler's formulas*

$$\cos y = \tfrac{1}{2}\{\exp iy + \exp(-iy)\}, \qquad \sin y = \frac{1}{2i}\{\exp iy - \exp(-iy)\} \tag{1.10–6}$$

1.10.4 – Circular functions

Hitherto we did not define the circular functions in a rigorous manner. The Euler formulas enable us to fill this gap, since they have still a meaning when y is a complex variable. Accordingly we may define the *circular functions* $\cos z$ and $\sin z$ of a complex variable z by putting

$$\boxed{\begin{aligned} \cos z &= \tfrac{1}{2}\{\exp iz + \exp(-iz)\}, \\ \sin z &= \frac{1}{2i}\{\exp iz - \exp(-iz)\}. \end{aligned}} \tag{1.10–7}$$

Obviously the circular functions are integral functions. They are represented by the power series

$$\boxed{\cos z = \sum_{\nu=0}^{\infty} (-1)^{\nu} \frac{z^{2\nu}}{(2\nu)!},} \tag{1.10–8}$$

$$\boxed{\sin z = \sum_{\nu=0}^{\infty} (-1)^{\nu} \frac{z^{2\nu+1}}{(2\nu+1)!}.} \tag{1.10–9}$$

By means of straight-forward algebraic computations the well-known addition theorems can be established. They turn out to be valid for all values of z. In particular we mention the *fundamental identity*

$$\boxed{\cos^2 z + \sin^2 z = 1.} \tag{1.10–10}$$

In many cases it is convenient to introduce the functions

$$\tan z = \frac{\sin z}{\cos z}, \quad \operatorname{ctn} z = \frac{\cos z}{\sin z}, \quad \sec z = \frac{1}{\cos z}, \quad \csc z = \frac{1}{\sin z}.$$

1.10.5 – Hyperbolic functions

Functions of a similar nature are the *hyperbolic functions*

$$\boxed{\begin{aligned} \cosh z &= \tfrac{1}{2}\{\exp z + \exp(-z)\}, \\ \sinh z &= \tfrac{1}{2}\{\exp z - \exp(-z)\}, \end{aligned}} \tag{1.10–11}$$

these functions also being integral functions. They are closely related to the circular functions. In fact, we have

$$\boxed{\cos iz = \cosh z, \qquad \sin iz = i \sinh z.} \tag{1.10–12}$$

The fundamental identity now appears as

$$\boxed{\cosh^2 z - \sinh^2 z = 1.} \tag{1.10–13}$$

Applying the addition theorems for circular functions we obtain the canonical equations, putting $z = x+iy$,

$$\cos z = \cos x \cosh y - i \sin x \sinh y, \tag{1.10–14}$$

$$\sin z = \sin x \cosh y + i \cos x \sinh y. \tag{1.10–15}$$

The modulus of these functions is now readily obtained. First we have, taking account of (1.10–10) and (1.10–12),

$$\begin{aligned}|\cos z|^2 &= \cos^2 x \cosh^2 y + \sin^2 x \sinh^2 y \\ &= \cos^2 x(1+\sinh^2 y) + \sin^2 x \sinh^2 y \\ &= \cos^2 x + (\cos^2 x + \sin^2 x) \sinh^2 y = \cos^2 x + \sinh^2 y\end{aligned}$$

and so

$$|\cos z| = \sqrt{\cos^2 x + \sinh^2 y}. \tag{1.10–16}$$

Similarly

$$|\sin z| = \sqrt{\sin^2 x + \sinh^2 y}. \tag{1.10–17}$$

1.10.6 – Zeros of the circular functions

Now we turn to the problem of finding the zeros of the circular functions. First we may state that *the zeros of the circular functions are real.* In fact, it follows from (1.10–16) and (1.10–17) that the zeros must satisfy the condition

$$\sinh y = 0,$$

i.e.,

$$\exp y = 1.$$

Since the real function $\exp y$ increases monotonously as y increases (this follows at once from the functional equation) we conclude that $y = 0$. Hence the problem is reduced to the case of functions of a real variable.

First we consider the following introductory problem, consisting in finding a real differentiable function $y(x)$ defined in the range $-1 \leqq x \leqq 1$ and satisfying the equation

$$\sin y = x, \tag{1.10–18}$$

taking the value 0 for $x = 0$.

Assuming we are already in possession of a function of this nature we find by differentiation

$$1 = \frac{d}{dx} \sin y(x) = \cos y(x) \cdot y' = y'\sqrt{1-x^2}.$$

Hence a function as desired can only be

$$y(x) = \int_0^x \frac{dt}{\sqrt{1-t^2}}, \qquad -1 \leqq x \leqq 1. \tag{1.10–19}$$

There could arise some doubt as to the convergence of the integral for $x = \pm 1$. But the integral is actually convergent, for, assuming $0 < x < 1$,

$$\int_0^x \frac{dt}{\sqrt{1-t^2}} < \int_0^x \frac{dt}{\sqrt{1-t}} = 2(1-\sqrt{1-x}) < 2,$$

whilst the function increases as x increases. Inserting (1.10–19) into (1.10–18) we find the function $\sin y(x)$ whose derivative turns out to be equal to 1. Hence $\sin y(x) = x$, since the function vanishes at $x = 0$.

Now we introduce the number π by means of the formula

$$\boxed{\tfrac{1}{2}\pi = \int_0^1 \frac{dt}{\sqrt{1-t^2}}.} \tag{1.10–20}$$

Obviously

$$\sin \tfrac{1}{2}\pi = 1 \tag{1.10–21}$$

and, by virtue of (1.10–10),

$$\cos \tfrac{1}{2}\pi = 0. \tag{1.10–22}$$

It is easy to prove that $\cos z$ does not possess zeros between 0 and $\frac{1}{2}\pi$, taking account of the fact that the integral (1.10–19) increases monotonously. The further development of the elementary theory of the circular function does not present any difficulty. On applying the addition theorem we get the result that *the zeros of the function* $\cos z$ *are at*

$$z = \tfrac{1}{2}\pi + k\pi, \qquad k = 0, \pm 1, \pm 2, \ldots, \tag{1.10–23}$$

and the zeros of the function $\sin z$ *are at*

$$z = k\pi, \qquad k = 0, \pm 1, \pm 2, \ldots. \tag{1.10–24}$$

Again by applying the additions theorem we find that *the circular functions are periodic with period* 2π. That means that the values of the functions are the same at the points z and $z+2\pi$. Consequently *the exponential function and the hyperbolic functions are periodic with period* $2\pi i$.

1.10.7 – Rigorous definition of the argument

We conclude with the remark that we are able to define rigorously the argument of z introduced in section 1.1.1. By Arg z we understand the set of values θ satisfying the equations

$$\cos\theta = \frac{\operatorname{Re} z}{|z|}, \qquad \sin\theta = \frac{\operatorname{Im} z}{|z|}, \qquad |z| \neq 0 \tag{1.10–25}$$

where z has been written in the form

$$z = \operatorname{Re} z + i \operatorname{Im} z. \tag{1.10–26}$$

An elementary discussion leads to the result that the solutions differ by a multiple of 2π. We may take a definite one satisfying $-\pi < \theta \leq \pi$. This is the principal argument introduced in section 1.1.1.

1.11 – The logarithm and the power

1.11.1 – The logarithm of a real variable

It is our aim to define a function which satisfies the equation

$$\exp w = z, \tag{1.11–1}$$

where z is any complex number different from zero. First we consider the equation

$$\exp y = x, \tag{1.11–2}$$

where $x > 0$ and y are real numbers. Assume that $y(x)$ is a real differentiable function satisfying (1.11–2) with $y(1) = 0$. By differentiation we find

$$y'(x) \exp y(x) = 1,$$

whence

$$y'(x) = \frac{1}{x}$$

and the desired function must be

$$\log x = \int_1^x \frac{dt}{t}, \qquad x > 0, \tag{1.11–3}$$

the *logarithm* of x. It is easily verified that this function is actually a solution of (1.11–2). For the derivative of exp log x is 1 and hence this function is the function x (since $\log x = 0$ for $x = 1$).

Taking account of

$$(\log ax)' = a \log' ax = \frac{1}{x},$$

we have

$$\log ax = C + \log x$$

and by putting $x = 1$ we find $C = \log a$. Thus we obtain the *functional equation* of the logarithm

$$\boxed{\log ax = \log a + \log x,} \tag{1.11–4}$$

where a and x are *real* numbers.

The elementary theory of the logarithmic function can now easily be developed. Since $\log 2^n = n \log 2$, n being an integer, we find that $\log x$ increases beyond any bound as $x \to \infty$. And from $\log 1/x = -\log x$ we find that $\log x \to -\infty$ as $x \to 0$.

The logarithm is, however, a weakly increasing function, i.e., $\log x$ tends to ∞ more slowly than x does. This is expressed by

$$\boxed{\lim_{x\to\infty} \frac{\log x}{x} = 0.} \tag{1.11–5}$$

A simple proof is the following. Let $t > 1$; then $t^{-1} < t^{-\frac{1}{2}}$. Hence, if $x > 1$,

$$\log x = \int_1^x \frac{dt}{t} \leqq \int_1^x \frac{dt}{\sqrt{t}} = 2(\sqrt{x}-1) < 2\sqrt{x}$$

and so

$$\frac{\log x}{x} < \frac{2}{\sqrt{x}}.$$

1.11.2 – THE LOGARITHM OF A COMPLEX VARIABLE

Now we turn to the consideration of the equation (1.11–1). Putting z in its polar form (1.1–3) and $w = u + iv$ we have the equivalent equation

$$\exp u \cdot (\cos v + i \sin v) = r(\cos \theta + i \sin \theta). \tag{1.11–6}$$

Equating real and imaginary parts and taking account of (1.10–10) and the remark at the end of section 1.10.6 we readily find

$$u = \log r, \qquad v = \theta + 2k\pi, \qquad k = 0, \pm 1, \pm 2, \ldots.$$

As a consequence all solutions of (1.11–5) are represented by

$$\operatorname{Log} z = \log |z| + i \operatorname{Arg} z. \tag{1.11–7}$$

The symbol $\operatorname{Log} z$ does not designate a function in the ordinary sense, for it lets correspond infinitely many values to a given value of z. On the other hand *the expression*

$$\boxed{\log z = \log |z| + i \arg z} \tag{1.11–8}$$

is a single-valued function defined in the principal region. It still has a meaning for negative real values of z when we take $\arg z = \pi$. The function (1.11–8) is called the *principal logarithm.*

It should be noticed that the principal logarithm does not satisfy a functional equation of the type (1.11–4), for the principal argument of the product of two numbers need not be equal to the sum of the principal arguments of the factors.

The principal logarithm is holomorphic throughout the principal region.

First we observe that on account of the theorem of section 1.2.2 and the expression (1.11–3) of $\log z$ for real values of z the function

$$w = \log |z| + i \arg z$$

is continuous throughout the principal region. Further it is apparent that it does not take the same values at two different points. Hence, if $|h|$ is sufficiently small and if we put

$$k = \log (z+h) - \log z$$

then $k \to 0$ as $h \to 0$, while $k \neq 0$ when $h \neq 0$. From

$$\frac{\log (z+h) - \log z}{h} = \frac{k}{z+h-z} = \frac{k}{\exp (w+k) - \exp w} \to \frac{1}{\exp' w} = \frac{1}{\exp w}$$

as $h \to 0$ we infer that

$$\boxed{\log' z = \frac{1}{z},} \qquad z + |z| \neq 0. \qquad (1.11\text{–}9)$$

Since

$$\frac{\log (1+z/n)}{1/n} \to z \log' 1 = z,$$

as $n \to \infty$, we easily deduce

$$\boxed{\exp z = \lim_{n\to\infty} \left(1 + \frac{z}{n}\right)^n.} \qquad (1.11\text{–}10)$$

The function $\operatorname{Log} z$ is an example of a *multiply valued function.* We shall not try to give here a general definition of a function of this nature. This problem will concern us in Vol. II. We may write

$$\operatorname{Log} z = \log z + 2k\pi i, \quad k = 0, \pm 1, \pm 2, \ldots, \qquad (1.11\text{–}11)$$

and we see that to every given value of k corresponds a holomorphic function defined in the principal region. A function of this kind is called a *branch* of the multiply valued function. As long as we are interested in the local properties of a function the study of a branch suffices.

1.11.3 – The power with variable exponent

If s is a real number and z a natural number then, by virtue of (1.11–4), $\log s^z = z \log s$. It is, therefore, natural to define,

$$\boxed{s^z = \exp(z \log s),} \qquad s \neq 0, \qquad (1.11\text{–}12)$$

where s is a fixed complex number and z a complex variable. Hence s^z is an integral function, its derivative being

$$(s^z)' = s^z \log s. \qquad (1.11\text{–}13)$$

The number e is defined by

$$\mathrm{e} = \exp 1, \qquad (1.11\text{–}14)$$

i.e.,

$$\boxed{\mathrm{e} = \sum_{\nu=0}^{\infty} \frac{1}{\nu!} = \lim_{n\to\infty} \left(1 + \frac{1}{n}\right)^n.} \qquad (1.11\text{–}15)$$

Hence $\log \mathrm{e} = 1$ and in accordance with (1.11–12)

$$\mathrm{e}^z = \exp z. \qquad (1.11\text{–}16)$$

This explains the name "exponential function" for $\exp z$.

1.11.4 – The power with variable basis

We may invert the roles of s and z in (1.11–12) and introduce the function

$$z^s = \exp(s \log z), \qquad z + |z| \neq 0. \qquad (1.11\text{–}17)$$

This function is holomorphic in the principal region its derivative being

$$(z^s)' = \frac{s}{z} z^s. \qquad (1.11\text{–}18)$$

The particular case $s = p/q$, where p and q are relatively prime integers, deserves special mention. It is customary to denote the function in this case by another symbol, viz.,

$$\sqrt[q]{z^p} = z^{p/q}. \qquad (1.11\text{–}19)$$

In particular we write $\sqrt{z}$ when $p = 1$, $q = 2$.

1.12 – The inverse circular and hyperbolic functions

1.12.1 – The inverse cosine

The equation

$$\cos w = z, \qquad (1.12\text{–}1)$$

where z is a given complex number possesses infinitely many solutions. In fact, by virtue of (1.10–7) we have

$$\exp^2 iw - 2z \exp iw + 1 = 0. \tag{1.12–2}$$

This equation, considered as a quadratic equation in terms of $\exp iw$, possesses two solutions whose product is equal to unity. One of the solutions is $\exp iw = z + i\sqrt{1-z^2}$ and so one of the solutions of (1.12–1) is the function

$$\boxed{\arccos z = \frac{1}{i} \log (z + i\sqrt{1-z^2})} \tag{1.12–3}$$

called the ***principal inverse cosine.***

The function $\sqrt{1-z^2}$ is holomorphic in the complex plane, supposed cut along the real axis from $-\infty$ to -1 and from $+1$ to $+\infty$ (fig. 1.12–1). The same statement holds for $\arccos z$. It is readily

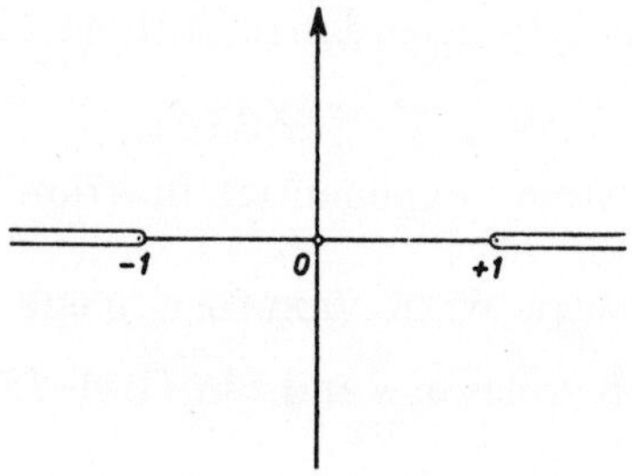

Fig. 1.12–1. Region of holomorphism of the inverse cosine

seen from (1.12–3) that the derivative is equal to

$$(\arccos z)' = \frac{-1}{\sqrt{1-z^2}} \tag{1.12–4}$$

and the function is still continuous at $z = \pm 1$.

It is easy to see that all solutions of (1.12–1) may be represented by

$$\operatorname{Arccos} z = \begin{cases} \arccos z + 2k\pi, \\ -\arccos z + 2k\pi, \end{cases} \quad k = 0, \pm 1, \pm 2, \ldots. \tag{1.12–5}$$

Hence there are two sequences of values at every point z, the difference between the values of the same sequence being a multiple of 2π.

1.12.2 – The inverse sine

The solutions of the equation

$$\sin w = z \tag{1.12–6}$$

are the same as those of $\cos(\frac{1}{2}\pi - w) = z$. The particular solution

$$\boxed{\arcsin z = \tfrac{1}{2}\pi + i\log(z + i\sqrt{1-z^2})} \qquad (1.12\text{–}7)$$

is the *principal inverse sine.* This function is holomorphic in the same region as arc cos z, its derivative being

$$(\arcsin z)' = \frac{1}{\sqrt{1-z^2}}. \qquad (1.12\text{–}8)$$

1.12.3 – The inverse tangent

The solutions of the equation

$$\tan w = z, \qquad (1.12\text{–}9)$$

where z is a given number, are found from

$$z = \frac{\sin w}{\cos w} = \frac{1}{i}\,\frac{\exp iw - \exp(-iw)}{\exp iw + \exp(-iw)} = -i\,\frac{\exp 2iw - 1}{\exp 2iw + 1}$$

or

$$\exp 2iw = \frac{1+iz}{1-iz}.$$

Hence we must suppose $z \neq \pm i$. The particular solution

$$\boxed{\arctan z = \frac{1}{2i}\log\frac{1+iz}{1-iz}} \qquad (1.12\text{–}10)$$

is called the ***principal inverse tangent.*** It is holomorphic in the complex plane, supposed cut along the imaginary axis from $-\infty i$ to $-i$ and from i to ∞i, (fig. 1.12–2), its derivative being

$$(\arctan z)' = \frac{1}{1+z^2}. \qquad (1.12\text{–}11)$$

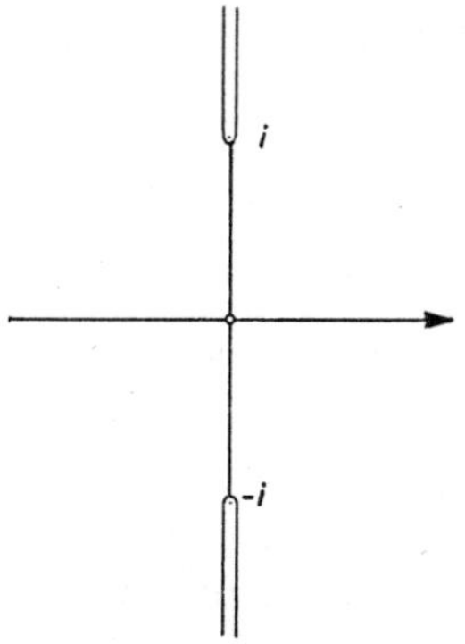

Fig. 1.12–2. Region of holomorphism of the inverse tangent

1.12.4 – The inverse hyperbolic functions

In an analogous manner we may also introduce the inverse of the hyperbolic functions.

First we consider the equation

$$\cosh w = z \tag{1.12–12}$$

or

$$\exp^2 w - 2z \exp w + 1 = 0.$$

The particular solution

$$\boxed{\operatorname{arcosh} z = \log (z+\sqrt{z^2-1})} \tag{1.12–13}$$

is called the ***principal inverse hyperbolic cosine.*** This function is holomorphic in the complex plane cut along the real axis from -1 to $+1$.

The equation

$$\sinh w = z \tag{1.12–14}$$

is equivalent to

$$\exp^2 w - 2z \exp w - 1 = 0$$

and the particular solution

$$\boxed{\operatorname{arsinh} z = \log (z+\sqrt{z^2+1})} \tag{1.12–15}$$

is called the ***principal inverse hyperbolic sine.*** The function is holomorphic in the same region as arctan z.

Finally we find that the equation

$$\tanh w = z \tag{1.12–16}$$

has the same solutions as

$$\exp 2w = \frac{1+z}{1-z}$$

and the particular solution

$$\boxed{\operatorname{artanh} z = \tfrac{1}{2} \log \frac{1+z}{1-z}} \tag{1.12–17}$$

is the ***principal inverse hyperbolic tangent.*** This function is holomorphic in the same region as arccos z.

The principal functions defined previously are special branches of certain multiple-valued functions. Until further notice we are only interested in single-valued functions and we may, therefore, henceforth omit the adjective "principal".

CHAPTER 2

CAUCHY'S INTEGRAL THEOREM AND ITS COROLLARIES - EXPANSION IN TAYLOR SERIES

2.1 - Chains and cycles

2.1.1 - DEFINITIONS OF A CHAIN AND A CYCLE

It is our aim to study integrals of complex functions along curves and systems of curves. In order to be able to state the theorems in a sufficiently general form we shall make some preliminary remarks of topological character.

By the *distance* of two point sets $\mathfrak{A}$ and $\mathfrak{B}$ we understand the greatest lower bound ϱ of the distances between any point a of $\mathfrak{A}$ and any point b of $\mathfrak{B}$. If $\mathfrak{A}$ and $\mathfrak{B}$ are closed and at least one of them is bounded, we can find a pair of points a and b with exactly the distance ϱ. If in addition the two sets are disjoint, we have $\varrho > 0$. This is well-known from elementary point set theory.

By a *smooth* arc C we understand a continuous curve

$$z(t) = x(t)+iy(t), \tag{2.1–1}$$

where t runs through a closed interval, say $0 \leqq t \leqq 1$ and $x(t)$ and $y(t)$ are continuously differentiable, i.e., the derivatives $x'(t)$, $y'(t)$ exist and are continuous throughout the range of t, while, moreover, the derivatives do not vanish simultaneously for any value of t.

Since a smooth arc is a continuous curve it can always be *oriented*; this means that we can describe the curve in a certain sense (see 1.2.4). By inverting this sense of description we obtain the *oppositely oriented* curve $-C$.

By a *chain* we shall mean a formal sum $\sum_{\nu} C_{\nu}$ of a finite number of continuous arcs C_n, each being oriented. One and the same arc can enter in this sum repeatedly and with either of its orientations. If these arcs are smooth the chain is called *regular*.

A chain is called *closed* or a *cycle* if each point is beginning point of just as many of the arcs C_n as it is end point.

A special case of a chain is obtained if a finite number of smooth arcs is joined in order in such a manner that the initial point of each coincides with the terminal point of the preceding arc; then *a regular curve* is formed. Such a curve is continuous and *piecewise smooth.*

The initial point and terminal point of a *closed regular curve* coincide. When the curve is also a contour (1.2.5) we term it a *regular contour.* The circumference of a circle is a regular contour, also the perimeter of a rectangle.

It is always possible to join two points of a region (1.2.4) by a regular curve, for a polygonal arc is such a curve.

Let $f(z)$ denote a complex function *continuous along the chain.* That means: given $\varepsilon > 0$ and a point z_0 on one of the arcs of C we can find a δ such that $|f(z)-f(z_0)| < \varepsilon$, provided $|z-z_0| < \delta$ and z is also on an arc of the chain.

The set of points belonging to all arcs of a chain is a bounded and closed set. Hence, according to the theorem of section 1.2.3, a function continuous along the chain is there uniformly continuous.

2.1.2 – The winding number

Let C denote a continuous arc $z(t)$, where t varies in a certain closed interval, say $0 \leqq t \leqq 1$. Let z be a point not on C and ζ a point of C. Assume in the first place that C is included in a circle that does not contain z, (fig. 2.1–1). In accordance with section 1.2.2. we

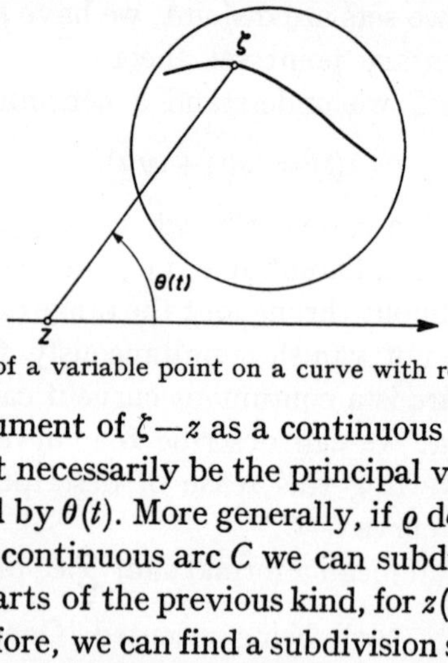

Fig. 2.1–1. Argument of a variable point on a curve with respect to a given point

can define the argument of $\zeta - z$ as a continuous function of t along the arc. It need not necessarily be the principal value. This function shall be designated by $\theta(t)$. More generally, if ϱ denotes the distance from a point z to a continuous arc C we can subdivide the arc into a finite number of parts of the previous kind, for $z(t)$ is uniformly continuous and, therefore, we can find a subdivision such that each part is included in a circle of radius $\frac{1}{2}\varrho$. The function $\theta(t)$ is uniquely determined but for a multiple of 2π. Now we introduce the number

$$2\pi\Omega_C(z) \tag{2.1–2}$$

being equal to $\theta(1)-\theta(0)$, the *increment* of the argument of $\zeta - z$ along the arc. It is easy to see that this number depends continuously on z and changes sign if we reverse the orientation of the arc. Moreover, if C is subdivided into the arcs C_1 and C_2, we have

$$\Omega_C(z) = \Omega_{C_1}(z) + \Omega_{C_2}(z). \tag{2.1–3}$$

If we replace C by an inscribed polygon L whose segments have a length less than ϱ, then obviously

$$\Omega_L(z) = \Omega_C(z). \tag{2.1–4}$$

If z is not on any arc C_ν of a chain C, we define

$$\Omega_C(z) = \sum_\nu \Omega_{C_\nu}(z). \tag{2.1–5}$$

It is easy to see that this definition is additive with respect to C.

A simple reasoning shows that $\Omega_C(z)$ is an integer whenever C is a cycle. In this event $\Omega_C(z)$ is called the *winding number* of the cycle with respect to z, (fig. 2.1–2). By definition the winding number

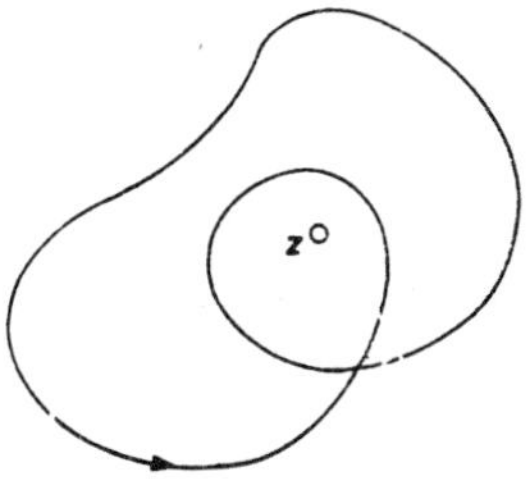

Fig. 2.1–2. The winding number of the cycle with respect to z is two

of a cycle with respect to $z = \infty$ is considered to be zero. The winding number is continuous as regards z and constant throughout any region that is disjoint from the arcs of C.

For instance, the winding number of the circumference of a circle traversed one time in the counter-clockwise sense is $+1$ with respect to each of its interior points and 0 with respect to a point outside.

2.1.3 – Homology

A cycle C is said to be *homologous* 0 in an open set $\mathfrak{A}$, written as

$$C \sim 0, \tag{2.1–6}$$

if the winding number of C with respect to each point not in $\mathfrak{A}$ is zero. It is understood that C is included in $\mathfrak{A}$.

A chain A and a chain B are said to be *homologous* in an open set $\mathfrak{A}$

$$A \sim B, \tag{2.1–7}$$

if $A - B$ is a cycle homologous 0 in $\mathfrak{A}$. It is easy to prove that the relation of homology is reflexive, symmetric and transitive.

2.2 – The connectivity of a region

2.2.1 – Simply connected regions

A region is said to be *simply connected* if each cycle in the region is homologous to zero. This means that the winding number of every cycle in the region with respect to a point outside the region is zero.

Thus, for instance, the interior of a circle or of a rectangle is simply connected. More generally:

A convex open set is a simply connected region.

We recall that a set is said to be convex if for each pair of points a, b belonging to the set the entire segment (a, b) also belongs to the set. It is plain that an open convex set is a region.

Let z denote a point outside the region. There exists a half ray issuing from z which has no point in common with the region, for in the contrary case two diametric half rays would meet the set and hence z would belong to the set.

Now we observe that a movement of the z-plane in itself (being the product of a translation and a rotation) does not affect the winding number. More precisely, if a movement carries z into z^* and C into C^* then

$$\Omega_{C^*}(z^*) = \Omega_C(z). \tag{2.2–1}$$

Accordingly we may suppose that $z = 0$ and that the half ray mentioned above coincides with the negative real axis. Under this assumption the cycle is contained in the principal region and the function $\theta(t)$ of section 2.1.2 necessary for the evaluation of $\Omega_C(0)$ can be taken as the principal argument of the corresponding number ζ on a component of C. From the definition of cycle it is now clear that $\Omega_C(0) = 0$.

In accordance with this theorem we shall consider the entire z-plane as simply connected.

2.2.2 – Multiply connected regions

A region which is not simply connected is called *multiply connected*. It may occur that we can find an *r-dimensional base*. By that is understood a set of r cycles $C_1, \ldots, C_r$ such that

(i) they are *linearly independent*, i.e., a homology

$$m_1C_1 + \ldots + m_rC_r \sim 0 \tag{2.2–2}$$

entails $m_1 = \ldots = m_r = 0$;

(ii) each cycle C is homologous to a *linear combination* (with integral coefficients)

$$C \sim m_1C_1 + \ldots + m_rC_r. \tag{2.2–3}$$

By virtue of (i) the coefficients $m_1, \ldots, m_r$ in (2.2–3) are uniquely determined. By well-known arguments of linear algebra it can be proved that all bases consist of the same number of elements. This number augmented by one, i.e., $r+1$, is called the *connectivity* of the region. If no base of a finite number of elements exists, the connectivity is said to be infinite. A base of a simply connected region is always empty.

2.2.3 – Illustrative examples

We may illustrate the previous considerations in simple examples. Consider the ring-shaped region $0 < R_1 < |z| < R_2$, (fig. 2.2–1).

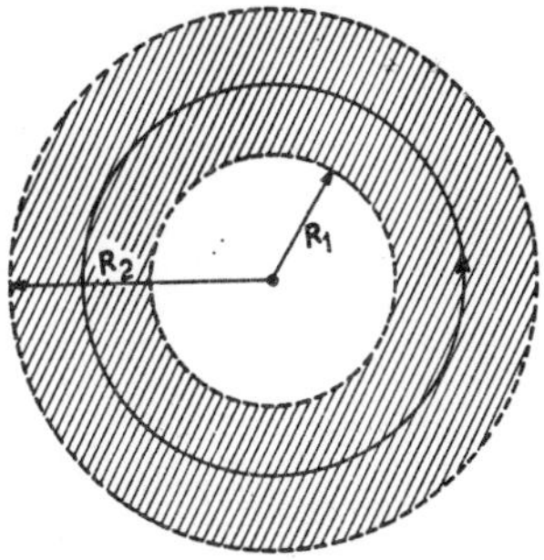

Fig. 2.2–1. The connectivity of a ring-shaped region

It is plain that the winding number of any cycle in the region with respect to a point outside the largest circle is zero. This can be proved by applying the same arguments as in the proof of the theorem of section 2.2.1. On the other hand, the winding number with respect to a point inside the smallest circle of the circumference $|z| = r$ with $R_1 < r < R_2$ is unity, provided the circumference is traversed in the counter-clockwise sense. Hence, if C_1 denotes this circumference we must have $C - mC_1 \sim 0$, or

$$C \sim mC_1,$$

where m denotes the winding number of C with respect to the origin. Thus we proved the existence of a base consisting of one element. The connectivity of an annulus is 2.

An example of an infinitely connected region is the z-plane from which the points $z = 0, 1, 2, \ldots$ are removed.

2.3 – The line integral of a complex function

2.3.1 – Definition of a line integral

We wish to define the *line integral* of a complex function $f(z)$ continuous along a smooth arc C. This may be done formally in the same way as for real integrals of one real variable. Divide the interval $0 \leqq t \leqq 1$ into n parts. Call the points of division t_0 $(= 0)$, $t_1, \ldots t_n$ $(= 1)$, with

$$t_0 < t_1 < \ldots < t_n.$$

The corresponding points $z(t_\nu)$ on the arc are denoted by z_ν. Select further n numbers τ_ν, $t_{\nu-1} \leqq \tau_\nu \leqq t_\nu$, $\nu = 1, \ldots, n$, and denote the corresponding points $z(\tau_\nu)$ on the arc by ζ_ν.

Now form the sum

$$s_n = \sum_{\nu=1}^{n} f(\zeta_\nu)(z_\nu - z_{\nu-1}). \tag{2.3-1}$$

We shall prove:

The sums s_n possess a limit s for $n \to \infty$ which is independent of the selection of the points of division and of the intermediate points, provided the maximal lengths of the rectilinear segments $(z_{\nu-1}, z_\nu)$ decrease to zero with increasing n.

Otherwise stated: Given $\varepsilon > 0$ a δ can be found such that

$$|s_n - s| < \varepsilon, \tag{2.3-2}$$

provided $\max |z_\nu - z_{\nu-1}| < \delta$, $\nu = 1, \ldots, n$.

The limiting value understood in this sense is called the *line integral of $f(z)$ taken along C* and denoted by

$$\int_C f(\zeta)\, d\zeta. \tag{2.3-3}$$

It is not necessary to use the symbol ζ under the sign of integration. We might also write $\int_C f(z)\, dz$, $\int_C f(u)\, du$, etc. if convenient.

2.3.2 – Existence of a line integral

We take the existence of real integrals of continuous functions for granted. Then, as we shall see, the complex case can be reduced to the real case in the following way. We may write

$$f\{z(t)\} = u\{x(t), y(t)\} + iv\{x(t), y(t)\} = \varphi(t) + i\psi(t). \tag{2.3-4}$$

Then (2.3–1) is

$$s_n = \sum_{\nu=1}^{n} \varphi(\tau_\nu)\{x(t_\nu) - x(t_{\nu-1})\} - \sum_{\nu=1}^{n} \psi(\tau_\nu)\{(y(t_\nu) - y(t_{\nu-1})\} +$$
$$+ i\left(\sum_{\nu=1}^{n} \psi(\tau_\nu)\{x(t_\nu) - x(t_{\nu-1})\} + \sum_{\nu=1}^{n} \varphi(\tau_\nu)\{y(t_\nu) - y(t_{\nu-1})\}\right). \tag{2.3-5}$$

The four separate sums on the right-hand side are all of the same type. Hence we may confine ourselves to the consideration of one of these sums. Let us take

$$\sigma_n = \sum_{\nu=1}^{n} \varphi(\tau_\nu)\{x(t_\nu)-x(t_{\nu-1})\}. \tag{2.3–6}$$

By virtue of the mean-value theorem of differential calculus we may write

$$\sigma_n = \sum_{\nu=1}^{n} \varphi(\tau_\nu)\, x'(\tau_\nu^{(1)})\,(t_\nu-t_{\nu-1}), \tag{2.3–7}$$

where

$$t_{\nu-1} < \tau_\nu^{(1)} < t_\nu, \qquad \nu = 1, \ldots, n.$$

It is natural to compare (2.3–7) with the Riemann sum

$$\sigma_n^* = \sum_{\nu=1}^{n} \varphi(\tau_\nu)\, x'(\tau_\nu)\,(t_\nu-t_{\nu-1}) \tag{2.3–8}$$

which has a limit as max $(t_\nu-t_{\nu-1})$ tends to zero. We wish to prove that σ_n has the same limit. An estimate of the difference $\sigma_n^*-\sigma_n$ is found from

$$|\sigma_n^*-\sigma_n| \leqq \sum_{\nu=1}^{n} |\varphi(\tau_\nu)|\;|x'(\tau_\nu)-x'(\tau_\nu^{(1)})|\;(t_\nu-t_{\nu-1}). \tag{2.3–9}$$

Since $\varphi(t)$ is continuous in a closed interval, this function is bounded, i.e., there exists a real constant A such that $|\varphi(t)| < A$. The function $x'(t)$, being continuous, is also uniformly continuous. Hence, given $\varepsilon > 0$, we can find an η_1 such that

$$|x'(\tau_\nu)-x'(\tau_\nu^{(1)})| < \frac{\varepsilon}{2A}, \tag{2.3–10}$$

provided max $(t_\nu-t_{\nu-1}) < \eta_1$. As a consequence we find

$$|\sigma_n^*-\sigma_n| < \tfrac{1}{2}\varepsilon. \tag{2.3–11}$$

Since σ_n^* approximates the Riemann integral

$$\int_0^1 \varphi(t)\,x'(t)\,dt, \tag{2.3–12}$$

we can find an η_2 such that

$$\left|\sigma_n^* - \int_0^1 \varphi(t)\,x'(t)\,dt\right| < \tfrac{1}{2}\varepsilon, \tag{2.3–13}$$

provided max $(t_\nu-t_{\nu-1}) < \eta_2$. Hence, we have from (2.3–11) and (2.3–13)

$$\left|\sigma_n - \int_0^1 \varphi(t)\,x'(t)\,dt\right| < \varepsilon, \tag{2.3–14}$$

provided max $(t_\nu-t_{\nu-1}) < \eta = \min(\eta_1, \eta_2)$.

Thus it appears that s_n tends to a limit s, provided max $(t_\nu-t_{\nu-1})$ tends to zero as $|z_\nu-z_{\nu-1}|$ tends to zero.

This proves to be true, for

$$\sqrt{\{x'(t)\}^2+(y'(t))^2}$$

is continuous for $0 \leqq t \leqq 1$ and does not vanish; hence it possesses a positive minimum μ. On the other hand we have

$$|z_\nu - z_{\nu-1}| = (t_\nu - t_{\nu-1})\sqrt{\{x'(\tau_\nu^{(1)})\}^2+\{y'(\tau_\nu^{(2)})\}^2} \qquad (2.3\text{–}15)$$

for suitably selected $\tau_\nu^{(1)}$, $\tau_\nu^{(2)}$ and we have, therefore,

$$|z_\nu - z_{\nu-1}| \geqq \mu(t_\nu - t_{\nu-1}), \qquad \nu = 1, \ldots, n. \qquad (2.3\text{–}16)$$

Hence we can make $\max\,(t_\nu - t_{\nu-1})$ arbitrarily small by taking $\max|z_\nu - z_{\nu-1}|$ sufficiently small. This completes the proof.

If we assume C to be a regular curve composed of r smooth arcs $C_1, \ldots, C_r$, we can maintain the definition of line integral along C. Take at first the vertices among the points of division. Then

$$\sum_{\nu=1}^{n} f(\zeta_\nu)(z_\nu - z_{\nu-1}) = \sum_{1}^{k_1} + \sum_{k_1+1}^{k_2} + \ldots + \sum_{k_{r-1}+1}^{k_r}, \quad k_r = n, \qquad (2.2\text{–}17)$$

where on the right-hand side the respective sums are denoted by the sign $\sum$ only. On the first arc there are k_1+1 points of division, on the second there are $k_2 - k_1 + 1$, etc. On refining the subdivision we find

$$\int_C f(\zeta)\,d\zeta = \int_{C_1} f(\zeta)\,d\zeta + \ldots + \int_{C_r} f(\zeta)\,d\zeta. \qquad (2.3\text{–}18)$$

We shall see, however, that we obtain the same result, when the vertices of C are not always chosen as the points of division. Let these vertices be a_λ, $\lambda = 0, \ldots, r$; we may add them to the points of division which occur in the definition of the sum. Then we get additional terms of the type

$$(a_\lambda - z_{\nu-1})\,f(\zeta_\nu^{(1)}) + (z_\nu - a_\lambda)\,f(\zeta_\nu^{(2)}).$$

Since $f(z)$ is bounded along the curve and only a finite number of these terms is added we find that s_n is modified by a number whose absolute value may be taken arbitrarily small. Hence it does not matter if we take or do not take some of the vertices of the curve C among the points of division.

This result makes it natural to define the line integral along any regular chain $C = \sum_\nu C_\nu$ by the formula

$$\int_C f(\zeta)\,d\zeta = \sum_\nu \int_{C_\nu} f(\zeta)\,d\zeta. \qquad (2.3\text{–}19)$$

The chain C is called the *path* of integration.

2.3.3 – Evaluation of simple integrals

In some simple cases a line integral can be evaluated on carrying out directly the process described by the definition.

Let C be a regular curve joining the points a and b. We wish to evaluate $\int_C d\zeta$. Now $f(z) = 1$ and every approximating sum is

$$(z_1-z_0)+(z_2-z_1)+\ldots+(z_n-z_{n-1}) = b-a.$$

Hence the limit is also $b-a$, independent of the choice of the curve C. We may write this as

$$\int_a^b d\zeta = b-a. \tag{2.3–20}$$

If C denotes a (regular) cycle, we have

$$\int_C d\zeta = 0. \tag{2.3–21}$$

In the same way we can find $\int_C \zeta\, d\zeta$. An approximating sum is

$$z_1(z_1-z_0)+z_2(z_2-z_1)+\ldots+z_n(z_n-z_{n-1}),$$

but also

$$z_0(z_1-z_0)+z_1(z_2-z_1)+\ldots+z_{n-1}(z_n-z_{n-1}).$$

Since these sums must have the same limit, we find by adding that this limit must be $\frac{1}{2}(b^2-a^2)$ and consequently

$$\int_a^b \zeta\, d\zeta = \tfrac{1}{2}(b^2-a^2). \tag{2.3–22}$$

If C denotes a cycle, we have

$$\int_C \zeta\, d\zeta = 0. \tag{2.3–23}$$

2.3.4 – Change of variable under the sign of integration

Let C denote a smooth arc represented by $z = z(t)$, $0 \leqq t \leqq 1$. Taking account of the considerations of section 2.3.2 we evidently have

$$\int_C f(\zeta)\, d\zeta = \int_0^1 \{u(x(t), y(t))+iv(x(t), y(t))\}(x'(t)+iy'(t))\, dt \tag{2.3–24}$$

or, more concisely,

$$\int_C f(\zeta)\, d\zeta = \int_0^1 f(z(t))\, z'(t)\, dt. \tag{2.3–25}$$

It should be noted that the integral on the left has been defined independently of the particular choice of a parameter along the arc.

It is now an easy matter to state a theorem which extends the formula for the change of a variable under the sign of integration to the complex case.

Let $g(z)$ be a continuous function, having in addition a continuous derivative at every point of a smooth arc C vanishing nowhere along C. It is evident that $g(z(t))$ defines another smooth arc C^*, briefly $C^* = g(C)$. Denoting the de.ivative of $g(z)$ with respect to z by $g'(z)$ we evidently have, when $f(z)$ is another function continuous along C^*,

$$\int_{C^*} f(\zeta)\,d\zeta = \int_0^1 f\{g(z(t))\}\frac{d}{dt}g(z(t))\,dt = \int_0^1 f(g\{z(t)\})\,g'\{z(t)\}z'(t)\,dt.$$

Hence

$$\boxed{\int_{C^*} f(\zeta)\,d\zeta = \int_C f\{g(\zeta)\}g'(\zeta)\,d\zeta,} \quad C^* = g(C). \qquad (2.3\text{–}26)$$

2.3.5 – The fundamental theorem of integral calculus

The following theorem is of frequent use.

Suppose that $f(z)$ is continuous and the derivative of another function $F(z)$ throughout a certain region $\mathfrak{R}$. Let C denote any smooth arc in $\mathfrak{R}$ connecting the points a and b, traversed from a to b. Then, integrating along C

$$\boxed{\int_a^b f(\zeta)\,d\zeta = F(b)-F(a),} \quad F'(z) = f(z), \qquad (2.3\text{–}27)$$

independent of the connecting arc.

Put

$$F(z) = U(x, y)+iV(x, y).$$

Taking account of the conditions of monogenity (1.3–7) we have

$$f(z) = u+iv = U_x+iV_x = U_x-iU_y = V_y+iV_x.$$

Hence, according to (2.3–24),

$$\begin{aligned}\int_a^b f(\zeta)\,d\zeta &= \int_0^1 (U_x x'+U_y y')\,dt+i\int_0^1 (V_x x'+V_y y')\,dt\\ &= U\{x(1), y(1)\}-U\{x(0), y(0)\}\\ &\quad +i\,(V\{x(1), y(1)\}-V\{(x(0), y(0)\})\\ &= F(b)-F(a).\end{aligned}$$

It is plain that the particular results (2.3–20) and (2.3–22) are included in this general theorem.

Another application is the following. We wish to evaluate the integral

$$\frac{1}{2\pi i}\int_C \frac{d\zeta}{\zeta - z} \qquad (2.3\text{–}28)$$

where z is a point not on the cycle C. A translation of the plane is expressed by the substitution $z^* = z+b$. If C is also translated we may assume $z = 0$. A rotation of the plane is expressed by $z^* = az$, where $|a| = 1$. According to (2.3–26) we have

$$\int_{C^*} \frac{d\zeta}{\zeta} = \int_C \frac{d\zeta}{\zeta}, \qquad (2.3\text{–}29)$$

where C^* arises from C by means of a rotation. Now C may be considered as the sum of smooth arcs such that either component is included in a region obtained from the z-plane by removing a half ray issuing from the origin. Let C_ν denote such an arc. By a suitable rotation we can place the half ray along the negative real axis. Now $1/z$ is the derivative of $\log z$ in the principal region. According to (2.3–27) we have

$$\int_{C_\nu^*} \frac{d\zeta}{\zeta} = \log \frac{r_2}{r_1} + 2\pi i \, \Omega_{C_\nu^*}(0),$$

where C_ν^* is the rotated arc C_ν and r_1, r_2 are the distances of the terminal points from the origin. Taking account of (2.3–29) and observing that the winding number is not affected by rotation or translation (in the sense described in section 2.2.1) we easily find by adding the contributions of all arcs

$$\boxed{\Omega_C(z) = \frac{1}{2\pi i} \int_C \frac{d\zeta}{\zeta - z},} \qquad (2.3\text{–}30)$$

an analytical expression for the winding number of a regular cycle.

In particular, *if C denotes a circle around the origin traversed in the counter-clockwise sense, then*

$$\int_C \frac{d\zeta}{\zeta} = 2\pi i. \qquad (2.3\text{–}31)$$

This result may be verified directly. Putting $z = re^{i\theta}$, r being the radius of the circle, we have by virtue of (2.3–25)

$$\int_C \frac{d\zeta}{\zeta} = \int_0^{2\pi} \frac{i r e^{i\theta} d\theta}{r e^{i\theta}} = i \int_0^{2\pi} d\theta = 2\pi i.$$

By the same method we find

$$\int_C \zeta^n d\zeta = 0, \qquad n \neq -1, \qquad (2.3\text{–}32)$$

where n is an integer, C being the same circle as before. In fact, the integral is equal to

$$i r^{n+1} \int_0^{2\pi} e^{i(n+1)\theta} d\theta = 0,$$

since the integral multiples of $2\pi i$ are zeros of the exponential function. But we can also use the argument that z^n is the derivative of $z^{n+1}/(n+1)$, provided that $n \neq -1$, and this function is holomorphic throughout the z-plane, except possibly at $z = 0$ (when $n < -1$).

2.3.6 – Integration by parts

Finally we wish to derive a formula which extends the rule for *integration by parts*.

If $f(z)$ and $g(z)$ are holomorphic throughout a region $\mathfrak{R}$ and if C denotes any regular path in $\mathfrak{R}$ connecting a and b, we evidently have by virtue of (2.3–27)

$$f(z)g(z)\Big|_a^b = f(b)g(b)-f(a)g(a) = \int_a^b \{f(\zeta)g(\zeta)\}' \, d\zeta$$
$$= \int_a^b f(\zeta)g'(\zeta)\,d\zeta + \int_a^b f'(\zeta)g(\zeta)\,d\zeta$$

and so

$$\boxed{\int_C f(\zeta)g'(\zeta)\,d\zeta = f(z)g(z)\Big|_a^b - \int_C f'(\zeta)g(\zeta)\,d\zeta.} \qquad (2.3\text{–}33)$$

2.4 – Properties of the line integrals of complex functions

2.4.1 – Fundamental properties

From the definition of line integral we easily deduce the following theorems (C denoting an arbitrary chain):

$$\int_{-C} f(\zeta)\,d\zeta = -\int_C f(\zeta)\,d\zeta. \qquad (2.4\text{–}1)$$

If a is a constant then

$$\int_C af(\zeta)\,d\zeta = a\int_C f(\zeta)\,d\zeta. \qquad (2.4\text{–}2)$$

Further

$$\int_C \Big(\sum_{\nu=1}^{n} f_\nu(\zeta)\Big)\,d\zeta = \sum_{\nu=1}^{n} \int_C f_\nu(\zeta)\,d\zeta. \qquad (2.4\text{–}3)$$

Under certain additional restrictions this result can be extended to the case of infinite series of functions, as we shall see in section 2.4.4.

Let $C_1, \ldots, C_r$ denote arbitrary chains. By $\sum_\nu C_\nu$ we understand a chain formed by all arcs that occur in $C_1, \ldots, C_r$ in such a fashion that if a certain arc occurs m_ν times in C_ν it occurs $\sum m_\nu$ times in $\sum C_\nu$. Then it is evident that

$$\int_{\Sigma C_\nu} f(\zeta)\, d\zeta = \sum_\nu \int_{C_\nu} f(\zeta)\, d\zeta. \tag{2.4–4}$$

2.4.2 – Estimate of a line integral

We now wish to establish a useful estimate of a line integral of a complex function.

If $f(z)$ is continuous then $|f(z)|$ is also continuous, since by virtue of the inequality (1.1–9)

$$\big|\,|f(z+h)|-|f(z)|\,\big| \leqq |f(z+h)-f(z)|. \tag{2.4–5}$$

We start from the inequality

$$\Big|\sum_{\nu=1}^{n} f(\zeta_\nu)\,(z_\nu - z_{\nu-1})\Big| \leqq \sum_{\nu=1}^{n} |f(\zeta_\nu)|\,|z_\nu - z_{\nu-1}|, \tag{2.4–6}$$

using the same notations as in the previous section. We shall prove that *the sum on the right tends to a limit,* whenever $\max|z_\nu - z_{\nu-1}|$ tends to zero. It is sufficient to give the proof in the case that C is a smooth arc, the complementary reasoning required for the case of a regular curve being the same as that in section 2.3.2.

Let

$$S_n = \sum_{\nu=1}^{n} |f(\zeta_\nu)|\,|z_\nu - z_{\nu-1}| = \sum_{\nu=1}^{n} |f(z(\tau_\nu)|\sqrt{\{x(t_\nu)-x(t_{\nu-1})\}^2+\{y(t_\nu)-y(t_{\nu-1})\}^2}$$

$$= \sum_{\nu=1}^{n} |f(z(\tau_\nu))|\sqrt{\{x'(\tau_\nu^{(1)})\}^2+\{y'(\tau_\nu^{(2)})\}^2}\,.\,(t_\nu - t_{\nu-1}). \tag{2.4–7}$$

Compare this last expression with the Riemann sum

$$S_n^* = \sum_{\nu=1}^{n} |f(z(\tau_\nu))|\sqrt{\{x'(\tau_\nu)\}^2+\{y'(\tau_\nu)\}^2}\cdot(t_\nu - t_{\nu-1}) \tag{2.4–8}$$

which tends to the limit

$$\int_0^1 |f\{z(t)\}|\sqrt{\{x'(t)\}^2+\{y'(t)\}^2}\,dt. \tag{2.4–9}$$

By virtue of the inequality (1.1–9) we have

$$|S_n^* - S_n| \leqq \sum_{\nu=1}^{n} |f(\zeta_\nu)|\sqrt{\{x'(\tau_\nu^{(1)})-x'(\tau_\nu)\}^2+\{y'(\tau_\nu^{(2)})-y'(\tau_\nu)\}^2}\,.\,(t_\nu - t_{\nu-1}). \tag{2.4–10}$$

By arguments analogous to those used in section 2.3.2 it is not difficult to complete the proof of the statement.

It is customary to write

$$\int_C |f(\zeta)|\,|d\zeta| = \lim \sum_{\nu=1}^{n} |f(\zeta_\nu)|\,|z_\nu - z_{\nu-1}|. \tag{2.4–11}$$

From (2.4–6) we deduce at once

$$\left|\int\limits_C f(\zeta)\,d\zeta\right| \leqq \int\limits_C |f(\zeta)|\,|d\zeta|. \tag{2.4–12}$$

2.4.3 – Darboux's theorem

Consider in particular the function $f(z) = 1$ along the regular curve C. The expression

$$l = \int\limits_C |d\zeta| \tag{2.4–13}$$

is called the *length* of the regular curve. From (2.4–12) it follows that

$$\left|\int\limits_C d\zeta\right| \leqq \int\limits_C |d\zeta|, \tag{2.4–14}$$

hence *the length of the line segment connecting two points does not exceed the length of the arc of the regular curve joining these points.* More generally, if $z_0, z_1, \ldots, z_n$ are vertices of an inscribed polygon of the curve C, then

$$\sum_{\nu=1}^{n} |z_\nu - z_{\nu-1}| \leqq l, \tag{2.4–15}$$

while l is the limit of the lengths of all these inscribed polygons as the maximum length of the sides tends to zero.

From (2.4–9) it follows that the length of a smooth arc can be evaluated from

$$l = \int_0^1 \sqrt{\{x'(t)\}^2 + \{y'(t)\}^2}\,dt = \int_0^1 |z'(t)|\,dt. \tag{2.4–16}$$

We now may state an important corollary of (2.4–12), viz. *Darboux's theorem:*

The modulus of the integral $\int\limits_C f(\zeta)\,d\zeta$ *taken along a regular curve does not exceed the product of the maximum modulus* M *of* $f(z)$ *on the curve and the length* l *of the curve,*

$$\left|\int\limits_C f(\zeta)\,d\zeta\right| \leqq Ml. \tag{2.4–17}$$

The proof is evident.

2.4.4 – Integration of a sequence and a series

We shall give an interesting application of Darboux's theorem. Consider the sequence

$$F_0(z),\ F_1(z), \ldots \tag{2.4–18}$$

of functions continuous along a regular curve C*, the sequence tending uniformly to its limit* $F(z)$*. Then*

$$\int_C (\lim_{n\to\infty} F_n(\zeta))\, d\zeta = \lim_{n\to\infty} \int_C F_n(\zeta)\, d\zeta. \tag{2.4–19}$$

An equivalent statement is the following: *The series*

$$f_0(z)+f_1(z)+\ldots \tag{2.4–20}$$

whose terms are continuous along a regular curve C, the series being uniformly convergent, is integrable along C term by term:

$$\int_C \{\sum_{\nu=0}^{\infty} f_\nu(\zeta)\} d\zeta = \sum_{\nu=0}^{\infty} \int_C f_\nu(\zeta)\, d\zeta. \tag{2.4–21}$$

The uniform convergence of the sequence (2.4–18) entails the continuity of its limit (1.5.2). Moreover, to a given $\varepsilon > 0$ we can find an n_0 such that $|F(z)-F_n(z)| < \varepsilon$, provided $n > n_0$ irrespective of the value of z on the curve. If l denotes the length of C, then by Darboux's theorem

$$\left|\int_C F(\zeta)\, d\zeta - \int_C F_n(\zeta)\, d\zeta\right| = \left|\int_C \{F(\zeta)-F_n(\zeta)\} d\zeta\right| \leqq \varepsilon l,$$

which proves the assertion.

2.4.5 – An approximation theorem

For a subsequent application we need the following theorem: *Let $f(z)$ be continuous throughout an open set $\mathfrak{A}$ and let C be a chain included in the set. Given $\varepsilon > 0$ we are able to find a polygon L whose points lie also in $\mathfrak{A}$ such that*

$$\left|\int_C f(\zeta)\, d\zeta - \int_L f(\zeta)\, d\zeta\right| < \varepsilon. \tag{2.4-22}$$

This means that we can approximate $\int_C f(\zeta) d\zeta$ as closely as we want by an integral taken along a suitably chosen polygon.

It is, of course, sufficient to prove the theorem for any arc of the chain. The complementary set of $\mathfrak{A}$, i.e., the set of all points not belonging to $\mathfrak{A}$, is closed. Hence the distance from C to this complementary set is a positive number ϱ. Consider an inscribed polygon whose segments have a length $< \frac{1}{2}\varrho$. This polygon lies certainly in $\mathfrak{A}$.

Additionally we take the lengths of these sides $< \delta$, where δ is a number such that

$$|f(z^{(1)})-f(z^{(2)})| < \frac{\varepsilon}{2l}, \tag{2.4–23}$$

l being the length of the arc, provided $z^{(1)}, z^{(2)}$ are points of C or at a distance from C of at most $\frac{1}{2}\varrho$, and $|z^{(1)}-z^{(2)}| < \delta$. This is possible for we can immerse C in a closed subset of $\mathfrak{A}$ whose points have a distance of at most $\frac{1}{2}\varrho$ to C. To construct such a set we may take all circular discs whose centres are on C and whose radii are $\frac{1}{2}\varrho$, observing that on account of the Heine-Borel theorem (1.2.4) already a finite number of these discs cover the arc.

Let $z_0, z_1, \ldots, z_n$ be the vertices of the inscribed polygon L. We can choose this polygon in such a fashion that all the mentioned conditions are satisfied for its segments and, moreover,

$$\left|\int_C f(\zeta)\,d\zeta - \sum_{\nu=1}^{n} f(\zeta_\nu)(z_\nu - z_{\nu-1})\right| < \tfrac{1}{2}\varepsilon, \tag{2.4-24}$$

where ζ_ν is a point on the part of the curve terminated by $z_{\nu-1}$ and z_ν, $\nu = 1, \ldots, n$. If now z is a point of the rectilinear segment $(z_{\nu-1}, z_\nu)$ we can set

$$f(z) = f(\zeta_\nu) + \varphi_\nu(z), \tag{2.4-25}$$

with

$$|\varphi_\nu| < \frac{\varepsilon}{2l}. \tag{2.4-26}$$

Taking account of (2.3–20) we have by integration along L

$$\int_L f(\zeta)\,d\zeta = \sum_{\nu=1}^{n} \int_{z_{\nu-1}}^{z_\nu} f(\zeta)\,d\zeta = \sum_{\nu=1}^{n} \int_{z_{\nu-1}}^{z_\nu} \left(f(\zeta_\nu) + \varphi_\nu(\zeta)\right) d\zeta$$

$$= \sum_{\nu=1}^{n} f(\zeta_\nu)(z_\nu - z_{\nu-1}) + \int_{z_{\nu-1}}^{z_\nu} \varphi_\nu(\zeta)\,d\zeta$$

and so, by Darboux's theorem,

$$\left|\int_L f(\zeta)\,d\zeta - \sum_{\nu=1}^{n} f(\zeta_\nu)(z_\nu - z_{\nu-1})\right| \leqq \frac{\varepsilon}{2l} \cdot l = \tfrac{1}{2}\varepsilon. \tag{2.4-27}$$

From (2.4–24) and (2.4–27) we easily deduce the truth of the theorem.

2.5 – Cauchy's integral theorem

2.5.1 – Goursat's lemma

The value of a line integral of a continuous function depends not only on the end-points of the path of integration but, in general, also essentially on this curve. Under a certain not very restrictive hypothesis this dependence does not exist. This is a marvellous discovery of Cauchy and is fundamental for the entire theory of functions.

The classical theory is based on the assumption that $f(z)$ is holomorphic throughout a region and admits a continuous derivative everywhere. Goursat made the fundamental remark that this latter assumption is redundant. Before formulating Cauchy's theorem in its modern form we shall establish a lemma, which we shall call *Goursat's lemma*:

Let $f(z)$ be holomorphic throughout an open set $\mathfrak{A}$. Consider a triangle T whose sides belong to the set as well as the interior points of the triangle. Then

$$\int_T f(\zeta)\,d\zeta = 0, \tag{2.5–1}$$

where T beneath the sign of integration denotes the chain consisting of the sides of the triangle.

We always integrate in the counter-clockwise sense. By joining the mid-points of the sides of the triangle T by straight segments we obtain four triangles of half the size, (fig. 2.5–1),

$$T_1^{(1)},\ T_1^{(2)},\ T_1^{(3)},\ T_1^{(4)}.$$

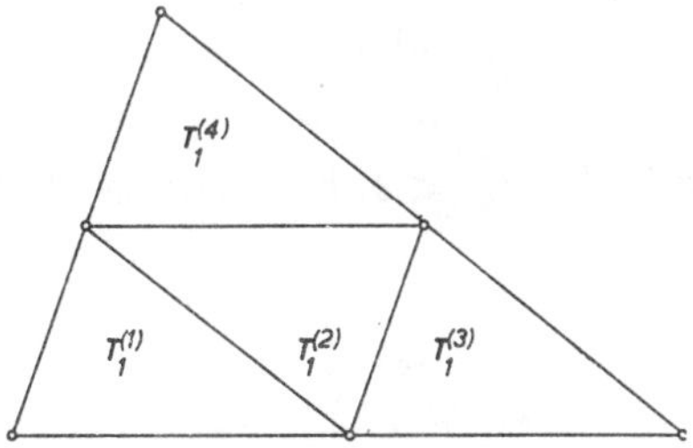

Fig. 2.5–1. Goursat's lemma

Then evidently

$$\int_T f(\zeta)\,d\zeta = \int_{T_1^{(1)}} f(\zeta)\,d\zeta + \int_{T_1^{(2)}} f(\zeta)\,d\zeta + \int_{T_1^{(3)}} f(\zeta)\,d\zeta + \int_{T_1^{(4)}} f(\zeta)\,d\zeta. \tag{2.5–2}$$

For, as we integrate over the sides of the four subtriangles, we integrate back and forth over the auxiliary segments, so that the integrals along these segments cancel. Of the four integrals on the right-hand side of (2.5–2) there must be one, the path of which we denote by T_1, for which

$$\left|\int_T f(\zeta)\,d\zeta\right| \leqq 4\left|\int_{T_1} f(\zeta)\,d\zeta\right|,$$

since not every one of the four integrals can have an absolute value less than one quarter of the whole. The subtriangle T_1 can be treated in the same manner: T_1 contains at least one subtriangle T_2 for which

$$\left|\int_{T_1} f(\zeta)\,d\zeta\right| \leqq 4\left|\int_{T_2} f(\zeta)\,d\zeta\right|,$$

so that

$$\left|\int_T f(\zeta)\,d\zeta\right| \leqq 4^2 \left|\int_{T_2} f(\zeta)\,d\zeta\right|.$$

Continuing in this manner, we obtain a sequence of similar triangles such that each lies inside the preceding one and

$$\left|\int_T f(\zeta)\,d\zeta\right| \leqq 4^n \left|\int_{T_n} f(\zeta)\,d\zeta\right|. \tag{2.5–3}$$

By a well-known theorem of point-set theory there is one and only one point z_0 common to all triangles and is a point of $\mathfrak{A}$. We assumed $f(z)$ to have a derivative at $z = z_0$. This implies: given $\varepsilon > 0$, we can find a δ such that for all z with $|z-z_0| < \delta$ we have

$$|f(z)-f(z_0)-(z-z_0)f'(z_0)| \leqq \varepsilon|z-z_0|$$

or

$$f(z) = f(z_0)+(z-z_0)f'(z_0)+(z-z_0)g(z), \tag{2.5–4}$$

with

$$|g(z)| \leqq \varepsilon.$$

Now take n so large that T_n lies entirely within the neighbourhood of z_0 characterised by $|z-z_0| < \delta$. By virtue of (2.3–21) and (2.3–23) we find

$$\int_{T_n} f(\zeta)\,d\zeta = \int_{T_n} f(z_0)\,d\zeta + \int_{T_n} \zeta f'(z_0)\,d\zeta - \int_{T_n} z_0 f'(z_0)\,d\zeta + \int_{T_n} (\zeta-z_0)\,g(\zeta)\,d\zeta$$

$$= 0+0-0 + \int_{T_n} (\zeta-z_0)\,g(\zeta)\,d\zeta.$$

Observing that $|\zeta-z_0|$ does not exceed the perimeter t_n of T_n, we deduce from Darboux's theorem that

$$\left|\int_{T_n} f(\zeta)\,d\zeta\right| \leqq \varepsilon t_n t_n = \frac{t^2\varepsilon}{4^n}$$

where t denotes the perimeter of T. Hence by (2.5–3)

$$\left|\int_T f(\zeta)\,d\zeta\right| \leqq t^2\varepsilon,$$

and since ε can be chosen as small as we please, we infer that (2.5–1) is true.

2.5.2 – Cauchy's integral theorem

In a very general form *Cauchy's integral theorem* may be stated as follows:

Let $f(z)$ be a holomorphic function in an open set $\mathfrak{A}$. If C is a cycle in the set, then

$$\int_C f(\zeta)\,d\zeta = 0 \tag{2.5–5}$$

whenever $C \sim 0$ *in the set.*

An equivalent statement is the following:

If $f(z)$ *is holomorphic in an open set* $\mathfrak{A}$ *and* C_1 *and* C_2 *are two chains in the set, then*

$$\int_{C_1} f(\zeta)\,d\zeta = \int_{C_2} f(\zeta)\,d\zeta \tag{2.5–6}$$

whenever $C_1 \sim C_2$ *in the set.*

The second statement follows from the first. For if $C_1 \sim C_2$ then $C_1 - C_2$ is a cycle and ~ 0. Hence

$$0 = \int_{C_1-C_2} f(\zeta)\,d\zeta = \int_{C_1} f(\zeta)\,d\zeta - \int_{C_2} f(\zeta)\,d\zeta, \tag{2.5–7}$$

on account of the properties of integrals mentioned in section 2.4.1.

Conversely, the first statement is a consequence of the second, for we can divide C into two chains C_1 and C_2 such that $C = C_1 - C_2$, whilst $C_1 \sim C_2$ is a consequence of $C \sim 0$.

It is sufficient to prove the theorem for the case that the path of integration is a polygon L, for we have already seen in section 2.4.5 that any curvilinear integral can be approximated as closely as we want by an integral taken along a polygon.

Let L, therefore, be a polygonal closed chain, each constituent segment being a straight segment L_ν. If the polygon approximating the closed chain is fine enough, it is on account of (2.1–4) also ~ 0. Hence we may assume $L \sim 0$. Draw all lines L_ν carrying these segments, (fig. 2.5–2). Each of them decomposes the plane into two

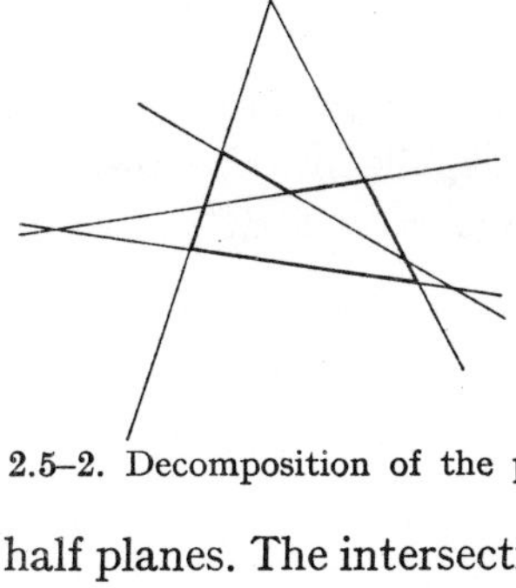

Fig. 2.5–2. Decomposition of the plane

convex sets, viz. two half planes. The intersection of a finite number of convex sets is either empty or it is itself convex. It thus follows that the straight lines L_ν decompose the plane into a finite number of convex sets, each of them having segments of the lines in their boundary. Each convex set is either bounded and therefore an ordinary convex polygon, or extends to infinity. In the case that it is bounded we select one of its vertices and draw all the diagonals from it. In this way we obtain a decomposition of the plane into triangles and into convex sets extending to infinity.

The winding number $\Omega_L(z)$ is constant in the interior of each of these parts of the plane. A point z at the boundary of such a part either belongs to L so that $\Omega_L(z)$ is undefined, or leads to a value of the winding number equal to that in the interior, because of the continuity of $\Omega_L(z)$.

Whenever $|z|$ is very large, then $\Omega_L(z) = 0$, as follows by an argument used in section 2.2.1. This shows that $\Omega_L(z) = 0$ in each part that extends to infinity.

Let $\mathfrak{T}$ denote a triangle with $\Omega_L(z) \neq 0$ for all points in the interior of $\mathfrak{T}$. Since $\Omega_L(z) = 0$ for all z that do not belong to $\mathfrak{A}$, all the points of $\mathfrak{T}$ belong to $\mathfrak{A}$, for those on the boundary T of $\mathfrak{T}$ belong to $\mathfrak{A}$ because they are either on L which is in $\mathfrak{A}$, or again $\Omega_L(z) \neq 0$ for them. Thus for such a triangle we get by Goursat's lemma (2.5.1)

$$\int_T f(\zeta)\, d\zeta = 0.$$

Let $\mathfrak{T}_1, \ldots, \mathfrak{T}_r$ all be triangles for which $\Omega_L(z) \neq 0$ whenever z is in $\mathfrak{T}_\nu$, $\nu = 1, \ldots, r$, and where $\Omega_L(z) = 0$ if z is in any other triangle. We assume T_ν, the boundary of $\mathfrak{T}_\nu$, to be oriented in such a fashion that $\Omega_{T_\nu}(z) = +1$ in the interior of $\mathfrak{T}_\nu$. Consider the new chain

$$L^* = L - \sum_\nu m_\nu T_\nu, \quad m_\nu = \Omega_L(z), \quad z \text{ in } T_\nu,\ \nu = 1, \ldots, r. \qquad (2.5\text{–}8)$$

We shall prove:

$$\Omega_{L^*}(z) = 0 \qquad (2.5\text{–}9)$$

for any z not on L^*.

If z is on the boundary of one of the parts, but not on L^*, we can shift it a little so that it falls into the interior of a part. If z is in $\mathfrak{T}_\nu$ then $\Omega_L(z) = m_\nu$, $\Omega_{T_\nu}(z) = +1$, $\Omega_{T_\mu}(z) = 0$, for $\mu \neq \nu$. Hence

$$\Omega_{L^*}(z) = \Omega_L(z) - m_\nu \Omega_{T_\nu}(z) = 0.$$

If z is in any other part, then $\Omega_L(z) = 0$, $\Omega_{T_\nu}(z) = 0$, so $\Omega_{L^*}(z) = 0$. Now

$$\int_{L^*} f(\zeta)\, d\zeta = \int_L f(\zeta)\, d\zeta - \sum_\nu m_\nu \int_{T_\nu} f(\zeta)\, d\zeta = \int_L f(\zeta)\, d\zeta,$$

since $\int_{T_\nu} f(\zeta)\, d\zeta = 0$. This reduces the proof of Cauchy's theorem to the chain L^*.

We may break up each arc of L^* into largest line segments S such that the interior of each S does not contain any vertex of L^*. Assume that S is contained h times in one and k times in opposite orientation, so that we have

$$L^* = hS-kS+Q,$$

where Q is a chain that does not contain S any more. Then $0 = \Omega_{L^*} = (h-k)\Omega_S+\Omega_Q$, where $2\pi\Omega_{L^*}$ means the increment of $\arg(\zeta-z)$, ζ on L^*, etc. Hence

$$\Omega_Q = (k-h)\Omega_S.$$

Ω_Q is defined and continuous also on S, but Ω_S is close to $+\frac{1}{2}$ on one side and close to $-\frac{1}{2}$ on the other side of S. It follows that $h = k$. As a consequence L^* contains each line segment equally often in both directions and we conclude: $\int\limits_{L^*} f(\zeta)\,d\zeta = 0$.

This completes the proof of Cauchy's integral theorem.

2.5.3 – Extension of Cauchy's integral theorem

A function is said to be *locally bounded* at a point $z = a$ if it is defined and holomorphic within a certain neighbourhood of a with possible exception of this point and bounded throughout the neighbourhood (from which a is removed).

The following theorem may be considered as an extension of Cauchy's integral theorem.

Let $\mathfrak{A}$ be an open set and assume $f(z)$ to be holomorphic in $\mathfrak{A}$ with possible exception of a finite number of points a_ν, where the function is locally bounded. If the cycle C is homologous 0 in $\mathfrak{A}$ and does not contain any of these points, then

$$\int\limits_C f(\zeta)d\zeta = 0. \tag{2.5–10}$$

The cycle is not necessarily ~ 0 in the set $\mathfrak{A}^*$ obtained from $\mathfrak{A}$ by omitting the points a_ν. Let m_ν be the winding number $\Omega_C(a_\nu)$ of C with respect to a_ν. Construct around each point a_ν a circle C_ν of so small a radius ϱ_ν that its interior, with exception of a_ν, belongs to $\mathfrak{A}^*$. By Darboux's theorem we have

$$\left|\int\limits_{C_\nu} f(\zeta)\,d\zeta\right| \leqq 2\pi\varrho_\nu M_\nu, \tag{2.5–11}$$

where M_ν is an upper bound of $f(z)$ in the circle C_ν. Since we can take ϱ_ν as small as we please we must have

$$\int\limits_{C_\nu} f(\zeta)\,d\zeta = 0, \tag{2.5–12}$$

for the value of the integral is independent of the value of ϱ_ν, as follows from Cauchy's integral theorem in the version (2.5–6).

In $\mathfrak{A}^*$ we have

$$C \sim \sum_{\nu} m_{\nu} C_{\nu}$$

and hence by Cauchy's integral theorem

$$\int_C f(\zeta)\, d\zeta = \sum_{\nu} m_{\nu} \int_{C_{\nu}} f(\zeta)\, d\zeta = 0,$$

the desired result.

2.6 – The fundamental theorem of algebra

2.6.1 – Statement and proof of the theorem

An interesting application of the previous results is a proof of the statement that *any polynomial of positive degree possesses at least one zero*. This statement is known as *the fundamental theorem of algebra*.

Let

$$f(z) = c_0 + c_1 z + \ldots + c_n z^n, \qquad c_n \neq 0, \quad n \geqq 0 \tag{2.6–1}$$

represent a polynomial with complex coefficients. First we observe that

$$f(z) \to \infty, \qquad \text{as } z \to \infty, \qquad \text{whenever } n > 0. \tag{2.6–2}$$

In fact,

$$\lim_{z \to \infty} \frac{f(z)}{z^n} = c_n \neq 0.$$

Hence

$$|f(z)| \geqq |z|^n \cdot \tfrac{1}{2} |c_n| \tag{2.6–3}$$

for sufficiently large $|z|$.

Assume that $f(z)$ is different from zero for all (finite) values of z. The function

$$g(z) = \frac{1}{f(z)} \tag{2.6–4}$$

is holomorphic throughout the entire plane and the same holds for the function

$$\frac{g(z) - g(0)}{z} \tag{2.6–5}$$

with exception at $z = 0$, where the function is locally bounded (since it tends to the derivative $g'(0)$ as $z \to 0$). By virtue of the extension of Cauchy's integral theorem of section 2.5.3 we have

$$\int_C \frac{g(\zeta) - g(0)}{\zeta}\, d\zeta = 0, \tag{2.6–6}$$

the integral taken along a circle of radius R around the origin. Hence, by (2.3–31),

$$\int_C \frac{g(\zeta)}{\zeta}\,d\zeta = \int_C g(0)\frac{d\zeta}{\zeta} = 2\pi i\, g(0).$$

If R is sufficiently large and $n > 0$ then $|g(z)| < \varepsilon$, whenever $|z| = R$, where ε denotes an arbitrary positive number. By Darboux's theorem we have

$$\left|\int_C \frac{g(\zeta)}{\zeta}\,d\zeta\right| \leqq \frac{\varepsilon}{R}\cdot 2\pi R = 2\pi\varepsilon$$

and therefore $|g(0)| < \varepsilon$. Since ε is arbitrary we must have $g(0) = 0$, contrary to $f(0)g(0) = 1$. Hence $n = 0$ and $f(z)$ is a non-vanishing constant. For other proofs we refer to subsequent sections.

2.6.2 – Decomposition of a polynomial

Let a_1 denote a zero of the polynomial $f(z)$. By virtue of the elementary identity

$$z^n - a^n = (z-a)(z^{n-1}+z^{n-2}a+\ldots+a^{n-1})$$

we infer that

$$f(z) = f(z)-f(a_1) = (z-a_1)f_1(z),$$

where $f_1(z)$ is a polynomial whose degree is $n-1$. If $n > 1$ the polynomial $f_1(z)$ has a zero a_2 and may therefore be written in the form

$$f_1(z) = (z-a_2)f_2(z).$$

Repeating the arguments we find that $f(z)$ can be represented as a product of a constant and n linear factors $c(z-a_1)\ldots(z-a_n)$. Since $f(z)z^{-n}$ tends to c_n as $z \to \infty$ we find $c = c_n$. As a consequence we may complete the fundamental theorem of algebra as follows:

A polynomial (2.6–1) *of positive degree n possesses just n (not necessarily distinct) zeros and can be represented as a product of n linear factors and a constant:*

$$\boxed{f(z) = c_n(z-a_1)\ldots(z-a_n),} \tag{2.6–7}$$

the constant being the coefficient of the highest power in $f(z)$.

2.7 – Cauchy's integral formula

2.7.1 – Cauchy's integral formula

Let $\mathfrak{A}$ be a bounded and open set and assume $f(z)$ to be holomorphic throughout $\mathfrak{A}$. If z is a point of $\mathfrak{A}$ the function

$$g(\zeta) = \frac{f(\zeta)-f(z)}{\zeta-z} \tag{2.7–1}$$

of the variable ζ is holomorphic throughout $\mathfrak{A}$ except at $\zeta = z$ where the function is locally bounded (tending to $f'(z)$ as $\zeta \to z$).

Let C be a cycle ~ 0 in $\mathfrak{A}$ and not passing through z. By Cauchy's integral theorem of section 2.5.3

$$0 = \int_C g(\zeta)\,d\zeta = \int_C \frac{f(\zeta)-f(z)}{\zeta-z}\,d\zeta \tag{2.7–2}$$

and so

$$\int_C \frac{f(\zeta)}{\zeta-z}\,d\zeta = f(z)\int_C \frac{d\zeta}{\zeta-z} = 2\pi i\, m f(z), \tag{2.7–3}$$

where m is the winding number $\Omega_C(z)$ of C with respect to z. Hence

$$\boxed{\Omega_C(z) f(z) = \frac{1}{2\pi i}\int_C \frac{f(\zeta)}{\zeta-z}\,d\zeta,} \tag{2.7–4}$$

whenever $C \sim 0$ in $\mathfrak{A}$. This is a general form of the famous *Cauchy integral formula.*

The formula (2.7–4) is also valid if there are a finite number of exceptional points in $\mathfrak{A}$, where the function is assumed to be locally bounded, provided they are not on C and are different from z. This is an immediate consequence of the theorem of section 2.5.3.

2.7.2 – A PARTICULAR CASE

A particular case deserves mention. Let $f(z)$ be holomorphic throughout an open set $\mathfrak{A}$ and be C a regular contour such that the interior of C is contained in $\mathfrak{A}$. As usual we describe C in the counter-clockwise sense. Then

$$\frac{1}{2\pi i}\int_C \frac{f(\zeta)}{\zeta-z}\,d\zeta = \begin{cases} f(z), & z \text{ inside } C, \\ 0, & z \text{ outside } C. \end{cases} \tag{2.7–5}$$

The proof is trivial in the case that C is a circle, a rectangle or a triangle, for then it is easily verified that $\Omega_C(z) = 1$ for an inner point whereas $\Omega_C(z) = 0$ if z is outside. It can be proved that the same result holds for an arbitrary regular contour, but since we are only concerned with those cases for which the statement is clear, we omit the general proof.

2.8 – Formula for the derivative. Riemann's theorem

2.8.1 – A LEMMA

Assume C to be an arbitrary regular curve, not necessarily closed, and z a point not on C. If $\varphi(\zeta)$ is continuous on C we may consider the function

$$\psi(z) = \int_C \frac{\varphi(\zeta)}{\zeta - z} d\zeta. \tag{2.8–1}$$

This function is defined in any bounded set of points not on C and we shall prove:

The function $\psi(z)$ defined in (2.8–1) is holomorphic throughout any bounded open set that does not contain points of C and the derivative is

$$\psi'(z) = \int_C \frac{\varphi(\zeta)}{(\zeta - z)^2} d\zeta. \tag{2.8–2}$$

Call ϱ the distance from z to C. Let $z+h$ be a point within a distance $\frac{1}{2}\varrho$ from z. Then

$$\frac{\psi(z+h)-\psi(z)}{h} - \int_C \frac{\varphi(\zeta)}{(\zeta-z)^2} d\zeta = \int_C \varphi(\zeta) \frac{h}{(\zeta-z)^2(\zeta-z-h)} d\zeta.$$

The function $\varphi(\zeta)$ admits an upper bound M on C. Now $|\zeta - z| \geqq \varrho$, $|\zeta - z - h| > \frac{1}{2}\varrho$. Hence

$$\left| \frac{\psi(z+h)-\psi(z)}{h} - \int_C \frac{\varphi(\zeta)}{(\zeta-z)^2} d\zeta \right| \leqq \frac{2|h|Ml}{\varrho^3}$$

where l denotes the length of C. The expression on the right tends to zero as $h \to 0$. This completes the proof.

2.8.2 – Formula for the derivative of a function

If $f(z)$ is holomorphic in an open set $\mathfrak{A}$ and if C is a regular contour within $\mathfrak{A}$ such that its interior is contained in $\mathfrak{A}$, then for every point z inside C we have

$$f'(z) = \frac{1}{2\pi i} \int_C \frac{f(\zeta)}{(\zeta-z)^2} d\zeta, \tag{2.8–3}$$

the path of integration being described in the counter-clockwise sense. This result is an immediate consequence of Cauchy's integral formula (2.7–5) and the theorem of section 2.8.1.

A more general result is the following: *If $f(z)$ is holomorphic in an open set $\mathfrak{A}$ and C an arbitrary cycle not passing through z, then*

$$\boxed{\Omega_C(z) f'(z) = \frac{1}{2\pi i} \int_C \frac{f(\zeta)}{(\zeta-z)^2} d\zeta,} \tag{2.8–4}$$

provided $C \sim 0$ in $\mathfrak{A}$. The proof is obvious.

2.8.3 – Riemann's theorem

We now wish to establish *Riemann's theorem* which makes the explicite mentioning of points, where a function is locally bounded, redundant.

Let $f(z)$ be holomorphic in an open set $\mathfrak{A}$ with possible exception of a point a, where the function is locally bounded. Then there exists a uniquely determined number b such that if we define $f(a) = b$ the extended function is also holomorphic at $z = a$.

Take C as a sufficiently small circle around a, described in the counter-clockwise sense. For all points $z \neq a$ in the interior of C we have by Cauchy's integral formula, taking account of the remark of section 2.7.1,

$$f(z) = \frac{1}{2\pi i}\int_C \frac{f(\zeta)}{\zeta - z}\,d\zeta.$$

We proved in section 2.8.1 that the function on the right is holomorphic throughout the interior of C. Hence we may take for b the value of the integral at $z = a$. For this reason the point $z = a$ is called a *removable singularity*.

2.9 – Differentiation inside the sign of integration

2.9.1 – Formula for the derivative with respect to a parameter

Consider the function $f(\zeta, z)$ of two variables ζ, z having the following properties:

(i) The function is defined for all points z of an open set $\mathfrak{A}$ and for all points ζ of a regular curve C. The function is, moreover, bounded for all those points ζ, z.

(ii) For every fixed ζ the function is holomorphic as regards z.

(iii) For every fixed z the function is continuous along C.

Under these conditions *the function*

$$F(z) = \int_C f(\zeta, z)\,d\zeta \tag{2.9–1}$$

is holomorphic throughout $\mathfrak{A}$, its derivative being

$$F'(z) = \int_C \frac{\partial f(\zeta, z)}{\partial z}\,d\zeta. \tag{2.9–2}$$

This means that the differentiation can be carried out inside the sign of integration.

Since $f(\zeta, z)$ is holomorphic for fixed ζ, we have by Cauchy's integral formula

$$f(\zeta, z) = \frac{1}{2\pi i}\int_{C^*} \frac{f(\zeta, \omega)}{\omega - z}\,d\omega, \tag{2.9–3}$$

where C^* denotes a sufficiently small circle of radius ϱ around z in $\mathfrak{A}$, described in the counter-clockwise sense. Hence

$$F(z) = \frac{1}{2\pi i}\int_C d\zeta \int_{C^*} \frac{f(\zeta, \omega)}{\omega - z}\, d\omega. \qquad (2.9\text{–}4)$$

By virtue of (2.8–3) we have

$$\frac{\partial f(\zeta, z)}{\partial z} = \frac{1}{2\pi i}\int_{C^*} \frac{f(\zeta, \omega)}{(\omega - z)^2}\, d\omega. \qquad (2.9\text{–}5)$$

Let $z+h$ be a point within a circle of radius $\frac{1}{2}\varrho$ around z. Then $|\omega - z| = \varrho$, $|\omega - z - h| > \frac{1}{2}\varrho$. Consider the difference quotient

$$\frac{F(z+h) - F(z)}{h} = \frac{1}{2\pi i}\int_C d\zeta \int_{C^*} \frac{f(\zeta, \omega)}{(\omega - z)^2}\, d\omega +$$

$$+ \frac{1}{2\pi i}\int_C d\zeta \int_{C^*} f(\zeta, \omega) \frac{h}{(\omega - z - h)(\omega - z)^2}\, d\omega.$$

Since $|f(\zeta, z)| < M$, we have on applying repeatedly Darboux's theorem, l denoting the length of C,

$$\left| \frac{F(z+h) - F(z)}{h} - \int_C \frac{\partial f(\zeta, z)}{\partial z}\, d\zeta \right| \leqq \frac{2|h|Ml}{\varrho^2} \qquad (2.9\text{–}6)$$

and this tends to zero as $h \to 0$.

2.9.2 – Formula for higher derivatives

Apply the above result to the function

$$\int_C (\zeta - z)^m \varphi(\zeta)\, d\zeta \qquad (2.9\text{–}7)$$

m being an integer and $\varphi(\zeta)$ being continuous along a regular curve C, while z varies throughout a bounded and open set that does not contain points of C. We immediately find

$$\frac{d}{dz}\int_C (\zeta - z)^m \varphi(\zeta)\, d\zeta = -m \int_C (\zeta - z)^{m-1} \varphi(\zeta)\, d\zeta. \qquad (2.9\text{–}8)$$

In particular, we may consider

$$f(z) = \frac{1}{2\pi i}\int_C \frac{f(\zeta)}{\zeta - z}\, d\zeta,$$

where C is a regular contour in the open set $\mathfrak{A}$ such that also the interior of C is contained in the set and z is inside C. It is assumed that $f(z)$ is holomorphic throughout the set. On carrying out repeatedly the process of differentiation described in section 2.9.1 we find, $f^{(n)}(z)$ denoting the derivative of order n of $f(z)$,

$$\frac{f^{(n)}(z)}{n!} = \frac{1}{2\pi i}\int_C \frac{f(\zeta)}{(\zeta-z)^{n+1}}\,d\zeta. \qquad (2.9\text{–}9)$$

This leads to the important and remarkable result:

A function holomorphic throughout an open set admits there derivatives of all orders and, consequently:

The derivative of a holomorphic function is itself a holomorphic function.

Another consequence is the following:

If $f(z) = u(x, y)+iv(x, y)$ is holomorphic throughout an open set, the functions $u(x, y)$ and $v(x, y)$ possess partial derivatives of all orders.

It should be noticed that the validity of this statement is already granted when the contour C in (2.9–9) is a circle. In this case the formula (2.9–9) is firmly established. In fact, a circle around z can always be imbedded in a slightly larger circle which is still included in the open set.

2.10 – Morera's theorem

2.10.1 – An integral as a function of the upper limit

If $f(z)$ is a continuous function in a bounded region $\mathfrak{R}$ and if a is an arbitrary but fixed point of $\mathfrak{R}$ and if the integral

$$\int_a^z f(\zeta)\,d\zeta \qquad (2.10\text{–}1)$$

is independent of the path connecting a and z, provided the path lies entirely within $\mathfrak{R}$, then the integral is a holomorphic function $F(z)$ whose derivative is

$$F'(z) = f(z). \qquad (2.10\text{–}2)$$

In fact, the function is uniquely determined by the integral. Let $z+h$ be another point of $\mathfrak{R}$. Then

$$F(z+h)-F(z) = \int_z^{z+h} f(\zeta)\,d\zeta, \qquad (2.10\text{–}3)$$

where, by hypothesis, the path may be taken arbitrarily, in particular as a rectilinear path if $|h|$ is sufficiently small. Since $f(z)$ is continuous we then have

$$f(\zeta) = f(z)+\varphi(\zeta),$$

where

$$|\varphi(\zeta)| < \varepsilon$$

for all ζ on the segment, provided $|h|$ is sufficiently small. Hence

$$F(z+h)-F(z) = hf(z)+\int_{z}^{z+h} \varphi(\zeta)\, d\zeta,$$

whence by Darboux's theorem

$$|F(z+h)-F(z)-hf(z)| \leqq |h|\varepsilon.$$

This proves the assertion.

2.10.2 – Morera's theorem

Now we are able to prove a converse of Cauchy's theorem, viz. *Morera's theorem*:

If $f(z)$ is continuous throughout a region and if

$$\int_C f(\zeta)\, d\zeta = 0 \tag{2.10–4}$$

for every closed path C lying in the region, then $f(z)$ is holomorphic throughout the region.

For, let C_1 and C_2 connect a fixed point a with z. Then C_1-C_2 is closed and therefore $\int_a^z f(\zeta)\, d\zeta$ independent of the path connecting a with z. The integral represents a holomorphic function, with derivative $f(z)$. In section 2.9.2 we observed that the derivative of a holomorphic function is itself holomorphic.

2.11 – Zeros of a holomorphic function

2.11.1 – Order of a zero

Let $f(z)$ be holomorphic in an open set $\mathfrak{A}$. If $f(z_0) = 0$ then $z = z_0$ is called a *zero* of $f(z)$. The function

$$\frac{f(z)}{z-z_0} = \frac{f(z)-f(z_0)}{z-z_0} \tag{2.11–1}$$

is holomorphic throughout the set, except at $z = z_0$, where the function is locally bounded, tending to $f'(z_0)$ as $z \to z_0$. By Riemann's theorem of section 2.8.3 there exists a function $g(z)$, holomorphic throughout $\mathfrak{A}$ which coincides with (2.11–1) for all $z \neq z_0$. Hence:

If z_0 is a zero of $f(z)$ we can find a holomorphic function $g(z)$ such that

$$f(z) = (z-z_0)\, g(z). \tag{2.11–2}$$

When to every positive integer n a holomorphic function $g_n(z)$ can be found such that

$$f(z) = (z-z_0)^n g_n(z), \tag{2.11–3}$$

then we say z_0 is a *zero of infinite order*. We shall prove the theorem:

The only function holomorphic throughout a region $\mathfrak{R}$ having a zero of infinite order is the constant 0.

Let z_0 be a zero of infinite order. Construct a circle C around z_0 which together with its interior belongs completely to the region. If we describe the circle in the counter-clockwise sense we have

$$g_n(z) = \frac{1}{2\pi i} \int_C \frac{g_n(\zeta)}{\zeta - z} \, d\zeta \qquad (2.11\text{–}4)$$

for any point in the interior of C. This leads to

$$f(z) = \frac{(z-z_0)^n}{2\pi i} \int_C \frac{f(\zeta)}{(\zeta-z)(\zeta-z_0)^n} \, d\zeta. \qquad (2.11\text{–}5)$$

Let r be the radius of C and ϱ the distance of z from C. If M is the maximum of the modulus of $f(\zeta)$ on C we have

$$|f(z)| \leqq \frac{|z-z_0|^n}{r^n} \frac{Mr}{\varrho} \to 0, \qquad \text{as } n \to \infty. \qquad (2.11\text{–}6)$$

As a consequence $f(z) = 0$ throughout the interior of C. Any point $z = z_1$ of this interior is also a zero of infinite order. For we can define the function $h_n(z)$ as the function 0 in the circle and as the function $f(z)/(z-z_1)^n$ outside or on the circumference, this function being evidently holomorphic throughout $\mathfrak{R}$. Then $f(z) = (z-z_1)^n h_n(z)$, n being an arbitrary positive integer.

Now we take an arbitrary point z_2 of the region. We may join it with z_0 by a continuous curve contained in $\mathfrak{R}$. Let σ denote a positive number smaller than the distance of this curve to the boundary of $\mathfrak{R}$. Subdivide the curve into a finite number of parts of diameter $\leqq \frac{1}{2}\sigma$. Then any point on the first part is a zero of infinite order and therefore any point on the second part, and so on. Thus we see that also z_2 is a zero of infinite order of $f(z)$ and $f(z) = 0$ throughout the region.

As a consequence we find that *for a function $f(z)$ holomorphic throughout a region $\mathfrak{R}$ not being identically equal to zero to any point z_0 of the region exists a maximal $n \geqq 0$ such that*

$$f(z) = (z-z_0)^n g(z), \qquad (2.11\text{–}7)$$

$g(z)$ being holomorphic and $g(z_0) \neq 0$.

Because of its continuity $g(z)$ is different from zero not only at z_0 but also in a certain neighbourhood of it. Within this neighbourhood $f(z)$ vanishes only at $z = z_0$. The zero turns out to be *isolated.* To sum up:

Every zero of $f(z)$ holomorphic in a region is isolated and of finite order, unless $f(z)$ is identically zero.

2.11.2 – The identity principle

An immediate and very important consequence of the previous theorem is the *identity principle* for holomorphic functions.

If two functions $f(z)$ and $g(z)$ are holomorphic in a region $\mathfrak{R}$ and assume the same values in a subset of $\mathfrak{R}$ having at least one accumulation point within $\mathfrak{R}$, then the two functions are equal everywhere in $\mathfrak{R}$.

For, on account of the continuity, the function $f(z)-g(z)$ admits the accumulation point as a non-isolated zero and must therefore vanish identically.

2.11.3 – Functions whose derivative is identically zero

A function holomorphic throughout a region admits only a derivative identically equal to zero if the function is a constant.

Let $f(z)$ be not a constant. At an arbitrary point z_0 we may put

$$f(z)-f(z_0) = (z-z_0)^n g(z), \quad g(z_0) \neq 0, \quad n \geqq 1. \tag{2.11–8}$$

Hence by differentiation

$$f'(z) = (z-z_0)^{n-1} h(z) \tag{2.11–9}$$

with

$$h(z) = ng(z)+(z-z_0)g'(z) \tag{2.11–10}$$

and also $h(z_0) \neq 0$. This is only possible if $f'(z)$ is not identically equal to zero.

By well-known arguments the following theorem may be deduced: *A function holomorphic throughout a region whose derivative of order n is identically equal to zero is a polynomial of degree not exceeding $n-1$.*

2.11.4 – Condition for a function to be a derivative

We conclude with the proof of a theorem which completes in a certain sense the theorem of section 2.3.5.

Let $f(z)$ be holomorphic throughout a simply connected region $\mathfrak{R}$. Then $f(z)$ is a derivative:

$$f(z) = \frac{d}{dz}\int_{z_0}^{z} f(\zeta)d\zeta. \tag{2.11–11}$$

In fact, the region being simply connected, every closed curve is homologous 0 and hence by Cauchy's integral theorem the function $\int_{z_0}^{z} f(\zeta)\,d\zeta$ is defined independently of the path of integration, z_0 being a fixed point in the region. According to section 2.10.1 this function is holomorphic throughout the region, its derivative being $f(z)$.

2.12 – The Cauchy-Liouville theorem

2.12.1 – Statement and proof of the theorem

A function which is holomorphic in the entire plane and is bounded, is a constant.

This statement is known as the *Cauchy-Liouville theorem.* In order to prove the theorem construct a circle C around the origin whose radius R is larger than $|z|$, where z is a given complex number. If $|f(z)| < M$ throughout the plane we find on applying the formula (2.8–3) for the derivative, taking account of Darboux's theorem:

$$|f'(z)| = \left| \frac{1}{2\pi i} \int_C \frac{f(\zeta)}{(\zeta-z)^2} d\zeta \right| \leqq \frac{MR}{(R-|z|)^2}. \qquad (2.12\text{–}1)$$

By taking R large enough we can obviously make the right-hand side as small as we please. Hence $f'(z) = 0$ and $f(z)$ is a constant, according to section 2.11.3.

2.12.2 – Extension of the Cauchy-Liouville theorem

The proof of the preceding theorem allows to state the following theorem:

If a function $f(z)$, holomorphic in the entire plane, is bounded on any sequence of concentric circumferences tending to infinity, then the function is a constant.

Along the same lines we may establish a more general theorem of similar nature:

Consider a sequence of concentric circumferences tending to infinity. If from a certain circumference upwards the function $f(z)z^{-k}$, $k > 0$, ($f(z)$ being holomorphic throughout the plane) remains bounded, then $f(z)$ is a polynomial of degree not exceeding k.

Let M be an upper bound for the function $|f(z)z^{-k}|$ on the circumferences mentioned in the theorem. If R is large enough we have by (2.9–9) and Darboux's theorem:

$$|f^{(n)}(z)| = \left| \frac{n!}{2\pi i} \int_C \frac{f(\zeta)}{(\zeta-z)^{n+1}} d\zeta \right| \leqq \frac{n!MR^{k+1}}{(R-|z|)^{n+1}}, \qquad (2.12\text{–}2)$$

which tends to zero as $R \to \infty$, whenever $n > k$. Hence $f^{(n)}(z) = 0$ for $n > k$ and therefore $f(z)$ is a polynomial of degree $\leqq k$.

The converse is trivial, for, whenever $|z| > 1$, then

$$|f(z)| = |c_0 + \ldots + c_n z^n| < (|c_0| + \ldots + |c_n|)\, |z|^n. \qquad (2.12\text{–}3)$$

2.12.3 – The fundamental theorem of algebra

From the Cauchy-Liouville theorem arises another and very simple proof of the fundamental theorem of algebra (2.6.1). Assume

$f(z)$ to be a polynomial without zeros of degree $n \geqq 0$. Then by (2.6–3)

$$|f(z)| \geqq |z|^n \cdot \tfrac{1}{2}|c_n|.$$

Hence the function $g(z) = 1/f(z)$ is holomorphic throughout the entire plane and bounded everywhere. Consequently $g(z)$ is a constant and so $f(z)$.

A non-vanishing constant is the only polynomial that does not possess zeros.

2.13 – The maximum modulus theorem

2.13.1 – The theorem of the arithmetical mean

Be a a point of a region $\mathfrak{R}$. Construct a circle C of radius r around a such that all interior points of the circle are points of the region. By Cauchy's integral formula we have

$$f(a) = \frac{1}{2\pi i} \int_C \frac{f(\zeta)}{\zeta - a}\, d\zeta \tag{2.13–1}$$

or, if we put $\zeta - a = re^{i\theta}$, whence $d\zeta = i(\zeta - a)\, d\theta$,

$$\boxed{f(a) = \frac{1}{2\pi} \int_0^{2\pi} f(a + re^{i\theta})\, d\theta.} \tag{2.13–2}$$

Thus the value of $f(z)$ at the centre of the circle is the arithmetical mean of the value of the function along the circumference.

2.13.2 – The maximum modulus theorem

Since $|f(z)|$ is continuous (2.4.2) it possesses a maximum on C which we denote by $M(r)$ and from (2.13–2) we deduce

$$|f(a)| \leqq \frac{1}{2\pi} \int_0^{2\pi} |f(a + re^{i\theta})|\, d\theta \leqq M(r). \tag{2.13–3}$$

We wish to prove

$$|f(a)| < M(r) \tag{2.13–4}$$

unless $f(z)$ is constant throughout the region. On the contrary, let $|f(a)| = M(r)$. We may write (2.13–3) in the form

$$\frac{1}{2\pi} \int_0^{2\pi} (|f(a)| - |f(a + re^{i\theta})|)\, d\theta \leqq 0 \tag{2.13–5}$$

where, by hypothesis, $|f(a)| - |f(a + re^{i\theta}| \geqq 0$. By a well-known argument borrowed from the theory of real integrals we infer that

$$|f(a)| = |f(a + re^{i\theta})|, \tag{2.13–6}$$

that is, $|f(\zeta)|$ is constant along C. If $f(a) = 0$ then $f(\zeta) = 0$ throughout $\mathfrak{R}$ (2.11.1). If, however, $f(a) \neq 0$ we may write

$$f(a+re^{i\theta}) = f(a)e^{i\varphi}. \tag{2.13–7}$$

From (2.13–2) we then deduce

$$1 = \frac{1}{2\pi}\int_0^{2\pi} e^{i\varphi}\, d\theta \tag{2.13–8}$$

or, taking the real part

$$1 = \frac{1}{2\pi}\int_0^{2\pi} \cos\varphi\, d\theta. \tag{2.13–9}$$

Hence $\cos\varphi = 1$ and, consequently, $f(\zeta) = f(a)$ along C. But then $f(z)$ is constant throughout the whole region (2.11.2).

This result leads to the following *maximum modulus theorem. Let $f(z)$ be holomorphic throughout a region $\mathfrak{R}$. If M denotes the least upper bound of $|f(z)|$, then*

$$|f(z)| < M$$

throughout $\mathfrak{R}$, unless $f(z)$ reduces to a constant.

In fact, any point of $\mathfrak{R}$ may be considered as centre of a circle which is included in $\mathfrak{R}$ together with all its interior points. A more imaginative proof of this important theorem will be given in section 3.12.2.

2.13.3 – Direct consequences of the maximum modulus theorem

An easy consequence of the preceding theorem is the following. *A holomorphic function in a region $\mathfrak{R}$ having a constant modulus is itself a constant.*

Another consequence is:

If $f(z)$ is continuous in the closure $\overline{\mathfrak{R}}$ of a bounded region $\mathfrak{R}$ and holomorphic throughout $\mathfrak{R}$, then $f(z)$ attains its maximum at a point of the boundary of $\mathfrak{R}$, unless $f(z)$ reduces to a constant.

In fact, Weierstrass's theorem on continuous functions states that on the bounded and closed set $\overline{\mathfrak{R}}$ there is at least one point z_0 where $|f(z)|$ attains its maximum. As we have seen this point cannot belong to $\mathfrak{R}$, unless $f(z)$ is constant throughout $\mathfrak{R}$.

The same property is not necessarily true for the minimum modulus of $f(z)$, for $f(z)$ might vanish in $\mathfrak{R}$. If we suppose, however, *that $f(z)$ does not vanish in $\mathfrak{R}$, then the minimum modulus is also attained at a point of the boundary, unless $f(z)$ is a constant.* This can be seen on applying the maximum modulus theorem to the function $1/f(z)$.

We also have: *If $f(z)$ is holomorphic in the interior of a circle whose* *radius is R, and is not constant, then the maximum modulus $M(r)$ of $f(z)$ on a concentric circumference of radius r, $0 \leqq r \leqq R$, is a steadily increasing function of r.*

In fact, if $0 \leqq r_1 < r_2 \leqq R$ then $M(r_1) < M(r_2)$, since $M(r_2)$ is the least upper bound of the values of $|f(z)|$ for $|z| < r_2$, as is easy to prove.

2.13.4 – Hadamard's three circles theorem

Assume that $f(z)$ is holomorphic in an open set containing the closed annulus $r_1 \leqq |z| \leqq r_2$. In this ring-shaped set we consider a circle $|z| = r$, such that $r_1 < r < r_2$. Let M_1, M, M_2 be the maxima of $|f(z)|$ on the three circumferences whose radii are r_1, r, r_2 respectively.

Now consider the function $z^p\{f(z)\}^q$, where $p, q > 0$ are integers. This function is also holomorphic in the same set, except possibly at $z = 0$. Restricting to values of z with $r_1 \leqq |z| \leqq r_2$ the maximum of this latter function can only occur on one of the bounding circles, i.e.,

$$r^p M^q \leqq \max(r_1^p M_1^q, r_2^p M_2^q). \qquad (2.13\text{–}10)$$

Now we take p, q such that

$$r_1^p M_1^q \geqq r_2^p M_2^q \qquad (2.13\text{–}11)$$

or

$$\frac{p}{q} \leqq -\frac{\log M_2 - \log M_1}{\log r_2 - \log r_1}. \qquad (2.13\text{–}12)$$

From (2.13–10) and (2.13–11) we then deduce

$$\log M \leqq \frac{p}{q}(\log r_1 - \log r) + \log M_1 \leqq \frac{\log r_1 - \log r}{\log r_2 - \log r_1}(\log M_1 - \log M_2) + \log M_1$$

$$= \frac{\log r_2 - \log r}{\log r_2 - \log r_1}\log M_1 + \frac{\log r - \log r_1}{\log r_2 - \log r_1}\log M_2.$$

Hence

$$(\log r_2 - \log r_1)\log M \leqq (\log r_2 - \log r)\log M_1 + (\log r - \log r_1)\log M_2. \qquad (2.13\text{–}13)$$

This inequality may be put in the form

$$\boxed{M^{\log \frac{r_2}{r_1}} \leqq M_1^{\log \frac{r_2}{r}} M_2^{\log \frac{r}{r_1}}.} \qquad (2.13\text{–}14)$$

This is *Hadamard's three circles theorem.*

An alternative form of (2.13–13) is

$$(\log r - \log r_2) \log M_1 + (\log r_1 - \log r) \log M_2 + \\ + (\log r_2 - \log r_1) \log M \leqq 0, \qquad (2.13\text{–}15)$$

that is,

$$\begin{vmatrix} \log r & \log M & 1 \\ \log r_1 & \log M_1 & 1 \\ \log r_2 & \log M_2 & 1 \end{vmatrix} \leqq 0. \qquad (2.13\text{–}16)$$

Hadamard's three-circles theorem may be expressed by saying *that* $\log M(r)$ *is a convex function of* $\log r$. This means that in a graphic representation the point whose rectangular coordinates are $(\log r, \log M(r))$ remains below or on the line passing through the points $(\log r_1, \log M_1)$ and $(\log r_2, \log M_2)$.

2.14 – Real parts of holomorphic functions

2.14.1 – The extreme values of the real part of a function

Let $u(x, y)$ be the real part of a holomorphic function throughout the region $\mathfrak{R}$ and continuous in the closure of the region. That is we can find a function $v(x, y)$ such that the function

$$f(z) = u(x, y) + iv(x, y) \qquad (2.14\text{–}1)$$

is holomorphic in $\mathfrak{R}$.

Under these circumstances also

$$\exp f(z) = \exp u(x, y) \cdot \exp iv(x, y) \qquad (2.14\text{–}2)$$

is holomorphic in $\mathfrak{R}$ and, consequently, $|\exp f(z)| = \exp u(x, y)$ and hence $u(x, y)$ cannot attain its maximum or its minimum at an interior point of $\mathfrak{R}$, unless the function reduces to a constant. Since we assumed $u(x, y)$ to be continuous on the closure of $\mathfrak{R}$ we have proved the following theorem:

If $u(x, y)$ *is the real part of a holomorphic function in a bounded region* $\mathfrak{R}$ *and continuous in the closure, then both the maximum and the minimum values of* $u(x, y)$ *are attained at the boundary, unless the function is constant throughout the region.*

From the established theorem follows the corollary: *If two functions* $u(x, y)$ *and* $u^*(x, y)$ *are real parts of holomorphic functions in a bounded region* $\mathfrak{R}$ *and continuous on the closure and if on the boundary always* $u(x, y) = u^*(x, y)$, *then throughout the entire region* $\mathfrak{R}$ *the functions* $u(x, y)$ *and* $u^*(x, y)$ *are identical.*

In fact, both the maximum and the minimum of the function $u(x, y) - u^*(x, y)$ are zero.

2.14.2 – A theorem about the increment of the real part

It is also worth-while to notice another consequence of the theorem established in section 2.14.1 analogous to that given in section 2.13.3 and which may be deduced by the same arguments.

If $f(z) = u(x, y)+iv(x, y)$ is holomorphic in the interior of a circle C with radius R and not equal to a constant and if $A(r)$ denotes the maximum of the real part $u(x, y)$ of $f(z)$ on the concentric circumference whose radius is r, $0 \leq r \leq R$, then $A(r)$ is a steadily increasing function of r.

2.15 – Representation of a holomorphic function by its real part

2.15.1 – Introductory remarks

In section 2.14.1 we pointed out that the values of the real part $u(x, y)$ of a holomorphic function in the interior of a contour C are completely determined by the values which it assumes on C. It is even true that a function holomorphic within and on a contour C is uniquely determined up to an additive constant by the values which the real part assumes on the contour. In fact, on account of the Cauchy-Riemann equations (1.3–7) a purely imaginary function cannot be holomorphic in a region, unless it is a constant. We conclude from this that the neat Cauchy integral formula is superabundant, for in order to determine the function in the interior of C we must know the values of $f(z)$ on C; hence the values of its real part as well as those of its imaginary part appear in the formula.

We shall now derive a formula which in the case of a circular contour represents the values of $f(z)$ within C by the values of the real part on the circumference only and by the value of the imaginary part of $f(z)$ at the centre of C. For the sake of convenience we shall take the centre of C at the origin.

2.15.2 – Schwarz's formula

The function $f(z)$ is assumed to be holomorphic in a region which contains the circular disc $|z| \leq R$. Let z denote a fixed point inside the circumference C represented by $|z| = R$. By Cauchy's integral formula

$$f(z) = \frac{1}{2\pi i}\int_C \frac{f(\zeta)}{\zeta - z}\,d\zeta = \frac{1}{2\pi}\int_0^{2\pi} f(\zeta)\,\frac{\zeta}{\zeta - z}\,d\varphi, \tag{2.15–1}$$

where $\zeta = Re^{i\varphi}$. On the other hand we have

$$0 = \frac{1}{2\pi i}\int_C \frac{f(\zeta)}{\zeta - z^*}\,d\zeta, \tag{2.15–2}$$

if z^* is a point outside the circumference C, since inside and on the boundary of the disc $|z| \leqq R$ the intregrand is holomorphic. A result of considerable importance is obtained if we take for z^* the inverse $R^2/\bar{z}$ of the point z with respect to C. Taking account of $R^2 = \zeta\bar{\zeta}$ we may bring (2.15–2) into the form

$$0 = \frac{1}{2\pi}\int_0^{2\pi} f(\zeta)\,\frac{\bar{z}}{\bar{z}-\bar{\zeta}}\,d\varphi. \tag{2.15–3}$$

Subtracting corresponding members of (2.15–1) and (2.15–3) we get

$$f(z) = \frac{1}{2\pi}\int_0^{2\pi} f(\zeta)\,A\,d\varphi \tag{2.15–4}$$

with

$$A = \frac{\zeta}{\zeta-z} - \frac{\bar{z}}{\bar{z}-\bar{\zeta}} = 1 + \frac{z}{\zeta-z} + \frac{\bar{z}}{\bar{\zeta}-\bar{z}}\,, \tag{2.15–5}$$

this being a real number. By adding the corresponding members we obtain

$$f(z) = \frac{1}{2\pi}\int_0^{2\pi} f(\zeta)(1+Bi)\,d\varphi \tag{2.15–6}$$

with

$$Bi = \frac{z}{\zeta-z} - \frac{\bar{z}}{\bar{\zeta}-\bar{z}}\,, \tag{2.15–7}$$

this number being purely imaginary. We may also write instead of (2.15–6), taking account of (2.13–2),

$$f(z) = f(0) + \frac{1}{2\pi}\int_0^{2\pi} f(\zeta)\,Bi\,d\varphi. \tag{2.15–8}$$

Assuming that ζ is on the circumference $|z| = R$, we shall write

$$f(\zeta) = u(R, \varphi) + iv(R, \varphi) \tag{2.15–9}$$

and

$$f(z) = u(r, \theta) + iv(r, \theta), \tag{2.15–10}$$

where $z = re^{i\theta}$. Then by equating real parts in (2.15–4)

$$u(r, \theta) = \frac{1}{2\pi}\int_0^{2\pi} u(R, \varphi)\,A\,d\varphi \tag{2.15–11}$$

and equating imaginary parts in (2.15–8)

$$iv(r, \theta) = iv(0) + \frac{1}{2\pi}\int_0^{2\pi} u(R, \varphi)\,Bi\,d\varphi. \tag{2.15–12}$$

Since

$$A + Bi = \frac{\zeta+z}{\zeta-z}\,,$$

we obtain by adding corresponding members of (2.15–11) and (2.15–12) *Schwarz's formula*

$$\boxed{f(z) = iv(0) + \frac{1}{2\pi}\int_0^{2\pi} u(R, \varphi)\,\frac{\zeta+z}{\zeta-z}\,d\varphi,} \quad \zeta = Re^{i\varphi}. \qquad (2.15\text{–}13)$$

It expresses the value of the function $f(z)$ at the point z in terms of the values of the real part $u(R, \varphi)$ on the circumference and the value of the imaginary part at the centre.

2.15.3 – Poisson's formulas

Put $z = re^{i\theta}$ and $\zeta = Re^{i\varphi}$. Then

$$\frac{\zeta+z}{\zeta-z} = \frac{Re^{i\varphi}+re^{i\theta}}{Re^{i\varphi}-re^{i\theta}} = \frac{(R\cos\varphi+r\cos\theta)+i(R\sin\varphi+r\sin\theta)}{(R\cos\varphi-r\cos\theta)+i(R\sin\varphi-r\sin\theta)}. \qquad (2.15\text{–}14)$$

The real part is

$$\frac{R^2-r^2}{R^2-2Rr\cos(\theta-\varphi)+r^2} \qquad (2.15\text{–}15)$$

and the coefficient of the imaginary part

$$\frac{2Rr\sin(\theta-\varphi)}{R^2-2Rr\cos(\theta-\varphi)+r^2}. \qquad (2.15\text{–}16)$$

This includes in the first place *Poisson's integral formula*:

$$\boxed{u(r, \theta) = \frac{1}{2\pi}\int_0^{2\pi} u(R, \varphi)\,\frac{R^2-r^2}{R^2-2Rr\cos(\theta-\varphi)+r^2}\,d\varphi,} \qquad (2.15\text{–}17)$$

and additionally

$$v(r, \theta) = v(0) + \frac{1}{2\pi}\int_0^{2\pi} u(R, \varphi)\,\frac{2Rr\sin(\theta-\varphi)}{R^2-2Rr\cos(\theta-\varphi)+r^2}\,d\varphi. \qquad (2.15\text{–}18)$$

These formulas are important in the theory of harmonic functions.

2.15.4 – Expansion in series

We may expand $\dfrac{\zeta+z}{\zeta-z}$ in a geometric series:

$$\frac{\zeta+z}{\zeta-z} = 1+\frac{2z}{\zeta-z} = 1+2\frac{z/\zeta}{1-z/\zeta} = 1+2\sum_{\nu=1}^{\infty}\left(\frac{z}{\zeta}\right)^{\nu} = 1+2\sum_{\nu=1}^{\infty}\left(\frac{r}{R}\right)^{\nu} e^{i\nu(\theta-\varphi)}. \qquad (2.15\text{–}19)$$

Term-by-term integration of the last series is justified whenever $r < R$ and we get

$$f(z) = iv(0)+\tfrac{1}{2}\alpha_0+\sum_{\nu=1}^{\infty}\left(\frac{r}{R}\right)^{\nu}\alpha_\nu\, e^{i\nu\theta} \tag{2.15–20}$$

with

$$\alpha_n = \frac{1}{\pi}\int_0^{2\pi} u(R,\varphi)\, e^{-in\varphi}\, d\varphi, \qquad n = 0, 1, 2, \ldots \tag{2.15–21}$$

or

$$u(r,\theta) = \tfrac{1}{2}a_0 + \sum_{\nu=1}^{\infty}\left(\frac{r}{R}\right)^{\nu}(a_\nu \cos\nu\theta + b_\nu \sin\nu\theta), \tag{2.15–22}$$

$$v(r,\theta) = v(0) + \sum_{\nu=1}^{\infty}\left(\frac{r}{R}\right)^{\nu}(-b_\nu \cos\nu\theta + a_\nu \sin\nu\theta), \tag{2.15–23}$$

with

$$a_n = \frac{1}{\pi}\int_0^{2\pi} u(R,\varphi)\cos n\varphi\, d\varphi, \quad b_n = \frac{1}{\pi}\int_0^{2\pi} u(R,\varphi)\sin n\varphi\, d\varphi. \tag{2.15–24}$$

The series (2.15–22) and (2.15–23) represent $u(r, \theta)$ and $v(r, \theta)$ in terms of very simple harmonic functions. Indeed $r^n \cos n\theta$ and $r^n \sin n\theta$ are respectively the real part and the coefficient of the imaginary part of the holomorphic function z^n.

2.16 – The Taylor expansion

2.16.1 – Proof of the Taylor expansion

Let $f(z)$ be holomorphic throughout an open set $\mathfrak{A}$ and let a denote a fixed point of $\mathfrak{A}$. Consider a circumference C with centre a and radius r lying together with all its interior points entirely in $\mathfrak{A}$. If z is a point inside C and if ζ moves along C, we have

$$\left|\frac{z-a}{\zeta-a}\right| < 1 \tag{2.16–1}$$

and therefore, on account of the formula for the sum of a geometric series,

$$\frac{1}{\zeta-z} = \frac{1}{(\zeta-a)-(z-a)} = \frac{1}{\zeta-a}\,\frac{1}{1-(z-a)/(\zeta-a)}$$
$$= \frac{1}{\zeta-a}\sum_{\nu=0}^{\infty}\left(\frac{z-a}{\zeta-a}\right)^{\nu} = \sum_{\nu=0}^{\infty}\frac{(z-a)^{\nu}}{(\zeta-a)^{\nu+1}}, \tag{2.16–2}$$

whence

$$\frac{f(\zeta)}{\zeta-z} = \sum_{\nu=0}^{\infty}(z-a)^{\nu}\frac{f(\zeta)}{(\zeta-a)^{\nu+1}}, \quad \zeta \text{ on } C. \tag{2.16–3}$$

Let M denote the maximum modulus of $f(\zeta)$ along C. The terms of the series of the moduli of the terms of the series on the right-hand side of (2.16–3) are dominated by

$$\frac{M}{r}\left|\frac{z-a}{r}\right|^n, \qquad n = 0, 1, 2, \ldots, \tag{2.16–4}$$

which brings on the uniform convergence of the series (2.16–3). We may therefore integrate term-by-term (2.4.4) and we obtain

$$\frac{1}{2\pi i}\int_C \frac{f(\zeta)}{\zeta-z}\,d\zeta = \sum_{\nu=0}^{\infty}(z-a)^\nu \frac{1}{2\pi i}\int_C \frac{f(\zeta)}{(\zeta-a)^{\nu+1}}\,d\zeta, \tag{2.16–5}$$

or, by virtue of (2.7–5) and (2.9–9),

$$\boxed{f(z) = \sum_{\nu=0}^{\infty} c_\nu (z-a)^\nu} \tag{2.16–6}$$

with

$$\boxed{c_n = \frac{1}{2\pi i}\int_C \frac{f(\zeta)}{(\zeta-a)^{n+1}}\,d\zeta = \frac{f^{(n)}(a)}{n!}.} \tag{2.16–7}$$

We thus obtain *Cauchy's series* which extends to the complex domain *Taylor's series* of the real domain. It is customary to use the name of *Taylor's series* for the expansion (2.16–6).

It is immediately seen that *the expansion of $f(z)$ in a power series of $z-a$ is uniquely determined.* For, if an expansion (2.16–6) is found, we can integrate the series term-by-term along a circumference C' within the circle of convergence around a. By virtue of (2.3–31) and (2.3–32) we have

$$\int_{C'} \frac{f(\zeta)}{(\zeta-a)^{m+1}}\,d\zeta = \sum_{\nu=0}^{\infty} c_\nu \int_{C'} (\zeta-a)^{\nu-m-1}\,d\zeta = 2\pi i\, c_m$$

and since $C' \sim C$ in the set $\mathfrak{A}$ we have the same result as (2.16–7). It turns out, moreover, that *the circle of convergence of* (2.16–6) *is the largest circle around $z=a$ whose interior is still entirely contained in the set.* In particular we find that *an integral function* (1.7.3) *can be represented by a power series which is convergent throughout the whole z-plane.*

2.16.2 – Illustrative examples

We wish to give some illustrative examples. Consider the function

$$f(z) = \log(1+z), \tag{2.16–9}$$

defined in the complex plane supposed cut along the real axis from $-\infty$ to -1. *The function is expansible in a power series of z in a* *circle around the origin of radius unity.* In fact, the function is in the interior of that circle a holomorphic function, whereas the function tends to infinity as $z \to -1$. From

$$f^{(n)}(z) = (-1)^{n-1}(n-1)!(1+z)^{-n} \qquad (2.16\text{–}10)$$

we get $f'(0) = 1$, $f''(0) = -1, \ldots, f^{(n)}(0) = (-1)^{n-1}(n-1)!$, while $f(0) = 0$. Hence, on account of (2.16–7):

For all values of z of modulus less than unity subsists the expansion

$$\boxed{\log(1+z) = \sum_{\nu=1}^{\infty} (-1)^{\nu-1}\frac{z^\nu}{\nu} = z - \frac{z^2}{2} + \frac{z^3}{3} - \ldots.} \qquad (2.16\text{–}11)$$

The series is not convergent for $z = -1$; in all other points of the circumference of convergence it is convergent as may be seen on applying Picard's theorem of section 1.8.1.

If $z \to 1$ radially then by Abel's theorem of section 1.8.2

$$\log 2 = 1 - \tfrac{1}{2} + \tfrac{1}{3} - \tfrac{1}{4} + \ldots. \qquad (2.16\text{–}12)$$

This is *Brouncker's series.*

A more general result may be obtained if we let $z \to e^{i\varphi}$ radially, whenever $\varphi \neq \pi$. Since $1+z$ is within a circle whose radius is unity around the point $+1$ the value of $\arg(1+z)$ is always between $-\frac{1}{2}\pi$ and $\frac{1}{2}\pi$. Now

$$1+e^{i\varphi} = 1 + \cos\varphi + i\sin\varphi = 2\cos^2\tfrac{1}{2}\varphi + 2i\sin\tfrac{1}{2}\varphi\cos\tfrac{1}{2}\varphi \qquad (2.16\text{–}13)$$

and hence

$$\arg(1+e^{i\varphi}) = \arctan(\tan\tfrac{1}{2}\varphi) = \tfrac{1}{2}\varphi, \qquad (2.16\text{–}14)$$

which is also evident geometrically, (fig. 2.16–1). In addition we have

$$|1+e^{i\varphi}| = \sqrt{4\cos^4\tfrac{1}{2}\varphi + 4\sin^2\tfrac{1}{2}\varphi\cos^2\tfrac{1}{2}\varphi} = 2\cos\tfrac{1}{2}\varphi.$$

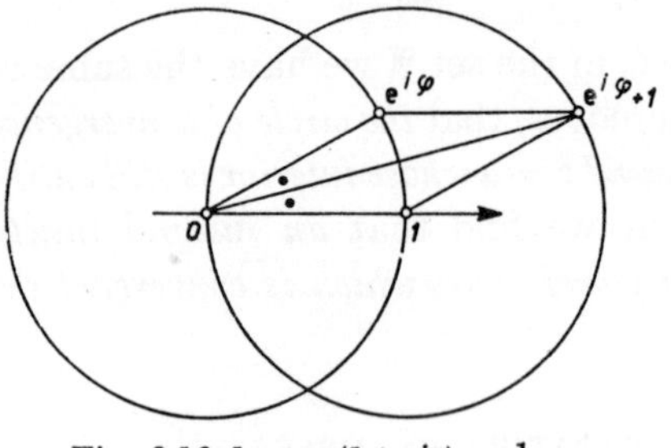

Fig. 2.16–1. $\arg(1+e^{i\varphi}) = \frac{1}{2}\varphi$

Thus we obtain from (2.16–11) on applying Abel's theorem

$$\log(2\cos\tfrac{1}{2}\varphi) = \sum_{\nu=1}^{\infty}(-1)^{\nu-1}\frac{\cos\nu\varphi}{\nu} = \cos\varphi - \frac{\cos 2\varphi}{2} + \frac{\cos 3\varphi}{3} - \ldots, \qquad (2.16\text{–}15)$$

and

$$\tfrac{1}{2}\varphi = \sum_{\nu=1}^{\infty}(-1)^{\nu-1}\frac{\sin \nu\varphi}{\nu} = \sin\varphi - \frac{\sin 2\varphi}{2} + \frac{\sin 3\varphi}{3} - \ldots, \tag{2.16–16}$$

whenever $-\pi < \varphi < \pi$.

The series (2.16–15) reduces to Brouncker's series when $\varphi = 0$. If we take $\varphi = \frac{1}{2}\pi$, we find from (2.16–16)

$$\tfrac{1}{4}\pi = 1 - \tfrac{1}{3} + \tfrac{1}{5} - \tfrac{1}{7} + \ldots, \tag{2.16–17}$$

the well-known *Leibniz series.*

Analogous considerations are valid for the function

$$f(z) = (1+z)^s \tag{2.16–18}$$

where s denotes a real or complex number. Taking account of

$$f^{(n)}(z) = s(s-1)\ldots(s-n+1)(1+z)^{s-n},$$

whence

$$f^{(n)}(0) = s(s-1)\ldots(s-n+1) = n!\binom{s}{n},$$

with

$$\binom{s}{n} = \frac{s(s-1)\ldots(s-n+1)}{n!}, \quad n = 1, 2, \ldots \tag{2.16–19}$$

we find, since $f(0) = 1$, that *within the circle of radius unity around the origin the function* (2.16–18) *is expansible in the binomial series*

$$(1+z)^s = 1 + \sum_{\nu=1}^{\infty}\binom{s}{\nu}z^\nu = 1 + \binom{s}{1}z + \binom{s}{2}z^2 + \ldots \tag{2.16–20}$$

The behaviour of the binomial series on the circumference of convergence has been fully investigated by N. H. Abel.

2.16.3 – Remark about the determination of the radius of convergence

The examples of section 2.16.2 throw light on a circumstance which deserves special mention. For the determination of the radius of convergence it is not sufficient to take only in consideration the values which $f(z)$ assumes along a line through the centre a, and that explains, for instance, that if $f(z)$ is real on the entire real axis and admits there derivatives of all orders, we can claim nothing about the range of validity of the expansion of $f(z)$ in a real Taylor series, since the values of the function for complex values of z are also of importance in this case. For example the function

$$g(z) = \operatorname{sech} z = \frac{2}{e^z + e^{-z}} \tag{2.16–21}$$

is real along the entire real axis and admits there derivatives of all orders. Nevertheless the radius of convergence of the power series representing $g(z)$ in the neighbourhood of the origin is $\frac{1}{2}\pi$. In fact, the zeros of $\cosh z$ are found from $e^z+e^{-z} = 0$, or $e^{2z} = -1$, and the zeros nearest to the origin are $\frac{1}{2}\pi i$ and $-\frac{1}{2}\pi i$. In these points the function $g(z)$ is not finite. Also the function

$$\arctan z = \frac{1}{2i} \log \frac{1+iz}{1-iz} \tag{2.16–22}$$

possesses along the real axis derivatives of all orders, but the radius of convergence of the power series that represents $\arctan z$ in a neighbourhood of the origin is unity, for the function becomes infinite at the points $z = \pm i$.

The expansion in series for the function (2.16–22) about the origin is obtained by subtracting the series for $\log(1+iz)$ and $\log(1-iz)$. An easy calculation yields

$$\boxed{\arctan z = \sum_{\nu=0}^{\infty} (-1)^{\nu} \frac{z^{2\nu+1}}{2\nu+1} = \frac{z}{1} - \frac{z^3}{3} + \frac{z^5}{5} - \ldots} \tag{2.16–23}$$

valid for $|z| < 1$. The series converges for $z = 1$ and by Abel's theorem we find Leibniz' series (2.16–17).

It should be noticed that we have applied the formula

$$\log \frac{1+iz}{1-iz} = \log (1+iz) - \log (1-iz).$$

This equation is exact, since in this case the difference of the principal arguments of $1+iz$ and $1-iz$ is between $-\pi$ and π.

2.17 – Some remarkable power series expansions

2.17.1 – The series for the inverse sine

In most cases the direct calculation of the derivatives of the function whose Cauchy-Taylor expansion is desired is rather tedious. Many artifices are devised to obtain the series. Sometimes it is very easy to find directly the series for the first derivative. Thus

$$\frac{d}{dz} \arctan z = \frac{1}{1+z^2} = \sum_{\nu=0}^{\infty} (-1)^{\nu} z^{2\nu} \tag{2.17–1}$$

valid for $|z| < 1$. Integration along a rectilinear path from 0 to z yields at once (2.16–23). Along the same lines we may proceed to find a series for $\arcsin z$. Whenever $|z| < 1$ we have

$$\frac{d}{dz}\arcsin z = (1-z^2)^{-\frac{1}{2}} = 1+\sum_{\nu=1}^{\infty}\binom{-\frac{1}{2}}{\nu}(-z)^{2\nu}$$

$$= 1+\frac{1}{2}z^2+\frac{1\cdot 3}{2\cdot 4}z^4+\frac{1\cdot 3\cdot 5}{2\cdot 4\cdot 6}z^6+\dots \qquad (2.17\text{–}2)$$

and by integrating along a rectilinear path from 0 to z we get

$$\boxed{\arcsin z = \frac{z}{1}+\frac{1}{2}\,\frac{z^3}{3}+\frac{1\cdot 3}{2\cdot 4}\,\frac{z^5}{5}+\frac{1\cdot 3\cdot 5}{2\cdot 4\cdot 6}\,\frac{z^7}{7}+\dots.} \qquad (2.17\text{–}3)$$

The series is convergent for $z = 1$. In fact, if $0 < z < 1$ the series represents $\arcsin z < \arcsin 1 = \frac{1}{2}\pi$. If $s_n(z)$ denotes the sum of n terms of the series we have $s_n(z) < \frac{1}{2}\pi$ and letting $z \to 1$ we infer that $s_n(1) \leqq \frac{1}{2}\pi$. The series (2.17–3) for $z = 1$ consists of positive terms. Hence it is convergent, since the partial sums are bounded. We may apply Abel's theorem (1.8.2) and get

$$\frac{1}{2}\pi = 1+\frac{1}{2}\cdot\frac{1}{3}+\frac{1\cdot 3}{2\cdot 4}\cdot\frac{1}{5}+\frac{1\cdot 3\cdot 5}{2\cdot 4\cdot 6}\cdot\frac{1}{7}+\dots. \qquad (2.17\text{–}4)$$

2.17.2 – Algebraic method

In other cases we may proceed by means of simple algebraic operations. Notice that the reciprocal $g(z)$ of a function $f(z)$ is holomorphic in an open set where $f(z)$ is holomorphic and does not present zeros.

Assume that $f(z)$ has the expansion

$$f(z) = \sum_{\nu=0}^{\infty} a_\nu z^\nu, \qquad a_0 \neq 0. \qquad (2.17\text{–}5$$

Then $g(z)$ is expansible as

$$g(z) = \sum_{\nu=0}^{\infty} b_\nu z^\nu. \qquad (2.17\text{–}6)$$

The radius of convergence of this latter series needs not be the same as that of the former one. It may occur, for instance, that $f(z)$ has a zero inside its circle of convergence. In that event the radius of convergence of (2.17–6) does not exceed the modulus of that zero. It is certainly true, however, that (2.17–6) converges in a sufficiently small neighbourhood of the origin.

Since the Taylor expansion is uniquely determined we may evaluate the coefficients in (2.17–5) from

$$1 = a_0b_0+(a_1b_0+a_0b_1)z+(a_2b_0+a_1b_1+a_0b_2)z^2+\dots,$$

whence the recurrent relations

$$1 = a_0 b_0,$$
$$0 = a_n b_0 + a_{n-1} b_1 + \ldots + a_0 b_n, \quad n > 0. \qquad (2.17\text{-}7)$$

These enable us to evaluate successively $b_0, b_1, \ldots$.

An explicit expression for the coefficients is

$$b_0 = \frac{1}{a_0}, \; b_n = \frac{(-1)^n}{a_0^{n+1}} \begin{vmatrix} a_1 & a_0 & 0 & \ldots & 0 \\ a_2 & a_1 & a_0 & \ldots & 0 \\ \cdot & \cdot & \cdot & \cdot & \cdot \\ a_{n-1} & a_{n-2} & a_{n-3} & \ldots & a_0 \\ a_n & a_{n-1} & a_{n-2} & \ldots & a_1 \end{vmatrix}, \; n = 1, 2, \ldots. \qquad (2.17\text{-}8)$$

2.17.3 – Euler's numbers

A first example arises from the series (1.10–9) of $\cos z$. For the sake of convenience we put in this case

$$\sec z = \sum_{\nu=0}^{\infty} \frac{b_\nu}{\nu!} z^\nu. \qquad (2.17\text{-}9)$$

Now we observe that all coefficients having an odd suffix vanish, since $\sec z$ is an even function. The numbers $E_{2n} = b_{2n}$, $n \geqq 1$, are called the *Euler numbers*. Inserting these in (2.17–8) we obtain the series

$$\boxed{\sec z = 1 + \sum_{\nu=1}^{\infty} \frac{E_{2\nu}}{(2\nu)!} z^{2\nu},} \qquad (2.17\text{-}10)$$

the radius of convergence being $\frac{1}{2}\pi$.

Taking account of (2.17–7) we can easily find recurrent relations for the Euler coefficients. By multiplying by $(2n)!$ we find

$$\boxed{E_{2n} - \binom{2n}{2n-2} E_{2n-2} + \binom{2n}{2n-4} E_{2n-4} + \ldots + (-1)^{n-1} \binom{2n}{2} E_2 + (-1)^n = 0.}$$
$$(2.17\text{-}11)$$

Since

$$E_{2n} = \frac{d^{2n}}{dz^{2n}} \sec z \Big|_{z=0}, \qquad n > 0, \qquad (2.17\text{-}12)$$

the Euler coefficients are positive integers. A simple computation yields

$$E_2 = 1, \quad E_4 = 5, \quad E_6 = 61, \quad E_8 = 1385,$$
$$E_{10} = 50521, \quad E_{12} = 2702765, \; \ldots.$$

The Euler coefficients are to be considered as "known" numbers.

2.17.4 – Bernoulli's numbers

A similar problem consists of finding the expansion of the reciprocal of the function

$$\int_0^1 e^{zt}\,dt = \frac{e^z-1}{z} = \sum_{\nu=0}^{\infty} \frac{z^\nu}{(\nu+1)!}. \tag{2.17–13}$$

Also in this case we put

$$\frac{z}{e^z-1} = \sum_{\nu=0}^{\infty} \frac{b_\nu}{\nu!} z^\nu. \tag{2.17–14}$$

The radius of convergence of the series is 2π. By virtue of (2.17–7) we have after multiplication by $(n+1)!$

$$0 = b_0 + \binom{n+1}{1} b_1 + \binom{n+1}{2} b_2 + \ldots + \binom{n+1}{n} b_n. \tag{2.17–15}$$

In particular $b_0 = 1$, $b_1 = -\frac{1}{2}$. It is easy to show that all numbers having an odd suffix > 1 are zero. In fact, the function

$$f(z) = \frac{z}{e^z-1} + \tfrac{1}{2}z \tag{2.17–16}$$

is an even function, as may readily be verified by the following expression for $f(z)$:

$$f(z) = \tfrac{1}{2}z\frac{e^z+1}{e^z-1} = \tfrac{1}{2}z \operatorname{ctnh} \tfrac{1}{2}z. \tag{2.17–17}$$

The numbers $B_{2n} = (-1)^{n-1} b_{2n}$, $n \geqq 1$, are called the *Bernoulli numbers*. They may be calculated from

$$\boxed{\binom{2n+1}{2n}B_{2n} - \binom{2n+1}{2n-2}B_{2n-2} + \ldots + (-1)^{n-1}\binom{2n+1}{2}B_2 + (-1)^n \frac{2n-1}{2} = 0.}$$

(2.17–18)

Thus we find for example

$$B_2 = \tfrac{1}{6},\quad B_4 = \tfrac{1}{30},\quad B_6 = \tfrac{1}{42},\quad B_8 = \tfrac{1}{30},\quad B_{10} = \tfrac{5}{66},$$
$$B_{12} = \tfrac{691}{2730},\quad B_{14} = \tfrac{7}{6},\quad B_{16} = \tfrac{3617}{510},\ \ldots$$

In section 3.7.4 we shall prove that all Bernoulli numbers are positive.

2.17.5 – Expansions involving Bernoulli's numbers

We shall list some expansions involving Bernoulli numbers. First we deduce from (2.17–14)

$$\boxed{\frac{1}{e^z-1}-\frac{1}{z}+\frac{1}{2}=\sum_{\nu=1}^{\infty}(-1)^{\nu-1}\frac{B_{2\nu}}{(2\nu)!}z^{2\nu-1},}\quad |z|<2\pi, \qquad (2.17\text{–}19)$$

a formula which will play an important role in the theory of the gamma function.

Taking account of (2.17–16) and (2.17–17) we have the alternative expression

$$\tfrac{1}{2}z \operatorname{ctnh} \tfrac{1}{2}z = 1-\sum_{\nu=1}^{\infty}(-1)^{\nu-1}\frac{B_{2\nu}}{(2\nu)!}z^{2\nu}. \qquad (2.17\text{–}20)$$

In this formula we replace z by $2iz$:

$$\boxed{z \operatorname{ctn} z = 1-\sum_{\nu=1}^{\infty}\frac{B_{2\nu}}{(2\nu)!}2^{2\nu}z^{2\nu},}\quad |z|<\pi. \qquad (2.17\text{–}21)$$

From

$$\operatorname{ctn} 2z = \frac{1}{\tan 2z} = \frac{1-\tan^2 z}{2\tan z} = \tfrac{1}{2}\operatorname{ctn} z - \tfrac{1}{2}\tan z$$

we have

$$\tan z = \frac{z \operatorname{ctg} z - 2z \operatorname{ctg} 2z}{z}$$

and hence, by virtue of (2.17–21),

$$\boxed{\tan z = \sum_{\nu=1}^{\infty}\frac{B_{2\nu}}{(2\nu)!}(2^{2\nu}-1)2^{2\nu}z^{2\nu},}\quad |z|<\tfrac{1}{2}\pi. \qquad (2.17\text{–}22)$$

Integrating the relation

$$\frac{d}{dz}\log\cos z = -\tan z$$

along a linear path from 0 to z, $|z|<\frac{1}{2}\pi$, we obtain from (2.17–22)

$$\boxed{\log\cos z = -\sum_{\nu=1}^{\infty}\frac{B_{2\nu}}{(2\nu)!}(2^{2\nu}-1)2^{2\nu}\frac{z^{2\nu}}{2\nu},}\quad |z|<\tfrac{1}{2}\pi. \qquad (2.17\text{–}23)$$

In a similar way we infer from

$$\frac{d}{dz}\log\frac{\sin z}{z} = \operatorname{ctn} z - \frac{1}{z} = \frac{1}{z}(z\operatorname{ctn} z - 1)$$

that

$$\boxed{\log\frac{\sin z}{z} = -\sum_{\nu=1}^{\infty}\frac{B_{2\nu}}{(2\nu)!}2^{2\nu}\frac{z^{2\nu}}{2\nu},}\quad |z|<\pi. \qquad (2.17\text{–}24)$$

Substracting corresponding members of (2.17–24) and (2.17–23) we have

$$\log \frac{\tan z}{z} = \sum_{\nu=1}^{\infty} \frac{B_{2\nu}}{(2\nu)!} (2^{2\nu}-2) \frac{z^{2\nu}}{2\nu}, \quad |z| < \tfrac{1}{2}\pi. \tag{2.17–25}$$

The derivative of this function is

$$(2z \csc 2z - 1)\frac{1}{z} = \sum_{\nu=1}^{\infty} \frac{B_{2\nu}}{(2\nu)!} (2^{2\nu}-2)\, 2^{2\nu} z^{2\nu-1},$$

whence

$$2z \csc 2z = 1 + \sum_{\nu=1}^{\infty} \frac{B_{2\nu}}{(2\nu)!} (2^{2\nu}-2)\, 2^{2\nu} z^{2\nu}$$

and so

$$\boxed{z \csc z = 1 + \sum_{\nu=1}^{\infty} \frac{B_{2\nu}}{(2\nu)!} (2^{2\nu}-2)\, z^{2\nu},} \quad |z| < \pi. \tag{2.17–26}$$

This result could also be obtained by observing that

$$\operatorname{ctn} z + \tan \tfrac{1}{2}z = \csc z.$$

Finally we wish to remark that the way in which we obtained (2.17–25) requires some comment. In fact, the difference of the logarithms of two functions is not always the logarithm of the quotient. The procedure is, however, exact in the case that z is real and hence also for complex z inside the region of convergence.

2.18 – Cauchy's inequality. Parseval's identity

2.18.1 – Cauchy's inequality

Denote the maximum of the modulus of the sum of the power series

$$f(z) = \sum_{\nu=0}^{\infty} c_\nu z^\nu \tag{2.18–1}$$

on a circumference $|z| = r$ within the region of convergence of the series by $M(r)$ (2.13.2). The following fundamental inequality

$$\boxed{|c_n| r^n \leqq M(r),} \quad n = 0, 1, 2, \ldots, \tag{2.18–2}$$

is known as *Cauchy's inequality*.

It may readily be proved on applying (2.16–7) that

$$c_n = \frac{1}{2\pi i} \int_C \frac{f(\zeta)}{\zeta^{n+1}}\, d\zeta,$$

where C is a circle of radius r around the origin. By virtue of Darboux's theorem (2.4.3) we have

$$|c_n| \leqq \frac{1}{2\pi}\frac{M(r)}{r^{n+1}}2\pi r = \frac{M(r)}{r^n}.$$

From Cauchy's inequality arises another proof of Liouville's theorem. If $f(z)$ is holomorphic throughout the entire plane, the series $\sum_{\nu=0}^{\infty} c_\nu z^\nu$ is convergent for all values of z. From $|f(z)| \leqq M$ we deduce $|c_n| \leqq Mr^{-n}$ and making $r \to \infty$ the right-hand member tends to zero whenever $n > 0$. Hence $f(z) = c_0$ is a constant. Along the same lines we can prove the more general theorem of section 2.12.2.

2.18.2 – Parseval's identity

Cauchy's inequality is included in a general formula, *Parseval's identity*. Put

$$f(z) = p_n(z)+\varphi_n(z) \qquad (2.18\text{–}3)$$

where $p_n(z)$ is a polynomial of degree n consisting of the first $n+1$ terms of the series (2.18–1). We consider only the values of z on C, that is $|z| = r$. Then $|\varphi_n(z)|$ is arbitrarily small whenever n is sufficiently large, while $p_n(z)$ is bounded. Hence also the expression $\chi_n(z, \bar{z})$ in

$$|f(z)|^2 = p_n(z)\overline{p_n(z)}+\chi_n(z, \bar{z})$$

is arbitrarily small for sufficiently large values of n. Let $z = re^{i\theta}$. Then

$$\int_0^{2\pi}|f(re^{i\theta})|^2 d\theta = \int_0^{2\pi} p_n(z)\overline{p_n(z)}\, d\theta+\int_0^{2\pi}\chi_n(z, \bar{z})\, d\theta, \qquad (2.18\text{–}4)$$

the last numbers tending to zero as $n \to \infty$. Observing that

$$\int_0^{2\pi} z^p \bar{z}^q\, d\theta = \int_0^{2\pi} r^{p+q} e^{(p-q)i\theta}\, d\theta = \begin{cases} 0, & \text{when } p \neq q, \\ 2\pi r^{2p}, & \text{when } p = q, \end{cases}$$

where p and q are non-negative integers, we readily find, by letting $n \to \infty$

$$\boxed{\frac{1}{2\pi}\int_0^{2\pi}|f(re^{i\theta})|^2 d\theta = \sum_{\nu=0}^{\infty}|c_\nu|^2 r^{2\nu},} \qquad (2.18\text{–}5)$$

the desired identity.

Since the expression on the left does not exceed $\{M(r)\}^2$ we must have

$$\sum_{\nu=0}^{\infty}|c_\nu|^2 r^{2\nu} \leqq \{M(r)\}^2, \qquad (2.18\text{–}6)$$

and it follows, each term of the series on the left being positive,

$$|c_n|^2 r^{2n} \leqq \{M(r)\}^2, \quad n = 0, 1, 2, \ldots, \tag{2.18–7}$$

and hence Cauchy's inequality (2.18–2).

A comparison of (2.18–6) and (2.18–7) shows that in (2.18–7) equality can only occur if all coefficients other than c_n vanish. The function $f(z)$ thus reduces to the monomial

$$f(z) = c_n z^n. \tag{2.18–8}$$

2.19 – An extension of the Cauchy-Liouville theorem

2.19.1 – Extension of Cauchy's inequality

In this section we shall derive a sharper form of Cauchy's inequality. Let $A(r)$ denote the maximum of the real part of the sum $f(z)$ of the series (2.18–1) on the circumference C defined by $|z| = r$ in the region of convergence.

For $n \geqq 1$ subsists the inequality

$$\boxed{|c_n| r^n \leqq \max\{4A(r), 0\} - 2 \operatorname{Re} f(0),} \tag{2.19–1}$$

where $\operatorname{Re} f(z)$ denotes the real part of $f(z)$.

Let $z = re^{i\theta}$, $f(z) = u(r, \theta) + iv(r, \theta)$. Then

$$c_n = \frac{1}{2\pi i} \int_C \frac{f(\zeta)}{\zeta^{n+1}}\, d\zeta = \frac{1}{2\pi} \int_0^{2\pi} \frac{f(re^{i\theta})}{r^{n+1} e^{i(n+1)\theta}}\, re^{i\theta}\, d\theta,$$

or

$$r^n c_n = \frac{1}{2\pi} \int_0^{2\pi} \{u(r, \theta) + iv(r, \theta)\} e^{-in\theta}\, d\theta, \quad n = 0, 1, \ldots. \tag{2.19–2}$$

On the other hand we have for $n \geqq 1$

$$\int_C f(\zeta)\, \zeta^{n-1}\, d\zeta = 0,$$

whence

$$0 = \frac{1}{2\pi} \int_0^{2\pi} \{u(r, \theta) + iv(r, \theta)\} e^{in\theta}\, d\theta, \tag{2.19–3}$$

and, if we replace i by $-i$,

$$0 = \frac{1}{2\pi} \int_0^{2\pi} \{u(r, \theta) - iv(r, \theta)\} e^{-in\theta}\, d\theta. \tag{2.19–4}$$

Now add the corresponding members of (2.19–2) and (2.19–4) for $n = 1, 2, \ldots$.

We get

$$c_n r^n = \frac{1}{\pi}\int_0^{2\pi} u(r,\theta)\, e^{-in\theta}\, d\theta, \quad n = 1, 2, \ldots \tag{2.19–5}$$

From this equation follows

$$|c_n|\, r^n \leqq \frac{1}{\pi}\int_0^{2\pi} |u(r,\theta)|\, d\theta, \quad n = 1, 2, \ldots \tag{2.19–6}$$

The particular case $n = 0$ of (2.19–2) is

$$c_0 = \frac{1}{2\pi}\int_0^{2\pi} \{u(r,\theta)+iv(r,\theta)\}\, d\theta, \tag{2.19–7}$$

whose real part is (multiplied by 2)

$$2\,\mathrm{Re}\, c_0 = 2\,\mathrm{Re}\, f(0) = \frac{1}{\pi}\int_0^{2\pi} u(r,\theta)\, d\theta. \tag{2.19–8}$$

If we add the members of this equation to the corresponding members of (2.19–6) we obtain

$$|c_n| r^n + 2\,\mathrm{Re}\, f(0) \leqq \frac{1}{\pi}\int_0^{2\pi} \{|u(r,\theta)|+u(r,\theta)\}\, d\theta. \tag{2.19–9}$$

Now $|u|+u = 0$, whenever $u \leqq 0$. Hence for $A(r) \leqq 0$ the right-hand side is zero. If instead $A(r) > 0$ we have

$$\frac{1}{\pi}\int_0^{2\pi} \{|u(r,\theta)| + u(r,\theta)\}\, d\theta \leqq \frac{1}{\pi}\int_0^{2\pi} 2A(r)\, d\theta = 4A(r),$$

and therefore, on account of (2.19–9),

$$|c_n| r^n + 2\,\mathrm{Re}\, f(0) \leqq 4A(r),$$

so that in every case (2.19–1) holds.

2.19.2 – Extension of the Cauchy-Liouville theorem

If $f(z)$ is holomorphic throughout the entire plane and $A(r)$ has an upper bound on a sequence of concentric circumferences tending to infinity, the function $f(z)$ is constant.

More generally, *if*

$$A(r) \leqq Ar^k,$$

A and k being constants, $k \geqq 0$, from a certain value r_0 of r upwards, then $f(z)$ is a polynomial of degree not exceeding k.

In fact, from (2.19–1) we have for $n > k$

$$|c_n| \leqq \frac{\max(4Ar^k, 0) - 2\,\mathrm{Re}\, f(0)}{r^n}$$

if $r > r_0$ and the right-hand member tends to zero as $r \to \infty$. It follows that $c_n = 0$, whenever $n > k$.

2.20 – Weierstrass's theorems about the limits of sequences of functions

2.20.1 – Weierstrass's theorem for sequences

The following theorems will be often referred to as *Weierstrass's theorems.* The functions of the sequence

$$F_0(z),\ F_1(z),\ F_2(z),\ \ldots \tag{2.20–1}$$

are assumed to be holomorphic throughout an open set $\mathfrak{A}$. Let the sequence converge uniformly on every closed and bounded set contained in $\mathfrak{A}$. Then we may prove:

(i) *The limiting function* $F(z)$ *is holomorphic throughout* $\mathfrak{A}$.

(ii) *The sequence*

$$F_0^{(k)}(z),\ F_1^{(k)}(z),\ F_2^{(k)}(z),\ \ldots, \tag{2.20–2}$$

obtained by differentiating k times the functions of the sequence (2.20–1) *is convergent throughout* $\mathfrak{A}$ *and uniformly convergent on every bounded and closed set within* $\mathfrak{A}$. *The limiting function is the corresponding derivative of* $F(z)$.

We already know from section 1.5.2 that $F(z)$ is continuous throughout $\mathfrak{A}$. Let z denote any point of $\mathfrak{A}$. Describe a sufficiently small circle C around z. By (2.9–9) we have

$$F_n^{(k)}(z) = \frac{k!}{2\pi i}\int_C \frac{F_n(\zeta)}{(\zeta - z)^{k+1}}\,d\zeta. \tag{2.20–3}$$

On C the sequence (2.20–1) tends uniformly to a limiting function $F(z)$. On account of a result of section 2.4.4 we have

$$\frac{k!}{2\pi i}\int_C \frac{F(\zeta)}{(\zeta - z)^{k+1}}\,d\zeta = \frac{k!}{2\pi i}\int_C \frac{\lim\limits_{n\to\infty} F_n(\zeta)}{(\zeta - z)^{k+1}}\,d\zeta$$

$$= \lim_{n\to\infty}\frac{k!}{2\pi i}\int_C \frac{F_n(\zeta)}{(\zeta - z)^{k+1}}\,d\zeta = \lim_{n\to\infty} F_n^{(k)}(z). \tag{2.20–4}$$

For $k = 0$ we find

$$F(z) = \lim_{n\to\infty} F_n(z) = \frac{1}{2\pi i}\int_C \frac{F(\zeta)}{\zeta - z}\,d\zeta, \tag{2.20–5}$$

hence $F(z)$ is differentiable at z (2.8.1) and, consequently, holomorphic throughout $\mathfrak{A}$. For $k > 0$ we have

$$F^{(k)}(z) = \frac{k!}{2\pi i}\int_C \frac{F(\zeta)}{(\zeta - z)^{k+1}}\,d\zeta = \lim_{n\to\infty} F_n^{(k)}(z). \qquad (2.20\text{–}6)$$

Let now $\mathfrak{C}$ denote a closed and bounded set within $\mathfrak{A}$. There is a positive constant ϱ such that all points of $\mathfrak{C}$ have a distance $\geqq \varrho$ to the boundary of $\mathfrak{A}$. Describe around a point z of $\mathfrak{C}$ a circle C of radius $\frac{1}{2}\varrho$. Given $\varepsilon > 0$, we have

$$|F(\zeta) - F_n(\zeta)| < \varepsilon, \qquad \zeta \text{ on } C,$$

whenever n is large enough, since the convergence of the sequence is uniform on C. Then also

$$|F^{(k)}(z) - F_n^{(k)}(z)| = \frac{k!}{2\pi}\left|\int_C \frac{F(\zeta) - F_n(\zeta)}{(\zeta - z)^{k+1}}\,d\zeta\right| \leqq \frac{k!\,\varepsilon}{r^{k+1}}, \qquad (2.20\text{–}7)$$

this estimate being independent of the choice of z in $\mathfrak{C}$.

2.20.2 – Modification of the previous result

The theorem of section 2.20.1 holds also in a slightly modified form if we suppose that *the functions* (2.20–1) *are continuous on the closure of a bounded region* $\mathfrak{R}$ *and the sequence is uniformly convergent on the boundary of the region.*

For, if n is sufficiently large, then for every $m > n$ we have

$$|F_m(\zeta) - F_n(\zeta)| < \varepsilon, \qquad (2.20\text{–}8)$$

ζ being on the boundary. On account of the maximum modulus principle (2.13.2) the inequality (2.20–8) holds certainly within $\mathfrak{R}$ and by Cauchy's convergence test (1.5.4) the sequence (2.20–1) is uniformly convergent on the closure of $\mathfrak{R}$.

2.20.3 – Weierstrass's theorem for series

An equivalent form of the theorem established in section 2.20.1 is the following.

The functions of the sequence

$$f_0(z),\ f_1(z),\ f_2(z),\ \ldots \qquad (2.20\text{–}9)$$

are assumed to be holomorphic throughout an open set $\mathfrak{A}$. Let the series

$$\sum_{\nu=0}^{\infty} f_\nu(z) \qquad (2.20\text{–}10)$$

converge uniformly on every closed and bounded subset of $\mathfrak{A}$.

Then the sum

$$f(z) = \sum_{\nu=0}^{\infty} f_\nu(z) \qquad (2.20\text{–}11)$$

is holomorphic throughout $\mathfrak{A}$ *and the series*

$$\sum_{\nu=0}^{\infty} f_\nu^{(k)}(z) \tag{2.20–12}$$

obtained by differentiating k times the terms of the given series converges in $\mathfrak{A}$ *and uniformly on every bounded and closed subset of* $\mathfrak{A}$, *its sum being the corresponding derivative of* $f(z)$.

2.20.4 – Weierstrass's double series theorem

A useful application is *Weierstrass's double series theorem*. Let all the series

$$f_m(z) = \sum_{\nu=0}^{\infty} c_{m\nu} z^\nu, \quad m = 0, 1, 2, \ldots \tag{2.20–13}$$

be convergent at least for $|z| < R$ and let

$$f(z) = \sum_{\mu=0}^{\infty} f_\mu(z) \tag{2.20–14}$$

be uniformly convergent for $|z| \leqq r < R$ for every $r < R$. Then *the coefficients of the same power of z in the respective series form a convergent series and if we set*

$$c_n = \sum_{\mu=0}^{\infty} c_{\mu n} \tag{2.20–15}$$

the series

$$\sum_{\nu=0}^{\infty} c_\nu z^\nu$$

represents $f(z)$ *at least for* $|z| < R$.

In fact, the function $f(z)$ is holomorphic for $|z| < R$ and can therefore be developed in a power series of z. The coefficient of z^n is

$$\frac{1}{n!} f^{(n)}(0) = \frac{1}{n!} \sum_{\mu=0}^{\infty} f_\mu^{(n)}(0) = \sum_{\mu=0}^{\infty} c_{\mu n}. \tag{2.20–16}$$

The theorem states that under certain conditions it is allowed to add infinitely many power series term-by-term.

2.20.5 – Weierstrass's theorem for infinite integrals

Another application may be made on functions that are defined by infinite integrals.

Let $f(t, z)$ be a function of the complex variable z and the real variable t, having the following properties:

(i) The function is defined for all points z of an open set $\mathfrak{A}$ and for all values of $t \geqq 0$. The function is, moreover, bounded.

(ii) For every fixed z the function is continuous as regards t.
(iii) For every fixed t the function is holomorphic throughout $\mathfrak{A}$.
(iv) The integral

$$F(z) = \int_0^\infty f(t, z)\, dt \qquad (2.20\text{–}17)$$

is convergent when z lies in $\mathfrak{A}$ and uniformly convergent on every closed and bounded subset of $\mathfrak{A}$. Under these assumptions we have:

The function $F(z)$ is a holomorphic function of z whose derivatives are found by differentiating inside the sign of integration and are represented by integrals that converge uniformly on every closed and bounded set contained in $\mathfrak{A}$.

The condition (iv) expresses that as the real number ω tends to infinity the integral

$$\int_0^\omega f(t, z)\, dt \qquad (2.20\text{–}18)$$

tends to $F(z)$ when z is a point of $\mathfrak{A}$ and that the convergence is uniform over any bounded and closed subset of $\mathfrak{A}$.

Now take any sequence of positive numbers

$$t_0 < t_1 < t_2 < \ldots, \qquad (2.20\text{–}19)$$

tending to infinity, and introduce the functions

$$F_n(z) = \int_0^{t_n} f(t, z)\, dt. \qquad (2.20\text{–}20)$$

By the theorem of section 2.9.1 these functions are holomorphic throughout $\mathfrak{A}$ and, moreover, they satisfy the conditions of the theorem of section 2.20.1. Hence

$$F(z) = \lim_{n\to\infty} F_n(z) \qquad (2.20\text{–}21)$$

is holomorphic within $\mathfrak{A}$ and $F_n^{(k)}(z)$ converges to $F^{(k)}(z)$. But

$$F_n^{(k)}(z) = \int_0^{t_n} \frac{\partial^k f(t, z)}{\partial z^k}\, dt \qquad (2.20\text{–}22)$$

and so, the sequence (2.20–9) being arbitrary,

$$F^{(k)}(z) = \int_0^\infty \frac{\partial^k f(t, z)}{\partial z^k}\, dt, \qquad (2.20\text{–}23)$$

the integral on the right-hand side being uniformly convergent on every closed and bounded subset of $\mathfrak{A}$.

2.20.6 – Change of order of integration

Now assume $\mathfrak{R}$ to be a *simply connected region* and let C denote a regular path within $\mathfrak{R}$. *If* $f(t, z)$ *satisfies the same conditions as in* 2.20.5 *then the relation*

$$\int_C \left\{\int_0^\infty f(t, \zeta)\, dt\right\} d\zeta = \int_0^\infty \left\{\int_C f(t, \zeta)\, d\zeta\right\} dt \qquad (2.20\text{–}24)$$

holds.

Let z_0 and z denote two points in $\mathfrak{R}$. Since $\mathfrak{R}$ is simply connected the integral

$$\int_{z_0}^{z} f(t, \zeta)\, d\zeta$$

represents a holomorphic function of z and it is easily shown that this function is continuous as regards t. Moreover, it is bounded in any closed and bounded subset of $\mathfrak{R}$. Then in view of the theorem of section 2.9.1 the integral

$$\int_0^\infty \left\{\int_{z_0}^{z} f(t, \zeta)\, d\zeta\right\} dt$$

can be differentiated with respect to z by carrying out the differentiation inside the sign of integration, the derivative being $\int_0^\infty f(t, z)\, dt$. But this is also the derivative of the function $\int_{z_0}^{z}\left\{\int_0^\infty f(t, \zeta)\, dt\right\} d\zeta$.

Hence

$$\int_0^\infty \left\{\int_{z_0}^{z} f(t, \zeta)\, d\zeta\right\} dt = \int_{z_0}^{z}\left\{\int_0^\infty f(t, \zeta) dt\right\} d\zeta, \qquad (2.20\text{–}25)$$

for both members coincide if we take $z = z_0$. Since $\int_0^\infty f(t, z)\, dt$ is uniformly convergent in every closed and bounded subset of $\mathfrak{R}$, in particular on C connecting the points z and z_0, we have, if ε is an arbitrary positive number, taking account of (2.20–25):

$$\left|\int_C \left\{\int_0^\infty f(t, \zeta)\, dt\right\} d\zeta - \int_0^\infty \left\{\int_C f(t, \zeta)\, d\zeta\right\} dt\right| = \left|\int_C \left\{\int_\omega^\infty f(t, \zeta)\, dt\right\} d\zeta\right| < \varepsilon l,$$

whenever ω is sufficiently large, l denoting the length of C.

2.20.7 – The representation of the logarithm as an infinite integral

We may illustrate the result of section 2.20.6 in a simple example which is of value in the theory of the gamma function.

It is easy to show that

$$\frac{1}{s} = \int_0^\infty e^{-st}\,dt, \qquad \operatorname{Re} s > 0. \tag{2.20–26}$$

The integral in (2.20–26) is uniformly convergent on any closed set $\mathfrak{C}$ in the right half plane Re $s > 0$. In fact, if ξ is the (positive) distance of $\mathfrak{C}$ to the imaginary axis, we have

$$\left|\int_0^\infty e^{-st}\,dt\right| \leqq \int_0^\infty e^{-xt}\,dt \leqq \int_0^\infty e^{-\xi t}\,dt = \frac{1}{\xi}$$

and the truth of the assertion follows from the last remark of section 1.5.5.

Integration from 1 to s yields

$$\boxed{\log s = \int_0^\infty \frac{e^{-t} - e^{-st}}{t}\,dt,} \qquad \operatorname{Re} s > 0, \tag{2.20–27}$$

a formula due to Euler.

2.21 – Schwarz's lemma

2.21.1 – Classical form of Schwarz's lemma

In the subsequent section 2.22.1 we shall establish a modern version of the theorem proved in section 2.20.1 due to G. Vitali and we may derive profit from a lemma due to H. A. Schwarz which he utilized in the theory of conformal mapping.

In its classical form *Schwarz's lemma* states:

If $f(z)$ is holomorphic for $|z| < 1$ where it satisfies

$$|f(z)| \leqq 1, \qquad f(0) = 0, \tag{2.21–1}$$

then the inequality

$$|f(z)| \leqq |z| \tag{2.21–2}$$

holds whenever $|z| < 1$. Moreover, equality can occur only when $f(z) = e^{i\alpha} z$, α being a real constant.

By virtue of Riemann's theorem (2.8.3), the function

$$g(z) = \begin{cases} \dfrac{f(z)}{z}, & \text{when } z \neq 0, \\ f'(0), & \text{when } z = 0, \end{cases} \tag{2.21–3}$$

is holomorphic for $|z| < 1$. Let z be a number whose modulus is less than 1. Select r in such a fashion that $|z| < r < 1$. Then by the principle of the maximum modulus (2.13.2) the function $g(z)$ attains its maximum modulus on $|z| \leqq r$ at some points of the circumference $|z| = r$, this maximum being $\leqq 1/r$.

Hence

$$|g(z)| \leqq \frac{1}{r}. \tag{2.21-4}$$

This inequality holds no matter how near r is to 1, and is independent of r. Making $r \to 1$ we deduce that

$$|g(z)| \leqq 1 \tag{2.21-5}$$

or

$$|f(z)| \leqq |z|, \tag{2.21-6}$$

whenever $|z| < 1$.

If there exists a number z of modulus less than 1 such that $|g(z)| = 1$, we know that $g(z)$ is a constant of modulus 1, i.e., $g(z) = e^{i\alpha}$ and we have $f(z) = e^{i\alpha}z$.

2.21.2 – Modification of Schwarz's lemma

A trivial modification of Schwarz's lemma is the following statement:

If $f(z)$ is holomorphic for $|z| < R$ where it satisfies the inequality $|f(z)| \leqq M$ and $f(0) = 0$, then the inequality

$$|f(z)| \leqq \frac{M}{R}|z| \tag{2.21-7}$$

holds whenever $|z| < R$. Equality can occur only when $f(z) = \frac{M}{R}e^{i\alpha}z$, α being a real constant.

For we may reduce this case to the preceding one by considering the function $\varphi(z) = f(zR)/M$.

2.21.3 – Estimate of a holomorphic function with positive real part inside the unit circle

Schwarz's lemma can be applied to obtain an estimate of a function whose real part is positive inside the unit circle. First we observe that

$$w = \frac{z-1}{z+1} \tag{2.21-8}$$

is numerically less than 1 when $x = \operatorname{Re} z > 0$. In fact,

$$|z-1| = \sqrt{(x-1)^2+y^2} < \sqrt{(x+1)^2+y^2} = |z+1|.$$

Now let $f(z)$ denote a function with $\operatorname{Re} f(z) > 0$ when $|z| < 1$. In view of the above result the modulus of the function

$$g(z) = \frac{f(z)-1}{f(z)+1} \tag{2.21-9}$$

is less than unity and we may write

$$f(z) = \frac{1+g(z)}{1-g(z)}, \tag{2.21-10}$$

where $|g(z)| < 1$, provided $|z| < 1$. Assuming, moreover, that $f(0) = 1$ we have $g(0) = 0$. Taking account of the inequalities (1.1–7) and (2.1–9), we find in view of Schwarz's lemma

$$|f(z)| = \frac{|1+g(z)|}{|1-g(z)|} \leqq \frac{1+|g(z)|}{1-|g(z)|} \leqq \frac{1+|z|}{1-|z|}, \tag{2.21-11}$$

whenever $|z| < 1$.

It is easy to obtain a lower bound for $|f(z)|$ by observing that

$$\mathrm{Re}\,(1/f(z)) = \mathrm{Re}\,(\overline{f(z)}/|f(z)|^2) = \mathrm{Re}\,(f(z)/|f(z)|^2) > 0.$$

Hence, in accordance with (2.21–11),

$$\frac{1}{|f(z)|} \leqq \frac{1+|z|}{1-|z|}. \tag{2.21-12}$$

The inequalities (2.21–11) and (2.21–12) combine into

$$\frac{1-|z|}{1+|z|} \leqq |f(z)| \leqq \frac{1+|z|}{1-|z|} \tag{2.21-13}$$

whenever $|z| < 1$.

The function

$$f(z) = \frac{1-z}{1+z}$$

shows that the inequalities (2.21–13) are the best possible. When $f(0) = a+bi$, $a > 0$, we may apply the above result to the function $(f(z)-bi)/a$.

2.22 – Vitali's theorem

2.22.1 – Statement and proof of the theorem

We are now in a position to prove an important theorem due to G. Vitali which is of fundamental importance in the theory of the so-called normal families of functions, that are classes of functions for which an analogue of the accumulation point principle holds. More precisely, a set of functions is called a *normal family* of holomorphic functions in a region $\mathfrak{R}$ if from any sequence $F_0(z)$, $F_1(z)$,

$F_2(z), \ldots$, of functions of the set it is possible to extract a subsequence $F_{n_0}(z), F_{n_1}(z), F_{n_2}(z), \ldots$, which either converges uniformly or tends uniformly to ∞ on every closed and bounded subset of $\mathfrak{R}$.

Vitali's theorem states:

Let the functions of the sequence

$$F_0(z),\ F_1(z),\ F_2(z), \ldots \tag{2.22–1}$$

be holomorphic throughout a region $\mathfrak{R}$ *and be uniformly bounded,* i.e., *there exists a constant M such that for all z in* $\mathfrak{R}$

$$|F_n(z)| \leqq M, \qquad n = 0, 1, 2, \ldots. \tag{2.22–2}$$

Moreover, the sequence may have finite limits at the points of a subset of $\mathfrak{R}$ *admitting at least one accumulation point contained in* $\mathfrak{R}$. *Then the sequence* (2.22–1) *converges throughout* $\mathfrak{R}$ *and uniformly in every bounded and closed subset within* $\mathfrak{R}$.

By means of a trivial substitution we can carry over the accumulation point into the origin. Let

$$F_m(z) = \sum_{\nu=0}^{\infty} a_{m\nu} z^\nu = a_{m0} + a_{m1} z + a_{m2} z^2 + \ldots, \tag{2.22–3}$$

within a circle C contained in $\mathfrak{R}$, the radius of this circle being r. Then

$$|F_m(z) - F_m(0)| \leqq |F_m(z)| + |F_m(0)| \leqq 2M \tag{2.22–4}$$

and since $F_m(z) - F_m(0)$ vanishes at $z = 0$, we have by Schwarz's lemma

$$|F_m(z) - F_m(0)| \leqq \frac{2M}{r}|z|, \qquad |z| < r. \tag{2.22–5}$$

Let $z^* \neq 0$ be a point within C where the sequence converges. Then

$$|F_m(0) - F_{m+p}(0)| \leqq |F_m(0) - F_m(z^*)| + |F_m(z^*) - F_{m+p}(z^*)| +$$
$$+ |F_{m+p}(z^*) - F_{m+p}(0)| \leqq \frac{4M}{r}|z^*| + |F_m(z^*) - F_{m+p}(z^*)|.$$

Since $z = 0$ is an accumulation point of the set of points where the sequence converges we may choose z^* in such a fashion that

$$|z^*| < \tfrac{1}{2}\varepsilon \frac{r}{4M},$$

ε being a given positive number. Moreover,

$$|F_m(z^*) - F_{m+p}(z^*)| < \tfrac{1}{2}\varepsilon,$$

whenever m is large enough, p being an arbitrary positive integer. Hence also

$$|F_m(0)-F_{m+p}(0)| < \varepsilon \tag{2.22–6}$$

or

$$|a_{m0}-a_{m+p,0}| < \varepsilon. \tag{2.22–7}$$

As a consequence

$$a_0 = \lim_{m\to\infty} a_{m0} \tag{2.22–8}$$

exists and is finite.

Next consider the function

$$G_m(z) = \frac{F_m(z)-F_m(0)}{z} = a_{m1}+a_{m2}z+\ldots. \tag{2.22–9}$$

The functions $G_m(z)$ are holomorphic for $|z| < r$ and from (2.22–5) we deduce

$$|G_m(z)| \leqq \frac{2M}{r} \tag{2.22–10}$$

whenever $|z| < r$, this estimate being independent of the choice of m. The sequence $G_0(z), G_1(z), G_2(z), \ldots,$ converges at the same points as the sequence (2.22–1). By the arguments used before we find that

$$a_1 = \lim_{m\to\infty} a_{m1} \tag{2.22–11}$$

exists and is finite.

Proceeding in this way we find that for an arbitrary n the limit

$$a_n = \lim_{m\to\infty} a_{mn} \tag{2.22–12}$$

exists and is finite.

From Cauchy's inequality we have

$$|a_{mn}| \leqq \frac{M}{r^n} \tag{2.22–13}$$

and hence also

$$|a_n| \leqq \frac{M}{r^n}. \tag{2.22–14}$$

This leads to the conclusion that the series

$$\sum_{\nu=0}^{\infty} a_\nu z^\nu = a_0+a_1z+a_2z^2+\ldots \tag{2.22–15}$$

converges for $|z| < r$. It represents, therefore, a function $F(z)$ which is holomorphic for $|z| < r$. We shall prove that $F(z)$ is the limiting function of the sequence (2.22–1) for these values of z. By virtue of (2.22–13) and (2.22–14) we have

$$|a_n - a_{mn}| \leqq \frac{2M}{r^n}. \tag{2.22–16}$$

Hence

$$|F(z) - F_m(z)| \leqq \sum_{\nu=0}^{p} |a_\nu - a_{m\nu}| \, |z|^\nu + 2M \sum_{\nu=p+1}^{\infty} \left(\frac{|z|}{r}\right)^\nu. \tag{2.22–17}$$

Given $\varepsilon > 0$ we can find a p such that $2M \sum_{\nu=p+1}^{\infty} \left(\frac{|z|}{r}\right)^\nu < \frac{1}{2}\varepsilon$. This p being fixed we can find an m_0 such that $|a_n - a_{mn}| \, |z|^n < \frac{1}{2}\varepsilon$, whenever $m > m_0$. This is possible because $a_{mn} \to a_n$, as $m \to \infty$. Hence, if m is sufficiently large

$$|F(z) - F_m(z)| < \varepsilon, \tag{2.22–18}$$

whenever $|z| < r$. Consequently, the sequence (2.22–1) is convergent for $|z| < r$, the convergence being uniform in every set $|z| \leqq r_1 < r$, for then p and m_0 can be chosen independently of z.

Now we wish to show that the sequence (2.22–1) converges throughout $\mathfrak{R}$. Let z^* be an arbitrary point of $\mathfrak{R}$. We may join z^* with an accumulation point z_0 of convergence points by a continuous curve within $\mathfrak{R}$. Let ϱ denote a positive number smaller than the distance from this curve to the boundary of $\mathfrak{R}$. On the curve we take a finite number of points $z_0, z_1, \ldots, z_n = z'$ such that $|z_\nu - z_{\nu-1}| < \varrho$, $\nu = 1, \ldots, n$. For $|z - z_0| < \varrho$ the sequence converges, as already has been proved. Hence z_1 is an accumulation point of a set of convergence points. Then, on applying the result obtained before, the sequence converges also for $|z - z_1| < \varrho$, and so on. Thus we find that the sequence converges also at z^* and uniformly in any closed circular disc within $\mathfrak{R}$ whose centre is z^*.

Let $\mathfrak{C}$ denote any closed and bounded subset of $\mathfrak{R}$. Every point of $\mathfrak{C}$ is the centre of a closed circular disc contained in $\mathfrak{R}$, where the sequence converges uniformly. By the Heine-Borel theorem (see section 1.2.4) a finite number of these discs are sufficient to cover $\mathfrak{C}$ and therefore the sequence (2.22–1) converges uniformly throughout $\mathfrak{C}$. This completes the proof of Vitali's theorem.

2.22.2 – Selection of a uniformly convergent subsequence

From Vitali's theorem we wish to deduce a remarkable consequence also due to Vitali.

Let

$$F_0(z),\ F_1(z),\ F_2(z),\ \ldots \tag{2.22–18}$$

be a sequence of functions which are holomorphic throughout a region $\mathfrak{R}$ and uniformly bounded. *From this sequence we can select a subsequence which converges uniformly in any closed and bounded set contained in* $\mathfrak{R}$. Hence the sequence (2.21–18) is a normal family.

Let $z_0, z_1, z_2, \ldots$ be a sequence of points converging towards a point z^* of $\mathfrak{R}$, no two of the points coinciding. Then the points $F_n(z_0)$, $n = 0, 1, 2, \ldots$, all lie in or on the boundary of the circular disc $|z| \leqq M$. Hence they have at least one accumulation point w_0 (if not, from a certain index upwards all are equal. If this should be the case we take w_0 as this number). It is possible to select a subsequence, say

$$F_{00}(z), F_{01}(z), F_{02}(z), \ldots, \tag{2.22–19}$$

such that for $z = z_0$ these functions converge to w_0, $|w_0| \leqq M$.

Similarly from this sequence of functions we can select a subsequence

$$F_{10}(z), F_{11}(z), F_{12}(z), \ldots, \tag{2.22–20}$$

such that these functions converge for $z = z_1$ to a number w_1, $|w_1| < M$. And then from this a third sequence

$$F_{20}(z), F_{21}(z), F_{22}(z), \ldots \tag{2.22–21}$$

which converges for $z = z_2$ to w_2, $|w_2| \leqq M$, and so on.

Now we form the sequence

$$F_{00}(z), F_{11}(z), F_{22}(z), \ldots \tag{2.22–22}$$

by taking the diagonal terms of the above double array. Each of these functions belongs to the sequence (2.22–19) and so the sequence converges at $z = z_0$; each function after the first belongs to the sequence (2.22–20) and so the sequence (2.22–22) converges at $z = z_1$; and so on. Therefore the sequence (2.22–22) converges at each of the points $z_0, z_1, z_2, \ldots$, and by Vitali's theorem this sequence converges uniformly in any closed and bounded subset of $\mathfrak{R}$.

2.23 – Laurent's expansion. The Fourier series

2.23.1 – Laurent's series

Assume that C_1 and C_2 are two concentric circles contained in an open set $\mathfrak{A}$ such that the ring-shaped region between these circles is also a subset of $\mathfrak{A}$. Let C_2 be the smallest of these circles. If they are both traversed in the counter-clockwise sense, they are homologous n $\mathfrak{A}$:

$$C_1 \sim C_2, \tag{2.23–1}$$

for the winding numbers of these circles with respect to any point not contained in $\mathfrak{A}$ are simultaneously either 0 or 1. The winding number of the cycle $C_1 - C_2$ with respect to a point z between C_1 and C_2 is $+1$. Hence, by virtue of the general Cauchy integral formula (2.7–4), $f(z)$ being holomorphic throughout $\mathfrak{A}$,

$$f(z) = \frac{1}{2\pi i}\int_{C_1} \frac{f(\zeta)}{\zeta - z}\, d\zeta - \frac{1}{2\pi i}\int_{C_2} \frac{f(\zeta)}{\zeta - z}\, d\zeta = f_1(z) + f_2(z). \qquad (2.23\text{–}2)$$

In this case $f_2(z)$ is not necessarily equal to zero, for $f(z)$ is not assumed to be holomorphic throughout the interior of C_2. In just the same way as in section 2.16.1 we deduce

$$f_1(z) = \frac{1}{2\pi i}\int_{C_1} \frac{f(\zeta)}{\zeta - z}\, d\zeta = \sum_{\nu=0}^{\infty} c_\nu (z-a)^\nu \qquad (2.23\text{–}3)$$

with

$$c_n = \frac{1}{2\pi i}\int_{C_1} \frac{f(\zeta)}{(\zeta - a)^{n+1}}\, d\zeta, \qquad n = 0, 1, 2, \ldots, \qquad (2.23\text{–}4)$$

where a denotes the centre of the circles C_1 and C_2.

Now let ζ move along C_2. Then $|(\zeta - a)/(z-a)| < 1$, hence

$$-\frac{1}{\zeta - z} = \frac{1}{(z-a)-(\zeta-a)} = \frac{1}{z-a}\,\frac{1}{1 - \dfrac{\zeta - a}{z - a}} = \sum_{\nu=1}^{\infty} \frac{(\zeta-a)^{\nu-1}}{(z-a)^\nu}.$$

The series in the last member converges uniformly along C_2 and therefore term-by-term integration is justified. Next we have

$$f_2(z) = \frac{-1}{2\pi i}\int_{C_2} \frac{f(\zeta)}{\zeta - z}\, d\zeta = \sum_{\nu=1}^{\infty} \frac{c_{-\nu}}{(z-a)^\nu} \qquad (2.23\text{–}5)$$

with

$$c_{-n} = \frac{-1}{2\pi i}\int_{C_2} (\zeta - a)^{n-1} f(\zeta)\, d\zeta, \qquad n = 1, 2, \ldots. \qquad (2.23\text{–}6)$$

The series (2.23–3) converges in C_1 and uniformly in any closed set in the interior of C_1; the series (2.23–5) converges outside C_2 and uniformly in any closed set in the exterior of C_2. From (2.23–3) and (2.23–5) we get *Laurent's series* for $f(z)$

$$\boxed{f(z) = \sum_{\nu=0}^{\infty} c_\nu (z-a)^\nu + \sum_{\nu=1}^{\infty} c_{-\nu}(z-a)^{-\nu} = \sum_{\nu=-\infty}^{\infty} c_\nu (z-a)^\nu.} \qquad (2.23\text{–}7)$$

Notice that within the set $\mathfrak{A}$, C being any circle concentric with C_1 and C_2 and between C_1 and C_2, the homologies $C \sim C_1$, $C \sim C_2$ are valid. Hence by Cauchy's integral theorem

$$c_n = \frac{1}{2\pi i} \int_C \frac{f(\zeta)}{(\zeta - a)^{n+1}} d\zeta, \quad n = 0, \pm 1, \pm 2, \ldots \qquad (2.23\text{–}8)$$

If $f(z)$ is holomorphic throughout the interior of C_1 then all coefficients with negative suffix are equal to zero and the Laurent series reduces to the Cauchy-Taylor series. In the general case, however, there are a finite or an infinite number of terms with negative exponents.

By the same arguments as used in the case of the Taylor expansion we may prove that Laurent's expansion is unique, i.e. the series (2.23–7) which represents $f(z)$ between C_1 and C_2 has the coefficients (2.23–8).

It is evident that Laurent's expansion is valid in the largest circular ring-shaped region around a that is still contained in the set $\mathfrak{A}$.

2.23.2 – Fourier's series

Consider a function $f(z)$ of period 1 and holomorphic in a strip $b_1 < \operatorname{Im} z < b_2$, (fig. 2.23–1), $\operatorname{Im} z$ denoting the coefficient of i in z.

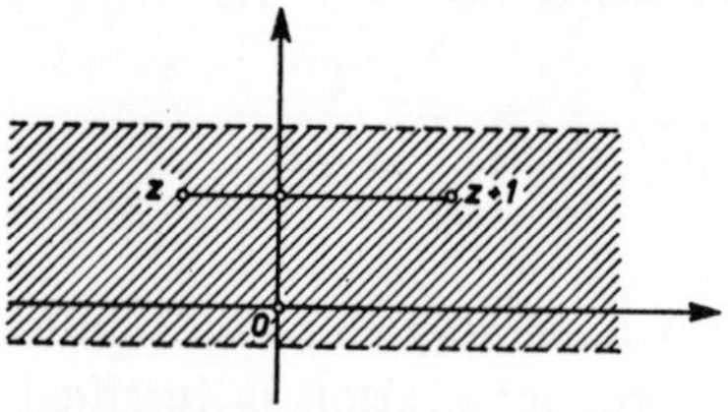

Fig. 2.23–1. Strip of holomorphism of a periodic function

The periodicity is expressed by

$$f(z+1) = f(z) \qquad (2.23\text{–}9)$$

for every z in the strip.

The equation

$$w = \exp 2\pi i z \qquad (2.23\text{–}10)$$

defines a mapping of the strip on the annulus $r_1 < |w| < r_2$, with $r_1 = \exp(-2\pi b_2)$, $r_2 = \exp(-2\pi b_1)$. In fact, $|w| = \exp(-2\pi \operatorname{Im} z)$. The transformation is of course not one-to-one. If w is an arbitrary point in the annulus we can find an infinity of numbers z satisfying (2.23–10), the difference of any two of these numbers being an integer. For all these values of z the function $f(z)$ takes the same value which we shall designate by $F(w)$. We wish to prove that $F(w)$ is holomorphic throughout the annulus.

Let w_0 be a fixed point in the annulus. The function

$$\log (w/w_0) + \log w_0$$

is holomorphic in the region $w/w_0 + |w/w_0| \neq 0$, i.e. the plane from which the points $w = -\lambda w_0$, $\lambda \geqq 0$ are removed, (fig. 2.23–2).

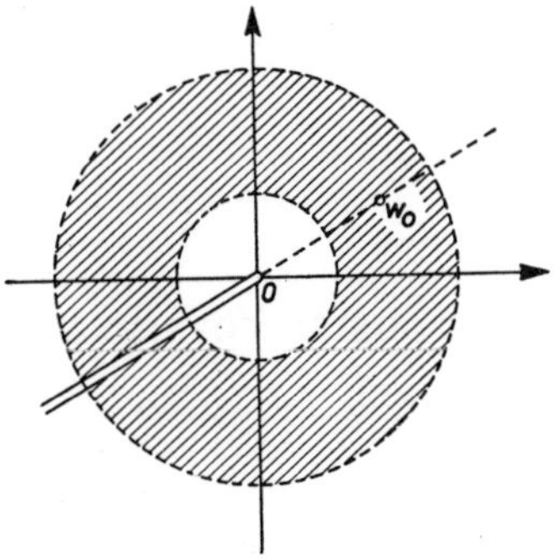

Fig. 2.23–2. Region of holomorphism of the logarithm of a periodic function

Hence the function

$$f\left\{\frac{1}{2\pi i}\left(\log\frac{w}{w_0} + \log w_0\right)\right\}$$

represents $F(w)$ in a neighbourhood of w_0, and it is now evident that $F(w)$ is differentiable at $w = w_0$.

Accordingly we may apply Laurent's expansion to the function $F(w)$, obtaining

$$F(w) = \sum_{\nu=-\infty}^{\infty} A_\nu w^\nu.$$

As a consequence we have

$$\boxed{f(z) = \sum_{\nu=-\infty}^{\infty} A_\nu \exp 2\pi i\, \nu z,} \tag{2.23–11}$$

the expansion of $f(z)$ as a *Fourier series*. Thus we proved:

A function being holomorphic in an infinite strip $b_1 < \operatorname{Im} z < b_2$ *and being periodic with period* 1 *possesses a Fourier expansion* (2.23–11). *The series is uniformly convergent in every closed strip included in the given strip.*

An easy example is provided by the function $\operatorname{ctn} \pi z$, this function being periodic of period 1 and holomorphic in the region $\operatorname{Im} z > 0$ as well in the region $\operatorname{Im} z < 0$. Accordingly we have two different expansions. First we may write

$$\operatorname{ctn} \pi z = i\frac{w+1}{w-1} = -i(1+2w+2w^2+ \ldots),$$

whenever $|w| < 1$, w being the expression (2.23–10). Hence

$$\operatorname{ctn} \pi z = -i(1+2\sum_{\nu=1}^{\infty} \exp 2\pi i \nu z), \quad \operatorname{Im} z > 0. \tag{2.23–12}$$

Secondly we have

$$\operatorname{ctn} \pi z = i\frac{1+w^{-1}}{1-w^{-1}} = i(1+2w^{-1}+2w^{-2}+\ldots),$$

whenever $|w| > 1$. Hence

$$\operatorname{ctn} \pi z = i(1+2\sum_{\nu=1}^{\infty} \exp(-2\pi i \nu z)), \quad \operatorname{Im} z < 0. \tag{2.23–13}$$

2.23.3 – The Euler-Fourier coefficients

The coefficients A_n, $n = 0, \pm 1, \pm 2, \ldots$, occurring in (2.23–11) are given by

$$A_n = \frac{1}{2\pi i}\int_C \frac{F(w)}{w}\, dw = \int_0^1 f(x+ib) \exp(-2\pi i n(x+ib))dx, \tag{2.23–14}$$

where $b_1 < b < b_2$ and C a circle around the origin of radius $\exp(-2\pi b)$.

An alternative representation of the series which is also of frequent use, is obtained by combining the coefficients A_n in pairs. It is customary to write

$$\tfrac{1}{2}a_0 = A_0, \quad a_n = A_n + A_{-n}, \quad b_n = i(A_n - A_{-n}), \quad n = 1, 2, \ldots.$$

Then (2.23–11) appears in the form

$$\boxed{f(z) = \tfrac{1}{2}a_0 + \sum_{\nu=1}^{\infty} (a_\nu \cos 2\pi\nu z + b_\nu \sin 2\pi\nu z),} \tag{2.23–15}$$

with

$$a_n = 2\int_0^1 f(x+ib) \cos 2\pi n(x+ib)\, dx, \quad n = 0, 1, 2, \ldots, \tag{2.23–16}$$

$$b_n = 2\int_0^1 f(x+ib) \sin 2\pi n(x+ib)\, dx, \quad n = 1, 2, \ldots. \tag{2.23–17}$$

These expressions are called the *Euler-Fourier coefficients* of $f(z)$.

In many cases we can put $b = 0$, but, as the example of $\operatorname{ctn} \pi z$ shows, this is not always permissible.

Finally we make the trivial remark that the case of a function being periodic in a certain strip having the period $\tilde{\omega}$ may be reduced to the previous case by considering the function $g(z) = f(\tilde{\omega} z)$.

2.23.4 – Poisson's summation formula

Let $f(z)$ denote a function which is holomorphic throughout a strip $-\varrho < \operatorname{Im} z < \varrho$, $\varrho > 0$. Assume, moreover, that the series

$$F(z) = \sum_{\nu=-\infty}^{\infty} f(\nu+z) \tag{2.23–18}$$

is uniformly convergent in every closed set including the segment $0 \leqq x \leqq 1$ and being a part of the strip. It is plain that $F(z)$ is periodic, its period being 1. Since $F(z)$ is holomorphic throughout the strip (by virtue of Weierstrass's theorem of section 2.20.3) the conditions of section 2.23.2 are fulfilled and, consequently, we have the Fourier expansion

$$F(z) = \sum_{\nu=-\infty}^{\infty} A_\nu \exp(-2\pi i\,\nu z) \tag{2.23–19}$$

with

$$A_n = \int_0^1 F(x) \exp(-2\pi i n x)\,dx, \quad n = 0, \pm 1, \pm 2, \ldots \tag{2.23–20}$$

Because of the uniform convergence of the series (2.23–19) in the interval $0 \leqq x \leqq 1$ we may apply term-by-term integration and we accordingly find

$$A_n = \sum_{\nu=-\infty}^{\infty} \int_0^1 f(\nu+x) \exp(-2\pi i\,nx)\,dx$$

$$= \sum_{\nu=-\infty}^{\infty} \int_\nu^{\nu+1} f(x) \exp(-2\pi i n x)\,dx = \int_{-\infty}^{\infty} f(x) \exp(-2\pi i\,nx)\,dx. \tag{2.23–21}$$

Inserting this into (2.23–19) and putting $z = 0$, we obtain *Poisson's summation formula*

$$\boxed{\sum_{\nu=-\infty}^{\infty} f(\nu) = \sum_{\nu=-\infty}^{\infty} \int_{-\infty}^{\infty} f(x) \exp(-2\pi i\,\nu x)\,dx.} \tag{2.23–22}$$

2.23.5 – Functional equation of a theta function

An interesting result is obtained when we apply Poisson's summation formula to the function

$$f(z) = \exp(-\pi z^2 t), \tag{2.23–23}$$

t being a positive number. For then we may deduce the functional equation of a so-called *theta function* defined as

$$\boxed{\vartheta(t) = \sum_{\nu=-\infty}^{\infty} \exp(-\pi \nu^2 t).} \tag{2.23–24}$$

Apart from a finite number of terms the series (2.23–18), where $f(z)$ is the expression (2.23–23), is dominated by the series $\sum_{\nu=-\infty}^{\infty} \exp(-|\nu|)$, whenever z remains in a bounded set, t being fixed.

By Weierstrass's theorem of section 1.5.4 the series is uniformly convergent as regards z in any bounded set of the z-plane. Hence the Poisson summation formula is applicable and we find

$$\vartheta(t) = \sum_{\nu=-\infty}^{\infty} \exp(-\pi\nu^2 t) = \sum_{\nu=-\infty}^{\infty} \int_{-\infty}^{\infty} \exp(-\pi x^2 t - 2\pi i\, \nu x)\, dx$$

$$= \sum_{\nu=-\infty}^{\infty} \exp\left(-\frac{\pi\nu^2}{t}\right) \int_{-\infty}^{\infty} \exp\left\{-\pi\left(x+\frac{i\nu}{t}\right)^2 t\right\} dx.$$

Writing x instead of $x\sqrt{\pi t}$ we may bring this result into the form

$$\vartheta(t) = \frac{1}{\sqrt{\pi t}} \sum_{\nu=-\infty}^{\infty} \exp\left(-\frac{\pi\nu^2}{t}\right) \int_{-\infty}^{\infty} \exp\left\{-\left(x+i\nu\sqrt{\frac{\pi}{t}}\right)^2\right\} dx. \qquad (2.23\text{–}25)$$

Now we observe that

$$\int_{-\infty}^{\infty} e^{-x^2}\, dx = \int_{-\infty}^{\infty} e^{-(x+ib)^2}\, dx, \qquad (2.23\text{–}26)$$

b being a real number.

The proof runs as follows. Integrate e^{-z^2} around the perimeter of a rectangle whose sides are along the lines $x = \pm R$, $y = ib$, $y = 0$, (fig. 2.23–3). Since the integrand is holomorphic in any region in-

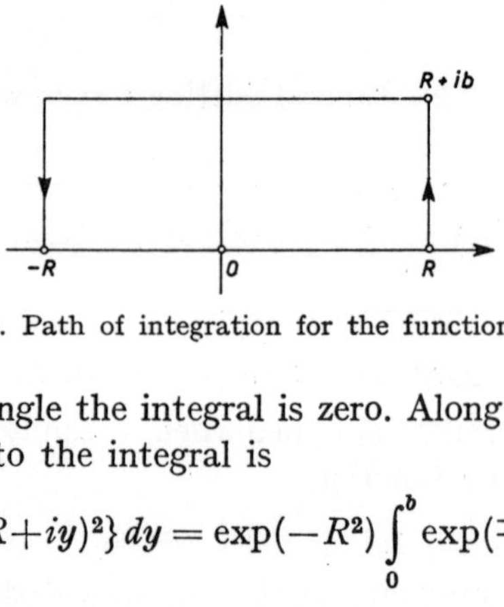

Fig. 2.23–3. Path of integration for the function exp $(-z^2)$

cluding this rectangle the integral is zero. Along the vertical sides the contribution to the integral is

$$\int_0^b \exp\{-(\pm R+iy)^2\}\, dy = \exp(-R^2) \int_0^b \exp(\mp 2iRy + y^2)\, dy.$$

The integral on the right is bounded when $R \to \infty$. Hence the expression on the right-hand side tends to zero and the equality (2.23–26) is an easy consequence. It is readily seen that the integrals occurring in (2.23–26) are convergent in the usual sense.

This result enables us to simplify (2.23–26) considerably. In fact, we may write

$$\vartheta(t) = \frac{1}{\sqrt{\pi t}}\, \vartheta\left(\frac{1}{t}\right) \int_{-\infty}^{\infty} e^{-x^2}\, dx. \qquad (2.23\text{–}27)$$

By putting $t = 1$ we may evaluate the integral (2.23–26). We get the important result

$$\boxed{\int_{-\infty}^{\infty} e^{-x^2}\,dx = \sqrt{\pi}.} \tag{2.23–28}$$

Inserting this value into (2.23–27) we finally obtain: *The theta function* (2.23–24) *satisfies the functional equation*

$$\boxed{\vartheta(t) = \frac{1}{\sqrt{t}}\,\vartheta\left(\frac{1}{t}\right),} \tag{2.23–29}$$

t being positive.

Chapter 3

REGULAR AND SINGULAR POINTS-RESIDUES-ZEROS

3.1 - Regular points

3.1.1 - Definition of regularity

A function $f(z)$ is said to be *regular* at $z = a$ whenever $f(z)$ is holomorphic in a neighbourhood of this point with possible exception of this point, where the function is locally bounded. By Riemann's theorem of section 2.8.3 the function may be identified with a function holomorphic throughout the entire neighbourhood. A point where a function $f(z)$ is regular is called a *regular point* of the function; a function is said to be regular throughout a set when it is regular at every point of the set.

We wish to include the point at infinity. A function $f(z)$ is said to be regular at $z = \infty$ if and only if the function $\varphi(z) = f(1/z)$ is regular at $z = 0$.

Within a sufficiently small circle around the (finite) point there exists the Taylor expansion

$$f(z) = \sum_{\nu=0}^{\infty} c_\nu (z-a)^\nu. \tag{3.1–1}$$

If $f(z)$ is regular at $z = \infty$ we can expand the function $\varphi(z)$ in a power series of z, whence

$$f(z) = \varphi(1/z) = \sum_{\nu=0}^{\infty} c_\nu z^{-\nu} \tag{3.1–2}$$

is valid for all sufficiently large values of $|z|$, i.e., in a neighbourhood of $z = \infty$.

3.1.2 - Order of the zeros of a derivative

We shall say that $z = \infty$ is a zero of $f(z)$ if $z = 0$ is a zero of $\varphi(z) = f(1/z)$. Let n be the order of this zero. Then according to (2.11–7)

$$\varphi(z) = z^n p(z), \qquad p(0) \neq 0 \tag{3.1–3}$$

where $p(z)$ is regular at $z = 0$; hence

$$f(z) = z^{-n} g(z), \qquad g(\infty) \neq 0, \tag{3.1–4}$$

$g(z)$ being regular at $z = \infty$.

From the result of section 2.9.2 we deduce: *At a point where $f(z)$ is* *regular the derivatives of all orders are also regular.* Now we may state the theorem:

A zero of order n of a function $f(z)$ is a zero of order $n-1$ of the derivative when the zero is a finite point, and a zero of order $n+1$ when the zero is at infinity.

Let $z = a$ be a zero of order n, a being a finite number:

$$f(z) = (z-a)^n g(z), \qquad g(a) \neq 0.$$

Then

$$f'(z) = (z-a)^{n-1} h(z)$$

with

$$h(z) = ng(z)+(z-a)g'(z), \qquad h(a) \neq 0.$$

If $z = \infty$ is a zero of order n, then $z = 0$ is a zero of order n of $f(1/z)$ and hence a zero of order $n-1$ of

$$-\frac{1}{z^2} f'\left(\frac{1}{z}\right).$$

As a consequence $z = 0$ is a zero of order $n+1$ of $f'(1/z)$.

This completes the proof.

3.2 – Isolated singularities

3.2.1 – Poles and essential singular points

The point $z = a$ is called an *isolated singularity* of the function $f(z)$ if the function is holomorphic throughout a neighbourhood of $z = a$ with exception of this point itself.

Assume the existence of a complex number b and of a certain neighbourhood of $z = a$ such that $f(z)$ does not come arbitrarily close to b in that neighbourhood. This means that there exists a positive number c such that

$$|f(z)-b| \geqq c \tag{3.2–1}$$

for all $z \neq a$ in that neighbourhood. The function

$$g(z) = \frac{1}{f(z)-b} \tag{3.2–2}$$

is holomorphic in that neighbourhood except at $z = a$, where it is, however, locally bounded, since $|g(z)| \leqq 1/c$. Hence, $g(z)$ is regular at $z = a$ and we may write

$$f(z) = b + \frac{1}{g(z)} \tag{3.2–3}$$

and

$$h(z) = \frac{1}{f(z)} = \frac{g(z)}{b\,g(z)+1}. \tag{3.2–4}$$

(i) Let $g(a) \neq 0$. Then (3.2–3) shows that $f(z)$ can be defined in such a fashion at $z = a$ that it is regular at this point.

(ii) Let $g(a) = 0$. Then $h(a)$ is regular at $z = a$ and admits this point as a zero. Assume

$$h(z) = (z-a)^n k(z), \qquad k(a) \neq 0.$$

We get

$$f(z) = (z-a)^{-n} \varphi(z), \tag{3.2–5}$$

where $\varphi(z)$ is regular at $z = a$ and $\varphi(a) \neq 0$. We shall say that $z = a$ is a *pole* with *order of multiplicity n* of the function $f(z)$.

Excluding the case of a regular point or of a pole the point is called an *essential singularity of* $f(z)$.

From the previous arguments it follows that the behaviour of a function in the vicinity of an essential singularity is described by the following *Casorati-Weierstrass theorem:*

Given any positive numbers ε, δ *and any complex number* b, *there is a point* z *inside the circle* $|z-a| = \delta$ *at which* $|f(z)-b| < \varepsilon$.

That is, $|f(z)|$ must come arbitrarily close to any complex number b in any neighbourhood of $z = a$.

Poles and essential singularities defined before are called *isolated singularities,* because the function is regular at every point of a certain neighbourhood, except at the point itself. In other words:

In the vicinity of an isolated singularity there are no other singular points.

3.2.2 – Condition for a pole

From (3.2–5) we deduce at once that

$$\lim_{z \to a} |f(z)| = \infty, \tag{3.2–6}$$

a being a pole. Conversely, let (3.2–6) hold at an isolated singular point. We shall prove that $z = a$ is a pole. In fact, we can find a positive number r such that

$$|f(z)| > 1$$

provided $0 < |z-a| < r$. The function $h(z) = 1/f(z)$ at all points $z \neq a$, where $f(z)$ is defined and different from zero, is holomorphic in the region $0 < |z-a| < r$ and locally bounded at $z = a$; hence $h(z)$ is regular at $z = a$ and admits there a zero. Let

$$h(z) = (z-a)^n k(z), \qquad k(a) \neq 0.$$

Then

$$f(z) = (z-a)^{-n} \varphi(z), \qquad \varphi(a) \neq 0, \tag{3.2–7}$$

and $\varphi(z)$ is regular at $z = a$. Thus we proved:

A necessary and sufficient condition that $z = a$ be a pole of $f(z)$ is expressed by (3.2–6).

An alternative statement is (see section **1.2.1**):

The function $f(z)$ is chordally continuous at any pole.

In the sections 3.3.5, 3.12.3 and 3.12.5 we shall describe in more detail the behaviour of a function in the neighbourhood of a zero or of a pole.

It is evident that *a pole of order n is a zero of the same order for the reciprocal of the function and conversely.* This follows at once from (3.2–5). It should be noticed that the considerations about isolated singularities can be extended to the case $z = \infty$. We then investigate the behaviour of $f(1/z)$ at $z = 0$.

A function which is regular at every point of the plane, the point at infinity included, is a constant.

For then $f(z)$ is necessarily bounded throughout the entire plane and is a constant according to Liouville's theorem (2.12.1).

3.2.3 – Behaviour of a function at an essential singular point

Let $z = a$ be an essential singular point of $f(z)$, this function being holomorphic for $0 < |z-a| < r$. Given the positive numbers p and r there exists a z_1 with $0 < |z_1-a| < r$ such that

$$|f(z_1)| = |f(z_1)-0| < p,$$

as follows from the Casorati-Weierstrass theorem. Moreover, the function not being bounded in a neighbourhood of $z = a$, there exists a z_2 with $0 < |z_2-a| < r$ such that

$$|f(z_2)| > p.$$

Now join z_1 and z_2 by a continuous arc. Since $|f(z)|$ is continuous along this arc there must be a point z on it such that $|f(z)| = p$. Thus:

Within every small neighbourhood, however small, of an isolated essential singularity of $f(z)$ there exist infinitely many points where the modulus takes any preassigned positive value.

This theorem is related to a famous theorem of Picard which we shall only state here.

In an arbitrarily small neighbourhood of an isolated essential singularity a function $f(z)$ takes every value with one exception at most.

Otherwise stated:

If $f(z)$ is holomorphic for $0 < |z-a| < r$ and there are two unequal numbers α, β such that $f(z) \neq \alpha$, $f(z) \neq \beta$ for $0 < |z-a| < r$ then $z = a$ is not an essential singularity.

Here we confine ourselves to the remark that *if $f(z)$ is holomorphic for $0 < |z-a| < r$ and if for a certain number α the function takes the value α at infinitely many points z which admit $z = a$ as an accumulation point, then $z = a$ is an essential singularity, unless $f(z)$ is constant.*

In fact, if $f(z)$ is regular at $z = a$, then $f(z)$ is a constant (2.11.2). If $f(z)$ is not regular at $z = a$, $f(z)$ cannot have a pole at $z = a$, for on account of (3.2–6) we can assign a neighbourhood of $z = a$ where $|f(z)| > \alpha+1$. The functions $\exp(1/z)$ and $\sin(1/z)$ admit $z = 0$ as an essential singularity. The equations $\exp(1/z) = 1$ and $\sin(1/z) = 1$ are satisfied by the infinitely many values $z = 1/2k\pi i$, $k = \pm 1, \pm 2, \ldots$, $z = 1/\frac{1}{2}(4k+1)\pi$, $k = 0, \pm 1, \pm 2, \ldots$, respectively, admitting $z = 0$ as an accumulation point.

Similarly $\exp z$ and $\sin z$ admit $z = \infty$ as an essential isolated singularity.

3.3 – Residues

3.3.1 – Residue at a finite point

Let $z = a$ be a regular or an isolated singular point of the function $f(z)$. If C denotes a sufficiently small circumference around $z = a$, then the integral

$$\operatorname*{Res}_{z=a} f(z) = \frac{1}{2\pi i} \int_{C+} f(\zeta)\, d\zeta \tag{3.3–1}$$

is independent of the radius of C, C being described in the counterclockwise sense (denoted by the index $+$). The integral (3.3–1) is called the ***residue of*** $f(z)$ ***at*** $z = a$.

The residue certainly vanishes if $z = a$ is a regular point but it may also vanish in other cases.

3.3.2 – Residue at infinity

Let $f(z)$ be regular at $z = \infty$ or have there an isolated singularity. Then outside a sufficiently large circle around the origin the function is holomorphic. If C is a sufficiently large circle the integral

$$\operatorname*{Res}_{z=\infty} f(z) = \frac{1}{2\pi i} \int_{C-} f(\zeta)\, d\zeta, \tag{3.3–2}$$

where C_- denotes the circle C described in the clockwise sense, is independent of the radius of C. It is called the ***residue of*** $f(z)$ ***at*** $z = \infty$.

Put $z = Re^{-i\theta}$, R being the radius of C. With $r = 1/R$ we have

$$\operatorname*{Res}_{z=\infty} f(z) = \frac{-1}{2\pi i}\int_0^{2\pi} f(Re^{-i\theta})i\,Re^{-i\theta}\,d\theta = \frac{-1}{2\pi}\int_0^{2\pi} f\left(\frac{1}{re^{i\theta}}\right)\frac{1}{re^{i\theta}}\,d\theta$$

$$= \frac{-1}{2\pi i}\int_0^{2\pi} f\left(\frac{1}{re^{i\theta}}\right)\frac{d(re^{i\theta})}{(re^{i\theta})^2} = \frac{-1}{2\pi i}\int_C f\left(\frac{1}{\zeta}\right)\frac{d\zeta}{\zeta^2}$$

where C denotes a circle of radius r around the origin described in the counter-clockwise sense. Hence:

$\operatorname*{Res}_{z=\infty} f(z)$ *is the opposite of the residue of the function* $f(1/z)/z^2$ *at the origin*

$$\boxed{\operatorname*{Res}_{z=\infty} f(z) = -\operatorname*{Res}_{z=0}\frac{f(1/z)}{z^2}.} \tag{3.3–3}$$

The reason that we describe the circle C in the clockwise sense in order to define the residue in infinity is the following. Project the complex plane stereographically on a complex sphere (1.1.3). For an observer outside the sphere none of the points ought to be preferred and a circle around the image of $z = \infty$ described positively corresponds to a circle around the origin in the complex plane described in the clockwise sense.

3.3.3 – Evaluation of residues

For the evaluation of residues in concrete examples the following remarks are of importance. *The residue at a pole of order n is equal to*

$$\operatorname*{Res}_{z=a} f(z) = \frac{1}{(n-1)!}\frac{d^{n-1}}{dz^{n-1}}\{(z-a)^n f(z)\}_{z=a}. \tag{3.3–4}$$

In fact, since

$$f(z) = (z-a)^{-n} g(z)$$

and $g(z)$ is regular at $z = a$, we have, according to (2.9–9),

$$\operatorname*{Res}_{z=a} f(z) = \frac{1}{2\pi i}\int_C \frac{g(\zeta)}{(\zeta-a)^n}\,d\zeta = \frac{1}{(n-1)!}\,g^{(n-1)}(a)$$

and the result follows at once. In the case $n = 1$ we may state this theorem in the form:

The residue at a simple pole $z = a$ *is found from*

$$\boxed{\operatorname*{Res}_{z=a} f(z) = \lim_{z\to a}\,(z-a)f(z).} \tag{3.3–5}$$

The following remark also deserves mention. *If* $f(z)$ *possesses a simple pole at* $z = a$ *with residue* c *and if* $\varphi(z)$ *is regular at that point, then the residue of* $f(z)\varphi(z)$ *is* $c\,\varphi(a)$.

In fact, if $\lim_{z\to a}(z-a)f(z) = c$, then $\lim_{z\to a}(z-a)f(z)\varphi(z) = c\,\varphi(a)$.

This result enables us to derive a useful formula for the evaluation of residues at simple poles.

Let $f(z)$ admit a simple pole at $z = a$. Then $g(z) = 1/f(z)$ has a simple zero there and

$$\lim_{z\to a} (z-a)f(z) = \lim_{z\to a} \frac{z-a}{g(z)} = \lim_{z\to a} \frac{z-a}{g(z)-g(a)} = \frac{1}{g'(a)}, \tag{3.3–6}$$

for $g'(a) \neq 0$ at a simple zero. Further, if $f(z)$ can be written in the form

$$f(z) = \frac{\varphi(z)}{g(z)}, \tag{3.3–7}$$

$\varphi(z)$ being regular at $z = a$ and $g(z)$ having a simple zero at $z = a$, *the residue of $f(z)$ at that point is equal to*

$$\boxed{\operatorname*{Res}_{z=a} \frac{\varphi(z)}{g(z)} = \frac{\varphi(a)}{g'(a)}.} \tag{3.3–8}$$

3.3.4 – Illustrative examples

We may illustrate these facts in some elementary examples. In section 1.10.6 we proved that the zeros of $\sin z$ are the numbers $k\pi$, $k = 0, \pm 1, \pm 2, \ldots$. The zeros are simple since $\sin z$ and $\sin' z = \cos z$ do not vanish simultaneously.

The poles of the function

$$\csc z = \frac{1}{\sin z} \tag{3.3–9}$$

are $z = k\pi$, $k = 0, \pm 1, \pm 2, \ldots$, and by (3.3.–8) we find for the residues, the poles being simple,

$$\operatorname*{Res}_{z=k\pi} \csc z = \sec k\pi = \frac{1}{\cos k\pi} = (-1)^k, \quad k=0, \pm 1, \pm 2, \ldots. \tag{3.3–10}$$

The points $z = k\pi$ are also simple poles of the function

$$\operatorname{ctn} z = \frac{\cos z}{\sin z}, \tag{3.3–11}$$

the residues being

$$\operatorname*{Res}_{z=k\pi} \operatorname{ctn} z = \frac{\cos k\pi}{\cos k\pi} = 1, \quad k = 0, \pm 1, \pm 2, \ldots. \tag{3.3–12}$$

3.3.5 – Residues calculated from Laurent's expansion

Describe a circular ring within a certain neighbourhood of $z = a$, a being finite. If $f(z)$ is regular at $z = a$ or admits there an isolated singularity we may take the inner circle as small as we please. According to Laurent's theorem we have

$$f(z) = \sum_{\nu=-\infty}^{\infty} c_\nu (z-a)^\nu \tag{3.3–13}$$

for all $z \neq a$ within a sufficiently small circle around $z = a$. On account of (2.23–4) we find:

The coefficient c_{-1} in Laurent's expansion of $f(z)$ in a neighbourhood of a finite isolated singularity is equal to the residue of the function at that point.

The following facts are evident:

The point $z = a$ is regular if the Laurent series possesses no terms with negative exponents. The point is a pole if there are a finite (non-zero) number of terms with negative exponents, whereas the point is an essential isolated singularity if there are an infinite number of terms with negative exponents.

Now let $f(z)$ be regular at $z = \infty$ or admit this point as an isolated singularity. Describe a circular ring around the origin, where the outer circle may be taken as large as is desired. Then

$$f(z) = \sum_{\nu=-\infty}^{\infty} c_\nu z^\nu \tag{3.3–14}$$

outside a sufficiently large circle around the origin. In this case we have:

The opposite of the coefficient c_{-1} in Laurent's expansion of $f(z)$ in a neighbourhood of an isolated singularity at infinity is equal to the residue of the function at that point.

The point at infinity is regular if there are no terms with positive exponents. Hence an integral function (1.7.3) which is not a constant admits $z = \infty$ as an essential singularity.

3.4 – Rational Functions

3.4.1 – Cluster point

Let $z = a$ be a point such that within an arbitrary small neighbourhood of $z = a$ there are infinitely many isolated singular points. Then $z = a$ is neither a regular nor an isolated singular point. Such a point is called a *cluster point.*

For example, the function $\text{ctn}(1/z)$ admits the poles $z = 1/k\pi$, $k = \pm 1, \pm 2, \ldots$. Hence $z = 0$ is a cluster point of this function. Similarly $z = \infty$ is a cluster pcint of $\text{ctn}\, z$.

3.4.2 – Characterization of a rational function

A function is said to be *meromorphic* throughout an open set $\mathfrak{A}$ if $f(z)$ is regular at the points of $\mathfrak{A}$ except for a finite or an infinite number of poles. Eventual cluster points are then points of the boundary of $\mathfrak{A}$. An elementary example is the *rational function*, that is a quotient of two polynomials.

The following theorem is easily proved.

A function which is meromorphic throughout the entire plane and admits no other singularity than a pole at $z = \infty$ is necessarily a rational function.

Since there are no cluster points there are only a finite number of poles. Let a be a pole of order n. By Laurent's theorem we have

$$f(z) = \sum_{\nu=0}^{\infty} c_\nu (z-a)^\nu + p(z) \tag{3.4–1}$$

with

$$p(z) = c_{-m}(z-a)^{-m} + \ldots + c_{-1}(z-a)^{-1}. \tag{3.4–2}$$

The function $p(z)$ being evidently a rational function is called the *meromorphic part* of $f(z)$ at $z = a$. It is regular at every point ($z = \infty$ included) save at $z = a$. The function $f(z) - p(z)$ possesses the same poles as $f(z)$ except at $z = a$, where it is regular. Let there be s finite poles and denote the corresponding meromorphic parts by $p_1(z), \ldots, p_s(z)$. The function

$$g(z) = f(z) - p_1(z) - \ldots - p_s(z) \tag{3.4–3}$$

is holomorphic throughout the entire plane and admits no other singularity than a pole at $z = \infty$. As a consequence $g(z)$ is a polynomial and hence

$$f(z) = g(z) + p_1(z) + \ldots + p_s(z) \tag{3.4–4}$$

is a rational function.

Conversely, it is easy to prove that *a rational function has no singularities other than poles*. Otherwise stated:

A rational function is chordally continuous throughout the extended plane.

We also obtain the following result:

Any rational function $f(z)$ possesses a decomposition (3.4–4) *into partial fractions of the form* (3.4–2) *and a polynomial.*

3.4.3 – Evaluation of the coefficients of the decomposition

In view of (3.3–4) it is easy to obtain general expressions for the coefficients occurring in the components of the type (3.4–2) in the decomposition into partial fractions.

In fact, c_{-1} is the residue of $f(z)$ at $z = a$, this point being a pole of order m. Hence

$$c_{-1} = \frac{1}{(m-1)!} \frac{d^{m-1}}{dz^{m-1}} \{(z-a)^m f(z)\}_{z=a}. \tag{3.4–5}$$

Now we observe that c_{-2} is the residue of $(z-a)f(z)$ at $z = a$, this point being a pole of order $m-1$. Hence

$$c_{-2} = \frac{1}{(m-2)!} \frac{d^{m-2}}{dz^{m-2}} \{(z-a)^m f(z)\}_{z=a}. \tag{3.4–6}$$

Proceeding in this way we have in general

$$\boxed{c_{-k} = \frac{1}{(m-k)!} \frac{d^{m-k}}{dz^{m-k}} \{(z-a)^m f(z)\}_{z=a},} \quad k = 1, \ldots, m. \tag{3.4–7}$$

The case $k = m$ means that we have only to evaluate $(z-a)^m f(z)$ at $z = a$.

3.5 – The theorem of residues

3.5.1 – Cauchy's theorem of residues

Consider an open set $\mathfrak{A}$ and assume the function $f(z)$ to be regular at the points of $\mathfrak{A}$ except for isolated singularities, $a_1, a_2, \ldots$. Let C denote a cycle not passing throughout any of the singular points within $\mathfrak{A}$ and *homologous zero* in the set. With respect to each of these singular points C has a winding number, but only a finite number of these winding numbers do not vanish. In fact, if there are infinitely many singular points they admit an accumulation point which is not contained in $\mathfrak{A}$ and hence the winding number of C with respect to this point is equal to zero and hence also for the singular points within a sufficiently small neighbourhood of that accumulation point. Around the points that provide non-vanishing winding numbers we describe small circles C_ν and in the set $\mathfrak{A}^*$ obtained from $\mathfrak{A}$ by removing the singular points the homology

$$C \sim \sum_{\nu=1}^{n} m_\nu C_\nu \tag{3.5–1}$$

is valid, where the singular points are appropriately numbered, and $m_\nu = \Omega_C(a_\nu)$, $\nu = 1, \ldots, n$. According to Cauchy's integral theorem we have

$$\boxed{\frac{1}{2\pi i} \int_C f(\zeta)\, d\zeta = \sum_{\nu=1}^{n} \Omega_C(a_\nu) \operatorname*{Res}_{z=a_\nu} f(z).} \tag{3.5–2}$$

This is a general form of *Cauchy's theorem of residues.*

In most applications the numbers $m_1, \ldots, m_n$ are ± 1, for instance when C is a circle or a rectangle, more generally when C is a regular contour (see the remark at the end of section 2.7.2).

Hence, if C is a regular contour described in the counter-clockwise sense and $a_1, \ldots, a_n$ are contained in its interior, we have

$$\frac{1}{2\pi i}\int_C f(\zeta)\,d\zeta = \sum_{\nu=1}^{n} \operatorname*{Res}_{z=a_\nu} f(z), \tag{3.5–3}$$

the classical form of the theorem of residues. It is assumed that C and its interior are contained in $\mathfrak{A}$.

3.5.2 – Sum of the residues

From (3.5–3) we may derive a result which deserves special mention.

If $f(z)$ admits only a finite number of isolated singularities in the extended plane then the sum of the residues (the residue at infinity included) is equal to zero.

By hypothesis there exists a circle C around the origin containing all singular points save $z = \infty$ in its interior. According to the definition of residue at $z = \infty$ we have

$$-\operatorname*{Res}_{z=\infty} f(z) = \frac{1}{2\pi i}\int_{C+} f(\zeta)\,d\zeta = \sum_{\nu=1}^{n} \operatorname*{Res}_{z=a_\nu} f(z) \tag{3.5–4}$$

or

$$\operatorname*{Res}_{z=a_1} f(z) + \ldots + \operatorname*{Res}_{z=a_n} f(z) + \operatorname*{Res}_{z=\infty} f(z) = 0. \tag{3.5–5}$$

3.6 – Evaluation of some integrals by means of the theorem of residues

3.6.1 – First example

The residue theorem is a powerful tool for evaluating definite integrals of a real variable which could not be obtained so easily otherwise. It is our aim to illustrate the method in some characteristic examples.

We start with a very simple case. The integral

$$\int_C \frac{e^\zeta}{\zeta}\,d\zeta \tag{3.6–1}$$

taken around a circumference of positive radius s around the origin has the value $2\pi i$. In fact the origin is a simple pole and (3.3–8) shows at once that the residue is 1. Putting $\zeta = se^{i\theta}$, we may write

$$\int_C \frac{e^\zeta}{\zeta}\,d\zeta = i\int_0^{2\pi} \exp(se^{i\theta})d\theta = 2\pi i,$$

whence

$$i\int_0^{2\pi} e^{s\cos\theta}\{\cos(s\sin\theta) + i\sin(s\sin\theta)\}\,d\theta = 2\pi i.$$

Equating imaginary parts we have

$$\int_0^{2\pi} e^{s\cos\theta}\cos(s\sin\theta)\,d\theta = 2\pi.$$

On applying the substitution $\theta' = 2\pi-\theta$ we readily find $\int_0^\pi = \int_\pi^{2\pi}$ and so

$$\int_0^\pi e^{s\cos\theta}\cos(s\sin\theta)\,d\theta = \pi. \tag{3.6–2}$$

This result is also valid when $s \leqq 0$.

3.6.2 – Second example

Another elementary example is the following. Consider the integral

$$\int_C \frac{d\zeta}{(\zeta-s)(\zeta-1/s)}, \tag{3.6–3}$$

taken along the circumference of the unit circle around the origin. We assume that s is a number between 0 and 1. The point $z = s$ is a simple pole of the integrand and the residue is

$$\lim_{z\to s}(z-s)\frac{1}{(z-s)(z-1/s)} = \frac{1}{s-1/s} = \frac{s}{s^2-1}.$$

Hence, if we put $\zeta = e^{i\theta}$, we find that (3.6–3) is

$$\int_0^{2\pi}\frac{i\,e^{i\theta}\,d\theta}{(e^{i\theta}-s)(e^{i\theta}-1/s)} = \frac{2\pi is}{s^2-1}$$

and so

$$\int_0^{2\pi}\frac{d\theta}{s^2-2s\cos\theta+1} = \frac{2\pi}{1-s^2}, \qquad 0 < s < 1. \tag{3.6–4}$$

3.6.3 – Elementary examples of infinite integrals

In most cases infinite integrals are obtained. A first example is provided by the integral

$$\int_C \frac{e^{si\zeta}}{1+\zeta^2}\,d\zeta, \quad s \geqq 0, \tag{3.6–5}$$

where C is a contour, (fig. 3.6–1), consisting of the real axis from

$x = -R$ to $x = R$ and that half of the circle $|z| = R > 1$ which lies above the real axis. The only pole within the contour of the inte-

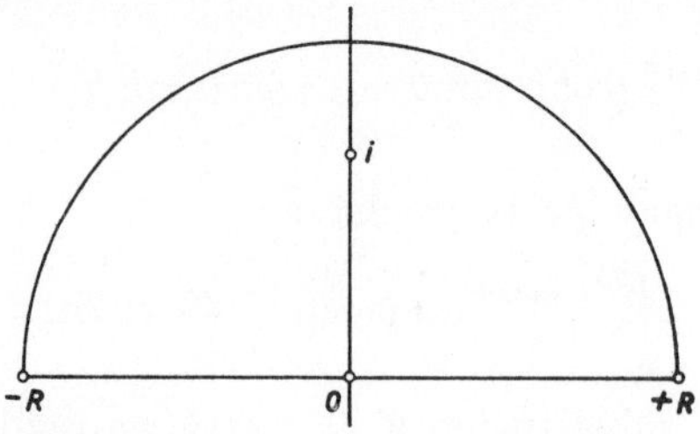

Fig. 3.6–1. Evaluation of the integral (3.6–5)

grand $f(z)$ is at $z = i$ and on applying (3.3–8) we find that the residue has the value $e^{-s}/2i$. Hence

$$\int_{-R}^{R} f(x)\, dx + \int_{0}^{\pi} f(Re^{i\theta}) Re^{i\theta} i\, d\theta = \pi e^{-s}.$$

Now we observe that

$$\int_{-R}^{R} f(x)\, dx = \int_{-R}^{R} \frac{\cos sx + i \sin sx}{1+x^2}\, dx = 2\int_{0}^{R} \frac{\cos sx}{1+x^2}\, dx,$$

since the part of the integral involving $\sin sx$ is odd and the part involving $\cos sx$ is even. Taking account of the inequality (1.1–9) we find

$$\left| \int_{0}^{\pi} f(Re^{i\theta}) Re^{i\theta} i\, d\theta \right| \leqq \int_{0}^{\pi} \frac{e^{-sR\sin\theta}}{R^2-1} R\, d\theta \leqq \frac{R}{R^2-1} \int_{0}^{\pi} d\theta = \frac{\pi R}{R^2-1}.$$

Hence the integral along the semi-circle tends to zero as $R \to \infty$. This leads to the result

$$\boxed{\int_{0}^{\infty} \frac{\cos sx}{1+x^2}\, dx = \tfrac{1}{2}\pi e^{-s},} \qquad s \geqq 0. \tag{3.6–6}$$

A particular case occurs when $s = 0$. Then we have the well-known result

$$\int_{0}^{\infty} \frac{dx}{1+x^2} = \tfrac{1}{2}\pi. \tag{3.6–7}$$

It should be observed that this method does not succeed in evaluating the integral

$$\int_{0}^{\infty} \frac{\sin sx}{1+x^2}\, dx.$$

This problem is more difficult and will be considered in section 8.13.3. In the next section, however, we shall prove that

$$\boxed{\int_0^\infty \frac{x \sin sx}{1+x^2}\, dx = \tfrac{1}{2}\pi e^{-s},} \qquad s > 0. \qquad (3.6\text{–}8)$$

The integral

$$\int_0^\infty \frac{x \cos sx}{1+x^2}\, dx$$

demands deeper considerations. It will also be evaluated in section 8.13.3

3.6.4 – Jordan's inequality

In many cases the inequality

$$\boxed{\frac{2\theta}{\pi} \leqq \sin \theta \leqq \theta,} \qquad 0 \leqq \theta \leqq \tfrac{1}{2}\pi, \qquad (3.6\text{–}9)$$

is extremely useful, (fig. 3.6–2). It is intuitively evident that if a

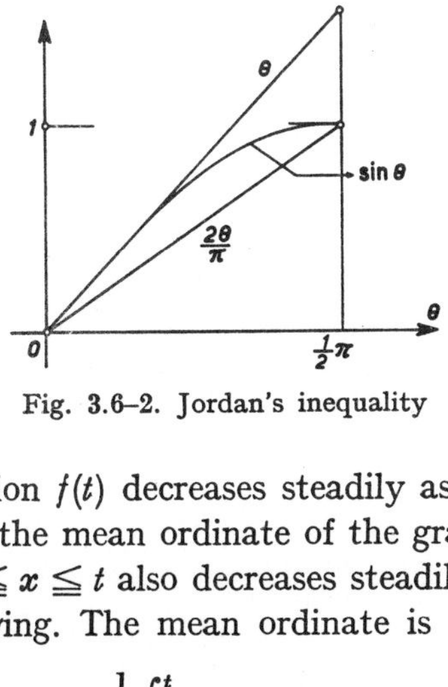

Fig. 3.6–2. Jordan's inequality

positive real function $f(t)$ decreases steadily as t increases from 0 to a certain value the mean ordinate of the graph of the function over the range $0 \leqq x \leqq t$ also decreases steadily. A more rigorous proof is the following. The mean ordinate is

$$F(t) = \frac{1}{t}\int_0^t f(x)\, dx, \qquad t > 0, \qquad (3.6\text{–}10)$$

and since $f(x)$ decreases steadily we have

$$F(t) \geqq \frac{1}{t}\int_0^t f(t)\, dx = f(t).$$

Hence

$$F'(t) = -\frac{1}{t^2}\int_0^t f(x)\, dx + \frac{f(t)}{t} = -\frac{F(t)}{t} + \frac{f(t)}{t} \leqq 0.$$

This proves the assertion.

We apply this result to the function $\cos\theta$ which decreases steadily as θ increases from 0 to $\frac{1}{2}\pi$. Then also

$$\frac{1}{\theta}\int_0^\theta \cos x\,dx = \frac{\sin\theta}{\theta}$$

decreases steadily and, consequently,

$$1 \geqq \frac{\sin\theta}{\theta} \geqq \frac{2}{\pi}$$

which is essentially (3.6–9).

Now we consider the integral

$$\int_C \frac{\zeta e^{si\zeta}}{1+\zeta^2}\,d\zeta, \qquad s > 0, \tag{3.6–11}$$

where C is the same contour as considered in section 3.6.3. If $f(z)$ denotes again the integrand, we have

$$\int_{-R}^{R} f(x)\,dx + \int_0^{R} f(Re^{i\theta})Re^{i\theta}i\,d\theta = \pi i e^{-s},$$

for the residue at $z = i$ is now $\frac{1}{2}e^{-s}$. Again

$$\int_{-R}^{R} f(x)\,dx = 2i\int_0^R \frac{x\sin sx}{1+x^2}\,dx.$$

Moreover

$$\left|\int_0^{\pi} f(Re^{i\theta})Re^{i\theta}i\,d\theta\right| < \int_0^{\pi}\frac{e^{-sR\sin\theta}}{R^2-1}R^2\,d\theta.$$

The occurrence of R^2 demands a more delicate argument. The last integral is equal to

$$2\int_0^{\frac{1}{2}\pi}\frac{e^{-sR\sin\theta}}{R^2-1}R^2\,d\theta$$

and on account of (3.6–9) does not exceed

$$\frac{2R^2}{R^2-1}\int_0^{\frac{1}{2}\pi} e^{-2sR\theta/\pi}\,d\theta = \frac{\pi R}{s(R^2-1)}(1-e^{-sR}) < \frac{\pi R}{s(R^2-1)}.$$

In fact this tends to zero as $R\to\infty$ and the formula (3.6–8) now follows easily.

3.6.5 – Jordan's lemma

The previous examples can also be established on applying a general lemma due to C. Jordan.

If $f(z)$ is continuous throughout the upper half of the complex plane, i.e., in the area $\operatorname{Im} z \geqq 0$ *and if $|f(z)|$ tends to zero as $z\to\infty$, uniformly as regards $\arg z$, $0 \leqq \arg z \leqq \pi$, then the integral*

$$J(R) = \int e^{si\zeta} f(\zeta)\, d\zeta, \qquad s > 0 \tag{3.6–12}$$

taken along that half of the circle $|z| = R$ *which is above the real axis, tends to zero as* $R \to \infty$.

As usual we put $\zeta = Re^{i\theta}$. Then

$$J(R) = \int_0^\pi e^{isR(\cos\theta + i\sin\theta)} f(Re^{i\theta}) Re^{i\theta} i\, d\theta$$
$$= iR \int_0^\pi e^{-sR\sin\theta} e^{i(sR\cos\theta + \theta)} f(Re^{i\theta})\, d\theta.$$

Whenever R is sufficiently large we have $|f(Re^{i\theta})| < \varepsilon$, ε being a given positive number. Hence

$$|J(R)| \leqq \varepsilon R \int_0^\pi e^{-sR\sin\theta}\, d\theta = 2\varepsilon R \int_0^{\frac{1}{2}\pi} e^{-sR\sin\theta}\, d\theta$$
$$\leqq 2\varepsilon R \int_0^{\frac{1}{2}\pi} e^{-2sR\theta/\pi}\, d\theta = \frac{\varepsilon\pi}{s}(1 - e^{-sR}) < \frac{\varepsilon\pi}{s}.$$

This proves the assertion. It is easily seen that the conditions of the lemma are satisfied by the examples (3.6–5) and (3.6–11).

3.6.6 – Cauchy's principal value

In many examples we find in a rather natural way the limit

$$\lim_{R \to +\infty} \int_{-R}^{R} f(x)\, dx. \tag{3.6–13}$$

This does not imply, however, that the infinite integral

$$\int_{-\infty}^{\infty} f(x)\, dx \tag{3.6–14}$$

is convergent, for then the integrals $\int_0^\infty f(x)\, dx$ and $\int_{-\infty}^0 f(x)\, dx$ exist separately. The expression (3.6–13) is, however, very useful and is called the *Cauchy principal value* of the integral (3.6–14). It is plain that (3.6–13) exists when (3.6–14) is convergent. In many cases the principal value will also be denoted by the symbol (3.6–14) with the additional remark, if necessary, that the principal value is meant.

A similar situation may occur in the case of the real integral

$$\int_a^b f(x)\, dx \tag{3.6–15}$$

where $f(x)$ has a singularity c between a and b. When the limit

$$\lim_{\varepsilon \to 0} \left(\int_a^{c-\varepsilon} f(x)\, dx + \int_{c+\varepsilon}^b f(x)\, dx \right) \tag{3.6–16}$$

exists, it is also called the Cauchy principal value of (3.6–15) and often denoted by the same symbol.

The following lemma states a sufficient condition for the existence of a principal value in the second case.

If $f(z)$ is holomorphic in an open set containing that part of the real axis for which $a \leqq x \leqq b$ except for a simple pole at a point c on the axis, where $a < c < b$, then the principal value (3.6–16) *of* (3.6–15) *exists.* By hypothesis we have

$$f(z) = \frac{A}{z-c} + g(z)$$

where $g(z)$ is holomorphic throughout the set.

Hence

$$\int_a^{c-\varepsilon} f(x)\, dx + \int_{c+\varepsilon}^b f(x)\, dx$$

$$= A \log \frac{\varepsilon}{c-a} + A \log \frac{b-c}{\varepsilon} + \int_a^{c-\varepsilon} g(x)\, dx + \int_{c+\varepsilon}^b g(x)\, dx$$

$$= A \log \frac{b-c}{c-a} + \int_a^{c-\varepsilon} g(x)\, dx + \int_{c+\varepsilon}^b g(x)\, dx,$$

and this tends to a limit as $\varepsilon \to 0$.

3.6.7 – The discontinuous factor

The path of integration is not necessarily the real axis. Consider, for example, the integral

$$\int_C \frac{e^{\zeta t}}{\zeta}\, d\zeta \qquad (3.6\text{–}17)$$

where t is a real number. We integrate along a contour consisting of the linear segment from $c-iR$ to $c+iR$, where c and R are positive, completed by a semi-circle on the left if $t > 0$ and a semi-circle on the right when $t < 0$, (fig. 3.6–3).

Along the semi-circular part we have $\zeta = c + Re^{i\theta}$, with $\frac{1}{2}\pi \leqq \theta \leqq \frac{3}{2}\pi$ when $t > 0$ and $\frac{1}{2}\pi \geqq \theta \geqq -\frac{1}{2}\pi$ when $t < 0$. In the first case we have along the semi-circular part

$$\left| \int_{\frac{1}{2}\pi}^{\frac{3}{2}\pi} \frac{\exp\{t(c+Re^{i\theta})\}}{|\zeta|} R\, d\theta \right| \leqq e^{tc} \int_{\frac{1}{2}\pi}^{\frac{3}{2}\pi} \frac{e^{tR\cos\theta}}{|\zeta|} R\, d\theta = e^{tc} \int_0^{\pi} \frac{e^{-tR\sin\varphi}}{|\zeta|} R\, d\varphi,$$

where $\varphi = \theta - \frac{1}{2}\pi$. By virtue of (3.6–9), taking account of $|\zeta| \geqq R-c$, if we assume $R > c$, the last integral does not exceed

$$2e^{tc} \int_0^{\frac{1}{2}\pi} \frac{e^{-2tR\varphi/\pi}}{|\zeta|} R\, d\varphi \leqq \frac{e^{tc}}{t(R-c)} \pi (1-e^{-tR}) < \frac{\pi e^{tc}}{(tR-c)}$$

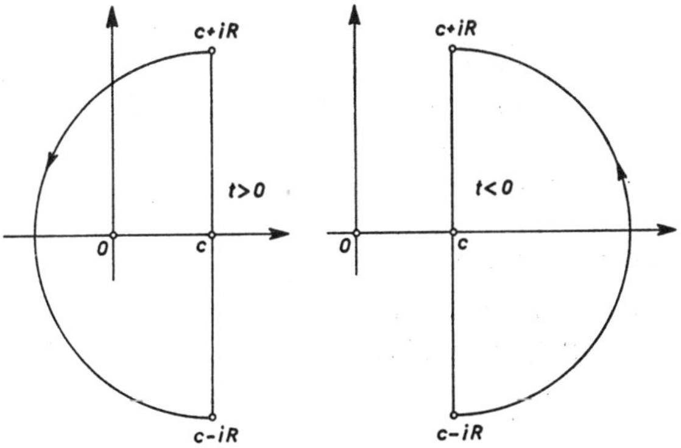

Fig. 3.6–3. Evaluation of the integral (3.6–17)

and hence tends to zero as $R \to \infty$. It follows that

$$\lim_{R\to\infty} \frac{1}{2\pi i} \int_{c-iR}^{c+iR} \frac{e^{\zeta t}}{\zeta}\, d\zeta = 1, \qquad t > 0,$$

for the integrand has a pole of residue 1 inside the contour.

If $t < 0$ we have the estimate, observing that $|\zeta| > R$,

$$\left| \int_{\frac{1}{2}\pi}^{-\frac{1}{2}\pi} \frac{\exp\{t(c+Re^{i\theta})\}}{|\zeta|} R\, d\theta \right| \leqq e^{tc} \int_{-\frac{1}{2}\pi}^{\frac{1}{2}\pi} \frac{e^{tR\cos\theta}}{|\zeta|} R\, d\theta$$

$$< 2e^{tc} \int_0^{\frac{1}{2}\pi} e^{tR\cos\theta}\, d\theta = 2e^{tc} \int_0^{\frac{1}{2}\pi} e^{tR\sin\theta}\, d\theta \leqq 2e^{tc} \int_0^{\frac{1}{2}\pi} e^{2tR\theta/\pi}\, d\theta$$

$$= \frac{-\pi}{tR} e^{tc}(1-e^{tR}) < \frac{-\pi}{tR} e^{tc},$$

and this tends to zero as $R \to \infty$. The integrand is regular throughout the entire interior of the contour. Hence

$$\lim_{R\to\infty} \int_{c-iR}^{c+iR} \frac{e^{\zeta t}}{\zeta}\, d\zeta = 0, \quad t < 0.$$

When $t = 0$ we have, on integrating along a vertical segment,

$$\frac{1}{2\pi i} \int_{c-iR}^{c+iR} \frac{d\zeta}{\zeta} = \frac{1}{2\pi i} \{\log(c+iR) - \log(c-iR)\} = \frac{1}{\pi} \arctan \frac{R}{c}$$

and this tends to $\frac{1}{\pi} \cdot \frac{1}{2}\pi = \frac{1}{2}$ as $R \to \infty$.

Thus we proved a theorem known as the *theorem of the discontinuous factor*:

If c is a positive number and if t is a real number then

$$\frac{1}{2\pi i}\int_{c-i\infty}^{c+i\infty}\frac{e^{\zeta t}}{\zeta}\,d\zeta=\begin{cases}1, \text{ when } t>0,\\ \tfrac{1}{2}, \text{ when } t=0,\\ 0, \text{ when } t<0,\end{cases} \tag{3.6–18}$$

the integral being understood as a Cauchy principal value.

3.6.8 – Two lemmas

The following lemmas are also frequently found useful.

Let AB (fig. 3.6–4) *be that arc of the circle* $|z| = R$ *for which*

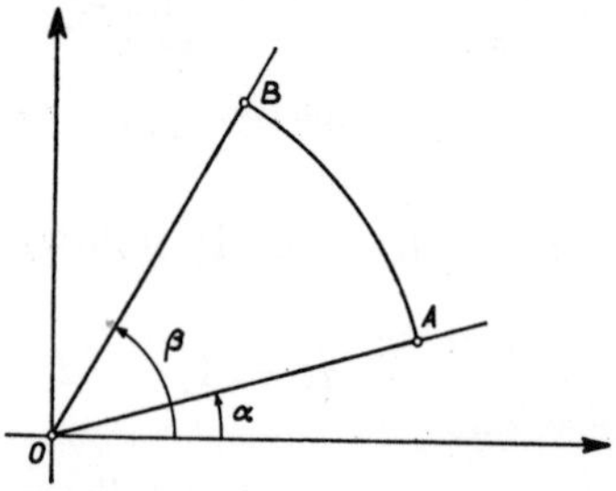

Fig. 3.6–4. The lemmas of 3.6.8

$\alpha \leqq \arg z \leqq \beta$ *and let* $z\,f(z)$ *tend uniformly to the limit* G *as* $R \to \infty$, *G being a constant. Then*

$$\lim_{R\to\infty}\int_A^B f(\zeta)\,d\zeta = i(\beta-\alpha)G. \tag{3.6–19}$$

We may write $z\,f(z) = G+\varphi(z)$ and choose R so great that $|\varphi(z)| < \varepsilon$. Then, if $\zeta = Re^{i\theta}$,

$$\int_A^B f(\zeta)\,d\zeta = \int_A^B \frac{G}{\zeta}\,d\zeta+\int_A^B \frac{\varphi(\zeta)}{\zeta}\,d\zeta = i\int_\alpha^\beta G\,d\theta+i\int_\alpha^\beta \varphi(\zeta)\,d\theta,$$

where

$$\left|\int_\alpha^\beta \varphi(\zeta)\,d\theta\right| < \varepsilon(\beta-\alpha).$$

This proves the assertion.

A similar statement is:

If AB is the same arc as mentioned in the above lemma and if $z\,f(z)$ *tends to a limit G as* $z \to 0$, *G being a constant, then*

$$\lim_{R\to 0}\int_A^B f(\zeta)\,d\zeta = i(\beta-\alpha)G. \tag{3.6–20}$$

Again we may write $z\,f(z) = G+\varphi(z)$, where $|\varphi(z)| < \varepsilon$, if $|z| = R$ is sufficiently small. The proof runs as in the above lemma.

It is plain that in the second case the centre of the arc may be any point $z = a$. The condition is then that $(z-a)f(z)$ has a limit G as $z \to a$.

3.6.9 – Application of the lemmas

The following example is an application of the lemmas considered previously.

First we wish to study the integral

$$\int_C \frac{e^{i\zeta}}{\zeta}\, d\zeta, \tag{3.6–21}$$

the contour C consisting of the real axis from r to R, $r < R$, the upper half of the circle $|z| = R$, the real axis from $-R$ to $-r$ and the upper half of the circle $|z| = r$, (fig. 3.6–5). The part of the small

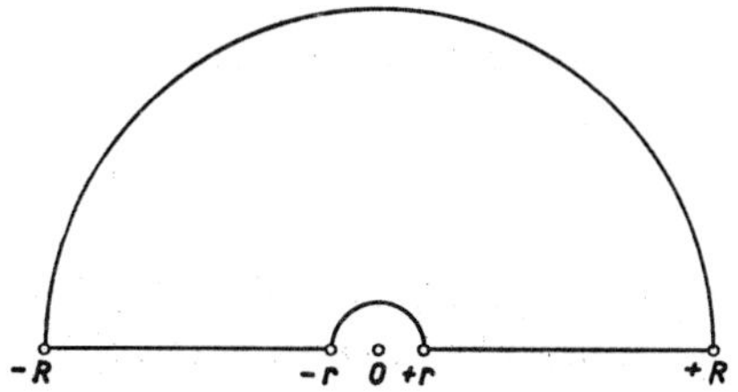

Fig. 3.6–5. Evaluation of the integral (3.6–21)

circle is described to avoid the singularity of the integrand. In a case of this kind we shall say that the contour is *indented* at the singularity.

Referring to Jordan's lemma of section 3.6.5 we see that the integral along the large circle tends to zero as $R \to \infty$. On applying the second lemma of section 3.6.8 we see that the integral along the small circle tends to $-i\pi$, since $ze^{iz}/z \to 1$ as $z \to 0$ and the circle is traversed from the left to the right. There are no singularities inside the contour. Hence

$$\int_{-\infty}^{\infty} \frac{e^{ix}}{x}\, dx = \pi i,$$

where the integral is a principal value at $x = 0$. On equating real and imaginary parts and taking account of the fact that $\sin x/x$ is an even function we obtain the important result

$$\boxed{\int_0^{\infty} \frac{\sin x}{x}\, dx = \tfrac{1}{2}\pi.} \tag{3.6–22}$$

An elementary computation yields another formula which is also useful. Introducing a new variable and applying integration by parts we have

$$\tfrac{1}{2}\pi = \int_0^\infty \frac{\sin x}{x}\,dx = \int_0^\infty \frac{\sin 2u}{u}\,du = 2\int_0^\infty \frac{\sin u \cos u}{u}\,du$$

$$= 2\,\frac{\sin^2 u}{u}\Bigg|_0^\infty - 2\int_0^\infty \frac{\sin u \cos u}{u}\,du + 2\int_0^\infty \frac{\sin^2 u}{u^2}\,du$$

$$= -\int_0^\infty \frac{\sin 2u}{u}\,du + 2\int_0^\infty \frac{\sin^2 u}{u^2}\,du = -\tfrac{1}{2}\pi + 2\int_0^\infty \frac{\sin^2 u}{u^2}\,du,$$

whence

$$\boxed{\int_0^\infty \frac{\sin^2 u}{u^2}\,du = \tfrac{1}{2}\pi.} \qquad (3.6\text{–}23)$$

3.6.10 – Two infinite integrals due to Euler

Another interesting example is provided by the integral

$$\int_C \frac{\zeta^{a-1}}{1-\zeta}\,d\zeta, \qquad 0 < a < 1, \qquad (3.6\text{–}24)$$

taken along the contour of section 3.6.9 but also indented at $z = 1$, (fig. 3.6–6). If $f(z)$ denotes the integrand we evidently have $z f(z) \to 0$

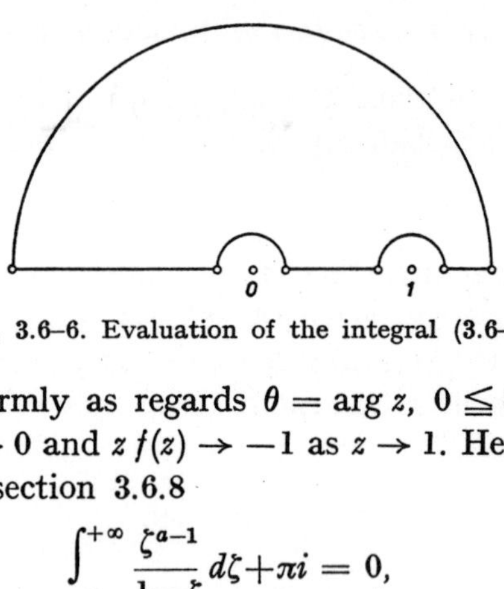

Fig. 3.6–6. Evaluation of the integral (3.6–24)

as $z \to \infty$, uniformly as regards $\theta = \arg z$, $0 \leqq \theta \leqq \pi$. Moreover $z f(z) \to 0$ as $z \to 0$ and $z f(z) \to -1$ as $z \to 1$. Hence, by virtue of the lemmas of section 3.6.8

$$\int_{-\infty}^{+\infty} \frac{\zeta^{a-1}}{1-\zeta}\,d\zeta + \pi i = 0, \qquad (3.6\text{–}25)$$

the integral on the left being a principal value. This integral decomposes into two parts $\int_{-\infty}^{0}$ and $\int_0^\infty$. Since

$$z^{a-1} = |z|^{a-1}\{\cos (a-1)\theta + i \sin (a-1)\theta\}$$

the integrand in the first part is (the argument θ being equal to π)

$$-\frac{x^{a-1}}{1+x}\,(\cos a\pi + i \sin a\pi),$$

where x is positive. In fact, z can be put into the form

$$z = x(\cos \pi + i \sin \pi).$$

The second part is the integral

$$\int_0^\infty \frac{x^{a-1}}{1-x}\,dx,$$

to be understood as a principal value, since there is a singularity at $x = 1$. Hence (3.6–24) may be written as

$$-(\cos a\pi + i \sin a\pi)\int_0^\infty \frac{x^{a-1}}{1+x}\,dx + \int_0^\infty \frac{x^{a-1}}{1-x}\,dx + \pi i = 0.$$

Equating real and imaginary parts we obtain

$$\boxed{\int_0^\infty \frac{x^{a-1}}{1+x}\,dx = \pi \csc a\pi,} \qquad 0 < a < 1, \tag{3.6–26}$$

and

$$\int_0^\infty \frac{x^{a-1}}{1-x}\,dx = \pi \operatorname{ctn} a\pi. \tag{3.6–27}$$

Let b denote another real number between 0 and 1. In (3.6–27) we may replace a by b and on subtracting corresponding members we find

$$\boxed{\int_0^\infty \frac{x^{a-1} - x^{b-1}}{1-x}\,dx = \pi(\operatorname{ctn} a\pi - \operatorname{ctn} b\pi)} \tag{3.6–28}$$

valid under the assumptions $0 < a < 1$, $0 < b < 1$. The formulas derived in this part of the section were discovered by Euler. The formula (3.6–26) is closely related to the gamma function as we shall see presently. In (3.6–28) the integral is convergent in the ordinary sense, for the integrand is regular at $z = 1$.

3.6.11 – The Euler integrals of the first and the second kind

In chapter 4 we shall study the gamma function $\Gamma(z)$ and we shall prove that for positive values of $z = x$ it may be represented by the so-called *Euler integral of the second kind*

$$\Gamma(x) = \int_0^\infty e^{-t} t^{x-1}\,dt, \qquad x > 0. \tag{3.6–29}$$

First we wish to show that this integral is convergent. As regards the lower limit the statement follows from

$$\int_\varepsilon^1 e^{-t} t^{x-1}\, dt \leqq \int_\varepsilon^1 t^{x-1}\, dt = \frac{1-\varepsilon^x}{x} < \frac{1}{x},$$

where ε is an arbitrary number between 0 and 1. Since the integral on the left increases as $\varepsilon \to 0$ the limit exists.

Since the derivative of the function $t-(x+1)\log t$ is $1-(x+1)/t > 0$, whenever t is sufficiently large, the function is steadily increasing and takes values > 1. Hence

$$t^{x+1} < e^t$$

or

$$e^{-t} t^{x-1} < t^{-2},$$

whenever t is sufficiently large. As a consequence, ω being $> a$ and a sufficiently large,

$$\int_a^\omega e^{-t} t^{x-1}\, dt < \int_1^\omega t^{-2}\, dt = 1 - \frac{1}{\omega} < 1,$$

and it follows that the integral on the left tends to a limit as $\omega \to \infty$, since it increases steadily. Finally we wish to observe that $\Gamma(x) > 0$ for $x > 0$.

A very remarkable theorem states that the integral

$$\int_0^\infty \frac{x^{p-1}}{(1+x)^{p+q}}\, dx, \tag{3.6–30}$$

where p and q are positive, can be expressed in terms of the integrals of the second kind. In fact, we shall prove that the integral represents the beta function

$$B(p, q) = \frac{\Gamma(p)\Gamma(q)}{\Gamma(p+q)} \tag{3.6–31}$$

for positive values of p and q.

First we wish to verify the convergence of (3.6–30). In fact

$$\int_\varepsilon^1 \frac{x^{p-1}}{(1+x)^{p+q}}\, dx < \int_\varepsilon^1 x^{p-1}\, dx = \frac{1}{p}(1-\varepsilon^p) < \frac{1}{p}, \qquad 0 < \varepsilon < 1$$

and, if $\omega > 1$,

$$\int_1^\omega \frac{x^{p-1}}{(1+x)^{p+q}}\, dx < \int_1^\omega \frac{x^{p-1}}{x^{p+q}}\, dx = \int_1^\omega \frac{dx}{x^{q+1}} = \frac{1}{q}\left(1-\frac{1}{\omega^q}\right) < \frac{1}{q},$$

and the truth of the statement follows at once.

On applying the substitution $x = t/(1-t)$ we see that (3.6–30) may be brought into the form

$$\int_0^1 t^{p-1}(1-t)^{q-1}\,dt, \qquad p > 0,\ q > 0, \tag{3.6–32}$$

the *Euler integral of the first kind.*

In order to prove the above statement we first observe that

$$\frac{x^{p-1}}{(1+x)^{p+q}}\Gamma(p+q)=\int_0^\infty e^{-t}t^{p+q-1}\frac{x^{p-1}}{(1+x)^{p+q}}dt=\int_0^\infty e^{-y(1+x)}y^{p+q-1}x^{p-1}dy$$

where $y(1+x) = t$. Upon integrating with respect to x we get

$$\Gamma(p+q)\int_0^\infty \frac{x^{p-1}}{(1+x)^{p+q}}\,dx = \int_0^\infty x^{p-1}\,dx\int_0^\infty e^{-y(1+x)}\,y^{p+q-1}\,dy.$$

By reversing the order of integration, which shall be justified below, the expression on the right appears as

$$\int_0^\infty e^{-y}\,y^{p+q-1}\,dy\int_0^\infty x^{p-1}\,e^{-xy}\,dx = \int_0^\infty e^{-y}\,y^{q-1}\,dy\,.\int_0^\infty e^{-u}\,u^{p-1}\,du,$$

where u stands for xy. Thus we see that

$$\boxed{\int_0^\infty \frac{x^{p-1}}{(1+x)^{p+q}}\,dx = \frac{\Gamma(p)\Gamma(q)}{\Gamma(p+q)}.} \tag{3.6–33}$$

The reasoning, in detail, is as follows. Let a, ε and ω denote positive numbers with $\varepsilon < \omega$. Then

$$\begin{aligned}\int_0^a x^{p-1}\,dx\int_\varepsilon^\omega e^{-y(1+x)}\,y^{p+q-1}\,dy &= \int_\varepsilon^\omega e^{-y}\,y^{p+q-1}\,dy\int_0^a e^{-xy}\,x^{p-1}\,dx\\ &= \int_\varepsilon^\omega e^{-y}\,y^{q-1}\,dy\int_0^{ay} e^{-u}\,u^{p-1}\,du.\end{aligned}$$

When y is between ε and ω, then the last integral $\int_0^{ay}$ is between $\int_0^{a\varepsilon}$ and $\int_0^{a\omega}$. Hence, by letting $a \to \infty$ we obtain

$$\int_0^\infty x^{p-1}\,dx\int_\varepsilon^\omega e^{-y(1+x)}\,y^{p+q-1}\,dy = \Gamma(p)\int_\varepsilon^\omega e^{-y}\,y^{q-1}dy.$$

Now

$$\begin{aligned}\int_0^\infty x^{p-1}\,dx\int_\omega^\infty e^{-y(1+x)}\,y^{p+q-1}\,dy &\leqq \int_0^\infty e^{-\omega x}\,x^{p-1}\,dx\int_\omega^\infty e^{-y}\,y^{p+q-1}\,dy\\ &= \omega^{-p}\,\Gamma(p)\int_\omega^\infty e^{-y}\,y^{p+q-1}\,dy < \omega^{-p}\,\Gamma(p)\,\Gamma(p+q) \to 0\end{aligned}$$

as $\omega \to \infty$. And so we arrive at the result

$$\int_0^\infty x^{p-1}\,dx\int_\varepsilon^\infty e^{-y(1+x)}\,y^{p+q-1}\,dy = \Gamma(p)\int_\varepsilon^\infty e^{-y}\,y^{q-1}\,dy.$$

It remains to show that in this formula ε may be replaced by 0. Since $q > 0$ we can find a positive number $q' < q$. Then

$$x^{p-1}\int_0^{\varepsilon} e^{-y(1+x)}\, y^{p+q-1}\, dy = x^{p-1}\int_0^{\varepsilon} e^{-y(1+x)}\, y^{p+q'-1}\, y^{q-q'}\, dy$$

$$< \varepsilon^{q-q'}\, x^{p-1}\int_0^{\varepsilon} e^{-y(1+x)}\, y^{p+q'-1}\, dy = \varepsilon^{q-q'}\,\frac{x^{p-1}}{(1+x)^{p+q'}}\int_0^{\varepsilon(1+x)} e^{-t}\, t^{p+q'-1}\, dt$$

$$< \varepsilon^{q-q'}\,\frac{x^{p-1}}{(1+x)^{p+q'}}\int_0^{\infty} e^{-t}\, t^{p+q'-1}\, dt,$$

whence

$$\int_0^{\infty} x^{p-1}\, dx \int_0^{\varepsilon} e^{-y(1+x)}\, y^{p+q-1}\, dy < \varepsilon^{q-q'}\,\Gamma(p+q')\int_0^{\infty}\frac{x^{p-1}}{(1+x)^{p+q'}}\, dx.$$

The expression on the right tends to zero as $\varepsilon \to 0$. This completes the proof of the theorem.

By inserting $p = a$, $q = 1-a$, $0 < a < 1$ into (3.6–33) and taking account of $\Gamma(1) = \int_0^{\infty} e^{-t}\, dt = 1$, we can bring (3.6–26) into the form

$$\boxed{\Gamma(a)\Gamma(1-a) = \pi \csc \pi a,} \qquad 0 < a < 1, \qquad (3.6\text{–}34)$$

In particular we may take $a = \frac{1}{2}$. Observing that $\Gamma(\frac{1}{2}) > 0$ we have

$$\Gamma(\tfrac{1}{2}) = \sqrt{\pi} \qquad (3.6\text{–}35)$$

or

$$\int_0^{\infty} e^{-t}\, t^{-1/2}\, dt = \sqrt{\pi}$$

whence, by putting $t = x^2$,

$$\int_0^{\infty} e^{-x^2}\, dx = \tfrac{1}{2}\sqrt{\pi}, \qquad (3.6\text{–}36)$$

in accordance with (2.23–28).

3.6.12 – Some integrals related to Euler's integral of the second kind

The gamma function is the starting point of many interesting considerations. The function

$$f(z) = e^{-z} z^{a-1}, \qquad (3.6\text{–}37)$$

where a is a number between 0 and 1, is regular at every point of the positive quadrant, i.e., at all points where $\operatorname{Re} z \geqq 0$, $\operatorname{Im} z \geqq 0$, except at $z = 0$.

Integrate the function along a contour, (fig. 3.6–7), consisting of the segment of the real axis from r to R, $0 < r < R$, a quadrant of

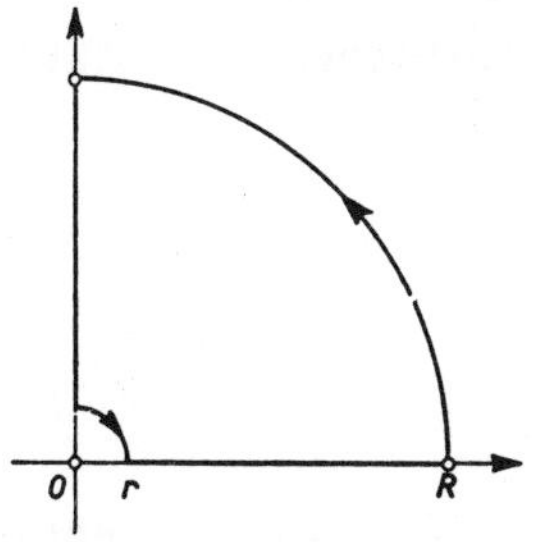

Fig. 3.6–7. Path of integration for the function (3.6–37)

the circle $|z| = R$, $0 \leqq \arg z \leqq \frac{1}{2}\pi$, the segment of the imaginary axis from iR to ir and finally a quadrant of the circle $|z| = r$, which completes the contour. By Cauchy's theorem the integral

$$\int_C e^{-\zeta} \zeta^{a-1}\, d\zeta \tag{3.6–38}$$

is zero. Since $z\,f(z) \to 0$ as $z \to 0$, we may let $r \to 0$ on account of the lemma of section 3.6.8. On the other hand, when $\zeta = R\,e^{i\theta}$, the integral taken along the large circular arc is

$$iR^a \int_0^{\frac{1}{2}\pi} e^{-R\cos\theta + ai\theta}\, d\theta$$

and its absolute value does not exceed

$$R^a \int_0^{\frac{1}{2}\pi} e^{-R\cos\theta}\, d\theta = R^a \int_0^{\frac{1}{2}\pi} e^{-R\sin\theta}\, d\theta.$$

On account of Jordan's lemma we find that this latter integral is dominated by

$$R^a \int_0^{\frac{1}{2}\pi} e^{-2R\theta/\pi}\, d\theta = \tfrac{1}{2}\pi R^{a-1}(1 - e^{-R}) \to 0$$

as $R \to \infty$. Hence

$$\Gamma(a) = \int_0^\infty e^{-x} x^{a-1}\, dx = \int_0^\infty e^{-iy}\, (iy)^{a-1}\, d(iy) = i^a \int_0^\infty e^{-iy}\, y^{a-1}\, dy,$$

whence

$$\int_0^\infty \frac{\cos y - i \sin y}{y^{1-a}}\, dy = i^{-a}\,\Gamma(a) = (\cos \tfrac{1}{2}\pi a - i \sin \tfrac{1}{2}\pi a)\, \Gamma(a).$$

Equating real and imaginary parts we obtain

$$\int_0^\infty \frac{\cos y}{y^{1-a}}\, dy = \Gamma(a) \cos \tfrac{1}{2}\pi a, \tag{3.6–39}$$

$$\int_0^\infty \frac{\sin y}{y^{1-a}}\,dy = \Gamma(a)\sin\tfrac{1}{2}\pi a. \qquad (3.6\text{–}40)$$

It will be convenient to introduce the variable u such that $y = au^{1/a}$. An easy computation yields

$$\int_0^\infty \cos(au^{1/a})\,du = a^{1-a}\,\Gamma(a)\cos\tfrac{1}{2}\pi a, \qquad (3.6\text{–}41)$$

$$\int_0^\infty \sin(au^{1/a})\,du = a^{1-a}\Gamma(a)\sin\tfrac{1}{2}\pi a. \qquad (3.6\text{–}42)$$

The particular case $a = \frac{1}{2}$ deserves mention. Taking account of (3.6–35) we find *Fresnel's integrals*

$$\boxed{\int_0^\infty \cos\tfrac{1}{2}u^2\,du = \int_0^\infty \sin\tfrac{1}{2}u^2\,du = \tfrac{1}{2}\sqrt{\pi}.} \qquad (3.6\text{–}43)$$

3.6.13 The klothoids

We wish to conclude with some geometrical considerations. It is our aim to study a curve C_a which is represented parametrically by

$$x(s) = \int_0^s \cos(au^{1/a})\,du, \quad y(s) = \int_0^s \sin(au^{1/a})\,du. \qquad (3.6\text{–}44)$$

Since

$$\frac{dx}{ds} = \cos(as^{1/a}), \qquad \frac{dy}{ds} = \sin(as^{1/a}),$$

we see that the angle ϑ between the tangent and the positive x-axis is

$$\vartheta = as^{1/a}. \qquad (3.6\text{–}45)$$

Moreover

$$\left(\frac{dx}{ds}\right)^2 + \left(\frac{dy}{ds}\right)^2 = 1$$

and thus we see that the parameter s may be interpreted as the arc length reckoned from the origin.

The curvature $\varkappa$ is defined by

$$\varkappa = \frac{d\vartheta}{ds}$$

and from (3.6–45) follows that

$$\varkappa = s^{1/a-1}. \qquad (3.6\text{–}46)$$

It is easily seen that a curve C_a represented by (3.6–44) is a spiral starting from the origin and winding infinitely many times around the point with co-ordinates

$$x = a^{1-a}\Gamma(a)\cos\tfrac{1}{2}\pi a, \qquad y = a^{1-a}\Gamma(a)\sin\tfrac{1}{2}\pi a.$$

These curves are called *klothoids*.

The special curve $C_{\frac{1}{2}}$ plays an important part in Fresnel's theory of the diffraction of light. It is known under the name of *Cornu's spiral*,

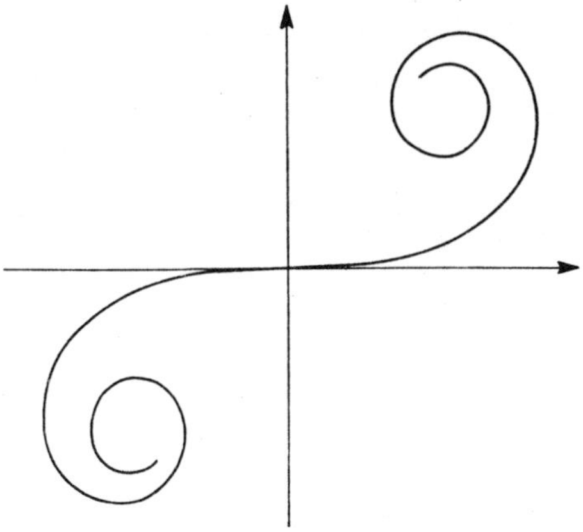

Fig. 3.6–8. Cornu's spiral

(fig. 3.6–8). It has the remarkable property that

$$\varkappa = s,$$

i.e., the curvature equals the arc length.

3.7 – Evaluation of the sum of certain series

3.7.1 – Gauss's sum

The residue theorem provides also a wonderful method for the summation of certain series. A famous example is the so-called *Gauss's sum*

$$S_n = \sum_{\nu=0}^{n-1} \exp\frac{2\pi i\nu^2}{n} = \sum_{\nu=0}^{n-1} T_\nu \tag{3.7–1}$$

where

$$T_k = \exp\frac{2\pi i k^2}{n}, \qquad k = 0, 1, \ldots, n-1. \tag{3.7–2}$$

On account of the relation

$$T_{n-m} = T_m, \qquad 0 < m < n, \tag{3.7–3}$$

we may write

$$S_n = T_0 + 2T_1 + \ldots + 2T_{\frac{1}{2}(n-1)}$$

or

$$S_n = T_0+2T_1+\ldots+2T_{\frac{1}{2}n-1}+T_{\frac{1}{2}n},$$

according as n is odd or even.

It is easy to see that the poles of the function

$$f(z) = \frac{2\exp(2\pi i z^2/n)}{e^{2\pi i z}-1} \tag{3.7–4}$$

are at $z = k$, $k = 0, \pm 1, \pm 2, \ldots$, these poles being simple. The residues are found on applying (3.3–8):

$$\frac{1}{\pi i}\frac{e^{2\pi i k^2/n}}{e^{2\pi i k}} = \frac{1}{\pi i}e^{2\pi i k^2/n}. \tag{3.7–5}$$

Now consider a rectangle of sides $x = 0$, $x = \frac{1}{2}n$, $y = \pm\omega$, indented at $z = 0$ and $z = \frac{1}{2}n$, (fig. 3.7–1).

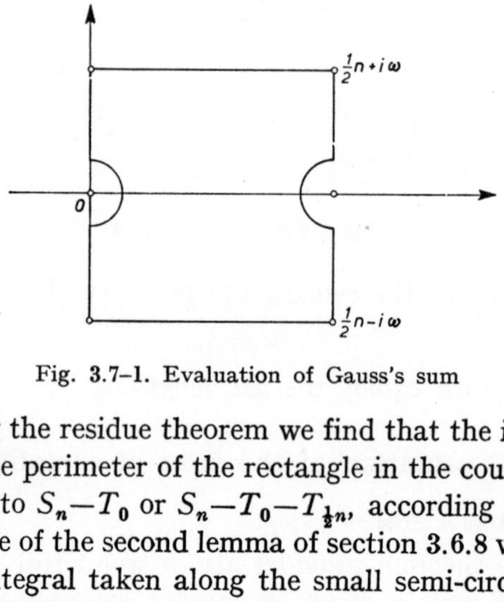

Fig. 3.7–1. Evaluation of Gauss's sum

On applying the residue theorem we find that the integral of $f(z)$ taken along the perimeter of the rectangle in the counter-clockwise sense is equal to $S_n - T_0$ or $S_n - T_0 - T_{\frac{1}{2}n}$, according as n is odd or even. By virtue of the second lemma of section 3.6.8 we see that the limit of the integral taken along the small semi-circle at $z = 0$ is $-T_0$, as the radius tends to zero. Similarly we see that the limit of the integral along the semi-circle at $z = \frac{1}{2}n$ is 0 or $T_{\frac{1}{2}n}$, according as n is odd or even.

By letting $\omega \to \infty$ we see that the integral taken along the rectilinear parts of left vertical side of the rectangle tends to

$$-2i\int_0^\infty \left(\frac{e^{-2\pi i y^2/n}}{e^{-2\pi y}-1}+\frac{e^{-2\pi i y^2/n}}{e^{2\pi y}-1}\right)dy = 2i\int_0^\infty e^{-2\pi i y^2/n}\,dy.$$

Similarly the integral along the rectilinear parts of the right-vertical side of the rectangle tends to

$$2i\int_0^\infty \left(\frac{e^{2\pi i(\frac{1}{2}n+iy)^2/n}}{(-1)^n e^{-2\pi y}-1}+\frac{e^{2\pi i(\frac{1}{2}n-iy)^2/n}}{(-1)^n e^{2\pi y}-1}\right)dy = 2i^{3n+1}\int_0^\infty e^{-2\pi i y^2/n}\,dy.$$

On the upper part of the rectangle we have the contribution

$$-2\int_0^{\frac{1}{2}n} \frac{e^{2\pi i(x+i\omega)^2/n}}{e^{2\pi i(x+i\omega)}-1}\,dx = -2\int_0^{\frac{1}{2}n} \frac{e^{2\pi i(x^2-\omega^2)/n}\,e^{-4\pi x\omega/n}}{e^{2\pi ix}\,e^{-2\pi\omega}-1}\,dx$$

and its modulus is less than

$$2\int_0^{\frac{1}{2}n} \frac{e^{-4\pi x\omega/n}}{1-e^{-2\pi\omega}}\,dx = \frac{n}{2\pi\omega}.$$

A similar consideration leads to the result that the contribution from the lower part is also numerically less than $n/2\pi\omega$. Hence the contributions from the horizontal sides tend to zero as $\omega \to \infty$. Thus we find

$$S_n = 2i(1+i^{3n})\int_0^{\infty} e^{-2\pi iy^2/n}\,dy = 2i(1+i^{3n})\sqrt{n}\int_0^{\infty} e^{-2\pi it^2}\,dt. \tag{3.7–6}$$

The last integral may be evaluated by taking $n = 4$.
Since

$$S_4 = 1+e^{2\pi i/4}+e^{2\pi i}+e^{2\pi i/4} = 2(1+i)$$

we have

$$2(1+i) = 8i\int_0^{\infty} e^{-2\pi it^2}\,dt,$$

whence

$$i\int_0^{\infty} e^{-2\pi it^2}\,dt = \tfrac{1}{4}(1+i) \tag{3.7–7}$$

and so, on inserting this value in (3.7–6),

$$\boxed{\sum_{\nu=0}^{n-1} \exp\frac{2\pi i\nu^2}{n} = \tfrac{1}{2}(1+i)(1+i^{3n})\sqrt{n}.} \tag{3.7–8}$$

Equating real and imaginary parts in (3.7–7) we find as a by-product

$$\int_0^{\infty} \cos 2\pi t^2\,dt = \int_0^{\infty} \sin 2\pi t^2\,dt = \tfrac{1}{4} \tag{3.7–9}$$

and it is easy to verify that this result is in accordance with (3.6–43).

3.7.2 – Some general sum formulas

We proceed to derive a general theorem which has many interesting applications.

(i) Let $\varphi(z)$ denote a meromorphic function having no other singularities than simple poles at $z = a,\ a\pm 1,\ a\pm 2, \ldots$ the residues being all equal to α_n, $n = 0, \pm 1, \pm 2, \ldots$. Assume $f(z)$ to be a holomorphic function within a certain open set $\mathfrak{A}$ except for isolated singularities. The sum of the residues of the function $f(z)\varphi(z)$ at the singular points of $f(z)$ inside a certain regular contour C may be designated by A. The residue theorem asserts

$$\sum_{\nu} \alpha_\nu f(\nu+a) = \frac{1}{2\pi i}\int_C f(\zeta)\varphi(\zeta)\, d\zeta - A, \qquad (3.7\text{–}10)$$

where on the left-hand side the summation has to be extended over the integers ν corresponding to points within C where $\varphi(z)$ has a pole and where $f(z)$ is regular.

(ii) Next we assume $f(z)$ to be a rational function such that $z\,f(z) \to 0$ as $z \to \infty$. Take for C a rectangle of sides $x = \pm(r+b)$, $y = \pm r$, where $b \neq a$, r being a positive integer.

(iii) Assuming that $\varphi(z)$ remains bounded on the perimeter of the rectangle as $r \to \infty$, we shall prove that the integral on the right of (3.7–10) tends to zero as $r \to \infty$. In fact, the smallest value of $|z|$ on the perimeter of the rectangle is r and the length of the path of integration is $2(4r+2b)$. If now $|\varphi(z)| < M$ for z on the perimeter we find by virtue of Darboux's inequality (2.4–17)

$$\left|\int_C f(\zeta)\varphi(\zeta)\, d\zeta\right| = \left|\int_C \zeta f(\zeta)\varphi(\zeta)\frac{d\zeta}{\zeta}\right| \leqq \frac{2(4r+2b)}{r} M\varepsilon < 10M\varepsilon,$$

where ε is an arbitrary positive number, provided r is sufficiently large. As a consequence we have

$$\sum_{\nu=-\infty}^{\infty} a_\nu f(\nu+a) = -A, \qquad (3.7\text{–}11)$$

where A denotes the sum of the residues of $f(z)\varphi(z)$ at the singularities of $f(z)$.

It should be noticed that on the left of (3.7–11) the terms corresponding to values of ν where $f(z)$ is singular must be omitted, for they contribute to A.

Some concrete examples will now be discussed for the sake of illustration. First we take

$$\varphi(z) = \pi \operatorname{ctn} \pi z. \qquad (3.7\text{–}12)$$

In this case $a=0$ and the number b introduced above may be taken as $\frac{1}{2}$. From (1.10–16) and (1.10–17) we infer that on the sides $x = \pm(r+\frac{1}{2})$ we have

$$|\operatorname{ctn} \pi z| \leqq \frac{|\sinh \pi y|}{\sqrt{1+\sinh^2 \pi y}} \leqq 1$$

and on the sides $y = \pm r$

$$|\operatorname{ctn} \pi z| \leqq \sqrt{\frac{1+\sinh^2 \pi r}{\sinh^2 \pi r}} \leqq 1 + \frac{1}{\sinh \pi r} \leqq 1 + \frac{1}{\pi r} < 2,$$

since $|\sinh y| \geqq |y|$, as may be deduced without difficulty. Since the residues are all equal to $+1$, we find a sum of the type

$$\sum_{\nu} f(\nu). \tag{3.7–13}$$

Treating the function

$$\varphi(z) = \pi \csc \pi z \tag{3.7–14}$$

in a similar way, we are led to an expansion of the type

$$\sum_{\nu} (-1)^{\nu} f(\nu). \tag{3.7–15}$$

If we consider the function

$$\varphi(z) = \pi \sec \pi z \tag{3.7–16}$$

we have $a = \frac{1}{2}$ and we may take $b = 0$. The residues at the poles are $(-1)^{n-1}$, $n = 0, \pm 1, \pm 2, \ldots$, and so we find a sum of the type

$$\sum_{\nu} (-1)^{\nu} f(\nu + \tfrac{1}{2}). \tag{3.7–17}$$

3.7.3 – Expansion of Bernoulli's and Euler's numbers in infinite series

Starting from (3.7–12) or (3.7–14) we wish to take

$$f(z) = z^{-2n}, \qquad n \geqq 1. \tag{3.7–18}$$

The conditions of section 3.7.2 are satisfied. Writing the expansion (2.17–19) in the form

$$\pi z \operatorname{ctn} \pi z = 1 - \sum_{\nu=1}^{\infty} \frac{B_{2\nu}}{(2\nu)!} 2^{2\nu} \pi^{2\nu} z^{2\nu},$$

we easily find that the residue of the function $\pi z^{-2n} \operatorname{ctn} \pi z$ at $z = 0$ is

$$-2^{2n} \pi^{2n} \frac{B_{2n}}{(2n)!}, \tag{3.7–19}$$

this being the coefficient of z^{-1} in the expansion of this function. Hence, (3.7–10) leads to the result

$$\boxed{\tfrac{1}{2} 2^{2n} \pi^{2n} \frac{B_{2n}}{(2n)!} = \sum_{\nu=1}^{\infty} \frac{1}{\nu^{2n}} = 1 + \frac{1}{2^{2n}} + \frac{1}{3^{2n}} + \ldots} \tag{3.7–20}$$

From this expression it follows that the Bernoulli numbers are positive.

Writing the expansion (2.17–25) in the form

$$\pi \csc \pi z = 1 + \sum_{\nu=1}^{\infty} \frac{B_{2\nu}}{(2\nu)!} (2^{2\nu} - 2) \pi^{2\nu} z^{2\nu}$$

we find that the residue of the function $\pi z^{-2n} \csc \pi z$ at $z = 0$ is

$$(2^{2n}-2)\pi^{2n} \frac{B_{2n}}{(2n)!}. \qquad (3.7\text{–}21)$$

In this case appears an expansion of the type (3.7–15),

$$\boxed{\tfrac{1}{2}(2^{2n} - 2)\pi^{2n} \frac{B_{2n}}{(2n)!} = \sum_{\nu=1}^{\infty} \frac{(-1)^{\nu-1}}{\nu^{2n}} = 1 - \frac{1}{2^{2n}} + \frac{1}{3^{2n}} - \cdots.} \qquad (3.7\text{–}22)$$

Adding corresponding members of (3.7–20) and (3.7–22) we get

$$\tfrac{1}{2}(2^{2n}-1)\pi^{2n} \frac{B_{2n}}{(2n)!} = \sum_{\nu=0}^{\infty} \frac{1}{(2\nu+1)^{2n}} = 1 + \frac{1}{3^{2n}} + \frac{1}{5^{2n}} + \cdots. \qquad (3.7\text{–}23)$$

Special cases are obtained by taking $n = 1$. We have successively

$$\frac{1}{6}\pi^2 = 1 + \frac{1}{2^2} + \frac{1}{3^2} + \cdots, \qquad (3.7\text{–}24)$$

$$\frac{1}{12}\pi^2 = 1 - \frac{1}{2^2} + \frac{1}{3^2} - \cdots, \qquad (3.7\text{–}25)$$

$$\frac{1}{8}\pi^2 = 1 + \frac{1}{3^2} + \frac{1}{5^2} + \cdots. \qquad (3.7\text{–}26)$$

Finally we consider the expansion (2.17–10) which we shall write in the form

$$\pi \sec \pi z = 1 + \sum_{\nu=1}^{\infty} \frac{E_{2\nu}}{(2\nu)!} \pi^{2\nu+1} z^{2\nu}.$$

The residue of the function $\pi z^{-(2n+1)} \sec \pi z$ at $z = 0$ is

$$\pi^{2n+1} \frac{E_{2n}}{(2n)!}, \qquad (3.7\text{–}27)$$

provided $n \geqq 1$; this result holds also for $n = 0$ when we put $E_0 = 1$. We now get a series of the type (3.7–17), which may be written as

$$\boxed{\tfrac{1}{2} \cdot (\tfrac{1}{2}\pi)^{2n+1} \frac{E_{2n}}{(2n)!} = \sum_{\nu=0}^{\infty} \frac{(-1)^{\nu}}{(2\nu+1)^{2n+1}} = 1 - \frac{1}{3^{2n+1}} + \frac{1}{5^{2n+1}} - \cdots.} \qquad (3.7\text{–}28)$$

When $n = 0$ the series reduces to Leibniz's series (2.16–17).

3.7.4 – Decomposition of some circular functions into partial fractions

Another remarkable application is the decomposition of π ctn πz and π csc πz into partial fractions. Let $f(z)$ denote the fraction

$$f(z) = \frac{1}{s^2 - z^2} \tag{3.7–29}$$

where s is not an integer. The singularities are at $z = s$ and $z = -s$. The residues of $\pi f(z)$ ctn πz and $\pi f(z)$ csc πz are $-\pi$ ctn $\pi s/2s$ and $-\pi$ csc $\pi s/2s$ respectively. Hence, by virtue of (3.7–11), replacing s by z,

$$\boxed{\pi \operatorname{ctn} \pi z = \frac{1}{z} + \sum_{\nu=1}^{\infty} \frac{2z}{z^2 - \nu^2}} \tag{3.7–30}$$

and

$$\boxed{\pi \csc \pi z = \frac{1}{z} + \sum_{\nu=1}^{\infty} \frac{2(-1)^\nu z}{z^2 - \nu^2}.} \tag{3.7–31}$$

It is easy to show that the series on the right of (3.7–30) is uniformly convergent on any closed and bounded set that avoids the points $z = 0, \pm 1, \pm 2, \ldots$. Hence the sequence

$$F_n(z) = \sum_{\nu=-n}^{n} \frac{1}{z-\nu} = \frac{1}{z} + \sum_{\nu=1}^{n} \frac{2z}{z^2 - \nu^2}$$

satisfies the conditions of section 2.20.1. Upon differentiation we get the expansion

$$\boxed{\pi^2 \csc^2 \pi z = \sum_{\nu=-\infty}^{\infty} \frac{1}{(z-\nu)^2},} \tag{3.7–32}$$

the series on the right being convergent for $z \neq 0, \pm 1, \pm 2, \ldots$, as seen by comparison with the series $\sum_{\nu=1}^{\infty} 1/\nu^2$.

3.8 – The logarithmic derivative

3.8.1 – Properties of the logarithmic derivative

If $f(z)$ is regular at $z = a$ and $f(a) \neq 0$ the *logarithmic derivative*

$$\frac{f'(z)}{f(z)} \tag{3.8–1}$$

is also regular at $z = a$. The logarithmic derivative has the following useful property:

$$\frac{(fg)'}{fg} = \frac{f'}{f} + \frac{g'}{g}. \tag{3.8–2}$$

If we assume $f(z)$ to be meromorphic in a region $\mathfrak{R}$ the singularities of the logarithmic derivative can only occur at the zeros and the poles of $f(z)$ since $f'(z)$ has no poles other than $f(z)$. Let $z = a$ be a zero of order n. Then

$$f(z) = (z-a)^n g(z), \qquad g(a) \neq 0, \tag{3.8–3}$$

and by virtue of (3.8–2)

$$\frac{f'(z)}{f(z)} = \frac{n}{z-a} + \frac{g'(z)}{g(z)}, \tag{3.8–4}$$

the second term on the right-hand side being regular at $z = a$. Hence:

If $z = a$ is a zero of order n of $f(z)$ then its logarithmic derivative admits this point as a simple pole with residue n.

If, instead, $z = a$ is a pole of order n, we have

$$f(z) = (z-a)^{-n} g(z), \qquad g(a) \neq 0, \tag{3.8–5}$$

and

$$\frac{f'(z)}{f(z)} = \frac{-n}{z-a} + \frac{g'(z)}{g(z)}. \tag{3.8–6}$$

Hence:

If $z = a$ is a pole of order n of $f(z)$ then its logarithmic derivative admits this point as a simple pole with residue $-n$.

We may summarize as follows:

The logarithmic derivative of a non-constant meromorphic function in a region $\mathfrak{R}$ is there meromorphic, its singularities being simple poles at the zeros and the poles of the given function, the residues being the orders or the opposite of the orders respectively. In fact, in a region a non-constant function can only have isolated zeros.

3.8.2 – Cauchy's theorem about the integral of the logarithmic derivative

Assume $f(z)$ to be a non-constant meromorphic function in a region $\mathfrak{R}$ and let C denote a cycle which is homologous 0 in $\mathfrak{R}$ avoiding the zeros and the poles of $f(z)$. Since the logarithmic derivative has only isolated singularities we may apply the general residue theorem of section 3.5.1. Let us assume that $a_1, \ldots, a_m$ are the zeros of $f(z)$ with orders $\alpha_1, \ldots, \alpha_m$ respectively, such that C has a non-vanishing winding number with respect to these points, whereas the winding numbers with respect to eventual other zeros vanish. Similarly let $b_1, \ldots, b_n$ denote the poles of $f(z)$ with orders $\beta_1, \ldots, \beta_n$ respectively, such that C has a non-vanishing winding-number with respect to these points only. Then we may infer from (3.5–2) that

$$\frac{1}{2\pi i}\int_C \frac{f'(\zeta)}{f(\zeta)}\,d\zeta = \sum_{\mu=1}^{m} \alpha_\mu\,\Omega_C(a_\mu) - \sum_{\nu=1}^{n} \beta_\nu\,\Omega_C(b_\nu), \tag{3.8–7}$$

where $C \sim 0$ in $\mathfrak{R}$.

If C is a regular contour traversed in the counter-clockwise sense and if $a_1, \ldots, a_m, b_1, \ldots, b_n$ are the zeros and poles inside C we may infer that

$$\boxed{\frac{1}{2\pi i}\int_C \frac{f'(\zeta)}{f(\zeta)}\,d\zeta = N_0 - N_\infty,} \tag{3.8–8}$$

where

$$N_0 = \sum_{\mu=1}^{m} \alpha_\mu \tag{3.8–9}$$

denotes the number of zeros of $f(z)$ inside C, each zero counted as many times as its order indicates, and

$$N_\infty = \sum_{\nu=1}^{n} \beta_\nu \tag{3.8–10}$$

is the number of poles inside C, each pole counted as many times as its order indicates. It must be assumed, of course, that C and its interior belong to $\mathfrak{R}$.

3.8.3 – Generalization of the previous theorem

It is an easy matter to generalize (3.8–7). Let $g(z)$ be holomorphic throughout $\mathfrak{R}$. The residues of

$$\frac{f'(z)}{f(z)}\,g(z) \tag{3.8–11}$$

may be evaluated on applying (3.3–5). From (3.5–2) we find

$$\boxed{\frac{1}{2\pi i}\int_C \frac{f'(\zeta)g(\zeta)}{f(\zeta)}\,d\zeta = \sum_{\mu=1}^{m} \alpha_\mu\,\Omega_C(a_\mu)g(a_\mu) - \sum_{\nu=1}^{n} \beta_\nu\,\Omega_C(b_\nu)g(b_\nu),} \tag{3.8–12}$$

where $C \sim 0$ in $\mathfrak{R}$.

A particular case occurs when $f(z) = z - a$. Then (3.8–12) reads

$$\frac{1}{2\pi i}\int_C \frac{g(\zeta)}{\zeta - a}\,d\zeta = \Omega_C(a)g(a),$$

i.e., Cauchy's integral formula (2.7–4).

3.8.4 – The number of zeros of a polynomial

From (3.8–8) we may deduce a proof of the assertion that a polynomial of degree $n > 0$ possesses a finite number of zeros, the sum of their orders being equal to n (see also section 3.10.3). Consider the polynomial

$$f(z) = c_0+c_1z+\ldots+c_nz^n, \qquad c_n \neq 0, \quad n > 0. \tag{3.8–13}$$

In section 2.6.1 we verified that $|f(z)| \to \infty$ as $|z| \to \infty$; hence for R sufficiently large we have $|f(z)| > 0$, whenever $|z| \geqq R$. We have only to prove

$$\frac{1}{2\pi i}\int_C \frac{f'(\zeta)}{f(\zeta)}\, d\zeta = n, \tag{3.8–14}$$

C being the circumference $|z| = R$ described in the counter-clockwise sense. The value of the left-hand member is the opposite of the residue of the integrand at $z = \infty$ and according to section 3.3.2 this is equal to the residue of $f'(1/z)/z^2 f(1/z)$ at $z = 0$. We therefore have to evaluate

$$\lim_{z\to 0} \frac{1}{z}\,\frac{f'(1/z)}{f(1/z)} = \lim_{z\to 0} \frac{c_1z^{n-1}+\ldots+nc_n}{c_0z^n+\ldots+c_n},$$

which turns out to be equal to n. This gives the desired result.

3.8.5 – Lucas's theorem

We conclude our considerations by establishing some theorems of a rather particular kind.

The relative position of the real zeros of a real differentiable function is described in Rolle's theorem, stating that between any two zeros of the function lies at least one zero of its derivative. However, Rolle's theorem is not generally true for holomorphic functions of a complex variable. Thus, for instance, the function $f(z)=e^z-1$ vanishes at $z = 0$ and $z = 2\pi i$, but the derivative $f'(z) = e^z$ has no zeros at all.

As to a polynomial we may, however, state the following theorem, due to F. Lucas:

Any convex polygon which contains all the zeros of a polynomial $f(z)$ also contains the zeros of the derivative $f'(z)$.

We assume of course, that the degree of $f'(z)$ is positive. According to (2.6–7) we may write

$$f(z) = c_n(z-a_1)\ldots(z-a_n),$$

where $a_1, \ldots, a_n$ are the zeros of $f(z)$. We consider the function

$$F(z) = \frac{f'(z)}{f(z)} = \sum_{\nu=1}^{n} \frac{1}{z-a_\nu} = \frac{1}{z-a_1}+\ldots+\frac{1}{z-a_n}. \tag{3.8–15}$$

If a zero a of $f'(z)$ were exterior to a convex polygon containing the points $a_1, \ldots, a_n$, it would not be a zero of $f(z)$. The differences $a_1 - a, \ldots, a_n - a$ are represented by segments, having their initial point at a and their end points at $a_1, \ldots, a_n$ respectively, (fig. 3.8–1) They are included in an angular area of measure ω, where

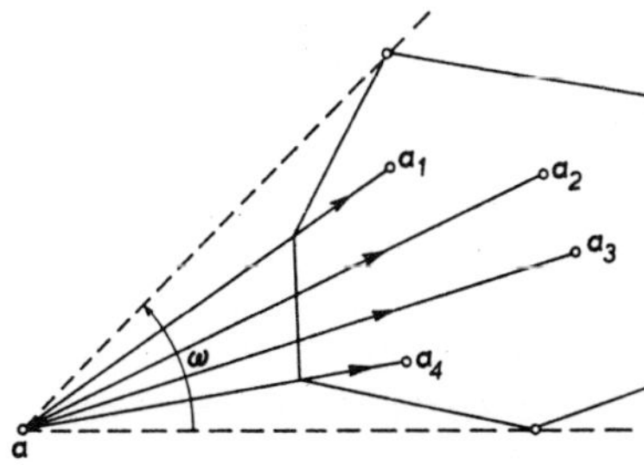

Fig. 3.8–1. Lucas's theorem

$0 \leqq \omega < \pi$, i.e. the angle subtended at a by the polygon. It is therefore possible to find a real constant α such that

$$\alpha - \pi < \arg (a_k - a) \leqq \alpha, \qquad k = 1, \ldots, n,$$

where $\arg (a_k - a)$ is one of the arguments of $a_k - a$. Since the direction of $1/(a_k - a)$ is found by reflection with respect to the real axis, we also have

$$\pi - \alpha > \arg \frac{1}{a_k - a} \geqq -\alpha$$

or

$$-\alpha \leqq \arg \frac{1}{a_k - a} < -\alpha + \pi, \qquad k = 1, \ldots, n,$$

whence

$$0 \leqq \arg \frac{e^{i\alpha}}{a_k - a} < \pi. \tag{3.8–16}$$

Hence, either $e^{i\alpha}/(a_k - a) > 0$ or $\operatorname{Im} e^{i\alpha}/(a_k - a) > 0$. As a consequence

$$\sum_{\nu=1}^{n} \frac{e^{i\alpha}}{a_\nu - a} = -e^{i\alpha} \frac{f'(a)}{f(a)} \neq 0, \tag{3.8–17}$$

contrary to $f'(a) = 0$.

3.8.6 – Jensen's circles theorem

The following theorem, due to Jensen, refers to a real polynomial, i.e., a polynomial whose coefficients are real numbers. It is easy to see that the non real zeros of $f(z)$ occur in conjugate imaginary pairs. The circles whose diameters are the line-segments joining the pairs of conjugate complex zeros of $f(z)$ are called the *Jensen circles* of $f(z)$, (fig. 3.8–2).

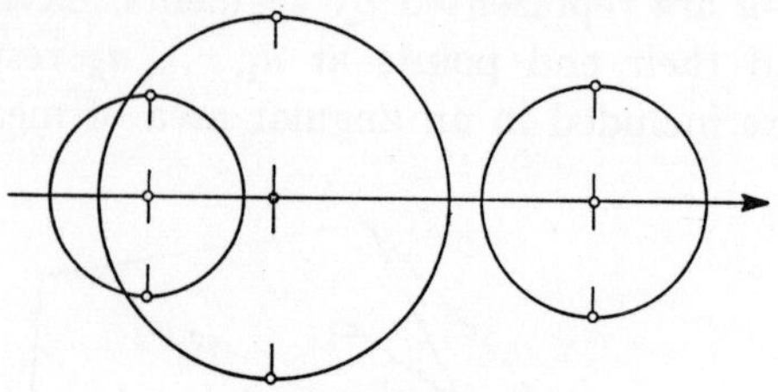

Fig. 3.8–2. Jensen's circles

Jensen's theorem about real polynomials states:

Every non-real zero of the derivative of a real polynomial $f(z)$ lies in or on at least one of the Jensen circles of the polynomial.

Let a denote a real zero of $f(z)$. Then

$$\frac{1}{z-a} = \frac{\bar{z}-a}{|z-a|^2}$$

and if $y = \operatorname{Im} z$,

$$\operatorname{Im} \frac{1}{z-a} = \frac{-y}{|z-a|^2}. \tag{3.8–18}$$

Next consider a non real zero $a = p+qi$. Then $\bar{a} = p-qi$ is also a zero and

$$\frac{1}{z-a} = \frac{\bar{z}-\bar{a}}{|z-a|^2} = \frac{x-iy-p+iq}{(x-p)^2+(y-q)^2},$$

whence

$$\operatorname{Im} \frac{1}{z-a} = \frac{-(y-q)}{(x-p)^2+(y-q)^2}.$$

Similarly

$$\operatorname{Im} \frac{1}{z-\bar{a}} = \frac{-(y+q)}{(x-p)^2+(y+q)^2}.$$

An easy computation yields

$$\operatorname{Im}\left(\frac{1}{z-a}+\frac{1}{z-\bar{a}}\right) = \frac{-2y\{(x-p)^2+y^2-q^2\}}{\{(x-p)^2+(y-q)^2\}\{(x-p)^2+(y+q)^2\}}, \tag{3.8–19}$$

and so we see from (3.8–18) and (3.8–19) that, when z is outside all Jensen circles,

$$\operatorname{Im} \frac{f'(z)}{f(z)} = \operatorname{Im} \sum_{\nu=1}^{n} \frac{1}{z-a_\nu} = -2y\,A(x, y) \tag{3.8–20}$$

where $A(x, y)$ is a positive expression. Hence $f'(z)$ is not zero outside all Jensen circles.

3.9 – Jensen's theorem. The Poisson-Jensen formula

3.9.1 – The arithmetical mean of the logarithm

If $f(z)$ is meromorphic then the function $\log |f(z)|$ is harmonic except at the zeros and the poles of $f(z)$. Assume $f(z)$ free from zeros and poles in $|z| \leqq R$. Then by (2.13–2) on taking real parts and inserting the harmonic function $\log |f(z)|$

$$\log |f(0)| = \frac{1}{2\pi} \int_0^{2\pi} \log |f(Re^{i\theta})| \, d\theta. \tag{3.9–1}$$

This formula remains true if $f(z)$ admits zeros or poles on the circumference $|z| = R$. If $Re^{i\varphi}$ is such a zero or a pole we can remove it by dividing or multiplying $f(z)$ by an appropriate power of $z-Re^{i\varphi}$ and we only have to verify that

$$\log R = \frac{1}{2\pi} \int_0^{2\pi} \log |Re^{i\theta}-Re^{i\varphi}| \, d\theta$$

or

$$\int_0^{2\pi} \log |e^{i\theta}-e^{i\varphi}| \, d\theta = 0. \tag{3.9–2}$$

Because of its periodicity we may take the integrand with $\varphi = 0$ and we have to verify

$$\int_0^{2\pi} \log |e^{i\theta}-1| \, d\theta = 0, \tag{3.9–3}$$

or

$$\int_0^{2\pi} \log \sin \tfrac{1}{2}\theta \, d\theta = -2\pi \log 2. \tag{3.9–4}$$

This is easily done, for (3.9–4) is equivalent to

$$\int_0^{\pi} \log \sin \theta \, d\theta = -\pi \log 2. \tag{3.9–5}$$

In order to prove this formula we observe first that the integral on the left is convergent. In fact, the integrand is equal to $\log (\sin \theta)/\theta + \log \theta$. The integral $\int_0^\pi \log \theta \, d\theta$ exists. The integral $\int_0^\pi \log (\sin \theta)/\theta \, d\theta$ is convergent at $\theta = 0$, for the integrand is bounded and on replacing θ by $\pi-\theta$ we conclude that the same statement holds for $\theta = \pi$. Next we write

$$\int_0^{\pi} \log \sin \theta \, d\theta = \pi \log 2 + \int_0^{\pi} \log \sin \tfrac{1}{2}\theta \, d\theta + \int_0^{\pi} \log \cos \tfrac{1}{2}\theta \, d\theta.$$

In the first integral on the right-hand side we put $\theta = 2\psi$, in the second $\theta = 2\psi-\pi$. We then get

$$\int_0^{\pi} \log \sin \theta \, d\theta = \pi \log 2 + 2 \int_0^{\frac{1}{2}\pi} \log \sin \psi \, d\psi + 2 \int_{\frac{1}{2}\pi}^{\pi} \log \sin \psi \, d\psi$$

$$= \pi \log 2 + 2 \int_0^{\pi} \log \sin \theta \, d\theta$$

and the desired result (3.9–5) follows.

3.9.2 – Jensen's formula

Let a be a point inside the circle C, $|z| = R$. Then $R^2/\bar{a}$ is its inverse with respect to the circle C. The function

$$\frac{z-a}{z-R^2/\bar{a}} \tag{3.9–6}$$

has a constant modulus along the circumference C as may be verified at once. This fact expresses a well-known theorem of elementary geometry (theorem of Apollonius). By multiplying by an appropriate constant we can get the function

$$\frac{R(z-a)}{R^2-\bar{a}z} \tag{3.9–7}$$

having modulus unity along C. We shall see presently that functions of this type are very useful in function theory.

If $f(z)$ possesses the zeros $a_1, \ldots, a_m$ and the poles $b_1, \ldots, b_n$ in the region $|z| < R$, multiple zeros and poles being repeated, the function

$$F(z) = f(z) \prod_{\mu=1}^{m} \frac{R^2-\bar{a}_\mu z}{R(z-a_\mu)} \prod_{\nu=1}^{n} \frac{R(z-b_\nu)}{R^2-\bar{b}_\nu z} \tag{3.9–8}$$

is free from zeros or poles inside $|z| = R$, it being assumed that $z = 0$ is not a zero or pole. But $|F(z)| = |f(z)|$ and according to (3.9–1) we have

$$\boxed{\log |f(0)| + \sum_{\mu=1}^{m} \log \frac{R}{|a_\mu|} - \sum_{\nu=1}^{n} \log \frac{R}{|b_\nu|} = \frac{1}{2\pi} \int_0^{2\pi} \log |f(Re^{i\theta})| \, d\theta.} \tag{3.9–9}$$

If $f(z)$ is meromorphic in an open set containing the interior and the boundary of a circular disc of radius R around the origin and does not vanish at the origin then the moduli of the zeros $a_1, \ldots, a_m$ and the poles $b_1, \ldots, b_n$, multiple zeros and poles being repeated, inside or on the boundary of the disc are related to the modulus of the function on the circumference $|z| = R$ by Jensen's formula (3.9–9).

3.9.3 – An application of Jensen's formula

Let $n(r)$ denote the number of zeros minus the number of poles inside the circle $|z| = r$. Assuming that there are no poles or zeros on the circumference we have on account of (3.8–8)

$$n(r) = \frac{1}{2\pi}\int_0^{2\pi} \frac{f'(re^{i\theta})}{f(re^{i\theta})}\, re^{i\theta}\, d\theta. \tag{3.9–10}$$

If we divide by r, integrate with respect to r and take real parts, we obtain

$$\int_0^R \frac{n(r)}{r}\, dr = \frac{1}{2\pi}\int_0^{2\pi} \log|f(Re^{i\theta})|\, d\theta - \log|f(0)|, \tag{3.9–11}$$

provided the origin is neither a zero nor a pole. Hence by Jensen's formula

$$\boxed{\int_0^R \frac{n(r)}{r}\, dr = \sum_{\mu=1}^{m} \log\frac{R}{|a_\mu|} - \sum_{\nu=1}^{n} \log\frac{R}{|b_\nu|}.} \tag{3.9–12}$$

We have to justify this process, for the integrand in (3.9–10) presents infinities which make the validity of the integration doubtful. It is, however, possible to verify (3.9–12) in a straight-forward manner.

We may arrange the moduli of the zeros $a_1, a_2, \ldots, a_m$ as a non-decreasing sequence and the same can be done for the moduli of the poles. Then

$$\begin{aligned}\sum_{\mu=1}^{m} \log\frac{R}{|a_\mu|} &= \log R^m - \log|a_1| - \ldots - \log|a_m| \\ &= (\log|a_2| - \log|a_1|) + 2(\log|a_3| - \log|a_2|) \\ &\quad + \ldots + (m-1)(\log|a_m| - \log|a_{m-1}|) + m(\log R - \log|a_m|) \\ &= \sum_{\mu=1}^{m-1} \mu(\log|a_{\mu+1}| - \log|a_\mu|) + m(\log R - \log|a_m|) \\ &= \sum_{\mu=1}^{m-1} \int_{|a_\mu|}^{|a_{\mu+1}|} \frac{dr}{r} + m\int_{|a_m|}^{R} \frac{dr}{r}.\end{aligned}$$

Let $n_0(r)$ denote the number of zeros of modulus $\leqq r$. Then $n_0(r) = 0$, when $0 \leqq r < |a_1|$, $n_0(r) = \mu$, when $|a_\mu| \leqq r < |a_{\mu+1}|$, $\mu = 1, \ldots, m-1$, $n_0(r) = m$, when $|a_m| \leqq r < R$. Hence

$$\sum_{\mu=1}^{m} \log\frac{R}{|a_\mu|} = \int_0^R \frac{n_0(r)}{r}\, dr. \tag{3.9–13}$$

Similarly, if n_∞ denotes the number of poles of modulus $\leqq r$ we have

$$\sum_{v=1}^{n} \log \frac{R}{|b_v|} = \int_0^R \frac{n_\infty(r)}{r}\, dr \tag{3.9–14}$$

and since $n(r) = n_0(r) - n_\infty(r)$ we obtain (3.9–12).

3.9.4 – The Poisson-Jensen formula

Let us apply the Poisson formula (2.15–17) to the function $\log |F(z)|$, where $F(z)$ is defined as (3.9–8). If z is a point inside the circle $|z| = R$, where $f(z)$ neither vanishes nor has a pole, we immediately infer that

$$\begin{aligned} \log |f(z)| + \sum_{\mu=1}^{m} \log \left| \frac{R^2 - \bar{a}_\mu z}{R(z-a_\mu)} \right| - \sum_{\nu=1}^{n} \log \left| \frac{R^2 - \bar{b}_\nu z}{R(z-b_\nu)} \right| \\ = \frac{1}{2\pi} \int_0^{2\pi} \log |f(Re^{i\theta})| \operatorname{Re} \frac{Re^{i\theta}+z}{Re^{i\theta}-z}\, d\theta. \end{aligned} \tag{3.9–15}$$

This formula due to R. Nevanlinna is referred to as the *Poisson-Jensen formula*. It reduces to Jensen's formula if we take $z = 0$. In its proof we assumed that there are no zeros or poles of $f(z)$ on the circumference. Now the integral on the right hand side of (3.9–9) turns out to be continuous as regards R and the same can therefore be asserted about the integral in (3.9–15). Since the left-hand member is also continuous as regards z, the relation (3.9–15) remains true if R tends to the modulus of a zero or of a pole of $f(z)$.

3.10 – Rouché's theorem

3.10.1 – The argument principle

For many purposes a more imaginative statement of (3.8–7) is to be preferred.

We consider a function $f(z)$ which is meromorphic in a region $\mathfrak{R}$. Let C denote a regular chain in $\mathfrak{R}$ that does not pass through any pole of $f(z)$. The chain is composed of smooth arcs, represented by $z = z_\nu(t)$. Excluding the trivial case that $f(z)$ is a constant, the equation

$$w = f(z) \tag{3.10–1}$$

defines a mapping of $\mathfrak{R}$ in the z-plane onto a point set in the w-plane. The points $w_\nu(t) = f\{z_\nu(t)\}$ constitute a smooth arc which we shall denote by $f(C_\nu)$. The chain $f(C)$ will be defined as the formal sum

$$f(C) = \sum_\nu f(C_\nu). \tag{3.10–2}$$

It is plain that $f(C)$ is a cycle when C is a cycle.

Assuming that $C \sim 0$ in $\mathfrak{R}$ and that C does not pass through a zero of $f(z)$, we evidently have, taking account of (2.3–26) and (2.3–30),

$$\boxed{\Omega_{f(C)}(0) = \sum_{\mu} \alpha_\mu \Omega_C(a_\mu) - \sum_{\nu} \beta_\nu \Omega_C(b_\nu).} \tag{3.10–3}$$

The theorem expressed by this equality will be referred to as the *argument principle.*

In the applications C is usually a regular contour described in the counter-clockwise sense, such that C and its interior belong to the region $\mathfrak{R}$. In this case we have the simpler formula

$$\Omega_{f(C)}(0) = N_0 - N_\infty. \tag{3.10–4}$$

3.10.2 – Rouché's theorem

Applying the argument principle we may prove an important statement, viz. *Rouché's theorem.*

Suppose that $f(z)$ is meromorphic and $g(z)$ is holomorphic in a region $\mathfrak{R}$ and satisfy the inequality

$$|g(z)| < |f(z)| \tag{3.10–5}$$

on a regular contour in $\mathfrak{R}$, such that the inner points of C are also included in $\mathfrak{R}$. Then the functions $f(z)$ and $f(z)+g(z)$ have the same number of zeros (each counted with the proper multiplicity) inside C.

Put

$$F(z) = \frac{f(z)+g(z)}{f(z)} = 1 + \frac{g(z)}{f(z)}. \tag{3.10–6}$$

By virtue of (3.10–5) the cycle $F(C)$ is inside a circumference of radius 1 and of centre 1. According to section 2.2.1 the cycle $F(C) \sim 0$ in the interior of the circumference, i.e., $\Omega_{F(C)}(0) = 0$. Since $f(z)$ and $f(z)+g(z)$ have the same number of poles inside C, the function $F(z)$ is free from poles inside or on C and (3.10–4) implies that the number of zeros of $F(z)$ inside C is also zero. Thus the assertion is proved.

3.10.3 – The fundamental theorem of algebra

Rouché's theorem provides an alternative proof of the fundamental theorem of algebra. Consider the polynomial

$$z^n + g(z), \qquad n > 0 \tag{3.10–7}$$

with

$$g(z) = c_0 + c_1 z + \ldots + c_{n-1} z^{n-1}. \tag{3.10–8}$$

Let R be a number exceeding 1 and $|c_0| + \ldots + |c_{n-1}|$. Then, if $|z| = R$,

$$|g(z)| \leqq |c_0|+\ldots+|c_{n-1}|R^{n-1} \leqq (|c_0|+\ldots+|c_{n-1}|)R^{n-1} < R^n.$$

Hence, by taking $f(z) = z^n$ we see that on account of Rouché's theorem the polynomial (3.10–7) has the same number of zeros inside the circumference $|z| = R$ as the function z^n, i.e., there are n zeros. On the other hand there are no zeros outside the circle. For, when $|z| \geqq R$ we have

$$|z^n+g(z)| \geqq |z|^n-|g(z)| > |z|^n-|z|^n = 0.$$

3.10.4 – Walsh's theorem

An interesting application of the argument principle is the following theorem, due to J. L. Walsh.

Let $p \leqq x \leqq q$ be a closed interval on the real axis such that neither p nor q is a zero of the real polynomial $f(z)$ or is a point in or on any Jensen circle (3.8.6) of $f(z)$. — Let $\mathfrak{R}$ be the set of points consisting of the points of the interval and of the closed discs of the Jensen circles which intersect the interval. Then the number of zeros of $f'(z)$ in $\mathfrak{R}$ differs by at most one from the number of zeros of $f(z)$ in $\mathfrak{R}$.

Let C denote the boundary of the smallest rectangle which has sides parallel to the real and imaginary axis and which encloses $\mathfrak{R}$, (fig. 3.10–1). In view of (3.8–20) C is mapped by the function

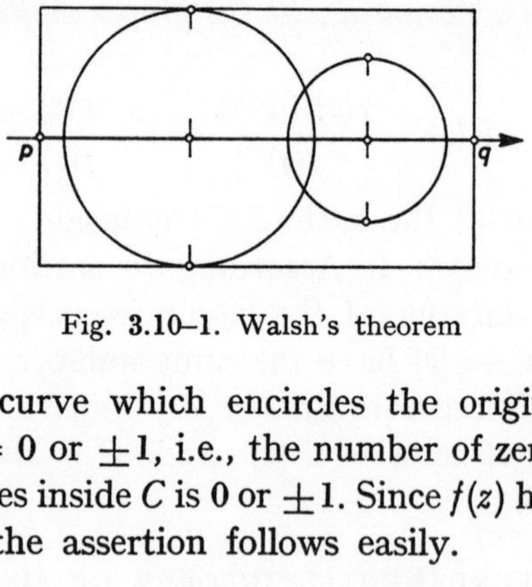

Fig. 3.10–1. Walsh's theorem

(3.8–15) onto a curve which encircles the origin at most once. Hence $\Omega_{F(C)}(0) = 0$ or ± 1, i.e., the number of zeros of $F(z)$ minus the number of poles inside C is 0 or ± 1. Since $f(z)$ has no poles inside C, the truth of the assertion follows easily.

3.11 – A theorem of Hurwitz

3.11.1 – Statement and proof of the theorem

Consider a sequence of functions

$$F_n(z), \qquad n = 1, 2, \ldots, \tag{3.11–1}$$

each being holomorphic in an open set $\mathfrak{A}$, and let

$$F_n(z) \to F(z) \tag{3.11–2}$$

uniformly in every closed and bounded subset of $\mathfrak{A}$ as $n \to \infty$, $F(z)$ *not being identically zero.* Then we assert: *A finite point z_0 of $\mathfrak{A}$ is a zero of $F(z)$ if and only if it is an accumulation point of the set of zeros of the functions $F_n(z)$, points which are zeros for an infinity of values of n being considered as accumulation points.*

Let C designate a circumference around z_0 such that $F(z)$ does not vanish inside or on C, save perhaps at $z = z_0$. Since $F(z)$ is continuous along C there exists a positive number m such that for z on C

$$|F(z)| \geqq m > 0. \tag{3.11–3}$$

On the other hand, the sequence (3.11–1) being uniformly convergent, we can find a number n_0 such that for $n > n_0$

$$|F_n(z) - F(z)| < m$$

if z is on C. We then have

$$F_n(z) = F(z) + G_n(z)$$

with

$$|G_n(z)| < |F(z)|$$

on C. According to Rouché's theorem $F_n(z)$, $n > n_0$, has the same number of zeros inside C as $F(z)$. It follows that $F_n(z)$ has at least one zero inside C if $F(z_0) = 0$, whenever $n > n_0$, whereas $F_n(z) \neq 0$ inside C if $F(z_0) \neq 0$.

3.11.2 – Comment

It is worth-while to notice that the assumptions of the theorem cannot be weakened. For instance, the sequence

$$F_n(z) = \frac{e^z}{n}$$

tends uniformly to zero, but inside a circle of radius unity $F_n(z)$ is always different from zero. Hence the condition that $F(z)$ is not identically zero is not superfluous.

Thus also

$$F_n(z) = 1 - \frac{z^n}{n}$$

considered inside the unit circle around the origin tends uniformly to 1 and the zeros of $F_n(z)$,

$$\sqrt[n]{n}\left(\cos\frac{2k\pi}{n} + i\sin\frac{2k\pi}{n}\right), \quad k = 0, 1, \ldots, n-1, \quad n = 1, 2, \ldots,$$

admit for accumulation points all points of the circumference, whereas on this circumference $F(z) = 1$. Hence in the statement of

Hurwitz's theorem it is necessary to assume that z_0 is a point not on the boundary of the set.

3.12 – The mapping of a region

3.12.1 – Behaviour of a function at a regular point

A geometric representation of a function $f(z)$ is obtained by regarding z and $w = f(z)$ as points in two different planes, the z-plane and the w-plane and interpreting the equation $w = f(z)$ as a *mapping* of points in the z-plane onto points in the w-plane. If $f(z)$ is defined on a set $\mathfrak{S}$ we shall say that the set of points in the w-plane which correspond to those of the set in the z-plane by means of the relation $w = f(z)$ is the *map* of $\mathfrak{S}$ as given by the function; we shall also use the word *image* in this connection. Our main task will consist in the proof of the statement that the image of a region is again a region, assuming, of course, that the mapping function is not constant.

First we wish to establish the theorem:

If a function $f(z)$, regular at a point z_0, is not constant in a neighbourhood of this point and assumes at z_0 the value $w_0 = f(z_0)$, then we can find a number A and a number ε such that every point inside the circumference $|w-w_0| = A$ is the image of at least one point inside the circumference $|z-z_0| = \varepsilon$.

Since $f(z)$ is regular at $z = z_0$ the point z_0 is an isolated zero of $f(z)-w_0$ and we can find a number ε such that $f(z)-w_0 \neq 0$ for $0 < |z-z_0| \leqq \varepsilon$. The function $f(z)$ is holomorphic in a region including the circumference $|z-z_0| = \varepsilon$, while $f(z)-w_0 \neq 0$ for $0 < |z-z_0| \leqq \varepsilon$ and we can, therefore, find a number A such that $|f(z)-w_0| > A > 0$ as long as z is on the circumference $|z-z_0| = \varepsilon$. Let w denote any point in the w-plane inside the circumference $|w-w_0| = A$. Since on $|z-z_0| = \varepsilon$ the inequality $|f(z)-w_0| > |w-w_0|$ holds, we may apply Rouché's theorem and we find that the functions $f(z)-w_0$ and $f(z)-w_0+(w_0-w) = f(z)-w$ have the same number of zeros inside $|z-z_0| = \varepsilon$. Since the first function has a zero at $z = z_0$ the truth of the statement follows.

3.12.2 – The invariance of the region

Now we are in a position to prove the following theorem which expresses the *invariance of the region* under holomorphic mapping.

If $f(z)$ is holomorphic in a region $\mathfrak{R}$ and does not reduce to a constant, the image of $\mathfrak{R}$ as given by the function is also a region.

In fact, if $w_0 = f(z_0)$, z_0 in $\mathfrak{R}$, the function $w_0-f(z)$ is not constant in any neighbourhood of z_0, since $\mathfrak{R}$ is a region (2.11.1).

By virtue of the previous theorem the image of $\mathfrak{R}$ is an open set.

The fact that every continuous arc in $\mathfrak{R}$ is mapped onto a continuous arc in the image of $\mathfrak{R}$ leads to the conclusion that the image is also connected.

This theorem throws light on the fact that a function holomorphic in a region $\mathfrak{R}$ cannot have a constant modulus (2.13.2) or a constant real or imaginary part (2.14.1), unless the function is itself a constant, for in this case the image as given by the function is not a region.

More generally, we can prove *that the maximum modulus theorem of section 2.13.2 is a consequence of the invariance of the region.*

In fact, assume $f(z)$ does not reduce to a constant. If $|f(z)|$ attained a maximum M at a certain point z_0 of $\mathfrak{R}$ we should have $M > 0$, for in the contrary case the function $f(z)$ would vanish identically. Next the function $f(z)$ would not assume in $\mathfrak{R}$ any value of the form $\lambda f(z_0)$ for $\lambda > 1$ which is, however, contrary to the fact that the image of $\mathfrak{R}$ is open.

3.12.3 – The inverse of a holomorphic function

Let $f(z)$ be regular at z_0 having the value w_0. Suppose $f'(z_0) \neq 0$. Without loss of generality we may assume $z_0 = w_0 = 0$. Analyzing the proof of the theorem of section 3.12.1 we conclude that we can find numbers ε and A such that $f(z)$ takes all values w inside $|w| = A$ within $|z| = \varepsilon$ exactly once. In fact, the function $f(z)$ has a simple zero at $z = 0$.

By virtue of this correspondence z may be considered as a function of w in a neighbourhood of the origin, the *inverse function* of $f(z)$ in this neighbourhood. We shall prove:

If $f(z)$ is regular at $z = z_0$ and $f'(z_0) \neq 0$ then the inverse function defined in a neighbourhood of $w_0 = f(z_0)$ is there holomorphic.

Assuming again $z_0 = w_0 = 0$ and observing that the equation $f(z) - w$ possesses one solution inside the circumference C around the origin of radius ε when $|w| < A$ we find on applying (3.8–12) (by taking $g(z) = z$ and writing $f(z) - w$ instead of $f(z)$)

$$z = \frac{1}{2\pi i} \int_C \frac{\zeta f'(\zeta)}{f(\zeta) - w} \, d\zeta. \qquad (3.12\text{–}1)$$

Referring to section 2.9.1 we conclude that actually z is a holomorphic function of w.

It is not difficult to expand z in terms of powers of w, for, when z is on C, we have

$$\left| \frac{w}{f(z)} \right| < \frac{|w|}{A} < 1,$$

Hence

$$\frac{z\,f'(z)}{f(z)-w} = \frac{zf'(z)}{f(z)}\,\frac{1}{1-w/f(z)} = \sum_{\nu=0}^{\infty} \frac{z\,f'(z)}{f^{\nu+1}(z)}\,w^{\nu}.$$

The series on the right is uniformly convergent on the circumference C. It is therefore justified to integrate term by term and so

$$\frac{1}{2\pi i}\int_C \frac{\zeta\,f'(\zeta)}{f(\zeta)-w}\,d\zeta = \sum_{\nu=0}^{\infty}\left(\frac{1}{2\pi i}\int_C \frac{\zeta f'(\zeta)}{f^{\nu+1}(z)}\,d\zeta\right) w^{\nu}.$$

But

$$\frac{1}{2\pi i}\int_C \frac{\zeta\,f'(\zeta)}{f(\zeta)}\,d\zeta = 0, \tag{3.12–2}$$

the integrand being holomorphic inside C.

Hence, by putting

$$b_n = \frac{1}{2\pi i}\int_C \frac{\zeta\,f'(\zeta)}{f^{n+1}(\zeta)}\,d\zeta, \qquad n = 1, 2, \ldots, \tag{3.12–3}$$

we obtain the expansion

$$z = \sum_{\nu=1}^{\infty} b_\nu w^{\nu}, \tag{3.12–4}$$

the series being certainly convergent for $|w| < A$.

We thus proved:

If in a neighbourhood of $z = 0$ the function $f(z)$ can be represented by the power series

$$f(z) = a_1 z + a_2 z^2 + \ldots, \tag{3.12–5}$$

where $a_1 \neq 0$, then in a sufficiently small neighbourhood of the origin we can invert the series (3.12–5) *obtaining a solution*

$$z = b_1 w + b_2 w^2 + \ldots \tag{3.12–6}$$

of the equation $w = f(z)$.

The coefficients $b_1, b_2, \ldots$, are given by (3.12–3), but they can also be determined from the coefficients $a_1, a_2, \ldots$ of (3.12–5) by means of rational operations.

We have indeed

$$z = b_1\left(\sum_{\nu=1}^{\infty} a_\nu z^{\nu}\right) + b_2\left(\sum_{\nu=1}^{\infty} a_\nu z^{\nu}\right)^2 + \ldots$$

and transforming the right-hand side into a power series of z on applying the double-series theorem of Weierstrass (2.20.4) we find the recurrence formulas

$$\begin{aligned} a_1 b_1 &= 1, \\ a_2 b_1 + a_1^2 b_2 &= 0, \\ a_3 b_1 + 2a_1 a_2 b_2 + a_1^3 b_3 &= 0, \\ \ldots\ldots&\ldots\ldots \end{aligned} \tag{3.12–7}$$

3.12.4 – Illustrative example

We wish to illustrate the previous theorem in an example. First we notice that on performing integration by parts we may replace (3.12–3) by

$$b_n = \frac{1}{2\pi i n} \int_C \frac{d\zeta}{f^n(\zeta)}. \tag{3.12–8}$$

Now we consider the equation

$$w = z e^{-z} \tag{3.12–9}$$

in a neighbourhood of the origin. Then, if w is sufficiently small, the series

$$\sum_{\nu=1}^{\infty} b_\nu w^\nu$$

with

$$b_n = \frac{1}{2\pi i n} \int_C \frac{d\zeta}{\zeta^n e^{-n\zeta}}, \tag{3.12–10}$$

where C is a small circle around the origin described in the counter-clockwise sense, is a solution of the equation (3.12–9). We may consider the number nb_n as the residue of the function $z^{-n}e^{nz}$ at the origin, this latter being a pole of order n. Hence by (3.3–4)

$$nb_n = \frac{1}{(n-1)!} \frac{d^{n-1}}{dz^{n-1}} e^{nz} \Big|_{z=0} = \frac{n^n}{n!}$$

whence

$$b_n = \frac{n^{n-1}}{n!}, \tag{3.12–11}$$

and we thus find that

$$z = \sum_{\nu=1}^{\infty} \frac{\nu^{\nu-1}}{\nu!} w^\nu \tag{3.12–12}$$

is a solution of (3.12–9). The radius of convergence is found on applying (1.6–12). The ratio of the coefficients of the $(n+1)$st term and the n-th term is

$$\frac{(n+1)^n}{(n+1)!} \cdot \frac{n!}{n^{n-1}} = \left(1 + \frac{1}{n}\right)^{n-1} \to e$$

as $n \to \infty$. As a consequence the radius of convergence of the series (3.12–12) is e^{-1}.

If $0 < w < e^{-1}$ the sum of the series (3.12–12) increases as w increases and if we make $w \to e^{-1}$ we have, since at the same time $z \to 1$,

$$1 = \sum_{\nu=1}^{\infty} \frac{\nu^{\nu-1}}{\nu!\, e^\nu}. \tag{3.12–13}$$

By a well-known theorem on convergent series $\sum_{\nu=0}^{\infty} c_\nu$ with positive monotonously decreasing terms there holds the relation $nc_n \to 0$ as $n \to \infty$. Hence we deduce from (3.12–13)

$$\lim_{n\to\infty} \frac{n^n}{n!\, e^n} = 0, \tag{3.12–14}$$

a result which we need subsequently in section 4.7.2.

3.12.5 – General inversion theorem

Suppose now that $f(z)$ has a zero of order $k > 1$ at $z = 0$. Then the equation $w = f(z)$ has the form

$$w = a_k z^k\{1+g(z)\},\ a_k \neq 0, \tag{3.12–15}$$

where $g(z)$ is a power series in z vanishing at $z = 0$. For sufficiently small $|z|$ we have $|g(z)| < 1$ and by means of the formula for the binomial series (2.16–20) we obtain

$$w^* = a_k^{1/k} z\{1+\frac{1}{k}\, g(z)+\ldots\},$$

where w^* is a number such that $w^{*k} = w$. On applying Weierstrass's double series theorem (2.20.4) we may also write

$$w^* = a_1^* z + a_2^* z^2 + \ldots, \qquad a_1^* \neq 0. \tag{3.12–16}$$

We can invert this series in a sufficiently small neighbourhood of $w^* = 0$. When w^* ranges over the interior of a circle around the origin then w covers the interior of a second circle in such a fashion that to every point $w \neq 0$ inside this latter circle there correspond just k points inside the former one, viz.

$$w^*,\ \omega w^*,\ \ldots,\ \omega^{k-1} w^*,$$

with

$$\omega = \exp 2\pi i/k.$$

Hence:

Around the origin in the z-plane and the w-plane we can describe two circles such that to any point $w \neq 0$ inside the second circle there correspond precisely k different points z inside the first circle for which the equation (3.12–15) *holds.*

To the point $w = 0$ corresponds only the point $z = 0$.

3.13 – Generalization of Taylor's and Laurent's series

3.13.1 – Bürmann's series

The Taylor expansion (2.16–6) is a particular case of an expansion of a holomorphic function if we replace $z-a$ by a more general function $h(z)$.

Let C denote a regular contour. We need only the property that the winding number of C with respect to every interior point is $+1$, when C is described in the counter-clockwise sense, and 0 with respect to every point outside (see also the remark made in section 2.7.2).

We assume that $g(z)$ and $h(z)$ are holomorphic throughout an open set $\mathfrak{A}$ containing C as well as its interior, that $h(z)$ has a simple zero $z = a$ inside C but vanishes neither elsewhere inside C nor on C. Finally we observe that we can find at least one point z such that

$$|h(z)| < r, \tag{3.13–1}$$

where r is the minimum of $|h(z)|$ along C, this minimum being evidently positive. This remark does not contradict the minimum principle of section 2.13.3, for $h(z)$ vanishes in the interior of C. Now we consider the integral

$$\frac{1}{2\pi i}\int_C \frac{g(\zeta)h'(\zeta)}{h(\zeta)-h(z)}\,d\zeta, \tag{3.13–2}$$

where z is a point inside C satisfying (3.13–1). It is plain, by virtue of Rouché's theorem applied on the functions $h(\zeta)$ and $h(\zeta)-h(z)$ considered as functions of the variable ζ, that this latter function has a simple zero $\zeta = z$ and therefore (3.13–2) represents the residue $g(z)$ of the integrand (3.3.3).

If now ζ denotes any point on C and z a point satisfying (3.13–1) we may write

$$\frac{g(\zeta)h'(\zeta)}{h(\zeta)-h(z)} = \frac{g(\zeta)h'(\zeta)}{h(\zeta)}\,\frac{1}{1-h(z)/h(\zeta)} = \frac{g(\zeta)h'(\zeta)}{h(\zeta)}\sum_{\nu=0}^{\infty}\left\{\frac{h(z)}{h(\zeta)}\right\}^{\nu}. \tag{3.13–3}$$

Let M denote the maximum modulus of $g(z)h'(z)$ on C. The series (3.13–3) is evidently dominated by the convergent geometric series

$$\frac{M}{r}\sum_{\nu=0}^{\infty} q^{\nu}$$

with $q = \max|h(z)/h(\zeta)| < 1$ on C and is therefore uniformly convergent along C. By virtue of the theorem of section 2.4.4 term-by-term integration is justified and so we find *Bürmann's series*

$$\boxed{g(z) = \sum_{\nu=0}^{\infty} c_{\nu} h^{\nu}(z)} \tag{3.13–4}$$

with

$$c_n = \frac{1}{2\pi i}\int_C \frac{g(\zeta)h'(\zeta)}{h^{n+1}(\zeta)}\,d\zeta, \qquad n = 0, 1, 2, \ldots. \tag{3.13–5}$$

The expansion is valid for any z that satisfies (3.13–1).

Next we wish to write the coefficients c_n in another form. Putting $z = a$ in (3.13—4) we find at once

$$c_0 = g(a), \tag{3.13–6}$$

since $h(a) = 0$. When $n > 0$ we apply integration by parts (2.3.6). We find

$$c_n = \frac{-1}{2\pi i}\int_C \frac{g(\zeta)}{n}\left\{\frac{1}{h^n(\zeta)}\right\}' d\zeta = \frac{1}{2\pi i n}\int_C \frac{g'(\zeta)}{h^n(\zeta)}\,d\zeta, \tag{3.13–7}$$

an expression which is frequently useful in the applications.

3.13.2 – Teixeira's series

It is natural to ask whether it is possible to generalize also Laurent's series (2.23–7). This is easily done in the following way. We assume that $h(z)$ is holomorphic in an open set containing a regular contour C_1 as well as its interior. Further it is supposed that $h(z)$ has a simple zero $z = a$ inside C_1 and vanishes neither elsewhere inside C_1 nor on C_1. Let C_2 denote a second regular contour inside C_1 and let $g(z)$ be holomorphic in an open set $\mathfrak{A}$, containing the closure of the ring-shaped region bounded by C_1 and C_2. Finally we assume that for every point z between C_1 and C_2

$$r_2 < |h(z)| < r_1, \tag{3.13–8}$$

where r_1 is the minimum of $|h(z)|$ along C_1 and r_2 the maximum of $|h(z)|$ along C_2. As already observed in the previous section the function $h(\zeta)-h(z)$ has the simple zero $\zeta = z$ inside C_1.

Describing C_1 and C_2 in the counter-clockwise sense we therefore have $C_1 \sim C_2$ in $\mathfrak{A}$ and so

$$g(z) = \frac{1}{2\pi i}\int_{C_1} \frac{g(\zeta)h'(\zeta)}{h(\zeta)-h(z)}\,d\zeta - \frac{1}{2\pi i}\int_{C_2} \frac{g(\zeta)h'(\zeta)}{h(\zeta)-h(z)}\,d\zeta. \tag{3.13–9}$$

The first integral can be expanded as in section 3.13.1. Operating in a similar manner on the second integral we find

$$-\frac{g(\zeta)h'(\zeta)}{h(\zeta)-h(z)} = \frac{g(\zeta)h'(\zeta)}{h(z)}\,\frac{1}{1-h(\zeta)/h(z)} = \frac{g(\zeta)h'(\zeta)}{h(z)}\sum_{\nu=0}^{\infty}\left\{\frac{h(\zeta)}{h(z)}\right\}^{\nu},$$

and it follows by the usual arguments that the series on the right is uniformly convergent along C_2.

On integrating we obtain *Teixeira's series*

$$g(z) = \sum_{\nu=-\infty}^{\infty} c_\nu h^\nu(z) \tag{3.13–10}$$

with

$$c_n = \frac{1}{2\pi i} \int_{C_1} \frac{g(\zeta)h'(\zeta)}{h^{n+1}(\zeta)}\, d\zeta, \qquad n = 0, 1, 2, \ldots, \tag{3.13–11}$$

and

$$c_{-n} = \frac{1}{2\pi i} \int_{C_2} g(\zeta)h'(\zeta)h^{n-1}(\zeta)\, d\zeta, \quad n = 1, 2, \ldots. \tag{3.13–12}$$

3.13.3 – Lagrange's series

From the expansion considered in section 3.13.1 we wish to derive a remarkable expansion due to Lagrange. Consider the function

$$h(z) = \frac{z-a}{\varphi(z)}, \tag{3.13–13}$$

where $\varphi(z)$ is holomorphic in an open set containing a regular contour C and its interior. It is assumed that $\varphi(z)$ does not vanish inside or on C. The point $z = a$ is inside C. We assume further that we can find a number w such that

$$|w| < |h(z)| \tag{3.13–14}$$

for all points z on C. By virtue of Rouché's theorem the functions $h(z)$ and $h(z)-w$ have the same number of zeros inside C. As a consequence we find that the equation

$$z = a+w\varphi(z) \tag{3.13–15}$$

has a simple root inside C. Taking account of (3.13–4), (3.13–6) and (3.13–7) we find that

$$g(z) = g(a)+ \sum_{\nu=1}^{\infty} c_\nu w^\nu, \tag{3.13–16}$$

where

$$c_n = \frac{1}{2\pi i n} \int_C \frac{g'(\zeta)\varphi^n(\zeta)}{(\zeta-a)^n}\, d\zeta. \tag{3.13–17}$$

In view of (2.9–9) we may also write

$$c_n = \frac{1}{n!} \{g'(a)\varphi^n(a)\}^{(n-1)}. \tag{3.13–18}$$

Thus we have proved the following important theorem:

Let $\varphi(z)$ denote a function which is holomorphic in an open set $\mathfrak{A}$ containing a regular contour C and its interior and with no zeros inside or on C. Let $z = a$ be a point inside C and w a number such that

$$|w\varphi(z)| < |z-a| \tag{3.13–19}$$

for all z on C. Under these assumptions the equation (3.13–15) possesses a simple root z inside C. If now g(z) is a function which is holomorphic in an open set containing C and its interior, we have Lagrange's expansion

$$\boxed{g(z) = g(a) + \sum_{\nu=1}^{\infty} \frac{\{g'(a)\varphi^{\nu}(a)\}^{(\nu-1)}}{\nu!} w^{\nu},} \tag{3.13–20}$$

where z denotes the root of (3.13–15). In particular

$$z = a + \sum_{\nu=1}^{\infty} \frac{\{\varphi^{\nu}(a)\}^{(\nu-1)}}{\nu!} w^{\nu}. \tag{3.13–21}$$

3.13.4 – Modification of Lagrange's series

A remarkable case occurs when we take

$$\varphi(z) = \frac{z}{f(z)},$$

where $f(z)$ is regular at $z = 0$, $f(0) = 0$ and $f'(0) \neq 0$. If C is a sufficiently small circle around the origin, then the function $\varphi(z)$ is free from zeros inside or on C. Since $f(z)$ is not constant we conclude from the maximum modulus principle that $|f(z)|$ for z inside C is smaller than on the circumference. It is therefore possible to find a number w such that

$$|w| < |f(z)| = \left|\frac{z}{\varphi(z)}\right|$$

for all z on C. Thus we find that the equation

$$w = f(z)$$

has a simple root inside C, being expansible as a power series in w. It is easy to verify that the coefficients computed by (3.13–7) are the same as (3.12–3). First we observe that $c_0 = 0$. When $n > 0$ we have in accordance with (3.12–8)

$$c_n = \frac{1}{2\pi i n} \int_C \frac{\zeta^n}{\zeta^n} \frac{d\zeta}{f^n(\zeta)} = \frac{1}{2\pi i n} \int_C \frac{d\zeta}{f^n(\zeta)},$$

whence, by integrating by parts,

$$c_n = \frac{1}{2\pi i} \int_C \frac{\zeta f'(\zeta)}{f^{n+1}(\zeta)} d\zeta.$$

An alternative expression for the coefficients occurring in (3.12–4) is therefore

$$b_n = \frac{1}{n!} \left\{ \left(\frac{a}{f(a)} \right)^n \right\}^{(n-1)}, \qquad a = 0. \tag{3.13–22}$$

Thus, for instance, when we take $f(z) = ze^{-z}$ we find at once

$$b_n = \frac{1}{n!}\,(e^{na})^{(n-1)}\big|_{a=0} = \frac{n^{n-1}}{n!},$$

in accordance with (3.12–11).

3.13.5 – Kepler's equation

A famous example is the application of Lagrange's expansion to the solution of Kepler's equation

$$u - \varepsilon \sin u = t \tag{3.13–23}$$

which occurs in the theory of the elliptic orbit of a planet. In this equation u denotes the so-called *excentric anomaly*, (fig. 3.13–1), t

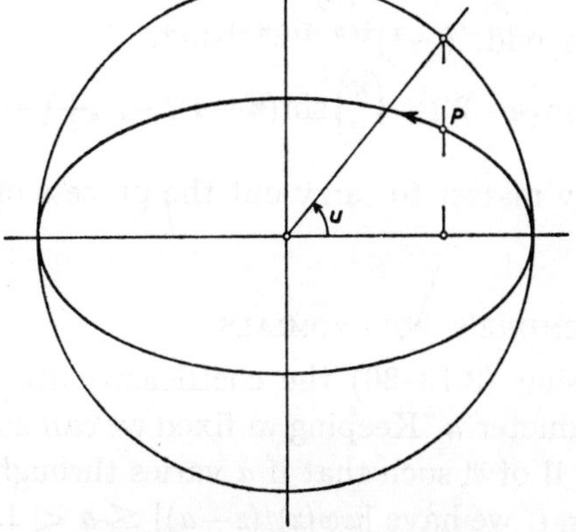

Fig. 3.13–1. Excentric anomaly

the *mean anomaly* (proportional to the time elapsed since the perihelion passage) and ε the *excentricity* of the orbit.

In the formula (3.13–15) we replace a by t, w by ε and z by u. If z is on a circumference of centre t and radius r, then the inequality (3.13–19)

$$|\varepsilon \sin u| < |u-t| = r$$

can be satisfied by sufficiently small ε and to such a value of ε corresponds a single value of u inside C which is a root of Kepler's equation. Applying Lagrange's expansion (3.13–21) we find that

$$u = t + \sum_{\nu=1}^{\infty} \frac{(\sin^{\nu} t)^{(\nu-1)}}{\nu!}\,\varepsilon^{\nu}, \tag{3.13–24}$$

the root tending to t as $\varepsilon \to 0$.

In practice it is not so easy to evaluate $(\sin^n t)^{(n-1)}$ directly, but the following trick facilitates this process considerably. Put

$$s = \cos t + i \sin t.$$

Then

$$s^{-1} = \cos t - i \sin t.$$

If k is an integer, we also have

$$s^k = \cos kt + i \sin kt, \qquad s^{-k} = \cos kt - i \sin kt,$$

and so

$$s^k + s^{-k} = 2 \cos kt, \qquad s^k - s^{-k} = 2i \sin kt, \qquad k = 0, 1, 2, \ldots. \tag{3.13–25}$$

On applying the binomial formula to $s - s^{-1}$ we easily find, taking account of (3.13–25),

(i) when n is even: $(-1)^{\frac{1}{2}n} 2^{n-1} \sin^n t$

$$= \cos nt - \binom{n}{1} \cos(n-2)t + \binom{n}{2} \cos(n-4)t - \ldots + (-1)^{\frac{1}{2}n} \binom{n}{\frac{1}{2}n};$$

(ii) when n is odd: $(-1)^{\frac{1}{2}(n-1)} 2^{n-1} \sin^n t$

$$= \sin nt - \binom{n}{1} \sin(n-2)t + \binom{n}{2} \sin(n-4)t - \ldots + (-1)^{\frac{1}{2}(n-1)} \binom{n}{\frac{1}{2}(n-1)} \sin t.$$

It is now an easy matter to carry out the process of differentiation in (3.13–24).

3.13.6 – Legendre's polynomials

In the expansion (3.13–20) the coefficients are holomorphic as regards the parameter a. Keeping w fixed we can assign a bounded and open subset $\mathfrak{U}$ of $\mathfrak{A}$ such that if a varies throughout the closure of $\mathfrak{U}$ and if z is on C we have $|w\varphi(z)/(z-a)| \leq q < 1$. It follows that the series is uniformly convergent as regards a on this closure and by virtue of the theorem of section 2.20.3 we may differentiate the series term-by-term. In particular we find that the root of (3.13–4) inside C is holomorphic as regards a, when a varies in $\mathfrak{U}$. Replacing $g'(z)$ by $F(z)$ we obtain on performing the process of differentiation

$$F(z) \frac{dz}{da} = F(a) + \sum_{\nu=1}^{\infty} \frac{d^\nu F(a) \varphi^\nu(a)/da^\nu}{\nu!} w^\nu, \tag{3.13–26}$$

a formula which is frequently useful.

We illustrate it with the following example. Let $g(z) = z$ and $\varphi(a) = \frac{1}{2}(a^2 - 1)$. Hence $F(z) = 1$ and (3.13–25) yields

$$\frac{dz}{da} = 1 + \sum_{\nu=1}^{\infty} \frac{d^\nu (a^2-1)^\nu/da^\nu}{2^\nu \nu!} w^\nu.$$

The coefficients of w^n in this expansion is evidently a polynomial $P_n(z)$ of degree n. It is called *Legendre's polynomial* of degree n. Replacing a by z we have *Rodrigues's formula*

$$\boxed{P_n(z) = \frac{1}{2^n n!} \frac{d^n}{dz^n} (z^2-1)^n.} \qquad (3.13\text{–}27)$$

From

$$w(z^2-1) = 2(z-a) \qquad (3.13\text{–}28)$$

we deduce, if we consider z as a function of a,

$$z \frac{dz}{da} w = \frac{dz}{da} - 1$$

or

$$\frac{dz}{da} = \frac{1}{1-wz}.$$

On the other hand we may write (3.13–28) as

$$(wz)^2 - w^2 = 2wz - 2aw$$

or

$$(1-wz)^2 = 1 - 2aw + w^2$$

whence

$$\frac{dz}{da} = (1-2aw+w^2)^{-\frac{1}{2}}.$$

Hence we may state that $P_n(z)$ is the coefficient of w^n in the powerseries expansion of $(1-2zw+w^2)^{-\frac{1}{2}}$ i.e.,

$$\boxed{(1+2zw+w^2)^{-\frac{1}{2}} = \sum_{\nu=0}^{\infty} P_\nu(z) w^\nu.} \qquad (3.13\text{–}29)$$

3.14 – Legendre's polynomials

3.14.1 – The differential equation of Legendre's polynomials

From Rodrigues's formula (3.13–27) it is at once evident that

$$\boxed{P_n(-z) = (-1)^n P_n(z).} \qquad (3.14\text{–}1)$$

Observing that

$$\frac{d^n}{dz^n} (z^2-1)^n = 2^n n! z^n + \text{ terms involving } (z^2-1)$$

we deduce that

$$\boxed{P_n(1) = 1.} \qquad (3.14\text{–}2)$$

Let us put

$$u = (z^2-1)^n.$$

Then

$$(z^2-1)u' = 2nzu.$$

Differentiating both members of this equation $n+1$ times we get

$$(z^2-1)u^{(n+2)}+\binom{n+1}{1}2zu^{(n+1)}+2\binom{n+1}{2}u^{(n)}=2nzu^{(n+1)}+\binom{n+1}{1}2nu^{(n)}$$

or

$$(z^2-1)u^{(n+2)}+2zu^{(n+1)}-n(n+1)u^{(n)} = 0.$$

It appears that $P_n(z)$ satisfies the differential equation

$$\boxed{(z^2-1)P_n''+2zP_n'-n(n+1)P_n=0.} \qquad (3.14\text{–}3)$$

It is easily shown that $P_n(z)$ *has no multiple zeros,* for when at a certain point z we should have $P_n(z) = P_n'(z) = 0$ then also $P''(z) = 0$, since $z \neq \pm 1$ and on differentiating (3.14–3) we successively find that the derivatives of all orders should vanish at z. This cannot be true, for the n-th derivative of $P_n(z)$ is a constant different from zero.

Next we shall show that $P_n(z)$ *has n real zeros between -1 and $+1$.* In fact, the function $u = (z^2-1)^n$ has $2n$ real zeros, n of them being $+1$, the others -1. By Rolle's theorem the derivative u' has at least one zero between -1 and $+1$. Since u' has $n-1$ zeros $+1$ and $n-1$ zeros -1 it has exactly one zero between -1 and $+1$. Proceeding in this way we find that u'' has exactly two zeros between -1 and $+1$, etc.

3.14.2 – Relations of orthogonality

We shall now derive some remarkable properties of integrals involving Legendre's polynomials.

Let m denote one of the integers $0, 1, \ldots, n$. On performing integration by parts we find

$$\int_{-1}^{1} x^m u^{(n)}(x)\,dx=-m\int_{-1}^{1} x^{m-1}u^{(n-1)}(x)\,dx=\ldots=(-1)^m m!\int_{-1}^{1} u^{(n-m)}(x)\,dx,$$

since the derivatives of u of order less than n vanish at $+1$ and -1. If $m < n$ we therefore have

$$\int_{-1}^{1} x^m u^{(n)}(x)\,dx = 0, \qquad (3.14\text{–}4)$$

whence the *relation of orthogonality*

$$\boxed{\int_{-1}^{1} P_m(x)P_n(x)dx = 0,} \qquad m < n. \qquad (3.14\text{–}5)$$

In the case $m = n$ we find

$$\int_{-1}^{1} x^n u^{(n)}(x)dx = (-1)^n n! \int_{-1}^{1} (x^2-1)^n dx = (-1)^n n! \int_{-1}^{1} (x-1)^n (x+1)^n dx$$

$$= (-1)^{n-1} n! \frac{n}{n+1} \int_{-1}^{1} (x-1)^{n-1}(x+1)^{n+1} dx = \frac{(n!)^2}{(n+1)\dots 2n} \int_{-1}^{1} (x+1)^{2n} dx,$$

whence

$$\int_{-1}^{1} x^n u^{(n)}(x)dx = \frac{2^{2n+1}(n!)^3}{(2n+1)(2n)!}. \qquad (3.14\text{–}6)$$

It is easy to see that the coefficient of x^n in $u^{(n)}(x)$ is $2n(2n-1)\dots(n+1) = (2n)!/n!$. Hence, taking account of (3.14–4),

$$\boxed{\int_{-1}^{1} P_n{}^2(x)dx = \frac{2}{2n+1}.} \qquad (3.14\text{–}7)$$

3.14.3 – Recurrent relations

We wish to draw some interesting conclusions from the obtained results.

First we observe that a relation of the type

$$z^n = c_0 P_0(z) + \dots + c_n P_n(z) \qquad (3.14\text{–}8)$$

holds, where $c_0, \dots, c_n$ are certain constants.

The statement is obvious for $n = 0$ or $n = 1$, for $1 = P_0(z)$ and $z = P_1(z)$. Assuming the truth of the statement for $1, \dots, z^{n-1}$, we find the truth for z^n from

$$P_n(z) = cz^n + \text{polynomial of degree} \leqq n-1.$$

As a consequence every polynomial $f(z)$ of degree n can be considered as a linear combination (with constant coefficients) of Legendre's polynomials.

We wish to apply this result to some particular polynomials. First we consider

$$zP_n(z) = \sum_{\nu=0}^{n+1} c_\nu P_\nu(z). \qquad (3.14\text{–}9)$$

Multiplying both members by $P_m(z)$, $m \leqq n+1$, and integrating between -1 and $+1$, we deduce from (3.14–5) and (3.14–7)

$$\int_{-1}^{1} xP_n(x)P_m(x)\, dx = \frac{2c_m}{2m+1}. \qquad (3.14\text{–}10)$$

In view of (3.14–4) the integral on the left can only be different from zero if $n+1 = m$ or $m+1 = n$. Hence in the expansion (3.14–9) only the coefficients c_{n+1} and c_{n-1} survive, i.e.,

$$zP_n(z) = c_{n-1}P_{n-1}(z)+c_{n+1}P_{n+1}(z),$$

whence, by putting $z = 1$, taking account of (3.14–1),

$$1 = c_{n-1}+c_{n+1}.$$

Equating the coefficients of z^{n+1} we find $c_{n+1} = (n+1)/(2n+1)$, whence $c_{n-1} = n/(2n+1)$.

From this result arises a relation connecting three Legendre polynomials of consecutive degrees

$$\boxed{(n+1)P_{n+1}(z)-(2n+1)zP_n(z)+nP_{n-1}(z) = 0.} \tag{3.14–11}$$

As a second example we consider

$$P'_{n+1}(z)-P'_{n-1}(z) = \sum_{\nu=0}^{n} c_\nu P_\nu(z). \tag{3.14–12}$$

Proceeding as before we find, when $m \leqq n$,

$$\begin{aligned}\frac{2c_m}{2m+1} &= \int_{-1}^{1} \{P'_{n+1}(x)P_m(x)-P'_{n-1}(x)P_m(x)\}\,dx\\ &= \{P_{n+1}(x)P_m(x)-P_{n-1}(x)P_m(x)\}\,\Big|_{-1}^{+1} +\\ &\qquad -\int_{-1}^{+1} \{P_{n+1}(x)P'_m(x)-P_{n-1}(x)P'_m(x)\}\,dx.\end{aligned}$$

By virtue of (3.14–1) and (3.14–2) the first term in the last expression vanishes. The last integral vanishes also when $m < n$, i.e., we have

$$P'_{n+1}(z)-P'_{n-1}(z) = c_n P_n(z).$$

Equating coefficients of z^n we find $c_n = 2n+1$ and so

$$\boxed{P'_{n+1}(z)-P'_{n-1}(z) = (2n+1)P_n(z).} \tag{3.14–13}$$

Differentiating (3.14–11) and eliminating $P'_{n+1}(z)$ between the result thus obtained and (3.14–13) we easily find

$$\boxed{zP'_n(z)-P'_{n-1}(z) = nP_n(z).} \tag{3.14–14}$$

Subtracting corresponding members of (3.14–13) and (3.14–14) we get

$$\boxed{P'_{n+1}(z)-zP'_n(z) = (n+1)P_n(z).} \tag{3.14–15}$$

Finally, writing $n-1$ for n in (3.14–15) and eliminating $P'_{n-1}(z)$ between the equation so obtained and (3.14–14) we find

$$\boxed{(z^2-1)P'_n(z) = nzP_n(z)-nP_{n-1}(z).} \tag{3.14–16}$$

3.14.4 – Schläfli's and Laplace's integral

By virtue of Cauchy's expression (2.9–9) for the n-th derivative we derive immediately from Rodrigues's formula

$$P_n(z) = \frac{1}{2\pi i} \int_C \frac{(\zeta^2-1)^n}{2^n(\zeta-z)^{n+1}} d\zeta, \tag{3.14–17}$$

where C is a circle around the point z traversed in the counter-clockwise sense. This integral is due to Schläfli.

Now we take for C a circle of radius $|\sqrt{z^2-1}|$ assuming, of course, that $z^2 \neq 1$. Then for ζ on C we may put

$$\zeta = z + \sqrt{z^2-1}e^{i\varphi}$$

where φ increases from $-\pi$ to π. Making the substitution we have

$$P_n(z) = \frac{1}{2^{n+1}\pi i} \int_{-\pi}^{\pi} \left(\frac{(z-1+\sqrt{z^2-1}e^{i\varphi})(z+1+\sqrt{z^2-1}e^{i\varphi})}{\sqrt{z^2-1}e^{i\varphi}} \right)^n id\varphi$$

$$= \frac{1}{2\pi} \int_{-\pi}^{\pi} (z+\sqrt{z^2-1}\cos\varphi)^n d\varphi.$$

Since the integrand is an even function of φ we may write

$$P_n(z) = \frac{1}{\pi} \int_0^{\pi} (z+\sqrt{z^2-1}\cos\varphi)^n d\varphi. \tag{3.14–18}$$

This expression is due to Laplace. It remains valid when $z = \pm 1$.

We conclude this section by evaluating a remarkable limit involving the Legendre polynomial for n tending to infinity.

Let $z = \cos(u/n)$. The integrand in (3.14–18) becomes

$$\left(\cos\frac{u}{n} + i \sin\frac{u}{n} \cos\varphi \right)^n$$

and its logarithm is

$$n \log \left(\cos\frac{u}{n} + i \sin\frac{u}{n} \cos\varphi \right) = n \log \left(1 + \frac{iu}{n} \cos\varphi + o\,(n^{-1}) \right)$$

where $o(n^{-1})$ is such that $n\,o(n^{-1}) \to 0$ as $n \to \infty$. Now

$$n \log \left(1 + \frac{iu}{n} \cos\varphi + o(n^{-1}) \right)$$

$$= \frac{\log \{1 + iu(\cos\varphi)/n + o(n^{-1})\}}{iu\,(\cos\varphi)/n + o(n^{-1})} \{iu\cos\varphi + no\,(n^{-1})\}$$

tending to $iu \cos\varphi$ as $n \to \infty$. We thus find

$$\lim_{n\to\infty} P_n\left(\cos\frac{u}{n}\right) = \frac{1}{\pi}\int_0^\pi \exp\,(iu\cos\varphi)\,d\varphi$$

$$= \frac{1}{\pi}\int_0^\pi \{\cos(u\cos\varphi) + i\sin(u\cos\varphi)\}\,d\varphi = \frac{1}{\pi}\int_0^\pi \cos(u\cos\varphi)\,d\varphi,$$

thus

$$\lim_{n\to\infty} P_n\left(\cos\frac{u}{n}\right) = J_0(u), \qquad (3.14\text{–}19)$$

where $J_0(u)$ is Bessel's function of order 0 represented by

$$J_0(u) = \frac{1}{\pi}\int_0^\pi \cos(u\cos\varphi)d\varphi. \qquad (3.14\text{–}20)$$

CHAPTER 4

WEIERSTRASS'S FACTORIZATION OF INTEGRAL FUNCTIONS - CAUCHY'S EXPANSION OF PARTIAL FRACTIONS - MITTAG-LEFFLER'S PROBLEM

4.1 – Infinite products

4.1.1 – CONVERGENCE

Given a sequence

$$c_0, c_1, c_2, \ldots, \tag{4.1–1}$$

of complex numbers, we may construct another sequence

$$p_n = \prod_{\nu=0}^{n} (1+c_\nu) = (1+c_0)\ldots(1+c_n), \quad n = 0, 1, 2, \ldots. \tag{4.1–2}$$

This sequence is called an *infinite product* and is represented symbolically by

$$\prod_{\nu=0}^{\infty} (1+c_\nu). \tag{4.1–3}$$

If p_n tends to a finite *non-zero* limit p as $n \to \infty$ we say that the infinite product is *convergent.* If, however, p_n tends to zero without any factor $1+c_n$ being equal to zero or does not tend to any finite limit, the product is called *divergent.* If there is a finite number of factors equal to zero the product is said to be convergent, when the product obtained by removing these factors turns out to be convergent. We then attribute the value zero to the product and, consequently, *a convergent infinite product is zero if at least one of its factors is equal to zero.*

Accordingly, in most cases there is no loss of generality if we assume that all factors are different from zero.
Since

$$p_n = p_{n-1}+c_n p_{n-1}, \tag{4.1–4}$$

an infinite product (4.1–3) converges only if $c_n \to 0$ as $n \to \infty$.

A useful theorem is the following:

A necessary and sufficient condition for the convergence of the infinite product (4.1–3) *is the convergence of the series*

$$\sum_{\nu=0}^{\infty} \log (1+c_\nu). \tag{4.1–5}$$

We assume that none of the factors of (4.1–3) vanish.

Let

$$s_n = \sum_{\nu=0}^{n} \log (1+c_\nu). \tag{4.1–6}$$

Then

$$e^{s_n} = \prod_{\nu=0}^{n} (1+c_\nu) \tag{4.1–7}$$

and since the exponential function is continuous, $s_n \to s$ implies $p_n \to e^s$ as $n \to \infty$. Hence the condition is sufficient.

If, conversely, the product is convergent then, ε being an arbitrary positive number < 1, we can find a number n_0 such that

$$|(1+c_{n+1})\ldots(1+c_{n+m})-1| < \tfrac{1}{2}\varepsilon,$$

provided $n \geqq n_0$, $m \geqq 1$. If $|z| < \frac{1}{2}\varepsilon < \frac{1}{2}$ we also have

$$|\log (1+z)| < \varepsilon, \tag{4.1–8}$$

for, if $|z| < \frac{1}{2}$ we deduce from the logarithmic series the estimate

$$|\log (1+z)| \leqq |z|+\tfrac{1}{2}|z|^2+\ldots \leqq |z|+|z|^2+\ldots = \frac{|z|}{1-|z|} \leqq 2|z|.$$

We thus may infer that

$$|\log (1+c_{n+1})\ldots(1+c_{n+m})| < \varepsilon \tag{4.1–9}$$

whenever $n \geqq n_0$, $m \geqq 1$.

Now we draw attention to the fact that in the complex case the logarithm of a product is not necessarily the sum of the logarithms of the factors, but may differ from it by a multiple of $2\pi i$. As a consequence there exists an integer q such that

$$|\log (1+c_{n+1})+\ldots+\log (1+c_{n+m})+2q\pi i\,| < \varepsilon, \tag{4.1–10}$$

and we desire to prove that $q = 0$. Take a fixed $n \geqq n_0$. Obviously the statement is true for $m = 1$. It follows that it is true for $m = 2$, for in

$$\log (1+c_{n+1})+\log (1+c_{n+2})+2q\pi i$$

each of the first terms has a modulus $< \varepsilon$ and since the entire sum has a modulus $<\varepsilon$ we infer that $q=0$. On applying this argument repeatedly we conclude that always $q = 0$ and the necessity of the condition follows at once.

4.1.2 – Absolute convergence

The infinite product (4.1–3) is said to be *absolutely convergent* if the series (4.1–5) is absolutely convergent. An absolutely convergent product is convergent.

An absolutely convergent infinite product is unconditionally convergent. The meaning of this statement is that the value of an absolutely convergent infinite product is not affected by changing the order in which the factors occur.

According to the previous definition the statement is equivalent to an analogous one for absolutely convergent series. For the sake of completeness we add the proof.

Suppose that the series $\sum_{\nu=0}^{\infty} a_\nu$ is absolutely convergent. Given a positive number ε we can find a natural number n such that for all $m > n$

$$|a_{n+1}+\ldots+a_m| \leqq |a_{n+1}|+\ldots+|a_m| < \varepsilon$$

or

$$|A_m - A_n| < \varepsilon,$$

where A_n denotes the sum of the first n terms of the series. Letting $m \to \infty$ we see that

$$|A - A_n| \leqq \varepsilon,$$

where A is the sum of the series.

Now we consider a second series $\sum_{\nu=0}^{\infty} a'_\nu$ formed by the same terms as the former one but in a different order. If m is sufficiently large then $a_0, \ldots, a_n$ are among the terms of the new series having a subscript $< m$. By the same argument as above we may infer that

$$|A'_m - A_n| < \varepsilon,$$

provided m is sufficiently large. And so

$$|A - A'_m| \leqq |A - A_n| + |A_n - A'_m| < 2\varepsilon,$$

in other words, the series $\sum_{\nu=0}^{\infty} a'_\nu$ converges to the same sum A. Since the theorem is certainly true for series with positive terms the rearranged series is also absolutely convergent.

The infinite product (4.1–3) *is absolutely convergent if and only if the series*

$$\sum_{\nu=0}^{\infty} c_\nu \tag{4.1–11}$$

is absolutely convergent.

A necessary condition for the product (4.1–3) or the series (4.1–5) to be convergent is $c_n \to 0$. Hence from a certain index upwards we have $|c_n| < \frac{1}{2}$ and then, omitting the terms $c_n = 0$,

$$\left|1-\frac{\log(1+c_n)}{c_n}\right| = |\tfrac{1}{2}c_n - \tfrac{1}{3}c_n^2 + \ldots| \leqq \tfrac{1}{2}(|c_n|+|c_n|^2+\ldots)$$
$$= \tfrac{1}{2}\frac{|c_n|}{1-|c_n|} \leqq \tfrac{1}{2},$$

and so

$$\tfrac{1}{2}|c_n| \leqq |\log(1+c_n)| \leqq \tfrac{3}{2}|c_n|, \qquad (4.1\text{–}12)$$

these inequalities also being valid for $c_n = 0$. This shows that the series $\sum_{\nu=0}^{\infty} \log(1+c_\nu)$ converges absolutely if and only if $\sum_{\nu=0}^{\infty} |c_\nu|$ is convergent. Since (4.1–12) remains true when we replace c_n by $|c_n|$ we find that the product (4.1–3) is absolutely convergent if the product

$$\prod_{\nu=0}^{\infty}(1+|c_\nu|) \qquad (4.1\text{–}13)$$

is convergent.

A product may be convergent without the series $\sum_{\nu=0}^{\infty} c_\nu$ being convergent. A simple example is the following. Let $c_{2n-1} = n^{-\frac{1}{2}}$ and $c_{2n} = -n^{-\frac{1}{2}}+n^{-1}$. The series $\sum_{\nu=1}^{\infty} c_\nu$, being the harmonic series, is divergent. The product $\prod_{\nu=1}^{\infty}(1+c_\nu)$ is equal to the product $\prod_{\nu=1}^{\infty}(1+\nu^{-3/2})$, this latter being convergent, since the series $\sum \nu^{-3/2}$ is convergent.

4.1.3 – Uniform convergence

Consider a sequence of functions

$$f_0(z), f_1(z), f_2(z), \ldots, \qquad (4.1\text{–}14)$$

each function being defined in a set $\mathfrak{S}$. Assume that the infinite product

$$\prod_{\nu=0}^{\infty}\{1+f_\nu(z)\} \qquad (4.1\text{–}15)$$

converges at each point of $\mathfrak{S}$. If the sequence

$$F_n(z) = \prod_{\nu=0}^{n}\{1+f_\nu(z)\} \qquad (4.1\text{–}16)$$

converges uniformly in $\mathfrak{S}$, we say that the infinite product (4.1–15) is *uniformly convergent* in $\mathfrak{S}$.

A useful theorem concerning these matters is the following:

Assume that the functions (4.1–14) *are all holomorphic in an open set* $\mathfrak{A}$ *and that the series*

$$\sum_{\nu=0}^{\infty} |f_\nu(z)| \tag{4.1–17}$$

is uniformly convergent in every closed and bounded subset of $\mathfrak{A}$. *Then the product* (4.1–15) *converges absolutely to a function* $F(z)$ *which is holomorphic throughout* $\mathfrak{A}$, *the convergence being uniform in every closed and bounded subset of* $\mathfrak{A}$.

In fact, since the series (4.1–17) converges at every point of $\mathfrak{A}$ the product (4.1–15) is also absolutely convergent by virtue of the last theorem of section 4.1.2 and hence the product represents a well-defined function.

If $\mathfrak{C}$ is a closed and bounded subset of $\mathfrak{A}$, by hypothesis we can find an index n such that

$$|f_{n+1}(z)|+\ldots+|f_{n+m}(z)| < 1 \tag{4.1–18}$$

at each point of $\mathfrak{C}$. Let us write

$$p_{n+m}(z) = \{1+f_0(z)\}\ldots\{1+f_n(z)\}q_m(z), \quad m \geqq 1. \tag{4.1–19}$$

Taking account of (4.1–19) we then have

$$\begin{aligned} |q_m(z)| &\leqq \{1+|f_{n+1}(z)|\}\ldots\{1+|f_{n+m}(z)|\} \\ &\leqq \exp\{|f_{n+1}(z)|+\ldots+|f_{n+m}(z)|\} < \mathrm{e}. \end{aligned} \tag{4.1–20}$$

Hence the sequence $q_1(z), q_2(z), \ldots$ tends uniformly to a limiting function and the same is true for the partial products $p_0(z), p_1(z), \ldots$ According to the theorem of section 2.20.1 the function $F(z)$ is holomorphic throughout $\mathfrak{A}$.

4.1.4 – Logarithmic derivative of a product

Under the same conditions as in section 4.1.3 we have:
At every point where $F(z) \neq 0$ *the following relation holds*

$$\boxed{\frac{F'(z)}{F(z)} = \sum_{\nu=0}^{\infty} \frac{f'_\nu(z)}{1+f_\nu(z)}.} \tag{4.1–21}$$

Since $F(z) \neq 0$ none of the factors $1+f_n(z)$ vanish. The sequence $p_0(z), p_1(z), \ldots$ tends uniformly to $F(z)$. By virtue of the theorem of section 2.20.1 also the sequence $p'_0(z), p'_1(z), \ldots$ tends uniformly to $F'(z)$ and therefore

$$\frac{p'_n(z)}{p_n(z)} \to \frac{F'(z)}{F(z)}$$

as $n \to \infty$. But

$$\frac{p'_n(z)}{p_n(z)} = \sum_{\nu=0}^{n} \frac{f'_\nu(z)}{1+f\ (z)}$$

and the result follows. – We may add that the series on the right-hand side of (4.1–21) is uniformly convergent in any bounded and closed subset of $\mathfrak{A}$ that does not contain zeros of $F(z)$.

4.2 – The factorization of integral functions

4.2.1 – Generalities

We already proved in section 2.6.2 that a polynomial

$$f(z) = c_0+c_1z+\ldots+c_nz^n, \qquad c_n \neq 0, \quad n > 0, \tag{4.2–1}$$

possesses n zeros $a_1, \ldots, a_n$ and can be expressed in the form

$$f(z) = c_n(z-a_1)\ldots(z-a_n), \tag{4.2–2}$$

or, alternatively,

$$f(z) = c_0\left(1-\frac{z}{a_1}\right)\ldots\left(1-\frac{z}{a_n}\right), \tag{4.2–3}$$

provided $c_0 \neq 0$.

These matters can be generalized. We consider the problem: To find whether an integral function possesses zeros and to express the function as an infinite product.

We observe first that there exist integral functions with no zeros, e.g., $\exp z$, more generally $\exp \varphi(z)$, where $\varphi(z)$ designates an integral function. Conversely, *if $g(z)$ is an integral function with no zeros, it must be of the form* $\exp \varphi(z)$, *where $\varphi(z)$ is itself an integral function.*

In fact, under this assumption the function $g'(z)/g(z)$ is an integral function. Integrating it along a path from 0 to z we find that

$$\varphi(z) = \log g(0) + \int_0^z \frac{g'(\zeta)}{g(\zeta)}\, d\zeta \tag{4.2–4}$$

is also an integral function. The logarithmic derivative of the function $(\exp \varphi(z))/g(z)$ is $\varphi'(z)-g'(z)/g(z) = 0$, whence

$$\frac{\exp \varphi(z)}{g(z)} = \frac{\exp \varphi(0)}{g(0)} = 1.$$

From this theorem we deduce that *if $g(z)$ is an integral function with a finite number of zeros and if we denote by $p(z)$ a polynomial which has the same zeros as $g(z)$, each counted with the proper multiplicity, then*

$$g(z) = p(z) \exp \varphi(z) \tag{4.2–5}$$

where $\varphi(z)$ is an integral function.

This follows from the fact that $g(z)/p(z)$ is an integral function with no zeros. – Applying the same arguments we have: *If $g(z)$ and $h(z)$ are integral functions having the same zeros with the same order of multiplicity, then*

$$g(z) = h(z) \exp \varphi(z) \tag{4.2–6}$$

where $\varphi(z)$ is an integral function.

4.2.2 – Examples

The problem of the factorization of an integral function with pre-assigned zeros by means of an infinite product or, as commonly stated, *the factorization of an integral function* shall be illustrated in a few examples.

A first example of the expansion of an integral function in an infinite product was provided by Euler who stated for $\sin \pi z$ the expression

$$\sin \pi z = \pi z \prod_{\nu=1}^{\infty} \left(1 - \frac{z^2}{\nu^2}\right). \tag{4.2–7}$$

At first sight the problem of constructing an integral function which vanishes at the points of a sequence

$$a_1, a_2, \ldots, \tag{4.2–8}$$

with the orders of multiplicity $m_1, m_2, \ldots$ respectively might be solved by taking for $g(z)$ the infinite product

$$\prod_{\nu=1}^{\infty} \left(1 - \frac{z}{a_\nu}\right)^{m_\nu}, \tag{4.2–9}$$

but a product of this type is, in general, not convergent. The difficulties inherent to the problem of factorization were surmounted by Weierstrass, inspired by a formula which represents the reciprocal of Euler's gamma function as an infinite product:

$$\frac{1}{\Gamma(z)} = z \exp \gamma z \cdot \prod_{\nu=1}^{\infty} \left(1 + \frac{z}{\nu}\right) \exp\left(-\frac{z}{\nu}\right),$$

γ being a universal constant, the Euler constant (see section 4.6.1).

Here the convergence arises from the coupling of the factor $\exp(-z/n)$ with the binomial $1+z/n$ and, in general, as we shall see, the adjunction of exponential factors enabled Weierstrass to achieve his purpose.

4.3 – **Primary factors of Weierstrass**

4.3.1 – Primary factors

According to Weierstrass we give the name *primary factors* to the integral functions

$$E(z;0)=1-z,\quad E(z;k)=(1-z)\exp\left(z+\tfrac{1}{2}z^2+\ldots+\frac{1}{k}z^k\right),\tag{4.3–1}$$

k being a positive integer. These functions vanish only at $z=1$.

The integral functions (4.3–1) can be expanded in a power series

$$E(z;k)=1-c_1z^{k+1}-c_2z^{k+2}-\ldots,\tag{4.3–2}$$

where $c_1, c_2, \ldots$ are positive rational numbers, provided $k>0$.

In fact the derivatives of the function

$$\exp\left(z+\tfrac{1}{2}z^2+\ldots+\frac{1}{k}z^k\right)\tag{4.3–3}$$

are products of polynomials with positive integral coefficients and the function itself. This function and all its derivatives assume therefore integral and positive values at $z=0$. As a consequence, the coefficients $c_1, c_2, \ldots$ in the Taylor expansion

$$\exp\left(z+\tfrac{1}{2}z^2+\ldots+\frac{1}{k}z^k\right)=(k+1)c_1+(k+2)c_2z+\ldots\tag{4.3–4}$$

are rational and positive.

We have further

$$E'(z;k)=\{-1+(1-z)(1+z+\ldots+z^{k-1})\}\exp\left(z+\tfrac{1}{2}z^2+\ldots+\frac{1}{k}z^k\right)$$

$$=-z^k\exp\left(z+\tfrac{1}{2}z^2+\ldots+\frac{1}{k}z^k\right)\tag{4.3–5}$$

and according to (4.3–4)

$$E'(z;k)=-(k+1)c_1z^k-(k+2)c_2z^{k+1}-\ldots,\tag{4.3–6}$$

and by integrating term-by-term, taking account of $E(0;k)=1$, we find (4.3–2). Making $z=1$ we find from (4.3–2)

$$\sum_{\nu=1}^{\infty}c_\nu=1.\tag{4.3–7}$$

4.3.2 – A FUNDAMENTAL INEQUALITY

For subsequent applications we need the following theorem: *The logarithm of a primary factor satisfies the inequality*

$$|\log E(z;k)|\leqq 2|z|^{k+1}\tag{4.3–8}$$

provided that $|z|\leqq\frac{1}{2}$.

In fact, we have for $|z|\leqq\frac{1}{2}$, $k\geqq 1$,

$$\log E(z;k) = \log(1-z) + z + \tfrac{1}{2}z^2 + \ldots + \frac{1}{k}z^k$$
$$= -\frac{1}{k+1}z^{k+1} - \frac{1}{k+2}z^{k+2} - \ldots,$$

whence

$$|\log E(z;k)| \leqq |z|^{k+1}\left(\frac{1}{k+1} + \frac{1}{k+2}|z| + \ldots\right)$$
$$\leqq |z|^{k+1}(1 + \tfrac{1}{2} + (\tfrac{1}{2})^2 + \ldots) = 2|z|^{k+1},$$

the result being also true when $k = 0$.

4.4 – Expansion of an integral function in an infinite product

4.4.1 – Theorem of Weierstrass

In any bounded region the integral function $g(z)$ possesses only a finite number of zeros, for there is no accumulation point of zeros at finite distance, unless $g(z)$ is identically equal to zero (a case which we shall exclude). It is easily shown that the zeros of $g(z)$ form an enumerable set and hence may be arranged in order such that the moduli do not decrease and that from two zeros having the same modulus the zero with the smallest principal argument precedes. Until further notice we exclude the case that $z = 0$ is among the zeros. We arrange the zeros in a sequence

$$a_1, a_2, \ldots \tag{4.4–1}$$

such that

$$0 < |a_1| \leqq |a_2| \leqq \ldots, \tag{4.4–2}$$

with $a_n \to \infty$ when there are infinitely many zeros.
We shall agree on repeating in the sequence (4.4–1) a zero as many times as is indicated by its order of multiplicity.

We wish to consider the following problem:

Given the sequence (4.4–1) which satisfies (4.4–2). To construct an integral function which vanishes at the points of this sequence and at these points only, agreeing that if a point is repeated μ times, then this point is a zero of order μ of the function.

The solution is given by the following *theorem of Weierstrass*:

If $k_1, k_2, \ldots$ is a sequence of non-negative integers such that the series

$$\sum_{\nu=1}^{\infty} \left|\frac{z}{a_\nu}\right|^{k_\nu+1} \tag{4.4–3}$$

is convergent for all values of z, then

$$g(z) = \exp \varphi(z) \cdot \prod_{\nu=1}^{\infty} \left(1 - \frac{z}{a_\nu}\right) \exp\left\{\frac{z}{a_\nu} + \frac{1}{2}\left(\frac{z}{a_\nu}\right)^2 + \ldots + \frac{1}{k_\nu}\left(\frac{z}{a_\nu}\right)^{k_\nu}\right\}, \tag{4.4–4}$$

where $\varphi(z)$ *is an integral function, the ultimate exponential factor being omitted when the corresponding* $k_\nu = 0$.

Referring to the considerations of section 4.2.1 it is sufficient to prove that the factor of $\exp \varphi(z)$ in (4.4.–4) represents an integral function with the prescribed zeros. In view of (4.3–1) we can represent this factor as

$$f(z) = \prod_{\nu=1}^{\infty} E\left(\frac{z}{a_\nu}; k_\nu\right) \tag{4.4–5}$$

and according to (4.3–8)

$$\left|\log E\left(\frac{z}{a_n}; k_n\right)\right| \leqq 2\left|\frac{z}{a_n}\right|^{k_n+1}, \qquad |a_n| \geqq 2|z|, \tag{4.4–6}$$

this being the case for sufficiently large values of n. Hence the series

$$\sum_{\nu=1}^{\infty} \log E\left(\frac{z}{a_\nu}; k_\nu\right)$$

is absolutely convergent at every point z different from the points (4.4–1) and therefore the product (4.4–5) also converges absolutely. The product, moreover, converges uniformly in any bounded set and hence represents an integral function. According to the theorem of Hurwitz (section 3.11.1) the only zeros of $f(z)$ are found from

$$E\left(\frac{z}{a_n}; k_n\right) = 0, \qquad n = 1, 2, \ldots,$$

i.e., the zeros are precisely the numbers of the sequence (4.4–1).

Since $|z/a_n| < 1$ for $|a_n| > |z|$ the series

$$\left|\frac{z}{a_1}\right| + \left|\frac{z}{a_2}\right|^2 + \left|\frac{z}{a_3}\right|^3 + \ldots$$

is convergent. On account of this fact it is always possible to find a sequence $k_1, k_2, \ldots$ having the property mentioned in Weierstrass's theorem, for we can take $k_n = n-1$.

We wish to find the logarithmic derivative of the function (4.4–5) which will enable us in section 4.12.1 to understand how the solution of the factorization problem can be made to depend on the solution of the so-called problem of Mittag-Leffler.

In view of (4.1–21) we have at once

$$\frac{f'(z)}{f(z)} = \sum_{\nu=1}^{\infty} \left(\frac{1}{z-a_\nu} + \frac{1}{a_\nu} + \frac{z}{a_\nu^2} + \ldots + \frac{z^{k_\nu-1}}{a_\nu^{k_\nu}} \right), \tag{4.4–7}$$

the series on the right hand side being uniformly convergent in any closed and bounded set that does not contain points of the sequence (4.4–1).

In the solution of Weierstrass's problem we assumed $a_1 \neq 0$. Whenever it is prescribed that the origin is a zero of order m of $g(z)$ it is sufficient to replace (4.4–4) by the formula

$$g(z) = z^m f(x) \exp \varphi(z). \tag{4.4–8}$$

4.4.2 – A THEOREM ABOUT MEROMORPHIC FUNCTIONS

Every function meromorphic throughout the whole plane is the quotient of two integral functions.

Let $g(z)$ denote an integral function having the zeros of the given function as zeros, each with the proper multiplicity and let $h(z)$ denote an integral function having the poles of the given function as zeros, of course also with the same multiplicity. If $f(z)$ is the given function, the function $f(z)h(z)/g(z)$ has no zeros and no poles and can be represented by exp $\varphi(z)$. Hence

$$f(z) = \frac{g(z) \exp \varphi(z)}{h(z)}, \tag{4.4–9}$$

the desired result.

As a consequence the study of functions which are meromorphic throughout the z-plane can be based on the theory of integral functions.

4.5 – Canonical products

4.5.1 – RANK OF A CANONICAL PRODUCT

A particularly noteworthy case of Weierstrass's factorization theorem presents itself if there exists a non-negative integer k such that the series

$$\sum_{\nu=1}^{\infty} \frac{1}{|a_\nu|^{k+1}} \tag{4.5–1}$$

is convergent. Then the series (4.4–3) is also convergent if we take $k_n = k$, $n = 1, 2, \ldots$.

It is not always possible to find such a number k. For instance the series

$$\frac{1}{(\log 2)^{k+1}} + \frac{1}{(\log 3)^{k+1}} + \ldots \tag{4.5–2}$$

is divergent, however large k may be. In fact, it is easily deduced by means of (1.11–5) that always

$$\lim_{n\to\infty} \frac{n}{\log^{k+1} n} = \infty \tag{4.5–3}$$

and hence from a certain number upwards the terms of the series (4.5–2) dominate the corresponding terms of the (divergent) harmonic series $\sum_{\nu=1}^{\infty} \nu^{-1}$.

If there exist non-negative integers k for which the series (4.5–1) is convergent, the smallest of them is called the *rank* of the sequence $a_1, a_2, \ldots$, and also of the *rank* of the corresponding *canonical product*, this being the function $f(z)$ defined in (4.4–5), where all exponents k_n are equal to the smallest number k for which (4.5–1) is convergent.

According to the results of section **4.4.1** we may state the following theorem:

If an integral function $g(z)$ has as zeros the numbers of the sequence (4.4—1) of rank k, then $g(z)$ is expressed by

$$g(z) = \exp \varphi(z) \cdot z^m \prod_{\nu=1}^{\infty} \left(1 - \frac{z}{a_\nu}\right) \exp \left\{\frac{z}{a_\nu} + \frac{1}{2}\left(\frac{z}{a_\nu}\right)^2 + \ldots + \frac{1}{k}\left(\frac{z}{a_\nu}\right)^k\right\} \tag{4.5–4}$$

where $\varphi(z)$ is an integral function and, when $m > 0$, m designates the order of multiplicity of the zero $z = 0$ of $g(z)$.

The infinite product in (4.5–4) is absolutely convergent and uniformly convergent in any bounded set and vanishes only at the points $z = 0, a_1, a_2, \ldots$ (the zero $z = 0$ not being present if $m = 0$). Further

$$\frac{g'(z)}{g(z)} = \varphi'(z) + \frac{m}{z} + \sum_{\nu=1}^{\infty} \left(\frac{1}{z - a_\nu} + \frac{1}{a_\nu} + \frac{z}{a_\nu^2} + \ldots + \frac{z^{k-1}}{a_\nu^k}\right), \tag{4.5–5}$$

the series on the right-hand side being uniformly convergent in any closed and bounded set which does not contain zeros of $g(z)$.

4.5.2 – Factorization of the sine

As an example we consider the function

$$\sin \pi z. \tag{4.5–6}$$

This function is an integral function which vanishes at $z = 0, \pm 1, \pm 2, \ldots$ and since the series

$$\sum_{\nu=-\infty}^{\infty}{}' \frac{1}{\nu^2} = 2 \sum_{\nu=1}^{\infty} \frac{1}{\nu^2} \tag{4.5–7}$$

(the prime indicating that on the left-hand side $\nu = 0$ must be excluded) is convergent, the rank of the sequence of the zeros is equal to 1. Hence we have

$$\sin \pi z = \exp \varphi(z) \cdot z \prod_{\nu=-\infty}^{\infty}{}' \left(1-\frac{z}{\nu}\right) \exp \frac{z}{\nu} \tag{4.5–8}$$

and by re-arranging the factors, since the product is unconditionally convergent,

$$\sin \pi z = \exp \varphi(z) \cdot z \prod_{\nu=1}^{\infty} \left(1-\frac{z^2}{\nu^2}\right). \tag{4.5–9}$$

The main difficulty is the determination of the function $\varphi(z)$. Taking the logarithmic derivative we find

$$\pi \operatorname{ctn} \pi z = \varphi'(z) + \frac{1}{z} + \sum_{\nu=1}^{\infty} \frac{2z}{z^2-\nu^2}. \tag{4.5–10}$$

Comparing this result with (3.7–30) we conclude that $\varphi'(z) = 0$ and hence that $\varphi(z)$ is a constant. As a consequence the factor $\exp \varphi(z)$ in (4.5–9) is also a constant and since

$$\lim_{z\to 0} \frac{\sin \pi z}{\pi z} = 1 \tag{4.5–11}$$

we find that the constant is equal to π. We thus derived the famous Euler expansion

$$\boxed{\sin \pi z = \pi z \prod_{\nu=1}^{\infty} \left(1-\frac{z^2}{\nu^2}\right).} \tag{4.5–12}$$

The Weierstrass formula for $\sin \pi z$ turns out to be

$$\boxed{\sin \pi z = \pi z \prod_{\nu=-\infty}^{\infty}{}' \left(1-\frac{z}{\nu}\right) \exp \frac{z}{\nu}.} \tag{4.5–13}$$

4.5.3 – Wallis's formula

If we insert $z = \frac{1}{2}$ in (4.5–12) we obtain the result

$$1 = \tfrac{1}{2}\pi \prod_{\nu=1}^{\infty} \left(1-\frac{1}{4\nu^2}\right) = \tfrac{1}{2}\pi \prod_{\nu=1}^{\infty} \frac{4\nu^2-1}{4\nu^2}$$

whence the important formula of Wallis

$$\boxed{\tfrac{1}{2}\pi = \prod_{\nu=1}^{\infty} \frac{(2\nu)^2}{(2\nu-1)(2\nu+1)} = \frac{2\cdot 2}{1\cdot 3}\,\frac{4\cdot 4}{3\cdot 5}\,\frac{6\cdot 6}{5\cdot 7}\cdots} \tag{4.5–14}$$

which may also be written in the form

$$\boxed{\sqrt{\pi} = \lim_{n\to\infty} \frac{2^{2n}(n!)^2}{(2n)!\sqrt{n}}.} \tag{4.5–15}$$

It is easy to give an independent proof of this result. In fact, if m is a positive integer then

$$\int_0^{\frac{1}{2}\pi} \sin^m x\, dx > \int_0^{\frac{1}{2}\pi} \sin^{m+1} x\, dx$$

and by integration by parts it is shown that $\frac{1}{2}\pi$ lies between the number

$$\frac{2}{1}\,\frac{2}{3}\,\frac{4}{3}\,\frac{4}{5}\,\frac{6}{5}\,\frac{6}{7}\cdots\frac{2n}{2n-1}\;\frac{2n}{2n+1}$$

and the number obtained by omitting from this product the last factor.

4.6 – The gamma function

4.6.1 – Definition of the gamma function

The most general integral function which vanishes simply at the points $z = 0, -1, -2, \ldots$ only has the form

$$g(z) = \exp\varphi(z)\cdot z \prod_{\nu=1}^{\infty}\left(1+\frac{z}{\nu}\right)\exp\left(-\frac{z}{\nu}\right),$$

where $\varphi(z)$ is an integral function. In fact, the sequence of the zeros is of rank 1, as already has been pointed out in the previous section in the case of the function $\sin \pi z$.

The case in which $\varphi(z) = \gamma z$, γ being a constant selected in such a fashion that $g(1) = 1$, is of utmost importance. The reciprocal of this function is called the *gammafunction* and is denoted by the symbol $\Gamma(z)$; thus

$$\boxed{\frac{1}{\Gamma(z)} = e^{\gamma z}\, z \prod_{\nu=1}^{\infty}\left(1+\frac{z}{\nu}\right)\exp\left(-\frac{z}{\nu}\right).} \tag{4.6–1}$$

The gamma function is meromorphic in the entire plane, having only simple poles, viz., at the points

$$z = 0, -1, -2, \ldots. \tag{4.6–2}$$

Moreover, the gamma function vanishes nowhere.

According to the definition we have

$$\boxed{\Gamma(1) = 1} \tag{4.6–3}$$

and as a consequence γ is determined by

$$e^{-\gamma} = \prod_{\nu=1}^{\infty} \left(1+\frac{1}{\nu}\right) e^{-\frac{1}{\nu}}. \tag{4.6–4}$$

Taking logarithms

$$-\gamma = \sum_{\nu=1}^{\infty} \left\{\log\left(\frac{\nu+1}{\nu}\right) - \frac{1}{\nu}\right\}$$

$$= \lim_{n\to\infty} \left\{\log\frac{2}{1}\cdot\frac{3}{2}\cdot\ldots\cdot\frac{n}{n-1} + \log\frac{n+1}{n} - \left(1+\frac{1}{2}+\ldots+\frac{1}{n}\right)\right\},$$

and since $\log\frac{n+1}{n}$ tends to zero as $n \to \infty$ we have

$$\boxed{\gamma = \lim_{n\to\infty} \left(1+\frac{1}{2}+\ldots+\frac{1}{n} - \log n\right).} \tag{4.6–5}$$

The constant γ is called the *Euler constant.* A crude estimate of this constant is obtained in the following way:

From

$$\frac{1}{n+1} < \int_n^{n+1} \frac{dx}{x} < \frac{1}{n}$$

we deduce

$$\frac{1}{n+1} < \log\frac{n+1}{n} < \frac{1}{n}. \tag{4.6–6}$$

Since for $n > 1$

$$\log n = \log\frac{2}{1}\cdot\frac{3}{2}\cdot\ldots\cdot\frac{n}{n-1} = \log\frac{2}{1} + \log\frac{3}{2} + \ldots + \log\frac{n}{n-1},$$

we also have

$$1+\frac{1}{2}+\ldots+\frac{1}{n} - \log n$$

$$= 1 - \left(\log\frac{2}{1} - \frac{1}{2}\right) - \left(\log\frac{3}{2} - \frac{1}{3}\right) - \ldots - \left(\log\frac{n}{n-1} - \frac{1}{n}\right)$$

$$= \left(\frac{1}{1} - \log\frac{2}{1}\right) + \left(\frac{1}{2} - \log\frac{3}{2}\right) + \ldots + \left(\frac{1}{n-1} - \log\frac{n}{n-1}\right) + \frac{1}{n}, \tag{4.6–7}$$

whence, according to (4.6–6),

$$1 - \left(\log 2 - \frac{1}{2}\right) > 1+\frac{1}{2}+\ldots+\frac{1}{n} - \log n > 1 - \log 2,$$

and this leads to

$$0 < \gamma < 1.$$

4.6.2 – Formula of Gauss

From (4.6–1), taking account of (4.6–5), we deduce

$$\frac{1}{\Gamma(z)} = \lim_{n\to\infty} \exp z\left(1+\frac{1}{2}+\ldots+\frac{1}{n}-\log n\right)\cdot z\prod_{\nu=1}^{n}\left(1+\frac{z}{\nu}\right)\exp\left(-\frac{z}{\nu}\right)$$

$$= \lim_{n\to\infty} \exp(-z\log n)\cdot z\prod_{\nu=1}^{n}\left(1+\frac{z}{\nu}\right)$$

$$= \lim_{n\to\infty} \frac{z\left(1+\frac{z}{1}\right)\left(1+\frac{z}{2}\right)\ldots\left(1+\frac{z}{n}\right)}{n^z}$$

and finally the *formula of Gauss*

$$\boxed{\Gamma(z) = \lim_{n\to\infty}\frac{n!\,n^z}{z(z+1)\ldots(z+n)}.} \qquad (4.6\text{–}8)$$

It is assumed, of course, that $z \neq 0, -1, -2, \ldots$.

4.6.3 – Functional equation

It is easy to derive a functional equation for $\Gamma(z)$. In fact, from (4.6–8) we have

$$\Gamma(z+1) = \lim_{n\to\infty}\frac{n!\,n^{z+1}}{(z+1)\ldots(z+n+1)}$$

$$= z\lim_{n\to\infty}\frac{n!\,n^z}{z(z+1)\ldots(z+n)}\cdot\lim_{n\to\infty}\frac{n}{z+n+1}$$

and hence the first fundamental relation for $\Gamma(z)$, the *functional equation*

$$\boxed{\Gamma(z+1) = z\,\Gamma(z).} \qquad (4.6\text{–}9)$$

In particular, when z is a positive integer m, we have

$$\Gamma(m+1) = m\Gamma(m) = \ldots = m!\,\Gamma(1)$$

or

$$\Gamma(m+1) = m!. \qquad (4.6\text{–}10)$$

Thus the gamma function coincides with the factorial when the variable takes positive integral values.

It is an easy matter to evaluate the residues of $\Gamma(z)$ at its poles. Let m denote a non-negative integer. Then by (4.6–9)

$$(z+m)\Gamma(z) = \frac{\Gamma(z+m+1)}{z(z+1)\ldots(z+m-1)}.$$

Letting $z \to -m$ we have

$$(z+m)\Gamma(z) \to \frac{\Gamma(1)}{(-m)(-m+1)\ldots(-1)} = \frac{(-1)^m}{m!}, \qquad (4.6\text{–}11)$$

this result being also valid for $m = 0$, for $z\Gamma(z) = \Gamma(z+1) \to \Gamma(1) = 1$. Hence

$$\boxed{\operatorname*{Res}_{z=-m} \Gamma(z) = \frac{(-1)^m}{m!}}, \quad m = 0, 1, 2, \ldots. \qquad (4.6\text{–}12)$$

4.6.4 – Formula of the complementary arguments

The formula (4.6–8) is equivalent to

$$z\Gamma(z) = \lim_{n\to\infty} \frac{n!n^z}{(z+1)\ldots(z+n)}.$$

Further

$$\Gamma(1-z) = \lim_{n\to\infty} \frac{n!n^{1-z}}{(1-z)(2-z)\ldots(n+1-z)} = \lim_{n\to\infty} \frac{n!n^{-z}}{(1-z)(2-z)\ldots(n-z)}.$$

Hence

$$z\Gamma(z)\Gamma(1-z) = \lim_{n\to\infty} \frac{(n!)^2}{(1^2-z^2)\ldots(n^2-z^2)} = \lim_{n\to\infty} \frac{1}{\left(1-\frac{z^2}{1^2}\right)\ldots\left(1-\frac{z^2}{n^2}\right)}.$$

In view of (4.5–12) we thus obtain the second fundamental relation, *the formula of the complementary arguments*

$$\boxed{\Gamma(z)\Gamma(1-z) = \pi \csc \pi z.} \qquad (4.6\text{–}13)$$

In particular, since $\Gamma(x) > 0$ whenever $x > 0$,

$$\boxed{\Gamma(\tfrac{1}{2}) = \sqrt{\pi}.} \qquad (4.6\text{–}14)$$

4.6.5 – Expansion of the logarithm of the gamma function

Taking logarithms on both sides of (4.6–1) we get

$$\log \Gamma(z) = -\log z - \gamma z - \sum_{\nu=1}^{\infty} \left\{\log\left(1+\frac{z}{\nu}\right) - \frac{z}{\nu}\right\}. \qquad (4.6\text{–}15)$$

The formula is valid in the principal region $z+|z| \neq 0$.

Expanding the logarithms occurring in the infinite series we get

$$\log \Gamma(z) = -\log z - \gamma z + \sum_{\nu=1}^{\infty} \sum_{\mu=2}^{\infty} (-1)^\mu \frac{1}{\mu}\left(\frac{z}{\nu}\right)^\mu, \quad |z| < 1, \quad z+|z| \neq 0,$$

and hence, by Weierstrass's double-series theorem of section 2.20.4 and the functional relation (4.6–9),

$$\log \Gamma(z+1) = -\gamma z + \sum_{\mu=2}^{\infty} \frac{(-1)^\mu z^\mu}{\mu} \zeta(\mu), \quad |z| < 1, \quad z+|z| \neq 0, \qquad (4.6\text{–}16)$$

with

$$\zeta(m) = \sum_{\nu=1}^{\infty} \nu^{-m}. \qquad (4.6\text{–}17)$$

For real values of z this series could be used for numerical computations, but the convergence is, however, rather bad. For large values of m the sums $\zeta(m)$ differ less from unity and we obtain a better result if we add the series for $\log(1+z)$. We then find, writing ν instead of μ,

$$\log \Gamma(1+z) = -\log(1+z) + z(1-\gamma) + \sum_{\nu=2}^{\infty} \frac{(-1)^\nu z^\nu}{\nu} \{\zeta(\nu) - 1\}. \qquad (4.6\text{–}18)$$

A much better series is obtained as follows. First we replace z by $-z$,

$$\log \Gamma(1-z) = -\log(1-z) - z(1-\gamma) + \sum_{\mu=2}^{\infty} \frac{z^\nu}{\nu} \{\zeta(\nu) - 1\}. \qquad (4.6\text{–}19)$$

By the functional relation (4.6–9) and the theorem of the complementary arguments (4.6–13) we have

$$\log \Gamma(1+z) + \log \Gamma(1-z) = \log(\pi z \csc \pi z). \qquad (4.6\text{–}20)$$

Adding corresponding members of (4.6–18) and (4.6–20) and subtracting from the resulting equation corresponding members of (4.6–19) we find after dividing by 2,

$$\log \Gamma(1+z) = \frac{1}{2}\left(\log(\pi z \csc \pi z) - \log \frac{1+z}{1-z}\right)$$
$$+ z(1+\gamma) - \sum_{\mu=1}^{\infty} \frac{z^{2\nu+1}}{2\nu+1} \{\zeta(2\nu+1) - 1\}. \qquad (4.6\text{–}21)$$

In particular, taking $z = \frac{1}{2}$ and observing that $\Gamma(\frac{3}{2}) = \frac{1}{2}\Gamma(\frac{1}{2})$, we have the following expansion of the Euler constant:

$$\gamma = 1 - \log \frac{3}{2} - \sum_{\nu=1}^{\infty} \frac{1}{(2\nu+1)2^{2\nu}} \{\zeta(2\nu+1) - 1\}. \qquad (4.6\text{–}22)$$

A table giving the values of $\zeta(m)$ has been computed by Legendre. If we take the terms up to and including $\zeta(9)$ we find γ in 16 places

$$\gamma = 0.57721\ 56649\ 01532\ 9.$$

It is unknown whether γ is rational or irrational.

4.6.6 – Duplication formula

The functions $\Gamma(z)\Gamma(z+\frac{1}{2})$ and $\Gamma(2z)$ have the same poles, viz. $z = 0, -\frac{1}{2}, -1, -\frac{3}{4}, -2, \ldots$. Hence their ratio is an integral function with no zeros and is of the form exp $\varphi(z)$ (see section 4.2.2). As a consequence the relation

$$\Gamma(z)\,\Gamma(z+\tfrac{1}{2}) = \exp\varphi(z)\cdot\Gamma(2z) \tag{4.6–23}$$

holds and from (4.6–1) we conclude that $\varphi(z)$ must be a polynomial whose degree does not exceed unity. Hence we may write

$$\Gamma(z)\,\Gamma(z+\tfrac{1}{2}) = ae^{bz}\Gamma(2z). \tag{4.6–24}$$

Replacing z by $z+\frac{1}{2}$ we obtain from (4.6–24), taking account of (4.6–9),

$$z\,\Gamma(z+\tfrac{1}{2})\,\Gamma(z) = ae^{bz+\frac{1}{2}b}\,2z\,\Gamma(2z). \tag{4.6–25}$$

Comparing this with (4.6–24) we infer that $2e^{\frac{1}{2}b} = 1$, or $e^b = \frac{1}{4}$. Putting $z = 0$ in (4.6–25) we have on account of (4.6–13), since $z\Gamma(z) = \Gamma(z+1)$ takes the value $\Gamma(1) = 1$,

$$\sqrt{\pi} = \tfrac{1}{2}a$$

and we arrive at the result

$$\boxed{\Gamma(z)\Gamma(z+\tfrac{1}{2}) = 2^{1-2z}\sqrt{\pi}\,\Gamma(2z),} \tag{4.6–26}$$

the third fundamental relation, the *duplication formula of Legendre.*

4.6.7 – Euler's formula

The previous result may be readily generalized. A generalization of (4.6–14) is Euler's formula

$$\prod_{\mu=1}^{m-1}\Gamma\left(\frac{\mu}{m}\right) = (2\pi)^{\frac{1}{2}(m-1)}\,m^{-\frac{1}{2}}, \tag{4.6–27}$$

m being an integer $\geqq 2$.

According to (4.6–13) the square of the expression on the left-hand side is

$$\prod_{\mu=1}^{m-1}\Gamma\left(\frac{\mu}{m}\right)\Gamma\left(1-\frac{\mu}{m}\right) = \frac{\pi^{m-1}}{\sin\dfrac{\pi}{m}\sin\dfrac{2\pi}{m}\cdots\sin\dfrac{(m-1)\pi}{m}}. \tag{4.6–28}$$

In order to evaluate the denominator on the right-hand side of the latter equation we use the identity

$$\frac{x^m-1}{x-1} = x^{m-1}+\ldots+1 = \prod_{\mu=1}^{m-1}\left(x-\exp\frac{2\mu\pi i}{m}\right)$$

whence, taking $x = 1$,

$$m = \prod_{\mu=1}^{m-1} \left(1 - \exp \frac{2\mu\pi i}{m}\right)$$

$$= \exp \frac{\pi i}{m} \ldots \exp \frac{(m-1)\pi i}{m} \prod_{\mu=1}^{m-1} \left\{\exp\left(-\frac{\mu\pi i}{m}\right) - \exp \frac{\mu\pi i}{m}\right\}$$

$$= \exp \tfrac{1}{2}(m-1)\pi i \prod_{\mu=1}^{m-1} \left\{\exp\left(-\frac{\mu\pi i}{m}\right) - \exp\frac{\mu\pi i}{m}\right\} = 2^{m-1} \prod_{\mu=1}^{m-1} \sin \frac{\mu\pi}{m}.$$

Hence

$$\sin \frac{\pi}{m} \cdot \sin \frac{2\pi}{m} \cdot \ldots \cdot \sin \frac{(m-1)\pi}{m} = \frac{m}{2^{m-1}}, \tag{4.6–29}$$

and the desired result follows easily.

4.6.8 – Gauss's multiplication formula

By a method similar to that used in section 4.6.6 we may derive a very general result due to Gauss, the *multiplication formula*

$$\prod_{\mu=0}^{m-1} \Gamma\left(z + \frac{\mu}{m}\right) = m^{\frac{1}{2}-mz} (2\pi)^{\frac{1}{2}(m-1)} \Gamma(mz), \tag{4.6–30}$$

where m is an integer $\geqq 2$. For $m = 2$ the result reduces to the Legendre duplication formula.

The function on the left-hand side has the same poles as $\Gamma(mz)$, viz. $z = 0, -\frac{1}{m}, -\frac{2}{m}, \ldots$, and the quotient of these functions is, consequently, an integral function with no zeros. It is therefore of the form

$$\exp \varphi(z) \cdot \Gamma(mz)$$

and as in section 4.6.6 we conclude that $\varphi(z)$ is a polynomial of degree not exceeding unity. We may therefore write

$$\prod_{\mu=0}^{m-1} \Gamma\left(z + \frac{\mu}{m}\right) = a e^{bz} \Gamma(mz). \tag{4.6–31}$$

Replacing z by $z + \frac{1}{m}$ we have

$$\prod_{\mu=1}^{m-1} \Gamma\left(z + \frac{\mu}{m}\right) z\Gamma(z) = a \exp\left(bz + \frac{b}{m}\right) \cdot mz\Gamma(mz) \tag{4.6–32}$$

and comparing this equation with the previous one we deduce $me^{b/m} = 1$, or $e^b = m^{-m}$. Putting $z = 0$ in (4.6–32) we have on account of (4.6–27), since $z\Gamma(z) = \Gamma(z+1)$ takes the value 1 for $z = 0$,

$$(2\pi)^{\frac{1}{2}(m-1)} m^{-\frac{1}{2}} = am^{-1},$$

and the desired result follows easily.

4.6.9 – CHARACTERIZATION OF THE GAMMA FUNCTION

On repeatedly applying (4.6–9) we have for any positive integer

$$\Gamma(z+n) = z(z+1)\dots(z+n-1)\Gamma(z).$$

Hence, taking account of (4.6–10),

$$\frac{\Gamma(z+n)}{n^z\Gamma(n)} = \frac{z(z+1)\dots(z+n-1)}{n!\,n^{z-1}}\Gamma(z),$$

and making $n \to \infty$ we obtain by virtue of

$$\lim_{n\to\infty}\frac{z(z+1)\dots(z+n-1)}{n!\,n^{z-1}} = \lim_{n\to\infty}\frac{z(z+1)\dots(z+n)}{n!\,n^{z}} = \frac{1}{\Gamma(z)}$$

the result

$$\lim_{n\to\infty}\frac{\Gamma(z+n)}{n^z\,\Gamma(n)} = 1. \tag{4.6–33}$$

Now we shall establish the interesting fact that the equations (4.6–9), (4.6–33) together with (4.6–3) determine the gamma function uniquely. We shall establish the theorem:

There is one and only one function $F(z)$ which satisfies the equations

$$F(1) = 1, \tag{4.6–34}$$

$$F(z+1) = zF(z), \tag{4.6–35}$$

$$\lim_{n\to\infty}\frac{F(z+n)}{n^z\,F(n)} = 1, \tag{4.6–36}$$

provided z is different from $z = 0, -1, -2, \dots$.

We know that there exists at least one solution of these equations. If $F(z)$ is such a solution then, according to (4.6–35),

$$F(z+n) = z(z+1)\dots(z+n-1)F(z)$$

and

$$F(n) = (n-1)!, \qquad n \geqq 1.$$

Hence by (4.6–36)

$$1 = \lim_{n\to\infty}\frac{F(z+n)}{n!\,n^{z-1}} = F(z)\lim_{n\to\infty}\frac{z(z+1)\dots(z+n-1)}{n!\,n^{z-1}} = \frac{F(z)}{\Gamma(z)},$$

and the theorem is proved.

4.7 – The Eulerian integrals

4.7.1 – THE INTEGRAL OF THE SECOND KIND

By the *Eulerian integral of the second kind* is understood the infinite integral

$$\int_0^\infty e^{-t} t^{z-1}\, dt, \qquad \operatorname{Im} t = 0. \tag{4.7–1}$$

We already discussed this integral in section 3.6.11, assuming z to be real. We shall prove that *this integral exists and is a holomorphic function, provided* $\operatorname{Re} z > 0$. We may write instead of (4.7–1)

$$\int_0^1 e^{-t} t^{z-1}\, dt + \int_1^\infty e^{-t} t^{z-1}\, dt \tag{4.7–2}$$

and we shall prove that these integrals exist.

Suppose that z lies in an arbitrary closed and bounded set. Then there is a constant A such that $\operatorname{Re} z \leqq A$ when z lies in the set, and so

$$|t^{z-1}| = t^{\operatorname{Re} z - 1} \leqq t^{A-1}$$

when $t \geqq 1$. Now $e^{-\frac{1}{2}t} t^{A-1}$ tends to zero as $t \to \infty$ and, consequently, there exists a constant B (depending on A) such that $t^{A-1} \leqq B e^{\frac{1}{2}t}$ when $t \geqq 1$. Hence we have

$$|e^{-t} t^{z-1}| \leqq B e^{-\frac{1}{2}t}$$

and so the second integral of (4.7–2) is uniformly and absolutely convergent in the closed set, (see section 1.5.5).

In the first integral of (4.7–2) we replace t by t^{-1} and obtain

$$\int_1^\infty e^{-t^{-1}} t^{-z-1}\, dt.$$

This integral is obviously not convergent when $\operatorname{Re} z \leqq 0$. If, however, z lies in a closed and bounded set which lies to the right of the imaginary axis the inequality $\operatorname{Re} z \geqq \xi$, $\xi > 0$, holds and hence

$$\left| e^{-t^{-1}} t^{-z-1} \right| \leqq t^{-\xi-1}$$

when $t \geqq 1$, and so also the first integral is uniformly convergent. By virtue of the theorem of section 2.20.5 each of the integrals (4.7–2) represents a function holomorphic throughout the region $\operatorname{Re} z > 0$.

In (4.7–1) we take $z = n$, n being a positive integer. We find by integration by parts

$$\int_0^\infty e^{-t} t^{n-1}\, dt = (n-1)! = \Gamma(n). \tag{4.7–3}$$

This leads to the conjecture

$$\boxed{\Gamma(z) = \int_0^\infty e^{-t} t^{z-1}\, dt,} \qquad \operatorname{Re} z > 0. \tag{4.7–4}$$

For $z = \frac{1}{2}$ this result reduces to

$$\sqrt{\pi} = \Gamma(\tfrac{1}{2}) = \int_0^\infty e^{-t} t^{-1/2}\, dt = 2\int_0^\infty e^{-t^2}\, dt, \tag{4.7–5}$$

a formula we already encountered before.

4.7.2 – Proof of the formula (4.7–4)

In view of the identity principle (2.11.2) it is sufficient to verify (4.7–4) in the case that z is an arbitrary real number x between 0 and 1. We proceed to show that the integral on the right-hand side satisfies the conditions mentioned in the last theorem of section 4.6.9. Call the integral $F(x)$. By integration by parts we find

$$F(x+1) = x F(x) \tag{4.7–6}$$

and it remains to verify the last condition, since $F(1) = 1$ is trivial. Now

$$F(x+n) = \int_0^\infty e^{-t} t^{x+n-1}\, dt$$

or, replacing t by nt,

$$F(x+n) = n^{x+n} \int_0^\infty e^{-nt} t^{x+n-1}\, dt$$

whence

$$\frac{F(x+n)}{F(n)n^x} = \frac{n^n}{\Gamma(n)} \int_0^\infty e^{-nt} t^{x+n-1}\, dt. \tag{4.7–7}$$

In order to show that the expression on the right-hand side tends to the limit 1 as $n \to \infty$ we proceed by a method due to A. Pringsheim.

Transforming the integrals

$$\Gamma(n) = \int_0^\infty e^{-t} t^{n-1}\, dt, \qquad \Gamma(n+1) = \int_0^\infty e^{-t} t^n\, dt$$

on replacing t by nt, we find

$$n^{-n}\Gamma(n) = \int_0^\infty e^{-nt} t^{n-1}\, dt, \tag{4.7–8}$$

$$n^{-n}\Gamma(n) = \int_0^\infty e^{-nt} t^n\, dt. \tag{4.7–9}$$

Now we integrate the identity

$$e^{-nt} t^{n-1} - e^{-nt} t^n = \frac{1}{n} \frac{d}{dt} (e^{-nt} t^n)$$

between the limits 0 and 1. We thus obtain

$$\int_0^1 e^{-nt} t^{n-1}\, dt - \int_0^1 e^{-nt} t^n dt = e^{-n} n^{-1}. \tag{4.7–10}$$

If we subtract corresponding members of this last equation and (4.7–8) we get

$$\int_1^\infty e^{-nt} t^{n-1}\, dt + \int_0^1 e^{-nt} t^n\, dt = n^{-n}\,\Gamma(n) - e^{-n} n^{-1} \tag{4.7–11}$$

and if we add corresponding members of (4.7–9) and (4.7–10)

$$\int_0^1 e^{-nt} t^{n-1}\, dt + \int_1^\infty e^{-nt} t^n\, dt = n^{-n}\,\Gamma(n) + e^{-n} n^{-1}. \tag{4.7–12}$$

We assumed $0 < x < 1$. Hence

$$t^n < t^{x+n-1} < t^{n-1} \quad \text{when } 0 < t < 1,$$

while

$$t^{n-1} < t^{x+n-1} < t^n \quad \text{when } 1 < t.$$

If everywhere in the integrands of (4.7–11) and (4.7–12) we replace t^{n-1} and t^n respectively by t^{x+n-1} we obtain the inequalities

$$n^{-n}\,\Gamma(n) - e^{-n} n^{-1} < \int_0^\infty e^{-nt} t^{x+n-1}\, dt < n^{-n}\,\Gamma(n) + e^{-n} n^{-1}$$

or

$$1 - \frac{n^n e^{-n}}{n!} < \frac{n^n}{\Gamma(n)} \int_0^\infty e^{-nt} t^{x+n-1}\, dt < 1 + \frac{n^n e^{-n}}{n!}, \tag{4.7–13}$$

and since on account of (3.12–14)

$$\lim_{n\to\infty} \frac{n^n e^{-n}}{n!} = 0 \tag{4.7–14}$$

the truth of the assertion follows.

4.7.3 – Independent proof of (4.7–14)

It is worth-while to give a direct proof of (4.7–14) which provides some more information. From the logarithmic series (2.16–11) we deduce

$$\log \frac{1+x}{1-x} = 2(x + \tfrac{1}{3}x^3 + \tfrac{1}{5}x^5 + \ldots), \qquad |x| < 1, \tag{4.7–15}$$

whence, if $0 < x < 1$,

$$2x < \log \frac{1+x}{1-x} < 2x + \tfrac{2}{3}x^2(x + x^3 + \ldots) = 2x + \frac{2}{3}\,\frac{x^3}{1-x^2},$$

or

$$1 < \frac{1}{2x} \log \frac{1+x}{1-x} < 1 + \frac{1}{3}\,\frac{x^2}{1-x^2}.$$

Take $x = 1/(2n+1)$, n being a positive integer. Then an easy calculation yields

$$1 < (n+\tfrac{1}{2}) \log\left(1+\frac{1}{n}\right) < 1+\frac{1}{12n(n+1)}. \qquad (4.7\text{–}16)$$

We may therefore write

$$(n+\tfrac{1}{2}) \log\left(1+\frac{1}{n}\right) = 1+r_n \qquad (4.7\text{–}17)$$

with

$$0 < r_n < \frac{1}{12}\left(\frac{1}{n}-\frac{1}{n+1}\right). \qquad (4.7\text{–}18)$$

Replacing n in (4.7–17) successively by 1, 2, . . ., $n-1$ we obtain by adding the corresponding members of the equalities thus obtained

$$\log\frac{2}{1}\left(\frac{3}{2}\right)^2\cdots\left(\frac{n}{n-1}\right)^{n-1}+\tfrac{1}{2}\log\frac{2}{1}\,\frac{3}{2}\cdots\frac{n}{n-1} = n-1+\sum_{\nu=1}^{n-1} r_\nu,$$

or

$$\log\frac{n^n}{n!}+\tfrac{1}{2}\log n = n-1+\sum_{\nu=1}^{n-1} r_\nu,$$

whence

$$\frac{e^n n!}{n^{n+\frac{1}{2}}} = e^{1-\sum_{\nu=1}^{n-1} r_\nu}. \qquad (4.7\text{–}19)$$

By virtue of (4.7–18) we have

$$\sum_{\nu=1}^{n-1} r_\nu < \frac{1}{12}\left(1-\frac{1}{n}\right) < \frac{1}{12}$$

whence

$$\frac{e^n n!}{n^n} > e^{\frac{11}{12}}\sqrt{n} \qquad (4.7\text{–}20)$$

and this inequality includes (4.7–14).

4.7.4 – Stirling's theorem for the factorial

The considerations of section 4.7.3 permit to derive an estimate of the factorial which is of utmost importance in pure and applied mathematics. The results are preliminary to a discussion of a much more extensive analogous problem concerning the gamma function which shall be dealt with in section 4.9.2.

In view of (4.7–19) it is plain that the expression on the left-hand side of (4.7–19) is steadily decreasing as $n \to \infty$ and consequently tends to a limit k, this limit being positive (as may be seen from (4.7–20)). In order to evaluate k we write

$$k = k^2 \frac{1}{k} = \lim_{n\to\infty} \frac{e^{2n}(n!)^2}{n^{2n+1}} \cdot \lim_{n\to\infty} \frac{(2n)^{2n+\frac{1}{2}}}{e^{2n}(2n)!} = \lim_{n\to\infty} \frac{2^{2n+\frac{1}{2}}(n!)^2}{(2n)!\sqrt{n}}.$$

Comparing the last member with the expression (4.5–15) in the Wallis formula we infer that $k = \sqrt{2\pi}$ and thus we have proved *Stirling's theorem*

$$\boxed{\lim_{n\to\infty} \frac{n!}{\sqrt{2\pi n}} \left(\frac{e}{n}\right)^n = 1.} \qquad (4.7\text{–}21)$$

This means that for large values of n the number $\left(\frac{n}{e}\right)^n \sqrt{2\pi n}$ is a good approximation for $n!$.

Let us write

$$n! = \left(\frac{n}{e}\right)^n \sqrt{2\pi n}\, e^{\mu(n)} \qquad (4.7\text{–}22)$$

where $\mu(n)$ is defined by

$$\mu(n) = \log n! - (n+\tfrac{1}{2}) \log n + n - \log \sqrt{2\pi}. \qquad (4.7\text{–}23)$$

From (4.7–21) and (4.7–19) it follows that

$$e^{1-\sum_{\nu=1}^{\infty} r_\nu} = \sqrt{2\pi}$$

and, consequently,

$$\mu(n) = \sum_{\nu=n}^{\infty} r_\nu. \qquad (4.7\text{–}24)$$

The estimate (4.7–18) leads at once to

$$0 < \mu(n) < \frac{1}{12n} \qquad (4.7\text{–}25)$$

and this shows again that

$$\lim_{n\to\infty} \mu(n) = 0. \qquad (4.7\text{–}26)$$

4.7.5 – Prym's decomposition

The expression of the gamma function by means of an integral is only valid in the region $\operatorname{Re} z > 0$. It is not difficult, however, to derive another expression involving the second integral of (4.7–2) and, as we already pointed out, this integral has a meaning throughout the entire z-plane. Let us denote the integrals in (4.7–2) by $P(z)$ and $Q(z)$ respectively. Hence

$$\Gamma(z) = P(z) + Q(z) \qquad (4.7\text{–}27)$$

where

$$P(z) = \int_0^1 e^{-t} t^{z-1}\, dt, \qquad Q(z) = \int_1^\infty e^{-t} t^{z-1}\, dt, \tag{4.7–28}$$

the function $Q(z)$ being an integral function. In the first integral (4.7–28) we replace e^{-t} by its Taylor expansion and we then integrate term-by-term, as is obviously permissible when $\operatorname{Re} z > 0$. The result is

$$P(z) = \sum_{\nu=0}^{\infty} \frac{(-1)^\nu}{\nu!(z+\nu)}. \tag{4.7–29}$$

This series is uniformly and absolutely convergent in any closed and bounded set that contains none of the points $z = 0, -1, -2, \ldots$, and so it represents a meromorphic function throughout the entire plane. Since the function obtained by adding $Q(z)$ to the series (4.7–29) coincides with $\Gamma(z)$ to the right of the imaginary axis, it represents $\Gamma(z)$ in the entire plane. We thus find *Prym's decomposition*

$$\boxed{\Gamma(z) = \sum_{\nu=0}^{\infty} \frac{(-1)^\nu}{\nu!(z+\nu)} + \int_1^\infty e^{-t} t^{z-1}\, dt,} \tag{4.7–30}$$

and we see again that the residue of $\Gamma(z)$ at $z = -m$ is $\dfrac{(-1)^m}{m!}$, $m = 0, 1, 2, \ldots$.

4.7.6 – Hankel's integral

A much more satisfactory solution of the problem of representing the gamma function by a single integral which is valid throughout the entire plane turns out to be possible when we take as a starting point the function

$$e^z z^{-s}$$

where s is a complex number. This function considered as a function of z is holomorphic in the principal region $z+|z| \neq 0$. We integrate along a path $L(a)$, that consists of the segment of the lower border of the cut in the z-plane from $-n$ to $-a$, n being a positive integer and a a positive number, a circle of radius a around the origin and the segment of the upper border of the cut from $-a$ to $-n$, (fig. 4.7–1). The integral under consideration is then

$$F_n(s) = \int_{-n}^{-a} e^t t^{-s}\, dt + \int_C e^t t^{-s}\, dt + \int_{-a}^{-n} e^t t^{-s}\, dt, \tag{4.7–31}$$

the variable t being complex. On the lower border we have $z = re^{-\pi i}$, $r \geqq 0$. On the upper border $z = re^{\pi i}$. Hence, the right-hand member of (4.7–31) is equal to

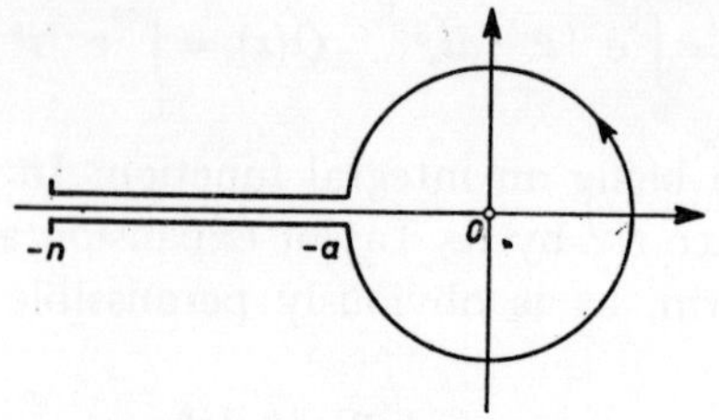

Fig. 4.7–1. Hankel's integral

$$-e^{\pi i s}\int_n^a e^{-r}r^{-s}\,dr - e^{-\pi i s}\int_a^n e^{-r}r^{-s}\,dr + \int_C e^t t^{-s}\,dt$$

$$= (e^{\pi i s} - e^{-\pi i s})\int_a^n e^{-r}r^{-s}\,dr + \int_C e^t t^{-s}\,dt,$$

or

$$F_n(s) = 2i\sin\pi s\int_a^n e^{-r}r^{-s}\,dr + \int_C e^t t^{-s}\,dt. \tag{4.7–32}$$

The function $F_n(s)$ is holomorphic as regards s and the integral $\int_a^\infty e^{-r}r^{-s}\,dr$ is uniformly convergent in any bounded set. According to the theorem of section 2.20.1 the sequence $F_n(s)$ tends to a limiting function $F(s)$ which is holomorphic throughout the entire s-plane. This function is equal to

$$2i\sin\pi s\int_a^\infty e^{-r}r^{-s}\,dr + \int_C e^t t^{-s}\,dt$$

and shall be denoted by

$$F(s) = \int_{L(a)} e^t t^{-s}\,dt. \tag{4.7–33}$$

Now we shall prove that $F(s)$ does not depend on a. In fact, the function

$$G(s) = \int_{L(b)} e^t t^{-s}\,dt - \int_{L(a)} e^t t^{-s}\,dt, \quad a < b,$$

is an integral along the boundary of a ringshaped region that is cut along a segment from $-a$ to $-b$, this segment occurring two times in the path of integration and bearing different values of the integrand, (fig. 4.7–2). Although the integrand is holomorphic throughout this region it is not permissible to apply Cauchy's integral theorem, since the path is not imbedded in a region where the integrand is single-valued. The function $G(s)$ is, however, equal to the integral obtained by replacing t by t^2,

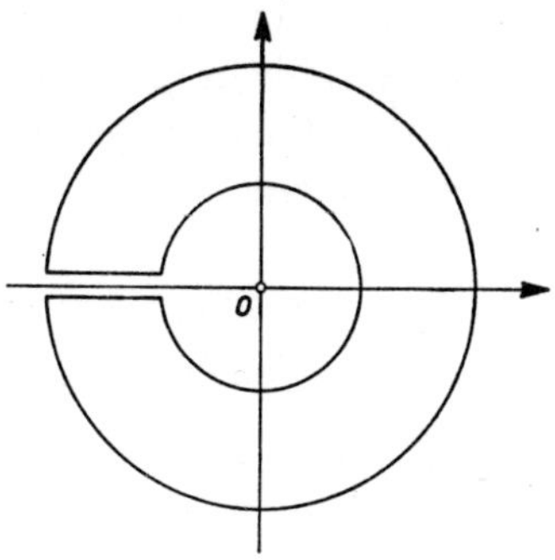

Fig. 4.7–2. Independence of Hankel's integral of the circular loop

$$G(s) = 2\int_{C'} e^{t^2} t^{-2s} t\, dt, \tag{4.7–34}$$

taken along a contour C' consisting of two semi circles to the right of the imaginary axis joined by two segments, (fig. 4.7–3), and it is

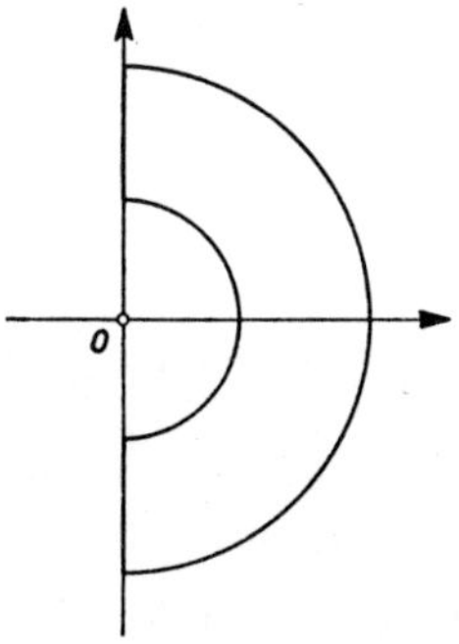

Fig. 4.7–3. Deformation of the path of fig. 4.7–2

now obvious that $G(s)$ vanishes since the contour C' lies in a region where the integrand is holomorphic. Since

$$\left|\int_C e^t t^{-s}\, dt\right| \leqq 2\pi a e^a a^{-\sigma} e^{\pi\omega}, \qquad s = \sigma + i\omega,$$

the left-hand member tends to zero as $a \to 0$, provided $\sigma = \operatorname{Re} s < 1$.

Hence we may infer that

$$F(s) = 2i \sin \pi s \int_0^\infty e^{-r} r^{-s}\, dr = 2i \sin \pi s\, \Gamma(1-s),$$

and by the theorem of the complementary arguments (4.6–13)

$$\boxed{\frac{1}{\Gamma(s)} = \frac{1}{2\pi i}\int_{L(a)} e^t t^{-s}\, dt,} \tag{4.7–35}$$

this equation being valid throughout the entire plane, for the functions at both sides are holomorphic in the entire plane and coincide when $\text{Re}\, s < 1$. The integral on the right-hand side of (4.7–35) shall be referred to as *Hankel's integral.*

4.7.7 – The integral of the first kind

By the *Eulerian integral of the first kind* is understood the integral

$$\int_0^1 t^{p-1}(1-t)^{q-1}dt \tag{4.7–36}$$

where p and q are complex quantities, the integration being performed along the real axis. It is easy to prove that this integral represents a holomorphic function with respect to p as well as q, provided $\text{Re}\, p > 0$, $\text{Re}\, q > 0$.

With Binet we introduce the so-called beta function

$$\boxed{\mathrm{B}(p, q) = \frac{\Gamma(p)\Gamma(q)}{\Gamma(p+q)},} \tag{4.7–37}$$

this function being meromorphic as regards each variable.

We have

$$\boxed{\mathrm{B}(p, q) = \int_0^1 t^{p-1}(1-t)^{q-1}dt,} \tag{4.7–38}$$

provided $\text{Re}\, p > 0$, $\text{Re}\, q > 0$.

On account of the identity principle it is sufficient to exhibit the connection in the case that p and q have real positive values but this has already been done in section 3.6.11.

Since t varies between 0 and 1 we may put $\sin^2\theta = t$, $0 \leqq \theta \leqq \frac{1}{2}\pi$. Then (4.7–38) appears in the trigonometric form

$$\mathrm{B}(p, q) = 2\int_0^{\frac{1}{2}\pi} \sin^{2p-1}\theta \cos^{2q-1}\theta \, d\theta \tag{4.7–39}$$

which is of frequent use in many applications.

4.8 – The Gaussian psi function

4.8.1 – Definition

A function of utmost importance, intimately connected with the gamma function, is the *psi function*, also called the *digamma function*, defined as the logarithmic derivative of the gamma function:

$$\boxed{\Psi(z) = \frac{\Gamma'(z)}{\Gamma(z)}.} \tag{4.8–1}$$

Since $\Gamma(z)$ is a meromorphic function with no zeros, having simple poles, *the psi function is also meromorphic throughout the entire plane, having simple poles with residues equal to* -1 *at the points* $z = 0, -1, -2, \ldots$.

From the Weierstrass product (4.6–1) we obtain

$$\Psi(z)+\gamma = -\frac{1}{z} - \sum_{\nu=1}^{\infty}\left(\frac{1}{z+\nu} - \frac{1}{\nu}\right), \tag{4.8–2}$$

the series being absolutely convergent and uniformly convergent in any closed and bounded set that does not contain the points $z = 0, -1, -2, \ldots$.

From

$$\sum_{\nu=1}^{\infty}\left(\frac{1}{1+\nu} - \frac{1}{\nu}\right) = -1$$

it follows that

$$\boxed{\Psi(1)+\gamma = 0.} \tag{4.8–3}$$

4.8.2 – Functional equations

The functional equation (4.6–9) yields at once

$$\boxed{\Psi(z+1) = \Psi(z) + \frac{1}{z},} \tag{4.8–4}$$

while the theorem of the complementary arguments (4.6–13) leads to

$$\boxed{\Psi(z)-\Psi(1-z) = -\pi \operatorname{ctn} \pi z.} \tag{4.8–5}$$

According to (4.8–4) we have more generally

$$\Psi(z+n) = \sum_{\nu=0}^{n-1} \frac{1}{z+\nu} + \Psi(z), \tag{4.8–6}$$

whence

$$\Psi(z+n)-\Psi(1+n) = \frac{1}{z} - \frac{1}{n} + \sum_{\nu=1}^{n-1}\left(\frac{1}{z+\nu} - \frac{1}{\nu}\right) + \Psi(z) - \Psi(1).$$

On account of (4.8–2) and (4.8–3) we may infer that

$$\lim_{n\to\infty} \{\Psi(z+n)-\Psi(1+n)\} = 0, \tag{4.8–7}$$

uniformly as regards z in any bounded and closed set that does not contain the poles of $\Psi(z)$.

The behaviour of $\Psi(z+n)$ for large values of n turns out to be very simple as we shall see presently. In the first place it is required to extend slightly the expression

$$\gamma = \lim_{n\to\infty} \left(\sum_{\nu=1}^{n} \frac{1}{\nu} - \log n\right).$$

Let s denote an arbitrary complex number. Then

$$\lim_{n\to\infty} \{\log (s+n) - \log n\} = \lim_{n\to\infty} \log \left(1+\frac{s}{n}\right) = 0$$

and, consequently, also

$$\gamma = \lim_{n\to\infty} \left\{\sum_{\nu=1}^{n} \frac{1}{\nu} - \log (s+n)\right\}. \tag{4.8–8}$$

Actually the right-hand member does not depend on s.

By (4.8–6) we have

$$\Psi(n+1) = \sum_{\nu=1}^{n} \frac{1}{\nu} + \Psi(1),$$

or, taking (4.8–3) into account,

$$\sum_{\nu=1}^{n} \frac{1}{\nu} = \Psi(n+1)+\gamma. \tag{4.8–9}$$

Inserting this in (4.8–8) we get

$$\lim_{n\to\infty} \{\Psi(n+1) - \log (s+n)\} = 0 \tag{4.8–10}$$

and comparing this result with (4.8–7) we finally have

$$\lim_{n\to\infty} \{\Psi(z+n) - \log (s+n)\} = 0. \tag{4.8–11}$$

Hence for large values of n the function $\Psi(z+n)$ behaves like the logarithm.

4.8.3 – Jensen's series

It is now easy to obtain a series for $\Psi(z)$ which is due to Jensen. Since

$$\log (z+n) - \log z = \sum_{\nu=1}^{n-1} \log \left(1+\frac{1}{z+\nu}\right) \tag{4.8–12}$$

we find from (4.8–6)

$$\Psi(z) = \log z - \sum_{\nu=0}^{n-1} \left\{\frac{1}{z+\nu} - \log \left(1+\frac{1}{z+\nu}\right)\right\} + \Psi(z+n) - \log (z+n) \tag{4.8–13}$$

and according to (4.8–11) we may infer that

$$\boxed{\Psi(z) = \log z - \sum_{\nu=0}^{\infty} \left\{ \frac{1}{z+\nu} - \log\left(1 + \frac{1}{z+\nu}\right) \right\},} \tag{4.8–14}$$

the expansion being valid for all values of z save, of course, $z = 0, -1, -2, \ldots$.

4.8.4 – Expression of the logarithm in terms of the psi-function

The previous considerations made it obvious that there is an intimate relation between the psi function and the logarithm. In the same direction we shall also establish another interesting result.

The functional equation (4.8–4) may be put into the form

$$\int_0^1 \Psi'(z+t)dt - \frac{1}{z} = 0 \tag{4.8–15}$$

and the left-hand member is obviously the derivative of

$$\int_0^1 \Psi(z+t)dt - \log z \tag{4.8–16}$$

whenever $z+|z| \neq 0$. Hence the latter function does not depend on z and we therefore have

$$\int_0^1 \{\Psi(z+t) - \log z\}dt = \int_0^1 \{\Psi(z+t+n) - \log(z+n)\}dt. \tag{4.8–17}$$

On account of (4.8–11) we may infer that

$$\boxed{\int_0^1 \Psi(z+t)dt = \log z,} \qquad z+|z| \neq 0. \tag{4.8–18}$$

4.8.5 – Raabe's integral

The integral (4.8–18) is the derivative of

$$\int_0^1 \log \Gamma(z+t)dt, \qquad z+|z| \neq 0, \tag{4.8–19}$$

and hence this integral is equal to

$$A + z \log z - z, \tag{4.8–20}$$

A being a constant. Letting $z \to 0$, for instance along the positive real axis, we have in particular

$$\int_0^1 \log \Gamma(t)dt = A. \tag{4.8–21}$$

We may evaluate the constant A by applying the formula (4.6–13) of the complementary arguments of the gamma function, for, in addition to (4.8–21),

$$\int_0^1 \log \Gamma(1-t)dt = A \tag{4.8–22}$$

is also valid, whence by adding corresponding members of (4.8–21) and (4.8–22)

$$\log \pi - \int_0^1 \log \sin \pi t \, dt = 2A. \tag{4.8–23}$$

Now by a simple substitution the equation (3.9–5) can be transformed into

$$\int_0^1 \log \sin \pi t \, dt = -\log 2, \tag{4.8–24}$$

whence by (4.8–23)

$$A = \log \sqrt{2\pi}, \tag{4.8–25}$$

and we thus find *Raabe's integral*

$$\boxed{\int_0^1 \log \Gamma(z+t)dt = z \log z - z + \log \sqrt{2\pi}.} \tag{4.8–26}$$

4.8.6 – Representation of the psi function as an infinite integral

It is not difficult to obtain in a purely formal way a representation of the psi function as an infinite integral. Assuming $\operatorname{Re} z > 0$ we have on account of (4.8–2)

$$\begin{aligned} \Psi(z)+\gamma &= -\frac{1}{z} - \sum_{\nu=1}^{\infty}\left(\frac{1}{z+\nu} - \frac{1}{\nu}\right) \\ &= -\int_0^\infty e^{-tz}\,dt - \sum_{\nu=1}^{\infty}\int_0^\infty (e^{-t(z+\nu)} - e^{-t\nu})\,dt, \end{aligned}$$

whence by the formula of the sum of a geometric series (reversing the order of summation and integration)

$$\Psi(z)+\gamma = -\int_0^\infty e^{-tz}\,dt - \int_0^\infty \frac{e^{-t(z+1)} - e^{-t}}{1-e^{-t}}\,dt,$$

or

$$\Psi(z)+\gamma = \int_0^\infty \frac{e^{-t} - e^{-tz}}{1-e^{-t}}\,dt. \tag{4.8–27}$$

Before justifying this result we wish to eliminate the constant γ. In the first place we observe that

$$\sum_{\nu=1}^{n}\frac{1}{\nu}=\sum_{\nu=1}^{n}\int_0^\infty e^{-\nu t}\,dt=\int_0^\infty\left(\sum_{\nu=1}^{n}e^{-\nu t}\right)dt=\int_0^\infty\frac{1-e^{-nt}}{1-e^{-t}}e^{-t}\,dt. \quad (4.8\text{–}28)$$

Now we recall the expression (2.20–27) for $\log s$ as an infinite integral. Taking $s = n$ we may write

$$\log n=\int_0^\infty\frac{e^{-t}-e^{-nt}}{t}\,dt.$$

Hence

$$\sum_{\nu=1}^{n}\frac{1}{\nu}-\log n=\int_0^\infty\left(\frac{1}{1-e^{-t}}-\frac{1}{t}\right)e^{-t}dt-\int_0^\infty\left(\frac{1}{e^{t}-1}-\frac{1}{t}\right)e^{-nt}\,dt, \quad (4.8\text{–}29)$$

both integrals being convergent, for the first integrand may be written as

$$\frac{1}{e^t-1}-\frac{e^{-t}}{t}=\frac{1}{e^t-1}-\frac{1}{t}+\frac{e^{-t}-1}{-t},$$

and since

$$\frac{1}{e^t-1}-\frac{1}{t}$$

is continuous at $t = 0$ the same is true for the integrand under consideration. The convergence at the upper limit needs no comment. In the second integral the factor of e^{-nt} is bounded and, consequently, letting $n \to \infty$

$$\boxed{\gamma=\int_0^\infty\left(\frac{1}{1-e^{-t}}-\frac{1}{t}\right)e^{-t}\,dt.} \quad (4.8\text{–}30)$$

Inserting this expression for γ into (4.8–28) we find

$$\boxed{\Psi(z)=\int_0^\infty\left(\frac{e^{-t}}{t}-\frac{e^{-tz}}{1-e^{-t}}\right)dt,} \quad \operatorname{Re} z>0, \quad (4.8\text{–}31)$$

an integral due to Gauss.

4.8.7 – Characterization of the psi function

It remains to prove (4.8–27). This can be readily done by applying the following theorem which states that the relations (4.8–3), (4.8–4) and (4.8–7) determine the psi function uniquely:

There exists one and only one function $F(z)$ which satisfies the conditions:

$$F(1)+\gamma=0, \quad (4.8\text{–}32)$$

$$F(z+1)-F(z)=\frac{1}{z}, \quad (4.8\text{–}33)$$

$$\lim_{n\to\infty} \{F(z+n)-F(1+n)\} = 0, \qquad (4.8\text{–}34)$$

z being different from 0, $-1, -2, \ldots$.

In fact, we deduce from (4.8–33)

$$F(z+n) = \frac{1}{z} + \sum_{\nu=1}^{n-1} \frac{1}{z+\nu} + F(z),$$

whence

$$F(1+n) = \sum_{\nu=1}^{n-1} \frac{1}{\nu} + \frac{1}{n} + F(1)$$

and, on account of (4.8–32),

$$F(z+n)-F(1+n) = \frac{1}{z} + \sum_{\nu=1}^{n-1}\left(\frac{1}{z+\nu} - \frac{1}{\nu}\right) - \frac{1}{n} + F(z)+\gamma.$$

Making $n \to \infty$ we find from (4.8–34)

$$F(z)+\gamma = -\frac{1}{z} - \sum_{\nu=1}^{\infty}\left(\frac{1}{z+\nu} - \frac{1}{\nu}\right)$$

and by virtue of (4.8–2) we have $F(z) = \Psi(z)$.

Next we shall verify that the function

$$F(z) = -\gamma + \int_0^\infty \frac{e^{-t}-e^{-tz}}{1-e^{-t}}\, dt \qquad (4.8\text{–}35)$$

satisfies the conditions mentioned in the theorem. It is not difficult to prove that the integral has a meaning whenever $\operatorname{Re} z > 0$, for the integrand can be written as

$$-1 + \frac{1-e^{-tz}}{1-e^{-t}}$$

and turns out to be continuous at $t = 0$. If $t \geqq 1$ we have

$$\left|\frac{e^{-t}-e^{-tz}}{1-e^{-t}}\right| \leqq \frac{e^{-t}+e^{-tx}}{1-e^{-t}} < \frac{2e^{-t}}{1-e^{-t}}, \qquad x = \operatorname{Re} z > 0,$$

and the integral proves to be convergent at the upper limit.

The relation (4.8–32) is trivially satisfied. Further

$$F(z+1)-F(z) = \int_0^\infty e^{-tz}\, dt = \frac{1}{z},$$

so that it remains to verify (4.8–34). Now

$$F(z+n)-F(1+n) = \int_0^\infty \frac{e^{-t(1+n)}-e^{-t(z+n)}}{1-e^{-t}}\, dt$$

$$= \int_0^\infty \frac{e^{-t}-e^{-tz}}{1-e^{-t}}\, e^{-tn}\, dt,$$

whence

$$|F(z+n)-F(1+n)| \leqq M\int_0^\infty e^{-tn}\,dt = \frac{M}{n} \to 0$$

as $n \to \infty$. Here M denotes an appropriate constant. This completes the proof.

4.8.8 – Representation of Bernoulli's numbers as an infinite integral

We wish to conclude our considerations with an interesting application of the integral for the psi function. In view of (4.8–5) we readily obtain

$$-\pi \operatorname{ctn} \pi z = \int_0^\infty \frac{e^{-t(1-z)}-e^{-tz}}{1-e^{-t}}\,dt = \int_0^\infty \frac{e^{tz}-e^{-t(z-1)}}{e^t-1}\,dt$$

$$= \int_0^\infty \frac{e^{tz}-e^{-tz}}{e^t-1}\,dt - \int_0^\infty e^{-tz}\,dt,$$

whence

$$\pi \operatorname{ctn} \pi z = \frac{1}{z} - \int_0^\infty \frac{e^{tz}-e^{-tz}}{e^t-1}\,dt = \frac{1}{z} - 2\int_0^\infty \frac{\sinh tz}{e^t-1}\,dt.$$

Replacing πz by z and t by $2\pi t$ we finally have a representation of the cotangent as an infinite integral:

$$\operatorname{ctn} z = \frac{1}{z} - 4\int_0^\infty \frac{\sinh 2tz}{e^{2\pi t}-1}\,dt. \tag{4.8–36}$$

Now we may expand both members of this equation in terms of powers of z. According to (2.17–20) the relation

$$\sum_{\nu=1}^\infty \frac{B_{2\nu}}{(2\nu)!}\, 2^{2\nu} z^{2\nu-1} = 4\int_0^\infty \frac{\sinh 2tz}{e^{2\pi t}-1}\,dt \tag{4.8–37}$$

holds.

The integral on the right is holomorphic with respect to z in a neighbourhood of the origin. By differentiating $2n-1$ times within the sign of integration we readily find

$$\boxed{B_{2n} = 4n\int_0^\infty \frac{t^{2n-1}}{e^{2\pi t}-1}\,dt,} \qquad n = 1, 2, \ldots, \tag{4.8–38}$$

a representation of the Bernoulli numbers by an infinite integral. In section 7.7.3 we shall meet this expression again in connection with the zeta function of Riemann.

4.9 – Binet's function

4.9.1 – Definition

Raabe's integral (4.8–27) may be taken as a starting point for interesting and important developments. Upon integration by parts we obtain

$$\log \Gamma(z+1) - \int_0^1 t\Psi(z+t)dt = z \log z - z + \log \sqrt{2\pi}, \qquad (4.9\text{–}1)$$

or

$$\log \Gamma(z+1) - z \log z + z - \log \sqrt{2\pi} = \int_0^1 t\Psi(z+t)dt. \qquad (4.9\text{–}2)$$

In view of the definition (4.7–23) of $\mu(n)$ it is natural to study the function

$$\mu(z) = \log \Gamma(z+1) - (z+\tfrac{1}{2}) \log z + z - \log \sqrt{2\pi}, \qquad (4.9\text{–}3)$$

which will be referred to as *Binet's function*. Taking account of (4.8–18), we evidently have

$$\boxed{\mu(z) = \int_0^1 (t-\tfrac{1}{2})\Psi(z+t)\, dt.} \qquad (4.9\text{–}4)$$

This integral can be thrown into a more convenient form if we introduce the function

$$\mathsf{P}_1(t) = t - [t] - \tfrac{1}{2}, \qquad (4.9\text{–}5)$$

$[t]$ denoting, as usual, the greatest integer not exceeding t. This function is periodic, with period 1. It is continuous everywhere, except when t is an integer, for then it presents a jump -1, (fig. 4.9–1). It has the pleasant property

$$\int_n^{n+1} \mathsf{P}_1(t)dt = 0 \qquad (4.9\text{–}6)$$

where n is any integer.

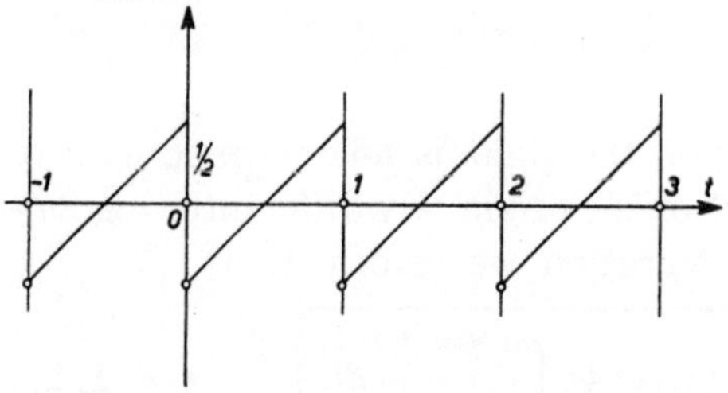

Fig. 4.9–1. Graph of the function $t-[t]-\frac{1}{2}$

Now we might argue as follows. By virtue of the functional equation (4.8–4) of the function $\Psi(z)$ we have

$$\begin{aligned}\int_0^\infty \frac{\mathsf{P}_1(t)}{z+t}\, dt &= \int_0^\infty \mathsf{P}_1(t)\Psi(z+t+1)dt - \int_0^\infty \mathsf{P}_1(t)\Psi(z+t)dt \\ &= \int_1^\infty \mathsf{P}_1(t)\Psi(z+t)\, dt - \int_0^\infty \mathsf{P}_1(t)\Psi(z+t)\, dt \\ &= -\int_0^1 \mathsf{P}_1(t)\Psi(z+t)dt,\end{aligned}$$

whence

$$\mu(z) = -\int_0^\infty \frac{\mathsf{P}_1(t)}{z+t}\,dt = -\int_0^\infty \frac{t-[t]-\frac{1}{2}}{z+t}\,dt. \qquad (4.9\text{–}7)$$

Unfortunately the integral $\int_0^\infty \mathsf{P}_1(t)\Psi(z+t)dt$ is not convergent, since for large values of t the function $\Psi(z+t)$ behaves like log $(z+t)$, as we pointed out in section 4.8.1.

The following reasoning, however, is sound. First we have to prove that the integral occurring in (4.9–7) is convergent. To this end we introduce the function $\mathsf{Q}(t) = \int_0^t \mathsf{P}_1(x)dx$, $t > 0$. By virtue of (4.9–6) the function $\mathsf{Q}(t)$ is bounded and its modulus remains below a certain constant A. By integration by parts we get

$$\int_{\omega_1}^{\omega_2} \frac{\mathsf{P}_1(t)}{z+t}\,dt = \frac{\mathsf{Q}(t)}{z+t}\bigg|_{\omega_1}^{\omega_2} + \int_{\omega_1}^{\omega_2} \frac{\mathsf{Q}(t)}{(z+t)^2}\,dt, \quad 0 \leqq \omega_1 < \omega_2. \qquad (4.9\text{–}8)$$

Since

$$\left|\frac{\mathsf{Q}(t)}{(z+t)^2}\right| < \frac{A}{|z+t|^2} \leqq \frac{A}{(x+t)^2}$$

we may conclude that the expression on the right of (4.9–8) tends to zero as $\omega_1 \to \infty$, and the statement follows.

Next, we have on account of (4.8–4)

$$\begin{aligned}\int_0^n \frac{\mathsf{P}_1(t)}{z+t}\,dt &= \int_0^n \mathsf{P}_1(t)\Psi(z+t+1)dt - \int_0^n \mathsf{P}_1(t)\Psi(z+t)\,dt\\ &= \int_1^{n+1} \mathsf{P}_1(t)\Psi(z+t)dt - \int_0^n \mathsf{P}_1(t)\Psi(z+t)dt\\ &= \int_n^{n+1} \mathsf{P}_1(t)\Psi(z+t)dt - \int_0^1 \mathsf{P}_1(t)\Psi(z+t)dt\end{aligned}$$

and it remains to prove that

$$\int_n^{n+1} \mathsf{P}_1(t)\Psi(z+t)dt = \int_0^1 \mathsf{P}_1(t)\Psi(z+t+n)dt \to 0,$$

as $n \to \infty$. Now by (4.9–6) and (4.8–7)

$$\int_0^1 \mathsf{P}_1(t)\Psi(z+t+n)dt = \int_0^1 \mathsf{P}_1(t)\{\Psi(z+t+n)-\Psi(1+n)\}dt \to 0,$$

as $n \to \infty$. This concludes the proof of (4.9–7).

In section 7.9.5 we shall find the same result by another method.

4.9.2 – Stirling's theorem for the gamma function

The equation (4.9–7) yields information about the behaviour of

$\mu(z)$ for large values of $|z|$. Put $z = re^{i\theta}$. Then

$$|t+z|^2 = (t+r\cos\theta)^2 + r^2\sin^2\theta = (t+r)^2 - 4tr\sin^2\tfrac{1}{2}\theta \geqq (t+r)^2\cos^2\tfrac{1}{2}\theta,$$

since $(t+r)^2 \geqq 4tr$. Hence

$$|t+z| \geqq (t+r)\cos\tfrac{1}{2}\theta \tag{4.9–9}$$

and

$$|\mu(z)| = \left|\int_0^\infty \frac{\mathsf{P}_1(t)}{z+t}\,dt\right| = \left|\int_0^\infty \frac{\mathsf{Q}(t)}{(z+t)^2}\,dt\right| \leqq \sec^2\tfrac{1}{2}\theta \int_0^\infty \frac{|\mathsf{Q}(t)|}{(r+t)^2}\,dt \leqq \frac{A}{r}\sec^2\tfrac{1}{2}\theta. \tag{4.9–10}$$

It is obvious that the ultimate expression tends to zero as $z \to \infty$ provided that $\theta = \arg z$ does not come arbitrarily near to $\pm\pi$. This result may be stated as:

Binet's function $\mu(z)$ *tends to zero when* z *goes to infinity, receding indefinitely from the negative real axis.* This theorem is often referred to as *Stirling's theorem*. It includes the results of section 4.7.4.

The situation mentioned in the above theorem presents itself, for instance, when z moves in a set determined by

$$|\arg z| \leqq \pi - \delta, \qquad \delta > 0, \tag{4.9–11}$$

i.e., the set obtained by deleting from the z-plane an angular region that contains the negative real axis, (fig. 4.9–2).

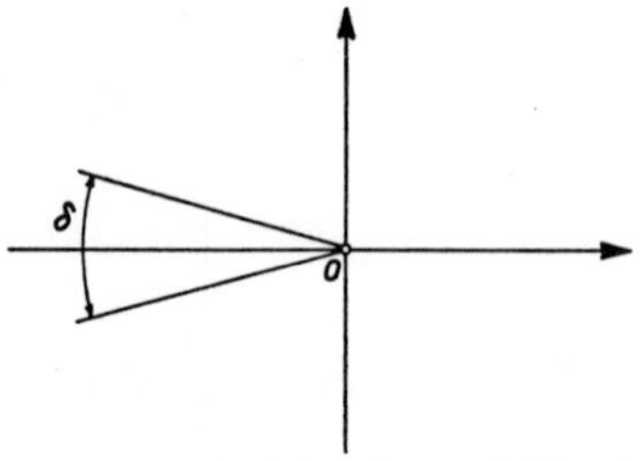

Fig. 4.9–2. Asymptotic behaviour of Binet's function

Since $\exp\mu(z) = 1 + o(1)$, where $o(1)$ denotes a function which tends to zero when $z \to \infty$ in the described manner, we have according to (4.9–11)

$$\boxed{\Gamma(z+1) = \left(\frac{z}{\mathrm{e}}\right)^z \sqrt{2\pi z}\,(1+o(1)).} \tag{4.9–12}$$

This is an alternative form of Stirling's theorem.

4.9.3 – Gudermann's series

From (4.9–3) we derive the following difference equation for

Binet's function

$$\mu(z+1)-\mu(z) = 1-(z+\tfrac{1}{2}) \log\left(1+\frac{1}{z}\right) \qquad (4.9\text{–}13)$$

whence

$$\mu(z+n)-\mu(z) = \sum_{\nu=0}^{n-1}\left\{1-(z+\nu+\tfrac{1}{2})\log\left(1+\frac{1}{z+\nu}\right)\right\}, \qquad (4.9\text{–}14)$$

and letting $n \to \infty$ we have on account of (4.9–8) the *Gudermann series*

$$\boxed{\mu(z) = \sum_{\nu=0}^{\infty}\left\{(z+\nu+\tfrac{1}{2})\log\left(1+\frac{1}{z+\nu}\right)-1\right\},} \qquad (4.9\text{–}15)$$

the expression being valid in the region $z+|z| \neq 0$.

4.9.4 – Binet's first integral

There are various representations of $\mu(z)$ as an infinite integral. In the first place we wish to deduce a classical representation due to Binet. The derivative of the function $\mu(z)$ is

$$\mu'(z) = \Psi(z)- \log z + \frac{1}{2z}. \qquad (4.9\text{–}16)$$

Under the assumption $\operatorname{Re} z > 0$ we have by (4.8–31) and (2.20–27)

$$\mu'(z) = \int_0^\infty \left(\frac{e^{-t}}{t} - \frac{e^{-zt}}{1-e^{-t}}\right) dt - \int_0^\infty \frac{e^{-t}-e^{-zt}}{t}\,dt + \tfrac{1}{2}\int_0^\infty e^{-zt}\,dt,$$

or

$$\mu'(z) = \int_0^\infty \left(\frac{1}{2}+\frac{1}{t}-\frac{1}{1-e^{-t}}\right) e^{-zt}\,dt. \qquad (4.9\text{–}17)$$

This result reduces to (4.8–30) if we take $z = 1$. Since

$$\frac{1}{2}-\frac{1}{1-e^{-t}} = -\frac{1}{e^t-1}-\frac{1}{2}$$

we may also write

$$\mu'(z) = \int_0^\infty \left(-\frac{1}{2}+\frac{1}{t}-\frac{1}{e^t-1}\right) e^{-zt}\,dt. \qquad (4.9\text{–}18)$$

The proof of the uniform convergence of the integral in any closed and bounded set to the right of the imaginary axis affords no serious difficulty. Accordingly it is permissible to integrate inside the sign of integration (2.20.6) and an easy calculation yields

$$\mu(z)-\mu(1) = \int_0^\infty \left(\frac{1}{e^t-1}-\frac{1}{t}+\frac{1}{2}\right)\frac{e^{-zt}}{t}\,dt - \int_0^\infty \left(\frac{1}{e^t-1}-\frac{1}{t}+\frac{1}{2}\right)\frac{e^{-t}}{t}\,dt. \qquad (4.9\text{–}19)$$

Letting $z \to \infty$ such that z recedes indefinitely from the negative real axis, we readily find

$$\mu(1) = \int_0^\infty \left(\frac{1}{e^t - 1} - \frac{1}{t} + \frac{1}{2}\right) \frac{e^{-t}}{t}\, dt \tag{4.9–20}$$

and thus (4.9–19) implies

$$\boxed{\mu(z) = \int_0^\infty \left(\frac{1}{e^t - 1} - \frac{1}{t} + \frac{1}{2}\right) \frac{e^{-zt}}{t}\, dt,} \qquad \operatorname{Re} z > 0, \tag{4.9–21}$$

Binet's first representation of $\mu(z)$.

4.9.5 – Schaar's integral and Binet's second integral

In order to transform the integral (4.9–21) we may use a device due to Cauchy. Observing that

$$\frac{1}{e^t - 1} - \frac{1}{t} + \frac{1}{2} = \frac{1}{2}\frac{e^t + 1}{e^t - 1} - \frac{1}{t} = \tfrac{1}{2} i \operatorname{ctn} \tfrac{1}{2} it - \frac{1}{t} \tag{4.9–22}$$

we have by virtue of (3.7–30)

$$\left(\frac{1}{e^t - 1} - \frac{1}{t} + \frac{1}{2}\right) \frac{1}{t} = 2 \sum_{\nu=1}^{\infty} \frac{1}{t^2 + 4\pi^2\nu^2}. \tag{4.9–23}$$

This result leads at once to the estimate

$$\left(\frac{1}{e^t - 1} - \frac{1}{t} + \frac{1}{2}\right) \frac{1}{t} < 2 \sum_{\nu=1}^{\infty} \frac{1}{4\pi^2\nu^2} = \frac{2}{4\pi^2} \cdot \frac{\pi^2}{6} = \frac{1}{12}, \qquad t > 0,$$

whence

$$|\mu(z)| < \frac{1}{12 \operatorname{Re} z}, \qquad \operatorname{Re} z > 0, \tag{4.9–24}$$

in accordance with (4.7–25).

Instead of (4.9–21) we may write

$$\mu(z) = \int_0^\infty 2 \sum_{\nu=1}^{\infty} \frac{e^{-zt}}{t^2 + 4\pi^2\nu^2}\, dt = 2 \sum_{\nu=1}^{\infty} \int_0^\infty \frac{e^{-zt}}{t^2 + 4\pi^2\nu^2}\, dt. \tag{4.9–25}$$

The reversal of the order of integration and summation may be justified as follows. The series

$$\sum_{\nu=1}^{\infty} \frac{e^{-zt}}{t^2 + 4\pi^2\nu^2}$$

is uniformly convergent in the interval $0 \leq t \leq \omega$. Hence

$$\int_0^\omega \sum_{\nu=1}^{\infty} \frac{e^{-zt}}{t^2 + 4\pi^2\nu^2}\, dt = \sum_{\nu=1}^{\infty} \int_0^\omega \frac{e^{-zt}}{t^2 + 4\pi^2\nu^2}\, dt.$$

The series on the right is uniformly convergent as regards ω, since

$$\left|\int_0^\infty \frac{e^{-zt}}{t^2+4\pi^2n^2}dt\right| < \int_0^\infty \frac{e^{-xt}}{t^2+4\pi^2n^2}dt < \frac{1}{4\pi^2n^2}\int_0^\infty e^{-xt}dt, x = \operatorname{Re} z, n = 1,2,\ldots.$$

Hence we can make $\omega \to \infty$, and the result follows.

Now

$$\int_0^\infty \frac{2e^{-zt}}{t^2+4\pi^2n^2}dt = \frac{1}{\pi}\int_0^\infty \frac{1}{1+t^2}\frac{e^{-2n\pi zt}}{n}dt, \quad n = 1, 2, \ldots,$$

and reversing the order of integration and summation again we find

$$\mu(z) = \frac{1}{\pi}\int_0^\infty \frac{1}{1+t^2}\sum_{\nu=1}^\infty \frac{e^{-2\nu\pi zt}}{\nu}dt,$$

or

$$\boxed{\mu(z) = -\frac{1}{\pi}\int_0^\infty \frac{1}{1+t^2}\log(1-e^{-2\pi zt})dt,} \qquad \operatorname{Re} z > 0, \qquad (4.9\text{–}26)$$

a representation of $\mu(z)$ due to Schaar. On performing integration by parts we obtain *Binet's second representation* of $\mu(z)$:

$$\boxed{\mu(z) = 2z\int_0^\infty \frac{\arctan t}{e^{2\pi zt}-1}dt,} \qquad \operatorname{Re} z > 0. \qquad (4.9\text{–}27)$$

By taking special values of z we find some interesting formulas. For instance, we may insert $z = 1$ into (4.9–27) and we get

$$2\int_0^\infty \frac{\arctan t}{e^{2\pi t}-1}dt = 1-\log\sqrt{2\pi}. \qquad (4.9\text{–}28)$$

By virtue of (4.9–16) we have on differentiating both sides of (4.9–26)

$$\Psi(z) = \log z - \frac{1}{2z} - 2\int_0^\infty \frac{t}{1+t^2}\frac{1}{e^{2\pi zt}-1}dt \qquad (4.9\text{–}29)$$

and by putting $z = 1$

$$\gamma = \frac{1}{2} + 2\int_0^\infty \frac{t}{1+t^2}\frac{1}{e^{2\pi t}-1}dt, \qquad (4.9\text{–}30)$$

an expression due to Poisson.

4.10 – Cauchy's method for the decomposition of meromorphic functions into partial fractions

4.10.1 – Description of the method

In section 3.4.2 we encountered a decomposition of a rational function into partial fractions. An example of a decomposition into partial fractions of a meromorphic function with infinitely many poles is provided by Prym's decomposition of the gamma function (4.7–30).

It is our intention to extend these results to functions $f(z)$ holomorphic in the entire plane except for isolated singularities.

Let $a_0 = 0, a_1, a_2, \ldots,$ denote these singular points. Since within any circle around the origin there can be only a finite number of singularities, we can arrange them in order of non-decreasing moduli, viz.,

$$a_0 < |a_1| \leqq |a_2| \leqq \ldots. \tag{4.10–1}$$

At every singular point a_n there is a Laurent expansion. The part of this expansion involving the negative powers shall be designated by

$$g_n\left(\frac{1}{z-a_n}\right), \tag{4.10–2}$$

where $g_n(z)$ is a power series (or a polynomial when a_n is a pole) with $g_n(0) = 0$. If the function is regular at $z = 0$ then $g_0(z) = 0$ identically.

In Cauchy's method the integral

$$\frac{1}{2\pi i}\int_C \frac{s^m}{\zeta^m}\frac{f(\zeta)}{\zeta-s}\,d\zeta \tag{4.10–3}$$

is taken as a starting point. C is a regular contour surrounding the origin but avoiding any of the singular points, s is an arbitrary regular point inside C and m is a positive integer.

Since

$$\frac{1}{z}+\frac{s}{z^2}+\ldots+\frac{s^{m-1}}{z^m} = \frac{1}{z}\frac{1-(s/z)^m}{1-s/z} = \frac{1-(s/z)^m}{z-s}$$

the integral (4.10–3) may also be written in the form

$$\frac{1}{2\pi i}\int_C f(\zeta)\left(\frac{1}{\zeta-s}-\frac{1}{\zeta}-\frac{s}{\zeta^2}-\ldots-\frac{s^{m-1}}{\zeta^m}\right)d\zeta. \tag{4.10–4}$$

We shall evaluate this integral by applying the residue theorem. To begin with we observe that s is a simple pole of the integrand, the residue being $f(s)$. Let us write

$$f(z) = g_n\left(\frac{1}{z-a_n}\right)+f_n(z-a_n)$$

where $f_n(z)$ is an ordinary power series in z. Then

$$\frac{f(z)}{z-s} = \frac{f(z)}{z-a_n-(s-a_n)}$$

$$= \frac{-1}{s-a_n}\,\frac{f(z)}{1-(z-a_n)/(s-a_n)} = -f(z)\sum_{\nu=1}^{\infty}\frac{(z-a_n)^{\nu-1}}{(s-a_n)^{\nu}}$$

$$= -\left\{f_n(z-a_n)+\sum_{\nu=1}^{\infty}\frac{c_{-\nu}^{(n)}}{(z-a_n)^{\nu}}\right\}\left\{\sum_{\nu=1}^{\infty}\frac{(z-a_n)^{\nu-1}}{(s-a_n)^{\nu}}\right\}$$

and it is easy to see that the coefficient of $1/(z-a_n)$ in this expansion is equal to $-g_n\{1/(s-a_n)\}$. Let $h_n(s)$ designate the coefficient of $1/(z-a_n)$ in the expansion of

$$-f(z)\left(\frac{1}{z}+\frac{s}{z^2}+\ldots+\frac{s^{m-1}}{z^m}\right) \tag{4.10–5}$$

in terms of powers of $z-a_n$. Clearly $h_n(s)$ is a polynomial of degree not exceeding $m-1$. Hence the residue of the integrand at $z = a_n$ is equal to

$$-\left\{g_n\left(\frac{1}{s-a_n}\right)-h_n(s)\right\}. \tag{4.10–6}$$

4.10.2 – Expansion of a meromorphic function into partial fractions

Consider the sequence

$$C_1, C_2, C_3, \ldots \tag{4.10–7}$$

of regular contours around the origin, each containing the preceding one in its interior, and such that to a given number of singular points $a_1, \ldots, a_k$ there always exists a contour C_p of the sequence (4.10–7) surrounding these points.

If we make the assumption that

$$\frac{1}{2\pi i}\int_{C_p}\frac{1}{\zeta^m}\,\frac{f(\zeta)}{\zeta-s}\,d\zeta \tag{4.10–8}$$

tends to zero for an appropriately chosen number m as $p\to\infty$ then $f(s)$ can be expanded in partial fractions

$$f(s) = \sum_{\nu=0}^{\infty}\left\{g\left(\frac{1}{s-a_\nu}\right)-h_\nu(s)\right\}, \tag{4.10–9}$$

this series being uniformly convergent in any closed and bounded set which does not contain a singular point.

This theorem is a direct consequence of the residue theorem.

4.10.3 – The polynomials $h_n(s)$

We wish to characterize the polynomials $h_n(s)$ in more detail. The cases $n = 0$ and $n > 0$ must be considered separately. The polynomial $h_0(s)$ is the residue of the function (4.10–5) at the origin. From the expansion of $f(z)$ in a neighbourhood of the origin we deduce at once that $h_0(s)$, being the coefficient of z^{-1} in the expansion of (4.10–5) in terms of powers of z, *is a polynomial consisting of the first m terms of the regular part of $f(s)$.*

In order to be able to characterize $h_n(s)$ in the case $n > 0$ we assume that s is sufficiently near to the origin. Then, if $C(a_n)$ is a small circle around the point a_n, we have, according to the statement at the end of section 4.10.1,

$$g_n\left(\frac{1}{s-a_n}\right) - h_n(s) = -\frac{s^m}{2\pi i}\int_{C(a_n)} \frac{1}{\zeta^m}\frac{f(\zeta)}{\zeta - s}\,d\zeta, \qquad (4.10\text{–}10)$$

and the expansion of the right-hand member as a power series of s begins with a term involving s^m. *Hence $h_n(s)$ is a polynomial consisting of the first m terms of the expansion of $g_n\{1/(s-a_n)\}$ as a power series in s,* on account of the fact that the coefficients of a Cauchy-Taylor expansion are uniquely determined.

If we assume that the contours of the sequence (4.10–7) expand to infinity in such a way that the distance of the origin to C_p exceeds any prescribed number whenever p is sufficiently large, then finally $|z/\zeta| < \varepsilon$, the number ε being arbitrarily chosen between 0 and 1 while ζ is on C_p. As a consequence the modulus of the integral (4.10–8) does not exceed

$$\frac{1}{1-\varepsilon}\,\frac{1}{2\pi}\int_{C_p}\left|\frac{f(\zeta)}{\zeta^{m+1}}\right|\,|d\zeta|,$$

whenever p is large enough, and we may conclude that (4.10–9) *is certainly valid when*

$$\int_{C_p}\left|\frac{f(\zeta)}{\zeta^{m+1}}\right|\,|d\zeta| \to 0 \qquad (4.10\text{–}11)$$

as $p \to \infty$, m being an appropriately chosen integer.

4.10.4 – Illustrative examples

We illustrate these results in some simple examples. In the first place we consider the function

$$f(z) = \pi \operatorname{ctn} \pi z. \qquad (4.10\text{–}12)$$

This function possesses simple poles at $z = 0, \pm 1, \pm 2, \ldots$, and is bounded on the circumference of a rectangle C_p whose sides are on the lines

$$x = \pm(p+\tfrac{1}{2}), \qquad y = \pm p,$$

p being an arbitrarily large positive integer, as we already pointed out in section 3.7.3. It follows that (4.10–11) is satisfied if we take $m = 1$.

The regular part of $f(z)$ at $z = 0$ begins with the term 0, for the function $f(z)$ is odd. The meromorphic part at $z = n$ is

$$\frac{1}{z-n} = \frac{-1}{n}\left(\frac{1}{1-z/n}\right) = \frac{-1}{n}\left(1+\frac{z}{n}+\dots\right)$$

and hence the associated polynomial $h(z)$ is $-1/n$. According to the general theory we have

$$\pi \operatorname{ctn} \pi z = \frac{1}{z} + \sum_{\nu=-\infty}^{\infty}{}' \left(\frac{1}{z-\nu} + \frac{1}{\nu}\right), \tag{4.10–13}$$

the prime indicating that the term corresponding to $\nu = 0$ is omitted.

By combining terms in which ν equals n, $-n$, $(n = 1, 2, \dots)$, we may also write

$$\pi \operatorname{ctn} \pi z = \frac{1}{z} + \sum_{\nu=1}^{\infty} \frac{2z}{z^2-\nu^2} \tag{4.10–14}$$

in accordance with (3.7–30).

As a second example we consider the function

$$f(z) = \pi \csc \pi z. \tag{4.10–15}$$

By nearly the same arguments as previously used we find

$$\pi \csc \pi z = \frac{1}{z} + \sum_{\nu=-\infty}^{\infty}{}' (-1)^{\nu} \left(\frac{1}{z-\nu} + \frac{1}{\nu}\right) \tag{4.10–16}$$

or, after combining terms in which ν equals n, $-n$, $(n = 1, 2, \dots)$,

$$\pi \csc \pi z = \frac{1}{z} + \sum_{\nu=1}^{\infty} (-1)^{\nu} \frac{2z}{z^2-\nu^2}. \tag{4.10–17}$$

Since it is legitimate to differentiate the series (4.10–13) term-by-term, we have in addition

$$\pi^2 \csc^2 \pi z = \sum_{\nu=-\infty}^{\infty} \frac{1}{(z-\nu)^2}. \tag{4.10–18}$$

4.11 – Mittag-Leffler's theorem

4.11.1 – Mittag-Leffler's formula

We wish to occupy us with the following problem: How to construct a single-valued function which is regular at the points of a certain open set except for a subset of isolated singularities within the given set where the function has prescribed singular parts. This is Mittag-Leffler's problem.

In the case that the subset consists only of a finite number of points the problem is trivial. For we can take the sum of all singular parts and add any function that is holomorphic throughout the given open set.

In this section we shall study the case in which the set of the singular points is infinite and admits only the point ∞ as an accumulation point. We already pointed out in section 4.4.1 that the singular points constitute an enumerable set and assuming first that the function is regular at $z = 0$ we may arrange them in a sequence

$$a_1, a_2, \ldots, \tag{4.11–1}$$

in order of non-decreasing moduli

$$0 < |a_1| \leqq |a_2| \leqq \ldots \tag{4.11–2}$$

where by hypothesis

$$\lim_{n\to\infty} a_n = \infty. \tag{4.11–3}$$

To each of these points let there correspond the singular parts

$$g_1\left(\frac{1}{z-a_1}\right), \quad g_2\left(\frac{1}{z-a_2}\right), \ldots \tag{4.11–4}$$

these expressions being integral functions with respect to their argument, with no constant term.

Now we take a convergent series

$$\varepsilon_1+\varepsilon_2+\ldots \tag{4.11–5}$$

with positive terms. The function

$$g_n\left(\frac{1}{z-a_n}\right) = g_n\left(\frac{-1/a_n}{1-z/a_n}\right),$$

where n denotes a positive integer, is holomorphic in the interior of a circle around the origin with radius $|a_n|$ and therefore can be expanded in a power series

$$g_n\left(\frac{1}{z-a_n}\right) = \sum_{\mu=0}^{\infty} b_{n\mu}\left(\frac{z}{a_n}\right)^{\mu}, \qquad n = 1, 2, \ldots. \tag{4.11–6}$$

Let ϑ denote a positive number less than unity. Then to the number ε_n corresponds an integer m_n such that within and on the boundary of the circle around the origin with radius $\vartheta|a_n|$ the inequality

$$\left| g_n\left(\frac{1}{z-a_n}\right) - \sum_{\mu=0}^{m_n} b_{n\mu}\left(\frac{z}{a_n}\right)^{\mu} \right| < \varepsilon_n \tag{4.11–7}$$

holds. For the sake of clearness we shall write

$$h_n(z) = \sum_{\mu=0}^{m_n} b_{n\mu}\left(\frac{z}{a_n}\right)^{\mu}, \qquad n = 1, 2, \ldots. \tag{4.11–8}$$

Now we shall prove that the series

$$\sum_{\nu=1}^{\infty} \left\{ g_\nu\left(\frac{1}{z-a_\nu}\right) - h_\nu(z) \right\} \tag{4.11–9}$$

converges absolutely and uniformly in any bounded and closed set $\mathfrak{C}$ which does not contain a point of the sequence (4.11–1).

In fact, let ϱ denote a positive number such that the points of the set $\mathfrak{C}$ are in a circle C around the origin with radius ϱ. Let a_{k+1} be the first point of the sequence (4.11–1) with $\vartheta|a_{k+1}| > \varrho$. We split the series (4.11–8) into two parts, as follows:

$$\sum_{\nu=0}^{k} \left\{ g_\nu\left(\frac{1}{z-a_\nu}\right) - h_\nu(z) \right\} + \sum_{\nu=k+1}^{\infty} \left\{ g_\nu\left(\frac{1}{z-a_\nu}\right) - h_\nu(z) \right\}. \tag{4.11–10}$$

In this expression the first sum consists of a finite number of terms. The moduli of the terms of the second series are dominated by the numbers $\varepsilon_{k+1}, \varepsilon_{k+2}, \ldots$, respectively, whenever $|z| \leqq \varrho$, and therefore this series is absolutely and uniformly convergent on $\mathfrak{C}$. By the theorem of section 2.20.3 the series (4.11–9) represents a function which is holomorphic throughout the entire plane from which the points of the sequence (4.11–1) are deleted. We thus proved:

The function

$$f_0(z) = \sum_{\nu=1}^{\infty} \left\{ g_\nu\left(\frac{1}{z-a_\nu}\right) - h_\nu(z) \right\} \tag{4.11–11}$$

is regular at the points of the entire plane except for the points of the sequence (4.11–1).

It is easily checked that this function solves Mittag-Leffler's problem in the case under consideration. For the difference

$$g^*(z) = f_0(z) - g_n\left(\frac{1}{z-a_n}\right)$$

is holomorphic in a circular neighbourhood of $z=a_n$, n being one of the numbers 1, 2, ... Within this neighbourhood

$$f_0(z) = g_n\left(\frac{1}{z-a_n}\right) + g^*(z)$$

and since $g^*(z)$ is regular at $z = a_n$ the singular part of $f_0(z)$ corresponding to this point is exactly $g_n\left(\frac{1}{z-a_n}\right)$.

If the origin should also be a singular point with singular part $g_0\left(\frac{1}{z}\right)$ we have only to add this function to the right member of (4.11–11).

It is clear that if $g(z)$ designates an integral function the function

$$\boxed{f(z) = g(z)+g_0\left(\frac{1}{z}\right) + \sum_{\nu=1}^{\infty}\left\{g_\nu\left(\frac{1}{z-a_\nu}\right)-h_\nu(z)\right\}} \qquad (4.11\text{–}12)$$

is the most general solution of Mittag-Leffler's problem in the case that the singular points admit only the point ∞ as an accumulation point. It is to be understood that g_0 vanishes identically whenever the function is regular at the origin. The expression (4.11–12) is referred to as *Mittag-Leffler's formula*.

In general the series

$$\sum_{\nu=1}^{\infty} g_\nu\left(\frac{1}{z-a_\nu}\right) \qquad (4.11\text{–}13)$$

is divergent. But the preceding theorem states that convergence can be obtained by adding suitably chosen polynomials to the terms of the series separately.

Finally we observe that $z = \infty$ is a non-isolated singularity of (4.11–12).

4.11.2 – Sufficient conditions for the validity of the expansion

In general it is a difficult task to determine the convergence producing polynomials in concrete examples. In the case that all singularities are simple poles we can give more information. In this case the meromorphic parts can be given as

$$g_n\left(\frac{1}{z-a_n}\right) = \frac{b_n}{z-a_n}, \qquad n = 0, 1, 2, \ldots \qquad (4.11\text{–}14)$$

with $a_0 = 0$. For $n > 0$ we may write

$$\frac{b_n}{z-a_n} = -\frac{b_n}{a_n}\left\{1+\frac{z}{a_n}+\ldots\right\}$$

and we have, consequently,

$$f_0(z) = \frac{b_0}{z} + \sum_{\nu=1}^{\infty}\left(\frac{b_\nu}{z-a_\nu} + \frac{b_\nu}{a_\nu}\left\{1+\left(\frac{z}{a_\nu}\right)+\ldots+\left(\frac{z}{a_\nu}\right)^{k_\nu-1}\right\}\right), \qquad (4.11\text{–}15)$$

a result that can also be written in the form

$$f_0(z) = \frac{b_0}{z} + \sum_{\nu=1}^{\infty} \left(\frac{z}{a_\nu}\right)^{k_\nu} \frac{b_\nu}{z-a_\nu}. \qquad (4.11\text{–}16)$$

There is some difficulty in determining the numbers k_n. Let z denote a fixed number. The number $1-z/a_n$ is as near to 1 as we wish, provided that n is sufficiently large. If ε is a positive number less than unity then for all numbers n exceeding a fixed number we have

$$1-\varepsilon < \left|1-\frac{z}{a_n}\right| < 1+\varepsilon,$$

whence

$$\left|\left(\frac{z}{a_n}\right)^{k_n} \frac{b_n}{a_n}\right| \frac{1}{1+\varepsilon} < \left|\left(\frac{z}{a_n}\right)^{k_n} \frac{b_n}{z-a_n}\right| < \left|\left(\frac{z}{a_n}\right)^{k_n} \frac{b_n}{a_n}\right| \frac{1}{1-\varepsilon}.$$

As a consequence the series (4.11–15) (or (4.11–16)) is absolutely convergent if and only if the series

$$\sum_{\nu=1}^{\infty} \left(\frac{z}{a_\nu}\right)^{k_\nu} \frac{b_\nu}{a_\nu} \qquad (4.11\text{–}17)$$

is absolutely convergent. But if this condition is satisfied for every value of z the series representing $f_0(z)$ is absolutely and uniformly convergent in every bounded and closed set which does not contain any of the prescribed singular points. In fact, let r denote the greatest upper bound of $|z|$ in such a set. Then from a certain index upwards the terms of the convergent series

$$\sum_{\nu=1}^{\infty} \left(\frac{r}{|a_\nu|}\right)^{k_\nu} \left|\frac{b_\nu}{a_\nu}\right| \frac{1}{1-\varepsilon} \qquad (4.11\text{–}18)$$

dominate the corresponding terms of the series (4.11–17). We have thus proved the theorem:

When the integers k_n, $n = 1, 2, \ldots$ can be chosen in such a way that the series (4.11–17) *is absolutely convergent for every value of z, then* (4.11–15) *represents a meromorphic function with simple poles at the points of the sequence* (4.11–1) (*to which eventually the origin is added*).

4.11.3 – Particular cases

Some particular cases deserve special mention.

When the upper limit

$$\limsup_{n\to\infty} b_n \qquad (4.11\text{–}19)$$

is a finite number, we may take $k_n = n$, $n = 1, 2, \ldots$.

This is true since the Cauchy-Hadamard test (1.6.5) shows that the series (4.11–17) is convergent throughout the entire plane, because $a_n \to \infty$ when $n \to \infty$.

The following statement requires no further comment:

We may take all numbers k_n equal to the same number k when the series

$$\sum_{\nu=1}^{\infty} \frac{b_\nu}{a_\nu^{k+1}} \tag{4.11–20}$$

is absolutely convergent.

This case occurs, for instance, *when the modulus of the difference of any two numbers a_p, a_q of the sequence (4.11–1) remains greater than a certain fixed positive number ϱ and when, at the same time, the numbers b_n form a bounded sequence.*

Then, as we shall prove presently, the series

$$\sum_{\nu=1}^{\infty} \frac{1}{|a_\nu|^3} \tag{4.11–21}$$

is convergent and, as a consequence, we may take $k = 2$.

It is possible to establish this fact by purely analytical means, but we prefer to give a more imaginative geometric reasoning.

Let A_n, $n = 1, 2, \ldots$ denote the number of points in the sequence which satisfy the condition

$$n \leqq |a_\lambda| < n+1. \tag{4.11–22}$$

If ε is a positive number $< \frac{1}{2}\varrho$ all circles around the points (4.11–1) of radius ε are mutually disjoint. The points which satisfy (4.11–22) are contained in a circular ring bounded by the circles around the origin having radii n and $n+1$ respectively. Suppose $A_n > 0$, i.e., there is at least one point in this ring. Then $2\varepsilon < |a_\lambda| < n+1$, whence $\varepsilon < \frac{1}{2}(n+1)$, $n-\varepsilon > \frac{1}{2}(n-1) \geqq 0$. All circles of radius ε around these A_n points lie between two circumferences around the origin with radii $n - \varepsilon$ and $n+1+\varepsilon$ respectively and cover therefore an area which is less than the area of the ring bounded by these circumferences. This leads to the estimate

$$A_n \varepsilon^2 \pi < (n+1+\varepsilon)^2 \pi - (n-\varepsilon)^2 \pi = (1+2\varepsilon)(2n+1)\pi$$

or

$$A_n < \frac{1+2\varepsilon}{\varepsilon^2}(2n+1) \leqq \eta n \tag{4.11–23}$$

with

$$\eta = \frac{3(1+2\varepsilon)}{\varepsilon^2}. \tag{4.11–24}$$

It is clear that (4.11–23) holds also in the case that $A_n = 0$. The contribution to the sum (4.11–21) by these points does not exceed

$$A_n \frac{1}{n^3} < \frac{\eta}{n^2}$$

and from the convergence of the series $\sum_{\nu=1}^{\infty} \nu^{-2}$ follows the desired result, for there is only a finite number of points in the sequence (4.11–1) whose distance from the origin is less than unity.

4.11.4 – The zeta function and the pe function of Weierstrass

A non-trivial example of a function with infinitely many poles is borrowed from the theory of elliptic functions.

Consider all points which may be represented as

$$2n\omega + 2n'\omega', \qquad n, n' = 0, \pm 1, \pm 2, \ldots, \qquad (4.11\text{–}25)$$

where ω and ω' are two non-zero numbers whose ratio is not real. Geometrically speaking this means that the points ω and ω' do not lie in a straight line through the origin. Let us now draw straight lines L and L' joining the origin to the points ω, ω' respectively, (fig. 4.11–1). We may mark the points $2n\omega$ on L and $2n'\omega'$ on $L)$

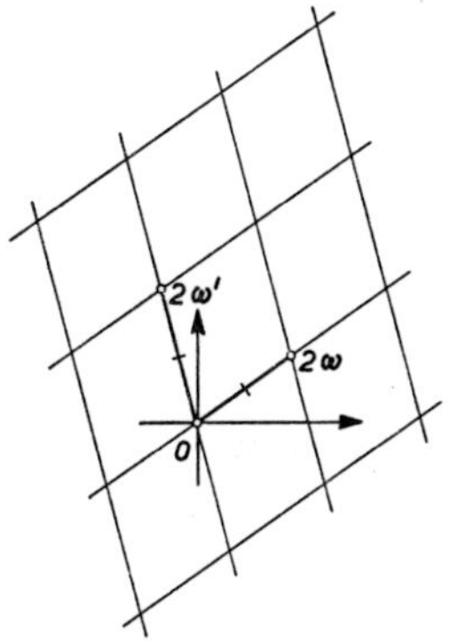

Fig. 4.11–1. The lattice-points (4.11–25)

and through each of these points draw a straight line parallel to L', L respectively. The points of intersection of these two families are precisely the points (4.11–25). They are the *lattice-points* of a network of parallelograms.

Obviously the mutual distances of the lattice points remain above a certain positive number. Hence, according to the last result of the previous part of this section, the series

$$\sum{}' \frac{1}{w^3} \qquad (4.11\text{–}26)$$

(where w runs through all lattice-points, the prime indicating that

$w = 0$ does not occur) is convergent. It is assumed that the lattice points are arranged in a certain order, but it is immaterial in which manner the arrangement has been made.

By virtue of Mittag-Leffler's theorem the infinite series

$$\boxed{\zeta(z) = \frac{1}{z} + \sum{}' \left(\frac{1}{z-w} + \frac{1}{w} + \frac{z}{w^2}\right) = \frac{1}{z} + \sum{}' \frac{z^2}{(z-w)w^2}} \tag{4.11–27}$$

represents a meromorphic function having simple poles with residues equal to unity at the lattice points (4.11–25). This function is the *Weierstrass zeta function.*

On account of the general results obtained before, term-by-term differentiation of the series (4.11–27) is permitted. Effecting this process we get a function of utmost importance:

$$\boxed{\wp(z) = -\zeta'(z) = \frac{1}{z^2} + \sum{}' \left(\frac{1}{(z-w)^2} - \frac{1}{w^2}\right),} \tag{4.11–28}$$

the famous *pe function of Weierstrass.*

This function possesses poles of order two at the lattice points, the residues being equal to zero. There are no other singular points in the finite plane.

A remarkable property of this function is its *double-periodicity,* the periods being 2ω, $2\omega'$; otherwise stated, the relation

$$\boxed{\wp(z+2n\omega+2n'\omega') = \wp(z),} \tag{4.11–29}$$

where n, n' are integers, is valid.

In order to prove this statement we consider the derivative

$$\wp'(z) = -\frac{2}{z^3} - 2\sum{}' \frac{1}{(z-w)^3} = -2\sum \frac{1}{(z-w)^3}. \tag{4.11–30}$$

Since w and $w-2\omega$ run through the same lattice points we evidently have

$$\wp'(z+2\omega) = -2\sum \frac{1}{\{z-(w-2\omega)\}^3} = -2\sum \frac{1}{(z-w)^3} = \wp'(z) \tag{4.11–31}$$

and this leads to

$$\wp(z+2\omega) = \wp(z)+c, \tag{4.11–32}$$

c being a constant.

It is easy to see that $\wp(z)$ is an even function, for

$$\wp(-z) = \frac{1}{z^2} + \sum{}' \left(\frac{1}{(z+w)^2} - \frac{1}{w^2}\right) = \frac{1}{z^2} + \sum{}' \left(\frac{1}{(z-w)^2} - \frac{1}{w^2}\right)$$

because of the fact that w and $-w$ run through the same lattice points. Hence

$$\wp(-z) = \wp(z). \tag{4.11–33}$$

If we now put $z=-\omega$ in (4.11–32) we readily find $c=0$ whence

$$\wp(z+2\omega) = \wp(z). \tag{4.11–34}$$

In exactly the same way we find

$$\wp(z+2\omega') = \wp(z) \tag{4.11–35}$$

and the general result (4.11–29) follows at once.

A more extensive study of this and allied functions is postponed to the next chapter.

4.12 – The Weierstrass factorization of an integral function deduced from Mittag-Leffler's theorem

4.12.1 – Deduction of Weierstrass's formula from Mittag-Leffler's formula

The special case of Mittag-Leffler's problem treated in section 4.11.3 affords a means for deriving the formula (4.4–4) which represents an integral function as an infinite product which vanishes at the points of the sequence (4.11–1). We assume that each point in this sequence is repeated as many times as the order of multiplicity indicates.

The logarithmic derivative $f'(z)/f(z)$ possesses at each point of (4.11–1) a simple pole with meromorphic part $1/(z-a_n)$, the residue being $b_n = 1$. Hence by (4.11–19) there exist integers k_n, $n = 1, 2, \ldots$, such that the series

$$\sum_{\nu=1}^{\infty} \frac{z^{k_\nu}}{a_\nu^{k_\nu+1}} \tag{4.12–1}$$

is absolutely convergent for every value of z. As a consequence the function represented by

$$\sum_{\nu=1}^{\infty}\left\{\frac{1}{z-a_\nu}+\frac{1}{a_\nu}+\frac{1}{a_\nu}\left(\frac{z}{a_\nu}\right)+\ldots+\frac{1}{a_\nu}\left(\frac{z}{a_\nu}\right)^{k_\nu-1}\right\} \tag{4.12–2}$$

represents a meromorphic function with simple poles, having there residues equal to unity and, if $g(z)$ denotes an integral function, we evidently have

$$\frac{f'(z)}{f(z)} = g(z)+\sum_{\nu=1}^{\infty}\left\{\frac{1}{z-a_\nu}+\frac{1}{a_\nu}+\ldots+\frac{1}{a_\nu}\left(\frac{z}{a_\nu}\right)^{k_\nu-1}\right\}. \tag{4.12–3}$$

Integrating along a regular path and putting

$$\varphi(z) = \log f(0) + \int_0^z g(\zeta)d\zeta$$

we get

$$\log f(z) = \varphi(z) + \sum_{\nu=1}^{\infty} \left\{ \log\left(1 - \frac{z}{a_\nu}\right) + \frac{z}{a_\nu} + \frac{1}{2}\left(\frac{z}{a_\nu}\right)^2 + \ldots + \frac{1}{k_\nu}\left(\frac{z}{a_\nu}\right)^{k_\nu} \right\}, \tag{4.12–4}$$

the logarithms depending on the path of integration. By taking another path only a finite number of terms are modified by a multiple of $2\pi i$. Hence the function

$$f(z) = \exp \varphi(z) \cdot \prod_{\nu=1}^{\infty} \left(1 - \frac{z}{a_\nu}\right) \exp\left\{\frac{z}{a_\nu} + \frac{1}{2}\left(\frac{z}{a_\nu}\right)^2 + \ldots + \frac{1}{k_\nu}\left(\frac{z}{a_\nu}\right)^{k_\nu}\right\} \tag{4.12–5}$$

is unambiguously determined and we find the desired formula (4.4–4).

4.12.2 – The sigma function of Weierstrass

We may illustrate the previous result in the following example. Evidently the function

$$\boxed{\sigma(z) = z \prod{}' \left(1 - \frac{z}{w}\right) \exp\left(\frac{z}{w} + \frac{z^2}{2w^2}\right)} \tag{4.12–6}$$

is an integral function with simple zeros at the lattice points (4.11–25), since, on account of the convergence of the series (4.11–26), we can take $k_n = 2$, $n = 1, 2, \ldots$.

This function is intimately connected with the Weierstrass pe function. In fact,

$$\zeta(z) = \frac{\sigma'(z)}{\sigma(z)} \tag{4.12–7}$$

and

$$\wp(z) = \frac{\sigma'^2(z) - \sigma(z)\sigma''(z)}{\sigma^2(z)}. \tag{4.12–8}$$

These latter expressions represent the meromorphic functions $\zeta(z)$ and $\wp(z)$ as quotients of integral functions.

When it is desirable to exhibit the dependence on the periods 2ω, $2\omega'$ we shall write $\wp(z|\omega, \omega')$, $\zeta(z|\omega, \omega')$ and $\sigma(z|\omega, \omega')$.

4.12.3 – Degenerate cases

The function $\sigma(z)$ is somewhat similar to the function $\sin z$. The rank of its zeros is, however, equal to two. The functions $\zeta(z)$ and $\wp(z)$ correspond to the functions $\operatorname{ctn} z$ and $\csc^2 z$ respectively.

More precisely: assume that the second period $2\omega'$ tends to infinity. In the expansion (4.11–27) for $\zeta(z)$ only the terms involving $2n\omega$ survive. The function degenerates into

$$\frac{1}{z}+\sum_{\nu=-\infty}^{\infty}{}'\left(\frac{1}{z-2\nu\omega}+\frac{1}{2\nu\omega}\right)+2z\sum_{\nu=1}^{\infty}\frac{1}{(2\nu\omega)^2}$$

whence, according to (4.10–13), taking account of (3.7–24),

$$\zeta(z|\omega,\infty)=\frac{\pi}{2\omega}\operatorname{ctn}\frac{\pi z}{2\omega}+\frac{1}{3}\left(\frac{\pi}{2\omega}\right)^2 z. \tag{4.12–9}$$

Since $\wp(z) = -\zeta'(z)$, we have at once

$$\wp(z|\omega,\infty)=\left(\frac{\pi}{2\omega}\right)^2\csc^2\frac{\pi z}{2\omega}-\frac{1}{3}\left(\frac{\pi}{2\omega}\right)^2. \tag{4.12–10}$$

It is not difficult to derive this formula from the expansion (4.11–28) taking account of (4.10–18) and (3.7–24).

Finally we obtain from (4.12–6), taking account of (4.5–13),

$$\sigma(z|\omega,\infty)=\frac{2\omega}{\pi}\sin\frac{\pi z}{2\omega}\cdot\exp\frac{1}{6}\left(\frac{\pi z}{2\omega}\right)^2. \tag{4.12–11}$$

4.13 – The general Mittag-Leffler problem

4.13.1 – Statement of the problem

The problem of constructing a single-valued function with prescribed singular points and corresponding singular parts has been solved in section 4.11.1 for the case that the set of prescribed singular points admits only the point at infinity as an accumulation point. We now turn to a more general problem by assuming that the set of prescribed singular points is an isolated set. A set $\mathfrak{S}$ is said to be *isolated* when it has no points in common with its derivative $\mathfrak{S}'$, i.e., the set of all its accumulation points.

Our first aim will be the proof of the statement:

An isolated set is always enumerable. In this statement the trivial case of a finite set is included.

In the first place we may observe that to every point $z = a$ of the set $\mathfrak{S}$ corresponds a positive number ϱ such that inside the circle around $z = a$ and of radius ϱ there are no other points of $\mathfrak{S}$. For in the contrary case $z = a$ should be an accumulation point of the set $\mathfrak{S}$ and this contradicts the hypothesis.

The circle $|z-a| = \frac{1}{3}\varrho$ where ϱ is defined as before shall be called a circle *associated* with a. When a and b are two distinct points of $\mathfrak{S}$ then their respective associated circles are mutually external, for, if $|z-a| = \frac{1}{3}\varrho$ and $|z-b| = \frac{1}{3}\sigma$ are these circles, then we obviously have

$$|b-a| \geqq \max(\varrho, \sigma) > \tfrac{1}{3}\varrho+\tfrac{1}{3}\sigma.$$

It follows that within a circumference of radius 1 around the origin there is only a finite number of points with associated circles of radius exceeding 1, a finite number of points with associated circles of radius $\leqq 1$ and $> \frac{1}{2}$, a finite number of points with associated circles of radius $\leqq \frac{1}{2}$ and $> \frac{1}{4}$, etc. Hence all points of $\mathfrak{S}$ at a distance from O less than unity constitute an enumerable set. Similarly the points of $\mathfrak{S}$ at a distance $\geqq 1$ and < 2 from O constitute an enumerable set, etc. Thus we see that the set $\mathfrak{S}$ is built up by enumerably many enumerable sets and is therefore itself enumerable. Hence it is possible to arrange the points of $\mathfrak{S}$ as a sequence

$$a_1, a_2, \ldots.$$

It is important to observe that there are infinitely many points in the complex plane which do not belong to the union $\mathfrak{S}+\mathfrak{S}'$ of $\mathfrak{S}$ and its derivative $\mathfrak{S}'$. Such are, for instance, the points within a circle $|z-a| = \frac{1}{3}\varrho$ considered before, distinct from the centre a.

Again, if a is a point not belonging to $\mathfrak{S}+\mathfrak{S}'$, it is centre of a circle which contains no points of $\mathfrak{S}'$, because of the fact that $\mathfrak{S}'$ is closed. There are only a finite number of points of $\mathfrak{S}$ within such a circle and hence there is a circle $|z-a| = \varrho$ that contains no point of $\mathfrak{S}$, nor of $\mathfrak{S}'$. We now make the assumption that $\mathfrak{S}$ is bounded. Then also the derivative $\mathfrak{S}'$ is bounded. Assuming further that $\mathfrak{S}$ is infinite then $\mathfrak{S}'$ is not an empty set and since $\mathfrak{S}'$ is a closed set every point a_n of $\mathfrak{S}$ has a positive distance ϱ_n from $\mathfrak{S}'$.

The sequence ϱ_n tends to zero as $n \to \infty$. In fact, if there should exist infinitely many values $\varrho_{n_1}, \varrho_{n_2}, \ldots$, greater than a given positive value ε, the corresponding points $a_{n_1}, a_{n_2}, \ldots$ should constitute a bounded infinite set of points having a distance $\geqq \varepsilon$ to $\mathfrak{S}'$. By Bolzano's principle this set should admit at least one accumulation point not contained in $\mathfrak{S}'$, which is absurd.

We conclude these considerations by establishing the following fact:

To each point a_n of the infinite isolated bounded set $\mathfrak{S}$ we can find a companion a_n' of $\mathfrak{S}'$ such that

$$\lim_{n\to\infty} |a_n-a_n'| = 0. \tag{4.13–1}$$

In fact, given $\varepsilon > 0$ there exists a point a_n' of $\mathfrak{S}'$ such that

$$|a_n-a_n'| < \varrho_n+\frac{\varepsilon}{n}, \qquad n = 1, 2, \ldots,$$

ϱ_n being defined as before. Since $\varrho_n \to 0$ as $n \to \infty$ the truth of the assertion follows at once.

4.13.2 – The main theorem

After these preliminaries we are in a position to establish the main theorem:

Given an infinite isolated set $\mathfrak{S}$ *of points*

$$a_1, a_2, \ldots, \tag{4.13–2}$$

and corresponding to each point a_n *a function*

$$g_n\left(\frac{1}{z-a_n}\right), \tag{4.13–3}$$

integral as regards its argument (and without constant term), it is possible to construct a single-valued function $f(z)$ *which is regular at each point distinct from the points of the set* $\mathfrak{S}$ *and from the accumulation points of this set, and which behaves at* $z = a_n$, $n = 1, 2, \ldots,$ *like the function* (4.13–3), that is, the function

$$f(z)-g_n\left(\frac{1}{z-a_n}\right)$$

is regular at $z = a_n$.

It is to be understood that if the point ∞ is among the points of $\mathfrak{S}$ the corresponding singular part is to be interpreted as an integral function $g(z)$. We may assume, however, that the set $\mathfrak{S}$ is bounded. For, if $z = a$ is a point not belonging to $\mathfrak{S}$ we can introduce the new variable z^* by

$$z^* = \frac{1}{z-a}. \tag{4.13–4}$$

The transformation (4.13–4) carries $\mathfrak{S}$ into a set $\mathfrak{S}^*$ which neither contains the point ∞ nor admits this point as an accumulation point. After performing the construction of a function of z^* satisfying the conditions mentioned in the theorem for the set $\mathfrak{S}^*$ the inverse transformation of (4.13–4) yields the desired function for the set $\mathfrak{S}$.

To every point a_n of $\mathfrak{S}$ we select from $\mathfrak{S}'$ a companion a_n' such that (4.13–1) is valid. Since (4.13–3) is an integral function as regards its argument it is certainly holomorphic as regards z outside the circumference around a_n' of radius $|a_n-a_n'|$. Hence in this region it can be expanded in terms of $(z-a_n')^{-1}$, the expansion being

$$g_n\left(\frac{1}{z-a_n}\right) = \sum_{\mu=1}^{\infty} b_{n\mu}(z-a_n')^{-\mu}. \tag{4.13–5}$$

In this Laurent expansion only terms with $\mu > 0$ occur, since (4.13–3) is regular and zero at $z = \infty$.

As in section 4.11.1 we take a convergent series of positive terms

$$\varepsilon_1 + \varepsilon_2 + \ldots . \tag{4.13–6}$$

To the number ε_n there corresponds an integer m_n such that

$$\left| g_n\left(\frac{1}{z-a_n}\right) - h_n\left(\frac{1}{z-a'_n}\right) \right| < \varepsilon_n \tag{4.13–7}$$

where for the sake of brevity we have put

$$h_n(z) = \sum_{\mu=1}^{m_n} b_{n\mu} z^{\mu}, \tag{4.13–8}$$

the estimate (4.13–7) being valid outside or on a circumference around a'_n of radius $q|a_n - a'_n|$ with $q > 1$, i.e., for the points z satisfying

$$\left| \frac{z-a'_n}{a_n-a'_n} \right| \geqq q > 1 . \tag{4.13–9}$$

It remains to show that

$$f(z) = \sum_{\nu=1}^{\infty} \left\{ g_\nu\left(\frac{1}{z-a_\nu}\right) - h_\nu\left(\frac{1}{z-a'_\nu}\right) \right\} \tag{4.13–10}$$

represents a function which is regular at every point $z = z_0$ not belonging to $\mathfrak{S} + \mathfrak{S}'$.

In fact, we already pointed out in section 4.13.1 that there exists a circle $|z-z_0| = \varrho$ which contains no point of $\mathfrak{S} + \mathfrak{S}'$. Let C denote the circle $|z-z_0| = \frac{1}{2}\varrho$. Then for all points z inside C we have

$$|z-a_n| > \tfrac{1}{2}\varrho, \qquad |z-a'_n| > \tfrac{1}{2}\varrho, \qquad n = 1, 2, \ldots .$$

On account of (4.13–1) we can find a number m such that for all $n > m$ we have

$$|a_n - a'_n| < \frac{1}{2}\frac{\varrho}{q}$$

and thus for all points z inside C the inequality (4.13–9) is valid. By virtue of (4.13–7) the series (4.13–10) is from a certain index upwards dominated by the series (4.13–6). Hence the former series converges absolutely and uniformly in each closed subset within C. On the other hand each term of the series (4.13–10) is holomorphic throughout the interior of C and by the theorem of section 2.20.3 the function $f(z)$ is holomorphic within C. This completes the proof of the theorem.

CHAPTER 5

ELLIPTIC FUNCTIONS

5.1 – Periodic functions

5.1.1 – THE BEHAVIOUR OF A PERIODIC FUNCTION AT INFINITY

In this chapter we wish to discuss more thoroughly certain types of periodic functions. We consider only functions which are holomorphic throughout the entire z-plane, save for isolated singularities.

We recall that a function is said to be periodic if we can find a number $w \neq 0$ such that

$$f(z+w) = f(z)$$

for all points z at which the function is regular.

A non-constant periodic function has an essential singularity at infinity.

Let z_1 and z_2 be two points such that $f(z_1) \neq f(z_2)$. In an arbitrary neighbourhood of $z = \infty$ there are infinitely many points z_1+nw and z_2+nw, where n is an integer. Hence infinitely many times $f(z) = f(z_1)$ and $f(z) = f(z_2)$ and so $f(z)$ cannot tend to a finite or infinite limit as $z \to \infty$. In accordance with the considerations of section 3.2.2 the point $z = \infty$ is an essential singular point.

5.1.2 – THE PERIODS

A periodic function has always infinitely many periods. In fact, if w_1 and w_2 are periods then w_1+w_2 is either zero or is also a period. Now we state the theorem:

The set of periods of a non-constant function has no finite accumulation point.

Assume that w_0 is a finite accumulation point of the periods of a function $f(z)$ and let z_0 be a regular point of the function. By hypothesis there are infinitely many points z_0+w in an arbitrary neighbourhood of z_0+w_0. Hence the function $f(z)-f(z_0)$ has infinitely many zeros which possess the accumulation point z_0+w_0. According to section 2.11.1 the function $f(z)-f(z_0)$ is identically zero, i.e., $f(z)$ is constant.

A non-constant function cannot possess periods with arbitrarily small modulus.

In fact, in the contrary case the set of periods would possess the origin as an accumulation point.

5.1.3 – Simply- and doubly-periodic functions

The main result of this section may be stated as the theorem: *The periods of a non-constant function are either integral multiples of one period or the sums of integral multiples of two periods whose ratio is not real.*

First it may happen that all periods are of the form λw_0, where w_0 is a period and λ real. In other words, it may happen that all periods are represented by points on a line through the origin. Since these periods have no accumulation point on the line, there is a period w_1 nearest to the origin. Any other period can be put in the form λw_1, λ being real. Now $\lambda = m+\alpha$, where m is an integer and $0 \leqq \alpha < 1$. Since $w-mw_1 = \alpha w_1$ is also a period if $\alpha \neq 0$ we conclude that $\alpha = 0$, for in the contrary case we should have found a period between the origin and w_1.

In this case the function is called *simply-periodic,* and w_1 is a *primitive period.* Of course $-w_1$ is also a primitive period. These are the only possible cases. Thus, for instance, the function sin z has 2π as a primitive period, whereas tan z has π as a primitive period.

Secondly we assume that not all periods are on the same line through the origin, that is to say, we can find two periods w_1 and w_2 such that 0, w_1 and w_2 are the vertices of a triangle.

Since the periods have no finite accumulation point we conclude that within and on the boundary of this triangle are only a finite number of periods. Let w_3 be such a period not coinciding with w_1 or w_2. The triangle with vertices 0, w_1, w_3 contains less periods within or on its boundary than the above triangle. Thus we see that we can find a triangle containing no periods within or on its boundary except for its vertices different from 0. Let us suppose that the triangle with vertices 0, w_1 and w_2 already satisfies this condition.

Next we consider the parallelogram whose vertices are the points 0, w_1, w_1+w_2, w_2. Let w denote a period within or on the boundary

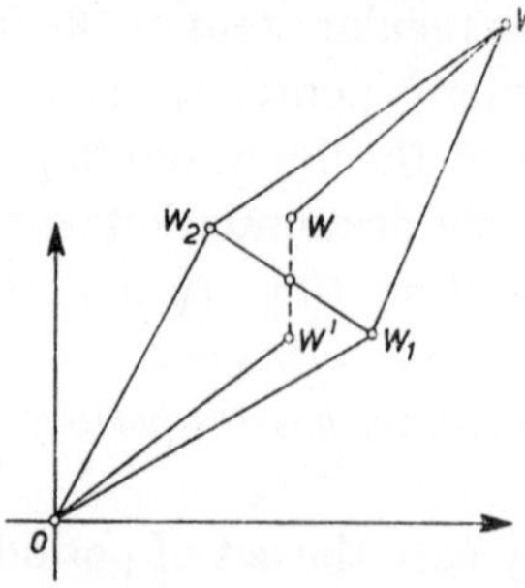

Fig. 5.1–1. $w+w = w_1+w_2$

of this parallelogram. It is necessarily contained inside or on the boundary of the triangle with vertices w_1, w_1+w_2, w_2. Then also $w' = w_1+w_2-w$ is a period or zero, and since $w+w' = w_1+w_2$ the segments (w, w') and (w_1, w_2) have a common centre, (fig. 5.1–1). As w' is within or on the boundary of the first triangle it must coincide with one of the vertices. Hence w is a vertex of the parallelogram.

Next we consider an arbitrary period w. It is evident that a number a can be written as the sum of two numbers a_1 and a_2, where a_1 is represented by a point on the line through 0 and w_1, and a_2 by a point on the line through 0 and w_2, (fig. 5.1–2). Hence $w = \lambda_1 w_1+\lambda_2 w_2$, where

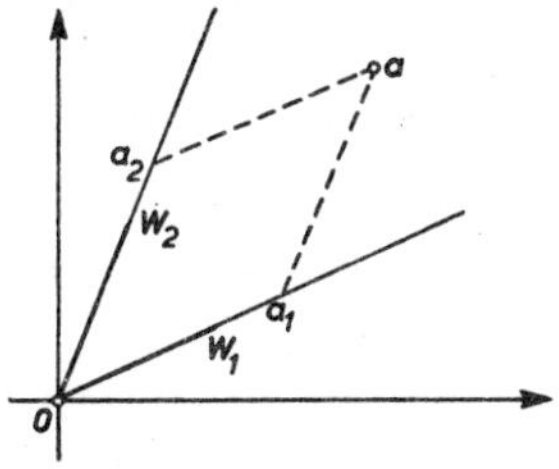

Fig. 5.1–2. Decomposition of the number a

λ_1 and λ_2 are real. Since $\lambda_1 = m_1+\alpha_1$, $\lambda_2 = m_2+\alpha_2$, where m_1 and m_2 are integers, while $0 \leqq \alpha_1 < 1$, $0 \leqq \alpha_2 < 1$, we conclude that $\alpha_1 w_1+\alpha_2 w_2 = w-m_1 w_1-m_2 w_2$ is either zero or also a period. But all points of the form $\alpha_1 w_1+\alpha_2 w_2$ belong to the parallelogram considered above and do not coincide with any vertex except the origin. As a consequence we have $\alpha_1 = \alpha_2 = 0$.

It appears that an arbitrary period can be written in the form

$$w = m_1 w_1+m_2 w_2, \qquad (5.1\text{–}1)$$

m_1 and m_2 being integers, the ratio of w_1 and w_2 being a non-real number.

The periods w_1 and w_2 are called *primitive periods*. They are not uniquely determined. It is easy to prove that

$$w_1^* = aw_1+bw_2,$$
$$w_2^* = cw_1+dw_2,$$

are also primitive periods, when a, b, c and d are integers such that $ad-bc = \pm 1$. Functions having two periods whose ratio is not real are called *doubly-periodic*. We encountered an example of such a function in section 4.11.4, where we defined the pe-function of Weierstrass.

5.1.4 – The period-parallelogram

Suppose that w_1 and w_2 are primitive periods of a doubly-periodic function. The points $n_1 w_1+n_2 w_2$; $n_1, n_2 = 0, \pm 1, \pm 2, \ldots$, are called the *lattice-points* in the plane (section **4.11.4**).

A parallelogram with vertices z_0, z_0+w_1, $z_0+w_1+w_2$, z_0+w_2 is called a *period-parallelogram* connected with z_0. It is clear that the z-plane may be covered by a network of equal and similarly situated period-parallelograms such that a given point belongs to the system of vertices. This system is obtained from the system of lattice-points by a translation which carries the origin to the point z_0.

We agree on taking w_1 and w_2 in such a way that $\text{Im}\,(w_2/w_1) > 0$. This does not mean any restriction, for when w_2 is a primitive period, so is $-w_2$. It results that the sense of description of the perimeter C of a period-parallelogram induced by the above order of vertices is always counter-clockwise.

On opposite sides of a period-parallelogram the function $f(z)$ assumes the same values. We agree on considering only the points $z_0+\alpha_1 w_1$, $z_0+\alpha_2 w_2$, $0 \leqq \alpha_1 < 1$, $0 \leqq \alpha_2 < 1$, as belonging to the period-parallelogram connected with z_0.

The period-parallelogram connected with the origin shall be referred to as the *fundamental period-parallelogram.*

Two points z, z' are said to be *congruent* modulo w_1, w_2 when

$$z-z' = m_1 w_1+m_2 w_2, \tag{5.1–2}$$

m_1 and m_2 being integers. We express this relation by the notation

$$z \equiv z'(w_1, w_2). \tag{5.1–3}$$

This relation is evidently reflexive, symmetric and transitive.

Any (finite) point in the z-plane is congruent to one and only one point in a given period-parallelogram.

In fact, we can write

$$z = z_0+\lambda_1 w_1+\lambda_2 w_2,$$

and since $\lambda_1 = m_1+\alpha_1$, $\lambda_2 = m_2+\alpha_2$, $0 \leqq \alpha_1 < 1$, $0 \leqq \alpha_2 < 1$, m_1 and m_2 being integers, we find that

$$z \equiv z_0+\alpha_1 w_1+\alpha_2 w_2 \ (w_1, w_2).$$

This proves the assertion.

A set of points is said to be *irreducible* if no two points of the set are congruent one to another. The points of an irreducible set are always congruent to the points of a set included in a period-parallelogram, no two points of this latter set being coincident.

It is evident that the values of a doubly-periodic function are known when we know the values of the points of a period-parallelogram. The values at other points are a mere repetition of its values in a period-parallelogram.

5.2 – Elliptic functions

5.2.1 – Definition

A doubly-periodic function which is meromorphic throughout the z-plane is called an *elliptic function*. The constant is a trivial example of an elliptic function. A non-trivial example is the Weierstrass pe function (**4**.11–28).

It is evident that if $f(z)$ and $g(z)$ are elliptic functions having the same set of periods, so are $f(z)+g(z)$, $f(z)g(z)$ and (when $g(z) \neq 0$) $f(z)/g(z)$. Hence the system of elliptic functions having the same set of periods is closed as regards rational operations. A system of this nature is called a *field*.

The simplest example of a field is the set of all rational functions. This field can be generated by the single function z, that is to say, we obtain all functions of the field by performing all possible rational operations on z.

A similar but not so simple theorem holds for a field of elliptic functions. In section 5.3.3 we shall prove that all elliptic functions of a field can be expressed rationally in terms of the pe function of Weierstrass and its derivative, having the same periods.

The following statement is almost trivial.

The derivative of an elliptic function is itself an elliptic function.

5.2.2 – Liouville's theorem

Next we turn to more significant theorems. The following theorem, known as *Liouville's theorem*, is of utmost importance in the theory of elliptic functions. It states:

An elliptic function with no poles in a period-parallelogram is a constant.

In fact, if an elliptic function $f(z)$ has no poles in a period-parallelogram it has no poles on adjacent period-parallelograms and is, therefore, bounded throughout the parallelogram. From the periodic properties of $f(z)$ it follows that the function is regular at every point of the z-plane and is bounded throughout the z-plane. From Liouville's theorem of section 2.12.1 we conclude that $f(z)$ is a constant.

It is clear that there are only a finite number of poles in a period-parallelogram, for the set of poles in such a parallelogram has no accumulation point.

Assume that $z = a$ is a pole of order n of the function $f(z)$, i.e.,

$$f(z)(z-a)^n = g(z),$$

where $g(z)$ is regular at $z = a$. If w is a period we have

$$g(z) = f(z)(z-a)^n = f(z+w)\{z+w-(a+w)\}^n = g(z+w).$$

Hence $f(z)\{z-(a+w)\}^n$ is regular at $a+w$, and so $a+w$ is a pole of $f(z)$, having the same order of multiplicity.

Each pole of a period-parallelogram is congruent to a pole with the same order of multiplicity in a fundamental period-parallelogram. The sum of the multiplicities of the poles in a fundamental period-parallelogram is called the *order* of an elliptic function.

Liouville's theorem states that *the order of an elliptic function is always positive.*

5.2.3 – The sum of the residues

Another important theorem is the following:

The sum of the residues of the poles in a period-parallelogram is zero.

Since there are only a finite number of poles in a period-parallelogram we may assume that none of them is on the boundary. For if this should be the case we shift it a little such that the perimeter is free from poles. Let C denote the perimeter of a period-parallelogram connected with z_0. Taking account of Cauchy's residue theorem of section 3.5.1 we have only to prove that

$$\int_C f(\zeta)d\zeta = 0. \tag{5.2–1}$$

The integral on the left may be written as the sum of four integrals taken along the sides

$$\int_{z_0}^{z_0+w_1} f(\zeta)d\zeta + \int_{z_0+w_1}^{z_0+w_1+w_2} f(\zeta)d\zeta + \int_{z_0+w_1+w_2}^{z_0+w_2} f(\zeta)d\zeta + \int_{z_0+w_2}^{z_0} f(\zeta)d\zeta.$$

In the second and third integral we write $\zeta+w_1$, $\zeta+w_2$ respectively. We find, after re-arranging the terms,

$$\int_{z_0}^{z_0+w_2} \{f(\zeta+w_1)-f(\zeta)\}d\zeta - \int_{z_0}^{z_0+w_1} \{f(\zeta+w_2)-f(\zeta)\}d\zeta,$$

and each of these integrals vanishes by virtue of the periodic properties of $f(z)$.

As a corollary we have:

The order of an elliptic function is never less than two.

In fact, if a function would have a simple pole, the residue would not be zero.

By a *fundamental set of poles* we understand an irreducible set (see section 5.1.4) of poles such that each pole is congruent to a pole included in the set.

So far as singularities are concerned the simplest elliptic functions are those of order two. Such functions may be divided into two classes:

(i) The functions having a fundamental system which consists of only one pole, this pole being double, and with residue zero at the pole. They are called the *elliptic functions of Weierstrass.*

(ii) The functions having a fundamental system which consists of two simple poles, the residues being numerically equal, but opposite in sign. They are called the *elliptic functions of Jacobi.*

5.2.4 – The sum of the zeros

A fundamental system of zeros may be defined in exactly the same way as a fundamental system of poles.

The sum of the multiplicities of the zeros of an elliptic function in a fundamental system is equal to the order of the function.

We may assume that neither zeros nor poles are on the sides of a period-parallelogram, for the zeros are also isolated. The sum of the multiplicities of the zeros minus the sum of the multiplicities of the poles are given by the equation (3.8–8). Since the integrand is elliptic we find by the argument applied in section 5.2.3 that this integral is zero.

If c is a constant then the functions $f(z)$ and $f(z)-c$ have the same poles. Hence:

The sum of the multiplicities of the roots of the equation $f(z) = c$ in a fundamental system is equal to the order of the function.

As a consequence an elliptic function assumes every value.

5.2.5 – The sum of the zeros in relation to the sum of the poles

Let $a_1, \ldots, a_r$ denote a fundamental system of zeros having certain multiplicities. By the sum of the roots we understand the sum of these numbers, each multiplied by its proper multiplicity. If n is the order we may also write the zeros as a sequence $a_1, \ldots, a_n$, where it is understood that a multiple zero is repeated. Similarly we define the sum of the poles in a fundamental system.

Now we wish to establish the remarkable theorem:

The sum of the zeros in a fundamental system is congruent to the sum of the poles in a fundamental system. Let also $b_1, \ldots, b_n$ denote the sequence of poles belonging to a fundamental system, multiple poles being repeated. In accordance with the formula (3.8–12), where we take $g(z) = z$, we have, on performing the same substitution as in section 5.2.3:

$$\sum_{\nu=1}^{n} a_\nu - \sum_{\nu=1}^{n} b_\nu = \frac{1}{2\pi i}\int_C \zeta \frac{f'(\zeta)}{f(\zeta)}\,d\zeta$$

$$= \frac{1}{2\pi i}\left\{\int_{z_0}^{z_0+w_1} + \int_{z_0+w_1}^{z_0+w_1+w_2} + \int_{z_0+w_1+w_2}^{z_0+w_2} + \int_{z_0+w_2}^{z_0}\right\} \zeta\frac{f'(\zeta)}{f(\zeta)}\,d\zeta$$

$$= \frac{1}{2\pi i}\int_{z_0}^{z_0+w_2}\left\{(\zeta+w_1)\frac{f'(\zeta+w_1)}{f(\zeta+w_1)} - \zeta\frac{f'(\zeta)}{f(\zeta)}\right\}d\zeta +$$

$$-\frac{1}{2\pi i}\int_{z_0}^{z_0+w_1}\left\{(\zeta+w_2)\frac{f'(\zeta+w_2)}{f(\zeta+w_2)} - \zeta\frac{f'(\zeta)}{f(\zeta)}\right\}d\zeta$$

$$= \frac{w_1}{2\pi i}\int_{z_0}^{z_0+w_2}\frac{f'(\zeta)}{f(\zeta)}\,d\zeta - \frac{w_2}{2\pi i}\int_{z_0}^{z_0+w_1}\frac{f'(\zeta)}{f(\zeta)}\,d\zeta.$$

Since $f(z)$ assumes the same values at z_0, z_0+w_1 and z_0+w_2, the point $f(z)$ describes a closed curve C_1 when z varies from z_0 to z_0+w_1, and a closed curve C_2 when z_0 varies from z_0 to z_0+w_2.

According to the considerations of section 3.10.1 we may infer that

$$\frac{1}{2\pi i}\int_C \zeta\frac{f'(\zeta)}{f(\zeta)}\,d\zeta = w_1\Omega_{C_1}(0) - w_2\Omega_{C_2}(0),$$

and since the winding numbers are integers, we actually have

$$\boxed{\sum_{\nu=1}^{n} a_\nu \equiv \sum_{\nu=1}^{n} b_\nu \ (w_1, w_2).} \tag{5.2–2}$$

5.3 – The pe function of Weierstrass

5.3.1 – Fundamental properties

We are now in a position to study more closely the elliptic function $\wp(z)$ introduced in section 4.11.4. We recall that $\wp(z)$ is a doubly-periodic function having periods 2ω, $2\omega'$, where $\text{Im}\,(\omega'/\omega) > 0$. The function is defined by the expansion

$$\wp(z) = \frac{1}{z^2} + \sum{}' \left(\frac{1}{(z-w)^2} - \frac{1}{w^2}\right) \tag{5.3–1}$$

where w runs through the periods $2n\omega + 2n\omega'$, the prime denoting that in the sum the term involving $w = 0$ does not occur.

It follows at once that

$$\wp'(z) = -\sum \frac{2}{(z-w)^3}, \tag{5.3–2}$$

the prime now being superfluous.

We already know that $\wp(z)$ is an even function and from (5.3–2) we easily deduce that $\wp'(z)$ is an odd function:

$$\boxed{\wp(-z) = \wp(z), \qquad \wp'(-z) = -\wp'(z).} \tag{5.3–3}$$

The function $\wp(z)$ assumes a double pole and the function $\wp'(z)$ assumes a triple pole at each lattice-point, the residues being zero. At all other points the functions are regular.

In a sufficiently small neighbourhood of the origin the function is represented by the Laurent series

$$\boxed{\wp(z) = \frac{1}{z^2} + \sum_{\nu=1}^{\infty} c_{2\nu} z^{2\nu},} \tag{5.3–4}$$

where

$$c_{2n} = (2n+1) \sum' \frac{1}{w^{2n+2}}, \quad n = 1, 2, \ldots. \tag{5.3–5}$$

In order to prove this statement we start with the zeta function (4.11–27)

$$\zeta(z) = \frac{1}{z} + \sum' \left(\frac{1}{z-w} + \frac{1}{w} + \frac{z}{w^2}\right). \tag{5.3–6}$$

Expanding each term occurring in the sum on the right, we have by virtue of Weierstrass's double series theorem (2.20.4)

$$\zeta(z) = \frac{1}{z} - z^2 \sum' \frac{1}{w^3} - z^3 \sum' \frac{1}{w^4} - \ldots. \tag{5.3–7}$$

Now the terms involving even powers of z vanish. In fact, since w and $-w$ run through the same set of lattice-points, we have

$$\sum' \frac{1}{w^{2n+1}} = \sum' \frac{1}{(-w)^{2n+1}} = -\sum' \frac{1}{w^{2n+1}}.$$

Accordingly we may write the series (5.3–7) in the form

$$\zeta(z) = \frac{1}{z} - \sum_{\nu=1}^{\infty} \frac{c_{2\nu}}{2\nu+1} z^{2\nu+1}, \tag{5.3–8}$$

c_{2n} being defined in (5.3–5).

We see that $\zeta(z)$ *is an odd function*:

$$\boxed{\zeta(-z) = -\zeta(z).} \tag{5.3–9}$$

Moreover

$$\zeta(z) - \frac{1}{z} = O(z^3), \qquad \text{as } z \to 0, \tag{5.3–10}$$

that is to say, the function $\zeta(z) - 1/z$ has a zero of order three at the origin.

Taking account of $\wp(z) = -\zeta'(z)$ the formula (5.3–4) follows at once from (5.3–8). Additionally we have

$$\wp'(z) = -\frac{2}{z^3} + \sum_{\nu=1}^{\infty} 2\nu c_{2\nu} z^{2\nu-1}. \tag{5.3–11}$$

Finally we wish to remark *that* 2ω *and* $2\omega'$ *are primitive periods of* $\wp(z)$ *and* $\wp'(z)$. If not, there would exist a network of period-parallelograms, each having smaller area than those formed by the lattice-points $2n\omega+2n'\omega'$. Some of them would evidently contain no singularity and this is impossible. Thus it appears *that* $\wp'(z)$ *is of order three, while* $\wp(z)$ *is of order two.*

5.3.2 – The zeros of the derivative

The problem of evaluating the zeros of the function $\wp'(z)$ is very easy. Since $\wp'(z)$ is odd we have

$$\wp'(w-z) = \wp'(-z) = -\wp'(z)$$

where w stands for 2ω, $2\omega+2\omega'$ or $2\omega'$. It is assumed, of course, that z is a regular point. Inserting $z = \frac{1}{2}w$ we find

$$\wp'(\tfrac{1}{2}w) = -\wp'(\tfrac{1}{2}w).$$

Since the order is three the sum of the multiplicities of the zeros in the fundamental period-parallelogram must be three. Since we have found three different zeros, viz., ω, $\omega+\omega'$ and ω', the zeros are necessarily simple.

In the fundamental period-parallelogram the function $\wp'(z)$ *has the zeros* $\omega, \omega+\omega', \omega'$, *each being simple.*

Since the order of $\wp(z)$ is two and the sum of the multiplicities of the zeros in a period-parallelogram is equal to the order, the equation

$$\wp(z) = \wp(a), \tag{5.3–12}$$

where a is not a period, has two sets of solutions, viz., the numbers congruent to a and those congruent to $-a$. When a and $-a$ are not congruent they form an irreducible set of roots of (5.3–12). It may happen, however, that a and $-a$ are congruent. That means that $2a \equiv 0$, or $a = n\omega+n'\omega'$, where not both numbers n, n' are even. Hence a is congruent to one of the zeros of $\wp'(z)$ in the fundamental period-parallelogram, in accordance with the fact that in this case a is a double root of (5.3–12).

The values of $\wp(z)$ at these points are finite. They play an important role in the theory of the pe-function. They are denoted as

$$\boxed{e_1 = \wp(\omega), \qquad e_2 = \wp(\omega+\omega'), \qquad e_3 = \wp(\omega').} \tag{5.3–13}$$

The previous result can also be stated in the form:
The equation

$$\wp(z) = c \tag{5.3–14}$$

has then and only then double roots if c is one of the numbers e_1, e_2, e_3.

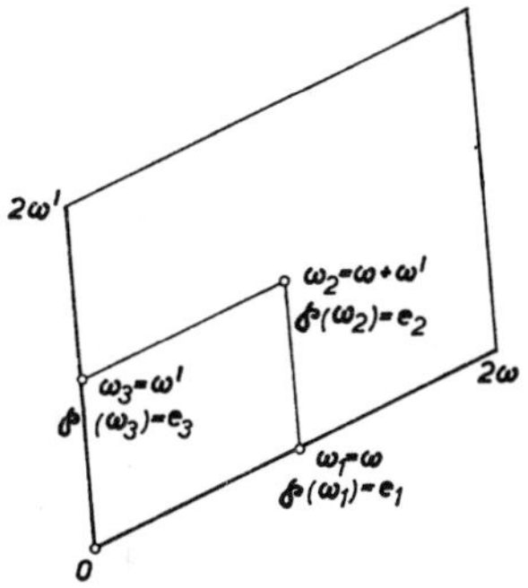

Fig. 5.3–1. Location of the half-periods of $\wp(z)$

For the sake of symmetry it is often convenient to denote the numbers ω, $\omega+\omega'$ and ω' by ω_1, ω_2, ω_3 respectively, (fig. 5.3–1), i.e.,

$$\omega_1 = \omega, \qquad \omega_2 = \omega+\omega', \qquad \omega_3 = \omega'. \tag{5.3–15}$$

We then have

$$\wp(\omega_\alpha) = e_\alpha, \qquad \alpha = 1, 2, 3. \tag{5.3–16}$$

It is easy to see that no two of the numbers e_1, e_2, e_3 are equal. For if e_α should be equal to e_β, $\alpha \neq \beta$, then the equation (5.3–14) would have the doubly counted root $z = \omega_\alpha$ and also the doubly counted root $z = \omega_\beta$. The sum of the multiplicities would be equal to 4 which is impossible.

5.3.3 – Expression of an elliptic function in terms of the pe function

We conclude our introductory considerations by establishing the following remarkable theorem:

Any elliptic function $f(z)$ can be expressed in terms of the functions $\wp(z)$ and $\wp'(z)$ with the same periods, the expression being rational in $\wp(z)$ and linear in $\wp'(z)$.

First we assume that $f(z)$ is an even function and is regular and non-zero at the lattice-points. If a_1 is a zero of $f(z)$ in the fundamental period-parallelogram then a point in this parallelogram congruent to $-a_1$ is also a zero. We can, therefore, choose n zeros $a_1, \ldots, a_n$ in the fundamental parallelogram, each multiple zero being repeated according to its multiplicity, in such a way that they, together with the points in the parallelogram congruent to $-a_1, \ldots,$

$-a_n$, are all zeros in the parallelogram. Similarly we can choose n poles $b_1, \ldots, b_n$ such that they, together with the points congruent to $-b_1, \ldots, -b_n$ in the parallelogram, are all poles in the fundamental parallelogram. The function

$$F(z) = \prod_{\nu=1}^{n} \frac{\wp(z) - \wp(a_\nu)}{\wp(z) - \wp(b_\nu)},$$

where $\wp(z)$ has the same primitive periods as $f(z)$, is an elliptic function having the same zeros and poles as $f(z)$. Hence the ratio $f(z)/F(z)$ is an elliptic function with no poles in the fundamental period-parallelogram and so is a constant by Liouville's theorem of section 5.2.2. Thus

$$f(z) = A \prod_{\nu=1}^{n} \frac{\wp(z) - \wp(a_\nu)}{\wp(z) - \wp(b_\nu)}. \qquad (5.3\text{–}17)$$

If $f(z)$ has a pole or a zero at the origin (and hence at all lattice points) such a pole or zero must be of even order. By choosing the integer m suitably the function $f(z)\,\wp^m(z)$ is an even elliptic function which is regular and non-zero at all lattice-points and is, therefore, expressible in the form (5.3–17).

If $f(z)$ is an odd function then $f(z)/\wp'(z)$ is even and therefore rationally expressible in terms of $\wp(z)$.

Finally we observe that any function can be written in the form

$$f(z) = \tfrac{1}{2}\{f(z)+f(-z)\}+\tfrac{1}{2}\{f(z)-f(-z)\}. \qquad (5.3\text{–}18)$$

The first term on the right-hand side of this equation is even, the second term is odd. Hence $f(z)$ can be put into the form

$$f(z) = R_1\{\wp(z)\}+\wp'(z)R_2\{\wp(z)\}, \qquad (5.3\text{–}19)$$

where R_1 and R_2 are rational functions of their argument $\wp(z)$. This is the result stated above.

5.4 – The differential equation of the pe function

5.4.1 – First form of the differential equation

The points $z = \omega, \omega+\omega', \omega'$ are double zeros of the functions $\wp(z)-e_1$, $\wp(z)-e_2$, $\wp(z)-e_3$ respectively and, at the same time, simple zeros of $\wp'(z)$. On the other hand the three above functions have poles of order two at the lattice-points, while $\wp'(z)$ has there poles of order three. Hence the ratio of the functions $\wp'^2(z)$ and $(\wp(z)-e_1)(\wp(z)-e_2)(\wp(z)-e_3)$ is an elliptic function with no poles and so is a constant. Multiplying denominator and numerator in this ratio by

z^6 and letting $z \to 0$ we see on account of (5.3–4) and (5.3–11) that this constant is 4. Thus:

The function $\wp(z)$ *satisfies the differential equation*

$$\boxed{\wp'^2(z) = 4(\wp(z)-e_1)(\wp(z)-e_2)(\wp(z)-e_3).} \qquad (5.4\text{–}1)$$

5.4.2 – Second form of the differential equation

An alternative method to derive the differential equation starts with the series (5.3–4) and (5.3–11). Cubing and squaring those respectively, we get

$$\wp^3(z) = \frac{1}{z^6} + \frac{3c_2}{z^2} + 3c_4 + O(z^2),$$

where $O(z^2)$ denotes a function having a zero at $z = 0$ of order two at least. Again

$$\wp'^2(z) = \frac{4}{z^6} - \frac{8c_2}{z^2} - 16c_4 + O(z^2),$$

whence

$$\wp'^2(z) - 4\wp^3(z) = -\frac{20c_2}{z^2} - 28c_4 + O(z^2)$$

and finally

$$\wp'^2(z) - 4\wp^3(z) + 20c_2\wp(z) + 28c_4 = O(z^2).$$

The function on the left-hand side is regular at $z = 0$ and hence at all lattice-points. But these are the only possible singularities and so it is an elliptic function with no poles. Hence it is a constant, which must be zero since the expression on the right-hand side is zero at $z = 0$.

It is customary to write

$$g_2 = 20c_2 = 60 \sum{}' \frac{1}{w^4}, \qquad g_3 = 28c_4 = 140 \sum{}' \frac{1}{w^6}. \qquad (5.4\text{–}2)$$

The numbers g_2 and g_3 are called the ***invariants*** of the function $\wp(z)$.

It follows that the function $\wp(z)$ satisfies the differential equation

$$\boxed{\wp'^2(z) = 4\wp^3(z) - g_2\wp(z) - g_3.} \qquad (5.4\text{–}3)$$

5.4.3 – The discriminant

Comparing (5.4–1) and (5.4–3) and observing that $\wp(z)$ assumes any value, we easily find the following relations for e_1, e_2, e_3:

$$e_1+e_2+e_3 = 0, \tag{5.4-4}$$

$$e_1 e_2+e_1 e_3+e_2 e_3 = -\tfrac{1}{4}g_2, \tag{5.4-5}$$

$$e_1 e_2 e_3 = \tfrac{1}{4}g_3. \tag{5.4-6}$$

By the *discriminant* of the function $\wp(z)$ one means the expression

$$\Delta = 16(e_1-e_2)^2(e_1-e_3)^2(e_2-e_3)^2. \tag{5.4-7}$$

We wish to express Δ in terms of g_2 and g_3. Differentiating the product

$$4(z-e_1)(z-e_2)(z-e_3) = 4z^3-g_2 z-g_3$$

and inserting in the result so obtained $z = e_1, e_2, e_3$ respectively, we find

$$(e_1-e_2)(e_1-e_3) = 3e_1^2-\tfrac{1}{4}g_2,$$
$$(e_2-e_1)(e_2-e_3) = 3e_2^2-\tfrac{1}{4}g_2,$$
$$(e_3-e_1)(e_3-e_2) = 3e_3^2-\tfrac{1}{4}g_2,$$

whence

$$\begin{aligned}-(e_1-e_2)^2(e_1-e_3)^2(e_2-e_3)^2 &= (3e_1^2-\tfrac{1}{4}g_2)(3e_2^2-\tfrac{1}{4}g_2)(3e_3^2-\tfrac{1}{4}g_2)\\ &=27(e_1 e_2 e_3)^2-\tfrac{9}{4}(e_1^2 e_2^2+e_1^2 e_3^2+e_2^2 e_3^2)g_2+\tfrac{3}{16}(e_1^2+e_2^2+e_3^2)g_2^2-\tfrac{1}{64}g_2^3.\end{aligned} \tag{5.4-8}$$

Squaring (5.4–4) we have on account of (5.4–5)

$$e_1^2+e_2^2+e_3^2 = \tfrac{1}{2}g_2. \tag{5.4-9}$$

Squaring (5.4–5) we easily find

$$e_1^2 e_2^2+e_1^2 e_3^2+e_2^2 e_3^2 = \tfrac{1}{16}g_2^2. \tag{5.4-10}$$

Inserting these results into (5.4–8) we finally have

$$\boxed{\Delta = 16(e_1-e_2)^2(e_1-e_3)^2(e_2-e_3)^2 = g_2^3-27g_3^2.} \tag{5.4-11}$$

5.4.4 – Degenerated pe functions

The case of degeneration (see section 4.12.3) is of some interest. From (3.7–20) we obtain, inserting the numerical values of the Bernoullinumbers listed in section 2.17.4,

$$\frac{\pi^4}{90} = \sum_{\nu=1}^{\infty}\frac{1}{\nu^4}, \quad \frac{\pi^6}{945} = \sum_{\nu=1}^{\infty}\frac{1}{\nu^6}.$$

Hence, according to (5.4–2), letting $\omega' \to \infty$,

$$g_2(\omega, \infty) = \frac{4}{3}\left(\frac{\pi}{2\omega}\right)^4, \quad g_3(\omega, \infty) = \frac{8}{27}\left(\frac{\pi}{2\omega}\right)^6. \tag{5.4-12}$$

From (4.12–10) we deduce at once

$$e_1 = \frac{2}{3}\left(\frac{\pi}{2\omega}\right)^2. \tag{5.4–13}$$

Inserting $z = \omega'$ or $z = \omega+\omega'$ into the expansion (5.3–1) and letting $\omega' \to \infty$ we find

$$e_2 = e_3 = -\sum{}' \frac{1}{w^2} = -2\sum_{\nu=1}^{\infty} \frac{1}{(2\nu\omega)^2},$$

whence

$$e_2 = e_3 = -\frac{1}{3}\left(\frac{\pi}{2\omega}\right)^2. \tag{5.4–14}$$

Expressed in terms of the invariants we have

$$e_1 = \frac{3g_3}{g_2}, \quad e_2 = e_3 = -\frac{3g_3}{2g_2}.$$

Finally we observe that *in the degenerated case the discriminant is zero.*

5.5 – Addition theorems

5.5.1 – The addition theorem of the pe function

Let a and b be two numbers not periods of $\wp(z)$. The equations

$$\wp'(a) = A\,\wp(a)+B, \qquad \wp'(b) = A\,\wp(b)+B \tag{5.5–1}$$

determine A and B unambiguously, unless $a \equiv \pm b(2\omega, 2\omega')$, i.e., unless $\wp(a) = \wp(b)$. The roots of the equation

$$\wp'(z) = A\,\wp(z)+B \tag{5.5–2}$$

are congruent to one of the points $a, b, -(a+b)$, for the sum of the poles in the fundamental period-parallelogram is zero. Hence, in accordance with (5.2–2), the sum of the roots in the fundamental parallelogram must be congruent to zero.

Taking account of (5.4–3) the roots must satisfy the equation

$$\begin{aligned}(A\,\wp(z)+B)^2 &= 4\wp^3(z)-g_2\wp(z)-g_3,\\ &= 4(\wp(z)-\wp(a))(\wp(z)-\wp(b))(\wp(z)-\wp(a+b))\end{aligned}$$

and, comparing equal powers of $\wp(z)$, we find that

$$\wp(a+b)+\wp(a)+\wp(b) = \tfrac{1}{4}A^2.$$

Solving for A in (5.5–1) we find the *addition theorem*

$$\boxed{\wp(a+b)+\wp(a)+\wp(b) = \frac{1}{4}\left(\frac{\wp'(a)-\wp'(b)}{\wp(a)-\wp(b)}\right)^2.} \tag{5.5–3}$$

We may remove the restriction that $a \not\equiv b(2\omega, 2\omega')$. Letting $b \to a$ in (5.5–3) we find the *duplication formula*

$$\wp(2a)+2\wp(a) = \frac{1}{4}\frac{\wp''^2(a)}{\wp'^2(a)}, \tag{5.5–4}$$

provided that not $a \equiv -a$, i.e., that a is not a zero of $\wp'(z)$.

5.5.2 – Addition of a half period

Putting $b = \omega$ in the addition theorem (5.5–3) we get, writing z instead of a,

$$\wp(z+\omega)+\wp(z)+\wp(\omega) = \frac{1}{4}\frac{\wp'^2(z)}{\{\wp(z)-\wp(\omega)\}^2},$$

or, taking account of (5.3–13) and (5.4–1),

$$\wp(z+\omega)+\wp(z)+e_1 = \frac{(\wp(z)-e_2)(\wp(z)-e_3)}{\wp(z)-e_1}.$$

By simple algebra it follows that

$$\wp(z+\omega) = A+\frac{B}{\wp(z)-e_1},$$

where A and B are constants. Referring to (5.4–4) and observing that $z = 0$ is a pole of $\wp(z)$ we find by taking $z = 0$ that $A = e_1$ and by taking $z = \omega'$ that $B = (e_2-e_1)(e_3-e_1)$. Hence

$$\boxed{\wp(z+\omega) = e_1+\frac{(e_2-e_1)(e_3-e_1)}{\wp(z)-e_1}.} \tag{5.5–5}$$

Similarly we find

$$\boxed{\wp(z+\omega+\omega') = e_2+\frac{(e_1-e_2)(e_3-e_2)}{\wp(z)-e_2}} \tag{5.5–6}$$

and

$$\boxed{\wp(z+\omega') = e_3+\frac{(e_1-e_3)(e_2-e_3)}{\wp(z)-e_3}.} \tag{5.5–7}$$

5.5.3 – The addition theorem of the zeta function

An alternative method for deriving the addition theorem makes use of some properties of the Weierstrass zeta function. Since

$$\zeta'(z) = -\wp(z) \tag{5.5–8}$$

we have

$$\zeta'(z+2\omega_\alpha) = \zeta'(z), \qquad \alpha = 1, 2, 3 \tag{5.5–9}$$

and by integration

$$\boxed{\zeta(z+2\omega_\alpha) = \zeta(z)+2\eta_\alpha,} \qquad \alpha = 1, 2, 3, \tag{5.5–10}$$

where η_α are constants.

Inserting $z = -\omega_\alpha$ we have

$$\zeta(\omega_\alpha) = \zeta(-\omega_\alpha)+2\eta_\alpha = -\zeta(\omega_\alpha)+2\eta_\alpha,$$

or

$$\boxed{\zeta(\omega_\alpha) = \eta_\alpha,} \qquad \alpha = 1, 2, 3. \tag{5.5–11}$$

The property expressed by (5.5–10) is often called the *quasi-periodicity* of the zeta function and the numbers η_α are the *quasi-periods*. Those corresponding to $\omega_1 = \omega$ and $\omega_3 = \omega'$ are also denoted by η and η' respectively.

Since $\omega_2 = \omega_1+\omega_3$, we have on account of (5.5–10)

$$\begin{aligned}\zeta(z)+2\eta_2 &= \zeta(z+2\omega_2) = \zeta(z+2\omega_1+2\omega_3)\\ &= \zeta(z+2\omega_1)+2\eta_3 = \zeta(z)+2\eta_1+2\eta_3,\end{aligned}$$

whence

$$\eta_2 = \eta_1+\eta_3 = \eta+\eta'. \tag{5.5–12}$$

It is clear that the function

$$\varphi(z) = \zeta(z-a)+\zeta(z+a)-2\zeta(z), \tag{5.5–13}$$

where a is not a lattice-point, is an elliptic function of periods 2ω, $2\omega'$. The expansion (5.3–8) exhibits that $z = 0$ is a pole of $\zeta(z)$, the residue at this pole being 1. Hence $\varphi(z)$ has poles at $z = a$, $z = -a$, $z = 0$, the residues there being 1, 1, -2 respectively. This function has the same poles as the function

$$f(z) = \frac{\wp'(z)}{\wp(z)-\wp(a)}, \tag{5.5–14}$$

the orders of multiplicity and the residues being the same. The difference $f(z)-\varphi(z)$ is therefore a constant (by Liouville's theorem) and since the function is odd, the constant is zero. Hence

$$\zeta(z-a)+\zeta(z+a)-2\zeta(z) = \frac{\wp'(z)}{\wp(z)-\wp(a)}. \tag{5.5–15}$$

Putting $z = b$ and interchanging a and b we get by adding

$$\boxed{\zeta(a+b)-\zeta(a)-\zeta(b) = \frac{1}{2}\,\frac{\wp'(a)-\wp'(b)}{\wp(a)-\wp(b)},} \tag{5.5–16}$$

the so-called *addition theorem for the zeta-function.*

Differentiation with respect to a yields

$$\wp(a+b)-\wp(a) = -\frac{1}{2}\frac{\partial}{\partial a}\left(\frac{\wp'(a)-\wp'(b)}{\wp(a)-\wp(b)}\right). \tag{5.5–17}$$

It is not difficult to show that (5.5–17) and (5.5–3) are identical. In fact, (5.5–17) can be written as

$$\wp(a+b)-\wp(a) = -\frac{1}{2}\frac{\wp''(a)}{\wp(a)-\wp(b)}+\frac{1}{2}\frac{\wp'(a)\{\wp'(a)-\wp'(b)\}}{\{\wp(a)-\wp(b)\}^2}.$$

By differentiating both sides of (5.4–3) we get

$$\wp''(a) = 6\wp^2(a)-\tfrac{1}{2}g_2. \tag{5.5–18}$$

Inserting this into the previous equation, interchanging a and b and adding we easily find the desired result (5.5–3).

5.5.4 – Legendre's relation

There is a narrow connection between the periods of the pe function and the quasi-periods of the allied zeta function. Since $\zeta(z)$ has a simple pole with residue one inside a suitably chosen period-parallelogram, we have by the residue theorem of Cauchy

$$\frac{1}{2\pi i}\int_C \zeta(z)dz = 1.$$

Proceeding as in section 5.2.3 we get

$$\frac{1}{2\pi i}\int_{z_0}^{z_0+2\omega'}\{\zeta(z+2\omega)-\zeta(z)\}dz-\frac{1}{2\pi i}\int_{z_0}^{z_0+2\omega}\{\zeta(z+2\omega')-\zeta(z)\}dz = 1,$$

whence, by virtue of (5.5–10),

$$\boxed{\eta\omega'-\eta'\omega = \tfrac{1}{2}\pi i.} \tag{5.5–19}$$

From this relation, *Legendre's relation,* we easily deduce the more general relations

$$\eta_\alpha\omega_\beta-\eta_\beta\omega_\alpha = \tfrac{1}{2}\pi i, \qquad \alpha<\beta, \qquad \alpha,\beta = 1, 2, 3. \tag{5.5–20}$$

Of course the expression on the left is zero for $\alpha = \beta$.

5.6 – The sigma functions of Weierstrass

5.6.1 – The sigma function

In this section we wish to study in more detail the sigma function introduced in section 4.12.2. It will appear that this function has remarkable properties and that it plays an important part in the theory of elliptic functions.

The sigma function is not an elliptic function but satisfies a functional equation of rather simple type which might also be called a relation of quasi-periodicity. This relation is readily obtained from (5.5–11), taking account of the fact that the zeta function is the logarithmic derivative of the sigma function. Hence

$$\sigma(z+2\omega_\alpha) = \sigma(z) \exp\,(2\eta_\alpha z+c) \tag{5.6–1}$$

where c is a constant. Now $\sigma(z)$ is an odd function

$$\sigma(-z) = -\sigma(z). \tag{5.6–2}$$

Inserting $z = -\omega_\alpha$ into (5.6–1) we find

$$\sigma(\omega_\alpha) = -\sigma(\omega_\alpha) \exp\,(-2\eta_\alpha \omega_\alpha+c)$$

whence

$$\exp\,(-2\eta_\alpha\omega_\alpha+c) = -1$$

or

$$\exp c = -\exp 2\eta_\alpha\omega_\alpha.$$

And so we finally have

$$\boxed{\sigma(z+2\omega_\alpha) = -\sigma(z) \exp 2\eta_\alpha(z+\omega_\alpha).} \tag{5.6–3}$$

The factor $-\exp 2\eta_\alpha(z+\omega_\alpha)$ is called the *periodicity-factor* of the function.

From the representation (4.12–6) of $\sigma(z)$ as an infinite product it follows immediately that

$$\boxed{\sigma(0) = 0, \qquad \sigma'(0) = 1.} \tag{5.6–4}$$

This is in accordance with the fact that all lattice-points are simple zeros of $\sigma(z)$.

5.6.2 – Expression of an elliptic function in terms of the sigma function

The importance of the sigma function is based on the fact that any elliptic function $f(z)$ can be expressed in terms of the sigma function.

Let $a_1, \ldots, a_n$ denote the system of zeros in the fundamental period-parallelogram, and $b_1, \ldots, b_n$ the system of poles in the same parallelogram, multiple zeros and poles being repeated. By virtue of the theorem of section 5.2.5 the sum of the zeros is congruent to the sum of the poles. By adding an appropriate period to b_n we may even suppose that

$$a_1+\ldots+a_n = b_1+\ldots+b_n, \tag{5.6–5}$$

where b_n need not lie in the fundamental period-parallelogram. Now consider the function

$$\prod_{\nu=1}^{n} \frac{\sigma(z-a_\nu)}{\sigma(z-b_\nu)}. \tag{5.6–6}$$

It has the same zeros and poles as $f(z)$. The effect of increasing z by $2\omega_r$ is to multiply the function by

$$\prod_{\nu=1}^{n} \frac{\exp 2\eta_\alpha(z-a_\nu)}{\exp 2\eta_\alpha(z-b_\nu)} = \exp 2\eta_\alpha\left(-\sum_{\nu=1}^{n} a_\nu + \sum_{\nu=1}^{n} b_\nu\right) = 1.$$

Hence the quotient of $f(z)$ and the function (5.6–6) is an elliptic function with no zeros and no poles. Accordingly we have by Liouville's theorem of section 5.2.2

$$\boxed{f(z) = A\prod_{\nu=1}^{n} \frac{\sigma(z-a_\nu)}{\sigma(z-b_\nu)}.} \tag{5.6–7}$$

Thus we see:

An elliptic function is determinate save for a multiplicative constant, when its period and a set of zeros and poles in a period-parallelogram are known.

5.6.3 – Expression of the pe function in terms of the sigma function

According to the previous result it must be possible to express the pe function in terms of the sigma function.

Assuming that a is not a period the function $\wp(z)-\wp(a)$ has zeros at $z = a$ and $z = -a$. If we take the (double) pole at the origin then (5.6–5) is satisfied and we conclude that

$$\wp(z)-\wp(a) = A\,\frac{\sigma(z+a)\sigma(z-a)}{\sigma^2(z)},$$

A being a constant. Multiplying both members by z^2 and letting $z \to 0$ we find, since $z^2\wp(z) \to 1$ and $\sigma(z)/z \to \sigma'(0) = 1$, that

$$1 = A\sigma(a)\sigma(-a) = -A\sigma^2(a).$$

Thus

$$\boxed{\wp(z)-\wp(a) = -\frac{\sigma(z+a)\sigma(z-a)}{\sigma^2(z)\sigma^2(a)}.} \tag{5.6–8}$$

Differentiating logarithmically we find again the equation (5.5–15).

5.6.4 – The associate sigma functions

Let us take ω_α for a in (5.6–8). We get

$$\wp(z)-e_\alpha = -\frac{\sigma(z+\omega_\alpha)\sigma(z-\omega_\alpha)}{\sigma^2(z)\sigma^2(\omega_\alpha)}. \tag{5.6–9}$$

In (5.6–3) we replace z by $z-\omega_\alpha$:

$$\sigma(z+\omega_\alpha) = -\sigma(z-\omega_\alpha) \exp 2\eta_\alpha z. \tag{5.6–10}$$

Hence (5.6–9) may be written as

$$\wp(z)-e_\alpha = \frac{\sigma^2(z+\omega_\alpha)}{\sigma^2(z)\sigma^2(\omega_\alpha)} \exp(-2\eta_\alpha z). \tag{5.6–11}$$

We may simplify the above result by introducing the functions

$$\boxed{\sigma_\alpha(z) = \frac{\sigma(z+\omega_\alpha)}{\sigma(\omega_\alpha)} \exp(-\eta_\alpha z),} \qquad \alpha = 1, 2, 3. \tag{5.6–12}$$

Then (5.6–11) appears in the simple form

$$\wp(z)-e_\alpha = \frac{\sigma_\alpha^2(z)}{\sigma^2(z)}, \quad \alpha = 1, 2, 3. \tag{5.6–13}$$

It is at once clear that the function $\sigma_\alpha(z)$ possesses simple zeros at the points congruent with $z = \omega_\alpha$, $\alpha = 1, 2, 3$:

$$\sigma_\alpha(\omega_\alpha) = 0, \qquad \alpha = 1, 2, 3, \tag{5.6–14}$$

whereas

$$\sigma_\alpha(0) = 1, \qquad \alpha = 1, 2, 3. \tag{5.6–15}$$

In contrast with the function $\sigma(z)$ *the functions* $\sigma_\alpha(z)$ *are even functions*

$$\sigma_\alpha(-z) = \sigma_\alpha(z). \tag{5.6–16}$$

In fact (5.6–10) can be written as

$$\sigma(z+\omega_\alpha) = \sigma(-z+\omega_\alpha) \exp 2\eta_\alpha z \tag{5.6–17}$$

and so

$$\sigma_\alpha(-z) = \frac{\sigma(z+\omega_\alpha)}{\sigma(\omega_\alpha)} \exp \eta_\alpha z \exp(-2\eta_\alpha z) = \sigma_\alpha(z).$$

The relations of quasi-periodicity of the functions $\sigma_\alpha(z)$ are readily found:

$$\begin{aligned}
\sigma_\alpha(z+2\omega_\beta) &= \frac{\sigma(z+\omega_\alpha+2\omega_\beta)}{\sigma(\omega_\alpha)} \exp(-\eta_\alpha(z+2\omega_\beta)) \\
&= -\frac{\sigma(z+\omega_\alpha)}{\sigma(\omega_\alpha)} \exp(-\eta_\alpha(z+2\omega_\beta)) \exp 2\eta_\beta(z+\omega_\alpha+\omega_\beta) \\
&= -\frac{\sigma(z+\omega_\alpha)}{\sigma(\omega_\alpha)} \exp 2\eta_\beta(z+\omega_\beta) \exp(-\eta_\alpha z) \exp(2\eta_\beta\omega_\alpha-2\eta_\alpha\omega_\beta).
\end{aligned}$$

Taking account of the relations (5.5–20) we find

$$\sigma_\alpha(z+2\omega_\alpha) = -\sigma_\alpha(z) \exp 2\eta_\alpha(z+\omega_\alpha), \tag{5.6–18}$$

$$\sigma_\alpha(z+2\omega_\beta) = \sigma_\alpha(z) \exp 2\eta_\beta(z+\omega_\beta), \quad \alpha \neq \beta. \tag{5.6–19}$$

5.6.5 – RELATIONS BETWEEN THE SIGMA FUNCTIONS

There are a large number of relations between the sigma functions. We shall list some of them.

In the first place it easily follows from (5.6–13) that

$$\boxed{\sigma_1^2(z)+e_1\sigma^2(z) = \sigma_2^2(z)+e_2\sigma^2(z) = \sigma_3^2(z)+e_3\sigma^2(z),} \tag{5.6–20}$$

and on eliminating $\sigma^2(z)$:

$$(e_2-e_3)\sigma_1^2(z)+(e_3-e_1)\sigma_2^2(z)+(e_1-e_2)\sigma_3^2(z) = 0. \tag{5.6–21}$$

The equation (5.4–1) may be written in the form

$$\wp'^2(z) = 4\frac{\sigma_1^2(z)\,\sigma_2^2(z)\,\sigma_3^2(z)}{\sigma^6(z)}.$$

Hence

$$\wp'(z) = -2\frac{\sigma_1(z)\,\sigma_2(z)\,\sigma_3(z)}{\sigma^3(z)}, \tag{5.6–22}$$

for multiplying both members by z^3 and letting $z \to 0$ the left hand-side tends to -2 and the factor of -2 of the right hand side to $+1$. This formula is another illustration of the theorem of section 5.6.2.

Differentiating (5.6–13) and comparing the result with (5.6–22) we obtain the curious relations

$$\left(\frac{\sigma_1(z)}{\sigma(z)}\right)' = -\frac{\sigma_2(z)\,\sigma_3(z)}{\sigma^2(z)}, \left(\frac{\sigma_2(z)}{\sigma(z)}\right)' = -\frac{\sigma_3(z)\,\sigma_1(z)}{\sigma^2(z)}, \left(\frac{\sigma_3(z)}{\sigma_1(z)}\right)' = -\frac{\sigma_1(z)\,\sigma_2(z)}{\sigma^2(z)}. \tag{5.6–23}$$

From these relations we easily deduce

$$\left(\frac{\sigma(z)}{\sigma_1(z)}\right)' = \frac{\sigma_2(z)\,\sigma_3(z)}{\sigma_1^2(z)}, \left(\frac{\sigma(z)}{\sigma_2(z)}\right)' = \frac{\sigma_3(z)\,\sigma_1(z)}{\sigma_2^2(z)}, \left(\frac{\sigma(z)}{\sigma_3(z)}\right)' = \frac{\sigma_1(z)\,\sigma_2(z)}{\sigma_3^2(z)}. \tag{5.6–24}$$

Finally we consider the integral function

$$f(z) = \sigma(z)\,\sigma_1(z)\,\sigma_2(z)\,\sigma_3(z).$$

It obviously has simple zeros at the points $z = m\omega+n\omega'$, m, $n = 0, \pm 1, \pm 2, \ldots$. From the relations of quasi-periodicity it follows that

$$f(z+2\omega_\alpha) = f(z) \exp 8\eta_\alpha(z+\omega_\alpha).$$

On applying (5.6–3) repeatedly, we find

$$\begin{aligned}\sigma(2z+4\omega_\alpha) &= -\sigma(2z+2\omega_\alpha)\exp 2\eta_\alpha(2z+2\omega_\alpha+\omega_\alpha)\\ &= \sigma(2z)\exp 2\eta_\alpha(2z+2\omega_\alpha+\omega_\alpha)\exp 2\eta_\alpha(2z+\omega_\alpha)\\ &= \sigma(2z)\exp 8\eta_\alpha(z+\omega_\alpha).\end{aligned}$$

Since $\sigma(2z)$ has the same zeros as $f(z)$ the quotient $\sigma(2z)/f(z)$ is an elliptic function with no poles, that is to say, a constant. Letting $z \to 0$ and observing that $\sigma(2z)/\sigma(z) \to 2\sigma'(0)/\sigma'(0) = 2$ we obtain the *duplication formula*

$$\boxed{\sigma(2z) = 2\sigma(z)\sigma_1(z)\sigma_2(z)\sigma_3(z).} \qquad (5.6\text{–}25)$$

5.6.6 – The sigma quotients

Combining the formulas for the quasi-periodicity of the sigma function we find the *sigma quotients*

$$\frac{\sigma_\alpha(z+2\omega_\beta)}{\sigma(z+2\omega_\alpha)} = \pm\frac{\sigma_\alpha(z)}{\sigma(z)}, \qquad \alpha, \beta = 1, 2, 3, \qquad (5.6\text{–}26)$$

where the upper sign has to be taken only when $\alpha = \beta$. Hence the functions are elliptic. One of the primitive periods of the function corresponding to a given index α is $2\omega_\alpha$, the other is $4\omega_\beta$, where β is one of the numbers 1, 2, 3 different from α. The poles are the zeros of $\sigma(z)$ and they are, therefore, simple. It is easy to verify that in any period-parallelogram there are two zeros of $\sigma(z)$. Hence the functions (5.6—26) represent elliptic functions of the Jacobian type (5.2.3). As we shall see they are of importance in the theory of the Jacobian functions which we shall introduce in section 5.8.3.

5.7 – The bisection formula of the pe function

5.7.1 – Preliminary form

According to the previous section the function

$$\frac{\sigma_1(z)\sigma_2(z)}{\sigma^2(z)} + \frac{\sigma_2(z)\sigma_3(z)}{\sigma^2(z)} + \frac{\sigma_3(z)\sigma_1(z)}{\sigma^2(z)} \qquad (5.7\text{–}1)$$

is an elliptic function with primitive periods 4ω, $4\omega'$. By virtue of (5.6–23) this function is the opposite of the derivative of

$$\frac{\sigma_1(z)}{\sigma(z)} + \frac{\sigma_2(z)}{\sigma(z)} + \frac{\sigma_3(z)}{\sigma(z)}, \qquad (5.7\text{–}2)$$

which is also an elliptic function with primitive periods 4ω, $4\omega'$. In the period-parallelogram with vertices 0, 4ω, $4\omega+4\omega'$, $4\omega'$ the poles are at the points 0, 2ω, $2\omega+2\omega'$, $2\omega'$, (fig. 5.7–1).

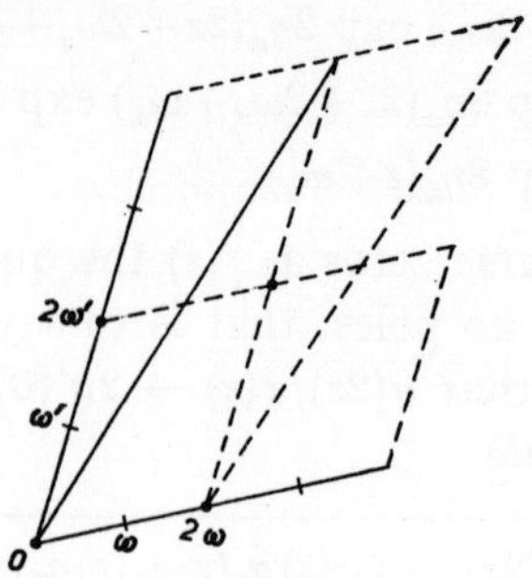

Fig. 5.7–1. Location of the poles of the function (5.7–2)

Now $\sigma_1(z)/\sigma(z)$ has primitive periods 2ω, $4\omega'$. The sum of the residues at the poles in the parallelogram with vertices 0, 2ω, $2\omega+4\omega'$, $4\omega'$ must be zero (5.2.3). Hence the residues at the above points are $+1$, $+1$, -1, -1 respectively. The function $\sigma_2(z)/\sigma(z)$ has the primitive periods 4ω, $2\omega+2\omega'$ and it follows that the residues at the above poles are $+1$, -1, $+1$, -1 respectively. Finally $\sigma_3(z)/\sigma(z)$ has the primitive periods 4ω, $2\omega'$ and it follows that the residues at the above poles are $+1$, -1, -1, $+1$ respectively. By adding we find that the residues of the function (5.7–2) at the poles in its primitive period-parallelogram are 3, -1, -1, -1 respectively.

Now it is easy to verify on account of the quasi-periodicity of the zeta function expressed by (5.5–10) that the function

$$2\zeta(\tfrac{1}{2}z)-\zeta(z)$$

is elliptic with primitive periods 4ω, $4\omega'$, having the same poles and residues as the function (5.7–2). Hence it differs from this function by a constant.

Differentiating we have the bisection formula

$$\wp(\tfrac{1}{2}z) = \wp(z)+\frac{\sigma_1(z)\,\sigma_2(z)}{\sigma^2(z)}+\frac{\sigma_1(z)\,\sigma_3(z)}{\sigma^2(z)}+\frac{\sigma_2(z)\,\sigma_3(z)}{\sigma^2(z)}. \qquad (5.7\text{–}3)$$

5.7.2 – Introduction of the Square Roots

In (5.6–13) the functions $\wp(z)-e_\alpha$ appear as the squares of the functions $\sigma_\alpha(z)/\sigma(z)$, $\alpha = 1, 2, 3$. It is convenient to define the square root of $\wp(z)-e_\alpha$ by the formula

$$\boxed{\sqrt{\wp(z)-e_\alpha}=\frac{\sigma_\alpha(z)}{\sigma(z)},} \qquad \alpha = 1, 2, 3. \qquad (5.7\text{–}4)$$

In particular we define $\sqrt{e_\alpha - e_\beta}$ as

$$\boxed{\sqrt{e_\alpha - e_\beta} = \frac{\sigma_\beta(\omega_\alpha)}{\sigma(\omega_\alpha)}.} \tag{5.7–5}$$

Since also

$$\sqrt{e_\alpha - e_\beta} = \frac{\sigma(\omega_\alpha + \omega_\beta)}{\sigma(\omega_\alpha)\sigma(\omega_\beta)} \mathrm{e}^{-\eta_\beta \omega_\alpha}$$

we easily find, taking account of Legendre's relation,

$$\sqrt{e_1 - e_2} = i\sqrt{e_2 - e_1}, \quad \sqrt{e_1 - e_3} = i\sqrt{e_3 - e_1}, \quad \sqrt{e_2 - e_3} = i\sqrt{e_3 - e_2}. \tag{5.7–6}$$

Inserting the expression (5.4–4) into (5.7–3) we obtain the *bisection formula* in the form

$$\boxed{\begin{aligned} \wp(\tfrac{1}{2}z) = \wp(z) + \sqrt{\wp(z) - e_1}\sqrt{\wp(z) - e_2} + \\ + \sqrt{\wp(z) - e_1}\sqrt{\wp(z) - e_3} + \sqrt{\wp(z) - e_2}\sqrt{\wp(z) - e_3}. \end{aligned}} \tag{5.7–7}$$

It is not difficult to obtain a similar formula for $\wp(\frac{1}{2}z + \omega_\alpha)$. In fact, by virtue of (5.6–26) we have

$$\sqrt{\wp(z + 2\omega_\alpha) - e_\beta} = \pm\sqrt{\wp(z) - e_\beta}$$

when the upper sign has to be taken only when $\alpha = \beta$. Thus we see that $\wp(\frac{1}{2}z + \omega_\alpha)$ has the same expression on the right as $\wp(\frac{1}{2}z)$, save that the sign of the terms involving $\sqrt{\wp(z) - e_\alpha}$ is changed.

Finally we wish to observe that the relations (5.5–5), (5.5–6) and (5.5–7) can be represented in the stronger form

$$\sqrt{\wp(z + \omega_\alpha) - e_\alpha} = \frac{\sqrt{e_\beta - e_\alpha}\sqrt{e_\gamma - e_\alpha}}{\sqrt{\wp(z) - e_\alpha}}, \quad \alpha \neq \beta, \ \alpha \neq \gamma, \ \beta \neq \gamma. \tag{5.7–8}$$

In fact, there can only be ambiguity in sign. But inserting for instance $z = \omega_\beta$ we find that the theorem is correctly stated. Similarly, we may write (5.4–1) in the stronger form

$$\wp'(z) = -2\sqrt{\wp(z) - e_1}\sqrt{\wp(z) - e_2}\sqrt{\wp(z) - e_3}, \tag{5.7–9}$$

this being the equation (5.6–22).

5.8 – The theta functions of Jacobi

5.8.1 – Introductory remarks

The Weierstrassian sigma functions are closely related to a certain class of rapidly converging series, discovered by Jacobi. These series are important from a theoretical point of view, but they are also of great value for numerical work.

The effect of increasing the argument z in a sigma function by a period is the multiplication by a periodicity-factor. This can be removed by multiplying the functions by the factor

$$\exp\left(-\frac{\eta}{2\omega}z^2\right).$$

In fact,

$$\exp\left(-\frac{\eta}{2\omega}(z+2\omega)^2\right) = \exp\left(-\frac{\eta}{2\omega}z^2\right)\exp\left(-2\eta(z+\omega)\right).$$

It is therefore natural to consider the functions $\varphi_1, \varphi_2, \varphi_3, \varphi_4$ defined as

$$\varphi_\alpha(z) = \sigma_{\alpha-1}(z)\exp\left(-\frac{\eta}{2\omega}z^2\right), \qquad \alpha = 1, 2, 3, 4, \qquad (5.8\text{–}1)$$

where $\sigma_0(z)$ stands for $\sigma(z)$. From the relations of quasi-periodicity of the sigma functions we get

$$\begin{aligned} \varphi_1(z+2\omega) &= -\varphi_1(z), & \varphi_2(z+2\omega) &= -\varphi_2(z), \\ \varphi_3(z+2\omega) &= \varphi_3(z), & \varphi_4(z+2\omega) &= \varphi_4(z), \end{aligned} \qquad (5.8\text{–}2)$$

that is to say, the functions φ_1 and φ_2 are periodic with periods 4ω and the functions φ_3 and φ_4 are periodic with period 2ω.

The effect of increasing z by $2\omega'$ is expressed by

$$\begin{aligned} \varphi_\alpha(z+2\omega') &= \pm\varphi_\alpha(z)\exp\left(-2\eta\frac{\omega'}{\omega}+2\eta'\right)(z+\omega') \\ &= \pm\varphi_\alpha(z)\exp\left(-\frac{\pi i z}{\omega}\right)\exp\left(-\pi i\frac{\omega'}{\omega}\right), \end{aligned} \qquad (5.8\text{–}3)$$

taking account of Legendre's relation. The upper sign has to be taken when $\alpha = 2, 3$, the lower when $\alpha = 1, 4$.

A further simplification may be acquired when we introduce the functions

$$f_1(z) = e^{\pi i z}\varphi_1(2\omega z),\ f_2(z) = e^{\pi i z}\varphi_2(2\omega z),\ f_3(z) = \varphi_3(2\omega z),\ f_4(z) = \varphi_4(2\omega z). \qquad (5.8\text{–}4)$$

These functions are simply-periodic, the period being 1:

$$f_\alpha(z+1) = f_\alpha(z), \qquad \alpha = 1, 2, 3, 4. \qquad (5.8\text{–}5)$$

We put

$$\boxed{\tau = \frac{\omega'}{\omega}} \tag{5.8–6}$$

and agree on taking ω and ω' in such a way that

$$\boxed{\operatorname{Im} \tau > 0.} \tag{5.8–7}$$

Hence the number

$$\boxed{q = \exp \pi i \tau} \tag{5.8–8}$$

is numerically less than unity.

From (5.8–3) we easily deduce that

$$f_1(z+\tau) = -f_1(z) \exp(-2\pi i z), \qquad f_2(z+\tau) = f_2(z) \exp(-2\pi i z),$$
$$f_3(z+\tau) = q^{-1} f_3(z) \exp(-2\pi i z), \quad f_4(z+\tau) = q^{-1} f_4(z) \exp(-2\pi i z). \tag{5.8–9}$$

5.8.2 – Expansions in Fourier series of the modified sigma functions

Since the functions $f_\alpha(z)$ are integral functions of period 1, we may expand them in a Fourier series (2.23–11), that is to say we can put

$$f_\alpha(z) = \sum_{\nu=-\infty}^{\infty} A_\nu \exp 2\nu\pi i z. \tag{5.8–10}$$

We wish to evaluate the coefficients A_n in the various cases $\alpha = 1, 2, 3, 4$.

(i) $\alpha = 1$. By virtue of (5.8–9) we have

$$\sum_{\nu=-\infty}^{\infty} A_\nu q^{2\nu} \exp 2\nu\pi i z = f_1(z+\tau) = -\sum_{\nu=-\infty}^{\infty} A_\nu \exp 2(\nu-1)\pi i z.$$

Observing that the coefficients in a Fourier expansion are uniquely determined we find for all integral values of n

$$A_n q^{2n} = -A_{n+1},$$

or, taking account of $(n+\frac{1}{2})^2-(n-\frac{1}{2})^2 = 2n$,

$$(-1)^n A_n q^{-(n-\frac{1}{2})^2} = (-1)^{n+1} A_{n+1} q^{-(n+\frac{1}{2})^2}. \tag{5.8—11}$$

The expression on the right-hand side arises from the expression on the left if we replace n by $n+1$. Hence its value is independent of

n and is therefore a constant C_1:

$$f_1(z) = C_1 \sum_{\nu=-\infty}^{\infty} (-1)^\nu q^{(\nu-\frac{1}{2})^2} \exp 2\nu\pi iz. \tag{5.8–12}$$

By d'Alembert's test it is easily seen that the series on the right is absolutely convergent for every value of z and uniformly convergent in any bounded set of the z-plane.

(ii) $\alpha = 2$. In a similar way as in the previous case we now find

$$A_n q^{2n} = A_{n+1}$$

or

$$A_n q^{-(n-\frac{1}{2})^2} = A_{n+1} q^{-(n+\frac{1}{2})^2}. \tag{5.8–13}$$

Both members are therefore independent of n and may be represented by a constant C_2. Hence

$$f_2(z) = C_2 \sum_{\nu=-\infty}^{\infty} q^{(\nu-\frac{1}{2})^2} \exp 2\nu\pi iz. \tag{5.8–14}$$

(iii) $\alpha = 3$. In this case we have

$$A_n q^{2n} = A_{n+1} q^{-1},$$

or, observing that $(n+1)^2 - n^2 = 2n+1$,

$$A_n q^{-n^2} = A_{n+1} q^{-(n+1)^2}. \tag{5.8–15}$$

The common value of both members will be designated by C_3 and so

$$f_3(z) = C_3 \sum_{\nu=-\infty}^{\infty} q^{\nu^2} \exp 2\nu\pi iz. \tag{5.8–16}$$

(iv) $\alpha = 4$. We now have

$$A_n q^{2n} = -A_{n+1} q^{-1}$$

or

$$(-1)^n A_n q^{-n^2} = (-1)^{n+1} A_{n+1} q^{-(n+1)^2}, \tag{5.8–17}$$

and so

$$f_4(z) = C_4 \sum_{\nu=-\infty}^{\infty} (-1)^\nu q^{\nu^2} \exp 2\nu\pi iz. \tag{5.8–18}$$

5.8.3 – Definition of the theta functions

The functions $f_1(z) \exp(-\pi iz)$ and $f_2(z) \exp(-\pi iz)$ assume the same periodicity factor as $f_3(z)$ and $f_4(z)$. It is therefore more convenient for the sake of uniformity to consider the expansions of these modified functions.

Jacobi introduced the series

$$
\begin{aligned}
\vartheta_1(z) &= i \sum_{\nu=-\infty}^{\infty} (-1)^\nu q^{(\nu-\frac{1}{2})^2} \exp (2\nu-1)\pi i z \\
&= 2q^{1/4} \sin \pi z - 2q^{9/4} \sin 3\pi z + 2q^{25/4} \sin 5\pi z + \ldots, \\
\vartheta_2(z) &= \sum_{\nu=-\infty}^{\infty} q^{(\nu-\frac{1}{2})^2} \exp (2\nu-1)\pi i z \\
&= 2q^{1/4} \cos \pi z + 2q^{9/4} \cos 3\pi z + 2q^{25/4} \cos 5\pi z + \ldots, \\
\vartheta_3(z) &= \sum_{\nu=-\infty}^{\infty} q^{\nu^2} \exp 2\nu\pi i z \\
&= 1 + 2q \cos 2\pi z + 2q^4 \cos 4\pi z + 2q^9 \cos 6\pi z + \ldots, \\
\vartheta_4(z) &= \sum_{\nu=-\infty}^{\infty} (-1)^\nu q^{\nu^2} \exp 2\nu\pi i z \\
&= 1 - 2q \cos 2\pi z + 2q^4 \cos 4\pi z - 2q^9 \cos 6\pi z + \ldots.
\end{aligned}
\tag{5.8–19}
$$

These function are called the *Jacobian theta functions*. The factor i in the first expression is added by obvious reasons. We are now able to express the functions $f_\alpha(z)$ in terms of the theta functions. The constants C_α are in the cases $\alpha = 2, 3, 4$ found by putting $z = 0$, whereas in the case $\alpha = 1$ we first divide by z and observe that $f_1(z)/z \to 2\omega$ as $z \to 0$. We thus obtain

$$
\begin{aligned}
&f_1(z) \exp(-\pi i z) = 2\omega \frac{\vartheta_1(z)}{\vartheta_1'(0)}, \quad f_2(z) \exp(-\pi i z) = \frac{\vartheta_2(z)}{\vartheta_2(0)}, \\
&f_3(z) = \frac{\vartheta_3(z)}{\vartheta_3(0)}, \quad f_4(z) = \frac{\vartheta_4(z)}{\vartheta_4(0)}.
\end{aligned}
\tag{5.8–20}
$$

The functions $\vartheta_\alpha(z)$ depend also on the variable τ. If it is desirable to exhibit this dependence we shall write $\vartheta_\alpha(z|\tau)$.

It should be noticed that the function $\vartheta(t)$ considered in section 2.23.5 is the special series $\vartheta_3(0|it)$ where $t > 0$.

It is also easy to express the sigma functions in terms of the theta function. We successively have

$$
\begin{aligned}
&\sigma(2\omega z) = 2\omega \frac{\vartheta_1(z)}{\vartheta_1'(0)} \exp 2\eta\omega z^2, \quad \sigma_1(2\omega z) = \frac{\vartheta_2(z)}{\vartheta_2(0)} \exp 2\eta\omega z^2, \\
&\sigma_2(2\omega z) = \frac{\vartheta_3(z)}{\vartheta_3(0)} \exp 2\eta\omega z^2, \quad \sigma_3(2\omega z) = \frac{\vartheta_4(z)}{\vartheta_4(0)} \exp 2\eta\omega z^2,
\end{aligned}
\tag{5.8–21}
$$

and so, according to (5.7–4),

$$
\boxed{\sqrt{\wp(2\omega z) - e_\alpha} = \frac{1}{2\omega} \frac{\vartheta_1'(0)}{\vartheta_{\alpha+1}(0)} \frac{\vartheta_{\alpha+1}(z)}{\vartheta_1(z)}}, \quad \alpha = 1, 2, 3. \tag{5.8–22}
$$

5.8.4 – General properties

We wish to list some general properties of the theta functions.

First we observe that $\vartheta_1(z)$ *is odd, whereas all the other theta functions are even*:

$$\vartheta_1(-z) = -\vartheta_1(z),\ \vartheta_2(-z) = \vartheta_2(z),\ \vartheta_3(-z) = \vartheta_3(z),\ \vartheta_4(-z) = \vartheta_4(z). \tag{5.8–23}$$

The effect of increasing the argument by 1 is expressed by

$$\begin{aligned} \vartheta_1(z+1) &= -\vartheta_1(z), & \vartheta_2(z+1) &= -\vartheta_2(z), \\ \vartheta_3(z+1) &= \vartheta_3(z), & \vartheta_4(z+1) &= \vartheta_4(z), \end{aligned} \tag{5.8–24}$$

whereas the effect of increasing z by τ is expressed by

$$\begin{aligned} \vartheta_1(z+\tau) &= -A\vartheta_1(z), & \vartheta_2(z+\tau) &= A\vartheta_2(z), \\ \vartheta_3(z+\tau) &= A\vartheta_3(z), & \vartheta_4(z+\tau) &= -A\,\vartheta_4(z), \end{aligned} \tag{5.8–25}$$

where A is the *periodicity factor*

$$A = q^{-1} \exp(-2\pi i z). \tag{5.8–26}$$

The effect of increasing z by $\frac{1}{2}$ or by $\frac{1}{2}\tau$ is also expressed by simple formulas. From the series expansions of the theta functions we find by a simple computation

$$\begin{aligned} \vartheta_1(z+\tfrac{1}{2}) &= \vartheta_2(z), & \vartheta_2(z+\tfrac{1}{2}) &= -\vartheta_1(z), \\ \vartheta_3(z+\tfrac{1}{2}) &= \vartheta_4(z), & \vartheta_4(z+\tfrac{1}{2}) &= \vartheta_3(z) \end{aligned} \tag{5.8–27}$$

and, introducing the *conversion factor*

$$B = q^{-\frac{1}{4}} \exp(-\pi i z), \tag{5.8–28}$$

$$\begin{aligned} \vartheta_1(z+\tfrac{1}{2}\tau) &= iB\vartheta_4(z), & \vartheta_2(z+\tfrac{1}{2}\tau) &= B\vartheta_3(z), \\ \vartheta_3(z+\tfrac{1}{2}\tau) &= B\vartheta_2(z), & \vartheta_4(z+\tfrac{1}{2}\tau) &= iB\vartheta_1(z). \end{aligned} \tag{5.8–29}$$

The formulas will be referred to as the *conversion formulas* of the theta functions.

The functions $\vartheta_1(z)$, $\vartheta_2(z)$, $\vartheta_3(z)$, $\vartheta_4(z)$ *have simple zeros at the points congruent to* 0, $\frac{1}{2}$, $\frac{1}{2}+\frac{1}{2}\tau$, $\frac{1}{2}\tau$ *respectively with respect to the lattice-points* $m+n\tau$, $m, n = 0, \pm 1, \pm 2, \ldots$, (fig. 5.8–1).

Hence the zeros are the vertices of a parallelogram whose measure is the half of the parallelogram of the network defined by the lattice-points.

5.8.5 – The differential equation

Considered as functions of the two variables z and τ the theta functions satisfy a simple partial differential equation. Since the series are also uniformly convergent as regards τ, when τ varies in a closed and bounded set in the region $\operatorname{Im}\tau > 0$, we may differentiate term-by-term with respect to this variable τ. Now the

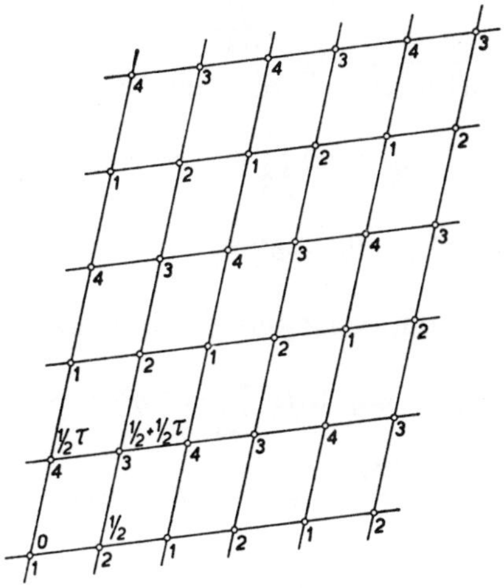

Fig. 5.8–1. Zeros of the theta functions

general term in each of the series is of the type

$$\varphi = \exp\,(\pi i \tau a^2 + 2\pi i a z).$$

From

$$\frac{\partial \varphi}{\partial z} = 2\pi i a \varphi, \frac{\partial^2 \varphi}{\partial z^2} = -4\pi^2 a^2 \varphi = 4\pi i (\pi i a^2 \varphi), \frac{\partial \varphi}{\partial \tau} = \pi i a^2 \varphi$$

we conclude that the theta functions satisfy the partial differential equation

$$\boxed{\frac{\partial^2 \vartheta}{\partial z^2} = 4\pi i \frac{\partial \vartheta}{\partial \tau}.} \tag{5.8–30}$$

5.9 – The expression for the theta functions as infinite products

5.9.1 – The infinite products

The zeros of $\vartheta_4(z)$ are at the points $m+n\tau+\frac{1}{2}\tau$ where $\exp 2\pi i z$ takes the values q^{2n+1} respectively. According to the general theory of section 4.1.2 the products

$$\prod_{\nu=1}^{\infty}(1-q^{2\nu-1} \exp 2\pi i z), \qquad \prod_{\nu=1}^{\infty}(1-q^{2\nu-1} \exp\,(-2\pi i z))$$

are absolutely and uniformly convergent in any finite set of values of z, for the series

$$\sum_{\nu=1}^{\infty} q^\nu$$

is absolutely convergent. Hence the function

$$\begin{aligned} f(z) &= \prod_{\nu=1}^{\infty} (1-q^{2\nu-1} \exp 2\pi iz) \prod_{\nu=1}^{\infty} (1-q^{2\nu-1} \exp (-2\pi iz)) \\ &= \prod_{\nu=1}^{\infty} (1-2q^{2\nu-1} \cos 2\pi z+q^{4\nu-2}) \end{aligned} \tag{5.9–1}$$

is an integral function, being periodic of period 1. On the other hand

$$\begin{aligned} f(z+\tau) &= \prod_{\nu=1}^{\infty} (1-q^{2\nu+1} \exp 2\pi iz) \prod_{\nu=1}^{\infty} (1-q^{2\nu-3} \exp (-2\pi iz)) \\ &= \frac{1-q^{-1} \exp (-2\pi iz)}{1-q \exp 2\pi iz} f(z) = -q^{-1} \exp (-2\pi iz) f(z) = -Af(z). \end{aligned}$$

In accordance with (5.8–25) we may conclude that $\vartheta_4(z)/f(z)$ is a doubly-periodic function with no poles, and therefore a constant. And so we find

$$\vartheta_4(z) = C\, f(z), \tag{5.9–2}$$

where $f(z)$ is the expression (5.9–1).

The expression for the other theta functions as infinite products may be obtained by applying the conversion formulas (5.8–27) and (5.8–29). Taking $z+\frac{1}{2}$ instead of z in (5.9–2) we get

$$\vartheta_3(z) = Cf(z+\tfrac{1}{2}) \tag{5.9–3}$$

where

$$f(z+\tfrac{1}{2}) = \prod_{\nu=1}^{\infty} (1+2q^{2\nu-1} \cos 2\pi z+q^{4\nu-2}), \tag{5.9–4}$$

while by taking $z+\frac{1}{2}\tau$ and observing that

$$\vartheta_1(z) = -iq^{\frac{1}{4}}\vartheta_4(z+\tfrac{1}{2}\tau) \exp \pi iz,$$

we find

$$\vartheta_1(z) = -Ciq^{\frac{1}{4}} f(z+\tfrac{1}{2}\tau) \exp \pi iz = Cq^{\frac{1}{4}} g(z) \tag{5.9–5}$$

where

$$\begin{aligned} g(z) &= -if(z+\tfrac{1}{2}\tau) \exp \pi iz \\ &= -i \prod_{\nu=1}^{\infty} (1-q^{2\nu} \exp 2\pi iz) \prod_{\nu=1}^{\infty} (1-q^{2\nu-2} \exp (-2\pi iz)) \cdot \exp \pi iz \\ &= -i \prod_{\nu=1}^{\infty} (1-q^{2\nu} \exp 2\pi iz) \prod_{\nu=1}^{\infty} (1-q^{2\nu} \exp (-2\pi iz)) \\ &\qquad \cdot (1-\exp (-2\pi iz)) \exp \pi iz, \end{aligned}$$

or

$$g(z) = 2 \sin \pi z \prod_{\nu=1}^{\infty} (1-2q^{2\nu} \cos 2\pi z+q^{4\nu}). \tag{5.9–6}$$

Finally we find from $\vartheta_2(z) = \vartheta_1(z+\frac{1}{2})$,

$$\vartheta_2(z) = Cq^{\frac{1}{4}}g(z+\tfrac{1}{2}), \tag{5.9–7}$$

where

$$g(z+\tfrac{1}{2}) = 2\cos\pi z \prod_{\nu=1}^{\infty}(1+2q^{2\nu}\cos 2\pi z+q^{4\nu}). \tag{5.9–8}$$

It should be noticed that in these formulas the quantity C has the same value. It is constant as regards z, but it depends on τ. The evaluation of C is not so easy and demands some further considerations.

5.9.2 – The fundamental relation

We wish to establish a remarkable simple relation between the values of $\vartheta_2(0)$, $\vartheta_3(0)$, $\vartheta_4(0)$ and $\vartheta_1'(0)$. Inserting the expressions (5.8–21) of the sigma functions in terms of the theta functions into (5.6–25) we get

$$\vartheta_1(2z)\,\vartheta_2(0)\,\vartheta_3(0)\,\vartheta_4(0) = 2\vartheta_1(z)\,\vartheta_2(z)\,\vartheta_3(z)\,\vartheta_4(z). \tag{5.9–9}$$

Logarithmic differentiation yields

$$2\frac{\vartheta_1'(2z)}{\vartheta_1(2z)} - \frac{\vartheta_1'(z)}{\vartheta_1(z)} = \frac{\vartheta_2'(z)}{\vartheta_2(z)} + \frac{\vartheta_3'(z)}{\vartheta_3(z)} + \frac{\vartheta_4'(z)}{\vartheta_4(z)}. \tag{5.9–10}$$

Since the functions on the right have each a simple zero at $z=0$ it is natural to divide by z and to let $z \to 0$. The right-hand side does not present any difficulty, but the expression on the left requires closer examination.

First we observe that the function $\vartheta_1(z)$ is odd and as a consequence all derivatives of even order vanish at $z = 0$. Expanding the function in a Taylor series we have

$$\frac{\vartheta_1'(z)}{\vartheta_1(z)} = \frac{\vartheta_1'(0)+\frac{1}{2}z^2\vartheta_1'''(0)+O(z^4)}{z\vartheta_1'(0)+\frac{1}{6}z^3\vartheta_1'''(0)+O(z^5)} = \frac{1}{z} + \frac{\frac{1}{3}z\vartheta_1'''(0)+O(z^3)}{\vartheta_1'(0)+O(z^2)},$$

whence

$$\frac{1}{z}\left(\frac{\vartheta_1'(z)}{\vartheta_1(z)} - \frac{1}{z}\right) \to \frac{1}{3}\frac{\vartheta_1'''(0)}{\vartheta_1'(0)} \tag{5.9–11}$$

as $z \to 0$. Similarly

$$\frac{1}{z}\left(\frac{\vartheta_1'(2z)}{\vartheta_1(2z)} - \frac{1}{2z}\right) \to \frac{2}{3}\frac{\vartheta_1'''(0)}{\vartheta_1'(0)}$$

and so

$$\frac{1}{z}\left(2\frac{\vartheta_1'(2z)}{\vartheta_1(2z)} - \frac{\vartheta_1'(z)}{\vartheta_1(z)}\right) \to \frac{\vartheta_1'''(0)}{\vartheta_1'(0)}.$$

Thus we find

$$\frac{\vartheta_1'''(0)}{\vartheta_1'(0)} = \frac{\vartheta_2''(0)}{\vartheta_2(0)} + \frac{\vartheta_3''(0)}{\vartheta_3(0)} + \frac{\vartheta_4''(0)}{\vartheta_4(0)}. \tag{5.9–12}$$

Now we lay stress upon the fact that the theta functions also depend on τ, that is to say, the equality (5.9–9) is actually a functional relation. This equation may be simplified by applying the differential equation (5.8–30) and the equality (5.9–12). We get

$$\frac{1}{\vartheta_1'(0)}\frac{\partial\vartheta_1'(0)}{\partial\tau} = \frac{1}{\vartheta_2(0)}\frac{\partial\vartheta_2(0)}{\partial\tau} + \frac{1}{\vartheta_3(0)}\frac{\partial\vartheta_3(0)}{\partial\tau} + \frac{1}{\vartheta_4(0)}\frac{\partial\vartheta_4(0)}{\partial\tau},$$

whence by integration

$$\vartheta_1'(0) = A\vartheta_2(0)\,\vartheta_3(0)\,\vartheta_4(0). \tag{5.9–13}$$

The constant A may be found by observing that

$$\vartheta_1'(0)q^{-\frac{1}{4}} \to 2\pi, \quad \vartheta_2(0)q^{-\frac{1}{4}} \to 2, \quad \vartheta_3(0) \to 1, \quad \vartheta_4(0) \to 1$$

as $q \to 0$, that is, as $\tau \to +i\infty$. We thus find that $A = \pi$ and we have derived the important relation

$$\boxed{\vartheta_1'(0) = \pi\vartheta_2(0)\,\vartheta_3(0)\,\vartheta_4(0).} \tag{5.9–14}$$

5.9.3 – Evaluation of a multiplicative constant

We are now sufficiently prepared to evaluate the factor C considered in section 5.9.1. First we shall list again the theta functions as infinite products.

$$\begin{aligned}
\vartheta_1(z) &= 2Cq^{\frac{1}{4}} \sin \pi z \prod_{\nu=1}^{\infty} (1-2q^{2\nu} \cos 2\pi z+q^{4\nu}),\\
\vartheta_2(z) &= 2Cq^{\frac{1}{4}} \cos \pi z \prod_{\nu=1}^{\infty} (1+2q^{2\nu} \cos 2\pi z+q^{4\nu}),\\
\vartheta_3(z) &= C \prod_{\nu=1}^{\infty} (1+2q^{2\nu-1} \cos 2\pi z+q^{4\nu-2}),\\
\vartheta_4(z) &= C \prod_{\nu=1}^{\infty} (1-2q^{2\nu-1} \cos 2\pi z+q^{4\nu-2}).
\end{aligned} \tag{5.9–15}$$

Dividing both members of the equation for $\vartheta_1(z)$ by z and letting $z \to 0$ we obtain

$$\vartheta_1'(0) = 2\pi Cq^{\frac{1}{4}} \prod_{\nu=1}^{\infty} (1-q^{2\nu})^2.$$

The equality (5.9–14) now leads to

$$\prod_{\nu=1}^{\infty} (1-q^{2\nu})^2 = C^2 \prod_{\nu=1}^{\infty} (1+q^{2\nu})^2 \prod_{\nu=1}^{\infty} (1-q^{4\nu-2})^2.$$

But

$$\prod_{\nu=1}^{\infty}(1-q^{2\nu}) = \prod_{\nu=1}^{\infty}(1-q^{4\nu})\prod_{\nu=1}^{\infty}(1-q^{4\nu-2}),$$

for the products are absolutely and therefore also unconditionally convergent. It follows that

$$C^2\prod_{\nu=1}^{\infty}(1+q^{2\nu})^2 = \prod_{\nu=1}^{\infty}(1-q^{4\nu})^2 = \prod_{\nu=1}^{\infty}(1-q^{2\nu})^2(1+q^{2\nu})^2,$$

whence

$$\boxed{C = \prod_{\nu=1}^{\infty}(1-q^{2\nu}).} \qquad (5.9\text{–}16)$$

In fact, there is no ambiguity in sign, for $C \to 1$ as $q \to 0$. This may be shown by applying the representation for $\vartheta_3(z)$ since $\vartheta_3(0) \to 1$ as $q \to 0$.

5.9.4 – Expression for the quasi-period of the zeta function

The result (5.9–11) enables us to express the quasi-period η of Weierstrass's zeta function in terms of ω and q. Differentiating both members of the first equation (5.8–21) logarithmically we find

$$2\omega\zeta(2\omega z) = 4\eta\omega z + \frac{\vartheta_1'(z)}{\vartheta_1(z)}, \qquad (5.9\text{–}17)$$

or

$$2\omega\left(\zeta(2\omega z) - \frac{1}{2\omega z}\right) = 4\eta\omega z + \frac{\vartheta_1'(z)}{\vartheta_1(z)} - \frac{1}{z}.$$

Taking account of (5.3–10), we find after dividing by z and letting $z \to 0$

$$4\eta\omega = -\frac{1}{3}\frac{\vartheta_1'''(0)}{\vartheta_1'(0)}. \qquad (5.9\text{–}18)$$

An easy computation leads to the result

$$\eta = \frac{\pi^2}{12\omega}\,\frac{\sum_{\nu=0}^{\infty}(-1)^\nu(2\nu+1)^3 q^{\nu(\nu+1)}}{\sum_{\nu=0}^{\infty}(-1)^\nu(2\nu+1)q^{\nu(\nu+1)}}. \qquad (5.9\text{–}19)$$

5.10 – Jacobi's imaginary transformation

5.10.1 – Definition of the transformation

In an elliptic function constructed with periods 2ω, $2\omega'$ such that $\operatorname{Im}\omega'/\omega = \operatorname{Im}\tau > 0$ it might be convenient to regard the periods as being $2\omega'$, -2ω. In the case of the pe function and also in the case of the associated sigma function the periods appear in a symmetrical manner and nothing is gained by this point of view. The situation is quite different in the case of the theta functions, for the parameter τ changes into $-1/\tau$, i.e., the replacement of 2ω, $2\omega'$ by $2\omega'$, -2ω induces the transformation

$$\tau' = -\frac{1}{\tau}. \tag{5.10–1}$$

This is *Jacobi's imaginary transformation* and we wish to study the effect of this on the theta functions.

5.10.2 – Some fundamental expressions

First we shall list some useful expressions. From (5.8–22) we deduce, when we take account of (5.8–27) and (5.8–28),

$$\sqrt{e_1-e_2} = \frac{1}{2\omega}\frac{\vartheta_1'(0)}{\vartheta_3(0)}\frac{\vartheta_3(\frac{1}{2})}{\vartheta_1(\frac{1}{2})} = \frac{1}{2\omega}\frac{\vartheta_1'(0)}{\vartheta_3(0)}\frac{\vartheta_4(0)}{\vartheta_2(0)},$$

$$\sqrt{e_2-e_3} = \frac{1}{2\omega}\frac{\vartheta_1'(0)}{\vartheta_4(0)}\frac{\vartheta_4(\frac{1}{2}+\frac{1}{2}\tau)}{\vartheta_1(\frac{1}{2}+\frac{1}{2}\tau)} = \frac{1}{2\omega}\frac{\vartheta_1'(0)}{\vartheta_4(0)}\frac{\vartheta_2(0)}{\vartheta_3(0)},$$

$$\sqrt{e_1-e_3} = \frac{1}{2\omega}\frac{\vartheta_1'(0)}{\vartheta_4(0)}\frac{\vartheta_4(\frac{1}{2})}{\vartheta_1(\frac{1}{2})} = \frac{1}{2\omega}\frac{\vartheta_1'(0)}{\vartheta_4(0)}\frac{\vartheta_3(0)}{\vartheta_2(0)},$$

whence, by inserting the values of $\vartheta_1'(0)$ given by (5.9–14),

$$\boxed{\sqrt{e_1-e_2} = \frac{\pi}{2\omega}\vartheta_4^2(0), \quad \sqrt{e_2-e_3} = \frac{\pi}{2\omega}\vartheta_2^2(0), \quad \sqrt{e_1-e_3} = \frac{\pi}{2\omega}\vartheta_3^2(0).} \tag{5.10–2}$$

An easy consequence is the *formula of the fourth powers*

$$\boxed{\vartheta_3^4(0) = \vartheta_2^4(0) + \vartheta_4^4(0).} \tag{5.10–3}$$

In particular we find that the discriminant is equal to

$$\Delta = 16\left(\frac{\pi}{2\omega}\right)^{12}\vartheta_2^8(0)\,\vartheta_3^8(0)\,\vartheta_4^8(0) = 16\frac{\pi^4}{(2\omega)^{12}}\vartheta_1'^8(0).$$

This may also be written in the form

$$\sqrt{\pi\omega}\,\sqrt[8]{\Delta} = \frac{\pi}{2\omega}\vartheta_1(\cup), \tag{5.10–4}$$

where $\sqrt[8]{\Delta}$ is an appropriately chosen eighth root of Δ.

5.10.3 – EFFECT OF THE TRANSFORMATION ON THE THETA FUNCTIONS

In accordance with (5.10–4) we may write the first formula of (5.8–21) in the form

$$\vartheta_1(z|\tau) = \sqrt{\frac{\omega}{\pi}}\,\sqrt[8]{\Delta}\,\sigma(2\omega z)\exp(-2\eta\omega z^2). \tag{5.10–5}$$

Now it is easy to see that Jacobi's transformation leaves Δ invariant, whereas $\sigma(2\omega z)$ is changed into $\sigma(2\omega' z)$ and η into η'. Since ω is replaced by $\omega' = \tau\omega$ we conclude that if z is replaced by z/τ the expression (5.10–5) is transformed into

$$\vartheta_1\left(\frac{z}{\tau}\,\middle|\,-\frac{1}{\tau}\right) = \varepsilon\sqrt{\tau}\sqrt{\frac{\omega}{\pi}}\,\sqrt[8]{\Delta}\,\sigma(2\omega z)\exp\left(-2\eta'\omega\frac{z^2}{\tau}\right), \tag{5.10–6}$$

where ε is a number such that $\varepsilon^8 = 1$.

Comparing (5.10–5) and (5.10–6) we may infer that

$$\vartheta_1\left(\frac{z}{\tau}\,\middle|\,-\frac{1}{\tau}\right) = \varepsilon\sqrt{\tau}\,\vartheta_1(z|\tau)\exp\left(2\eta\omega-2\eta'\frac{\omega}{\tau}\right)z^2.$$

But by virtue of (5.5–19)

$$2\eta\omega-2\eta'\frac{\omega}{\tau} = \frac{2\eta\omega'-2\eta'\omega}{\tau} = \frac{\pi i}{\tau},$$

and so

$$\vartheta_1\left(\frac{z}{\tau}\,\middle|\,-\frac{1}{\tau}\right) = \varepsilon\sqrt{\tau}\,\vartheta_1(z|\tau)\exp\frac{\pi i z^2}{\tau}. \tag{5.10–7}$$

It remains to evaluate the exact value of ε. Dividing both members of (5.10–7) by z and letting $z \to 0$ we get

$$\frac{1}{\tau}\vartheta_1'\left(0\,\middle|\,-\frac{1}{\tau}\right) = \varepsilon\sqrt{\tau}\,\vartheta_1'(0|\tau),$$

whence by taking $\tau = i$

$$\varepsilon = \frac{1}{i\sqrt{i}}.$$

We thus obtain one of the famous transformation formulas for the theta functions

$$\vartheta_1\left(\frac{z}{\tau}\,\middle|\,-\frac{1}{\tau}\right) = \frac{1}{i}\sqrt{\frac{\tau}{i}}\,\vartheta_1(z|\tau)\exp\frac{\pi i z^2}{\tau}. \tag{5.10–8}$$

In a similar way we may derive transformation formulas for the other theta functions. But it is much easier to apply the conversion formulas (5.8–27) and (5.8–29). We thus easily deduce

$$\vartheta_2(z) = \vartheta_1(z+\tfrac{1}{2}),$$
$$\vartheta_3(z) = q^{\frac{1}{4}}\vartheta_1(z+\tfrac{1}{2}+\tfrac{1}{2}\tau)e^{\pi iz},$$
$$\vartheta_4(z) = -iq^{\frac{1}{4}}\vartheta_1(z+\tfrac{1}{2}\tau)e^{\pi iz}.$$

An easy computation yields the following formulas, where for the sake of completeness we have also reproduced (5.10–8):

$$\boxed{\begin{aligned} i\vartheta_1\left(\frac{z}{\tau}\middle|-\frac{1}{\tau}\right) &= \sqrt{\frac{\tau}{i}}\,\vartheta_1(z|\tau)\exp\frac{\pi iz^2}{\tau}, \\ \vartheta_2\left(\frac{z}{\tau}\middle|-\frac{1}{\tau}\right) &= \sqrt{\frac{\tau}{i}}\,\vartheta_4(z|\tau)\exp\frac{\pi iz^2}{\tau}, \\ \vartheta_3\left(\frac{z}{\tau}\middle|-\frac{1}{\tau}\right) &= \sqrt{\frac{\tau}{i}}\,\vartheta_3(z|\tau)\exp\frac{\pi iz^2}{\tau}, \\ \vartheta_4\left(\frac{z}{\tau}\middle|-\frac{1}{\tau}\right) &= \sqrt{\frac{\tau}{i}}\,\vartheta_2(z|\tau)\exp\frac{\pi iz^2}{\tau}. \end{aligned}} \tag{5.10–9}$$

It should be noticed that the third equation is identical with (2.23–29) when we take $z = 0$, $\tau = it$.

5.11 – The logarithmic derivative of the theta functions

5.11.1 – The expansion in series of the logarithmic derivatives

On applying the formula (4.1–22) we readily obtain expansions in series of the logarithmic derivative of the theta functions.

First we consider the function $\vartheta_1(z)$. From (5.9–15) we deduce

$$\frac{\vartheta_1'(z)}{\vartheta_1(z)} = \pi \operatorname{ctn} \pi z + 4\pi \sum_{\nu=1}^{\infty} \frac{q^{2\nu}\sin 2\pi z}{1-2q^{2\nu}\cos 2\pi z + q^{4\nu}}. \tag{5.11–1}$$

Next we wish to represent the series on the right as a Fourier series. Putting $w = \exp 2\pi iz$, this series can be written as

$$\frac{1}{2i}\sum_{\nu=1}^{\infty}\frac{q^{2\nu}(w-w^{-1})}{(1-q^{2\nu}w)(1-q^{2\nu}w^{-1})} = \frac{1}{2i}\sum_{\nu=1}^{\infty}\left(\frac{q^{2\nu}w}{1-q^{2\nu}w} - \frac{q^{2\nu}w^{-1}}{1-q^{2\nu}w^{-1}}\right).$$

When w ranges in the region

$$|wq^2| < 1$$

we may apply Weierstrass's double-series theorem of section 2.20.4 to the series

$$\sum_{\nu=1}^{\infty}\frac{q^{2\nu}w}{1-q^{2\nu}w}. \tag{5.11–2}$$

In fact, this series is uniformly convergent on the closed set

$$|wq^2| \leqq r < 1,$$

for, whenever n is sufficiently large, we have

$$|q^{2n}w| \leqq |q|^{2n} r |q|^{-2} < \tfrac{1}{2}$$

on account of the fact that $|q| < 1$. Hence, from a certain term upwards the series (5.11–2) is dominated by the convergent geometric series

$$\sum_{\nu=1}^{\infty} 2|q|^{2\nu} r |q|^{-2}.$$

This proves the assertion.

Expanding each term of (5.11–2) in a geometric series we readily find by reversing the order of summation

$$\sum_{\nu=1}^{\infty} \frac{q^{2\nu}w}{1-q^{2\nu}w} = \sum_{\nu=1}^{\infty}\sum_{\mu=1}^{\infty} q^{2\nu\mu}w^{\mu} = \sum_{\mu=1}^{\infty}\sum_{\nu=1}^{\infty} q^{2\nu\mu}w^{\mu} = \sum_{\mu=1}^{\infty} \frac{q^{2\mu}w^{\mu}}{1-q^{2\mu}}. \tag{5.11–3}$$

In the same way we find by assuming

$$|w^{-1}q^2| < 1$$

the equality

$$\sum_{\nu=1}^{\infty} \frac{q^{2\nu}w^{-1}}{1-q^{2\nu}w^{-1}} = \sum_{\mu=1}^{\infty} \frac{q^{2\mu}w^{-\mu}}{1-q^{2\mu}}.$$

Hence, if w satisfies the condition

$$|q^2| < |w| < |q^{-2}|,$$

i.e., when z ranges in the open strip

$$-\operatorname{Im}\tau < \operatorname{Im} z < \operatorname{Im}\tau, \tag{5.11–4}$$

we readily find

$$\sum_{\nu=1}^{\infty} \frac{q^{2\nu}\sin 2\pi z}{1-2q^{2\nu}\cos 2\pi z+q^{4\nu}} = \sum_{\mu=1}^{\infty} \frac{q^{2\mu}}{1-q^{2\mu}} \sin 2\mu\pi z. \tag{5.11–5}$$

The function $\vartheta_2(z)$ gives rise to

$$\frac{\vartheta_2'(z)}{\vartheta_2(z)} = -\pi \tan \pi z - 4\pi \sum_{\nu=1}^{\infty} \frac{q^{2\nu}\sin 2\pi z}{1+2q^{2\nu}\cos 2\pi z+q^{4\nu}}. \tag{5.11–6}$$

Replacing z by $z+\frac{1}{2}$ in (5.11–5) we have

$$-\sum_{\nu=1}^{\infty} \frac{q^{2\nu}\sin 2\pi z}{1+2q^{2\nu}\cos 2\pi z+q^{4\nu}} = \sum_{\mu=1}^{\infty} \frac{(-1)^{\mu}q^{2\mu}}{1-q^{2\mu}} \sin 2\mu\pi z.$$

The situation in the case of $\vartheta_3(z)$ and $\vartheta_4(z)$ is a little different. We now have

$$\frac{\vartheta_3'(z)}{\vartheta_3(z)} = 4\pi \sum_{\nu=1}^{\infty} \frac{-q^{2\nu-1}\sin 2\pi z}{1+2q^{2\nu-1}\cos 2\pi z+q^{4\nu-2}} \tag{5.11–7}$$

and

$$\frac{\vartheta_4'(z)}{\vartheta_4(z)} = 4\pi \sum_{\nu=1}^{\infty} \frac{q^{2\nu-1} \sin 2\pi z}{1-2q^{2\nu-1} \cos 2\pi z + q^{4\nu-2}}. \tag{5.11–8}$$

The series on the right of (5.11–8) may be written as

$$\frac{1}{2i} \sum_{\nu=1}^{\infty} \frac{q^{2\nu-1}(w-w^{-1})}{(1-q^{2\nu-1}w)(1-q^{2\nu-1}w^{-1})} = \frac{1}{2i} \sum_{\nu=1}^{\infty} \left(\frac{q^{2\nu-1}w}{1-q^{2\nu-1}w} - \frac{q^{2\nu-1}w}{1-q^{2\nu-1}w^{-1}} \right).$$

Under the assumption

$$|q| < |w| < |q^{-1}|,$$

i.e.,

$$-\tfrac{1}{2} \operatorname{Im} \tau < \operatorname{Im} z < \tfrac{1}{2} \operatorname{Im} \tau, \tag{5.11–9}$$

we find, proceeding as in the case for $\vartheta_1(z)$,

$$\sum_{\nu=1}^{\infty} \frac{q^{2\nu-1} \sin 2\pi z}{1-2q^{2\nu-1} \cos 2\pi z + q^{4\nu-2}} = \sum_{\mu=1}^{\infty} \frac{q^{\mu}}{1-q^{2\mu}} \sin 2\mu\pi z \tag{5.11–10}$$

whence, by replacing z by $z+\frac{1}{2}$,

$$-\sum_{\nu=1}^{\infty} \frac{q^{2\nu-1} \sin 2\pi z}{1+2q^{2\nu-1} \cos 2\pi z + q^{4\nu-2}} = \sum_{\mu=1}^{\infty} \frac{(-1)^{\mu} q^{\mu}}{1-q^{2\mu}} \sin 2\mu\pi z. \tag{5.11–11}$$

We thus obtain the following expansions for the logarithmic derivative of the theta functions

$$\begin{aligned}
\frac{\vartheta_1'(z)}{\vartheta_1(z)} &= \pi \operatorname{ctn} \pi z + 4\pi \sum_{\nu=1}^{\infty} \frac{q^{2\nu}}{1-q^{2\nu}} \sin 2\nu\pi z, \\
\frac{\vartheta_2'(z)}{\vartheta_2(z)} &= -\pi \tan \pi z + 4\pi \sum_{\nu=1}^{\infty} \frac{(-1)^{\nu} q^{2\nu}}{1-q^{2\nu}} \sin 2\nu\pi z, \\
\frac{\vartheta_3'(z)}{\vartheta_3(z)} &= 4\pi \sum_{\nu=1}^{\infty} \frac{(-1)^{\nu} q^{\nu}}{1-q^{2\nu}} \sin 2\nu\pi z, \\
\frac{\vartheta_4'(z)}{\vartheta_4(z)} &= 4\pi \sum_{\nu=1}^{\infty} \frac{q^{\nu}}{1-q^{2\nu}} \sin 2\nu\pi z,
\end{aligned} \tag{5.11–12}$$

the first two expansions being valid in the strip $|\operatorname{Im} z| < \operatorname{Im} \tau$, the last two being valid in the strip $|\operatorname{Im} z| < \frac{1}{2} \operatorname{Im} \tau$.

5.11.2 – Applications

We wish to make some interesting applications of the formulas (5.11–12). Differentiating both members of (5.9–17) we have

$$4\omega^2 \wp(2\omega z) = -4\eta\omega - \frac{d}{dz} \frac{\vartheta_1'(z)}{\vartheta_1(z)}. \tag{5.11–13}$$

On account of the uniform convergence of the series occurring in

(5.11–12) in any closed and bounded set within the strip of convergence we may differentiate the series term-by-term. We thus obtain

$$4\omega^2 \wp(2\omega z) = -4\eta\omega+\pi^2 \csc^2 \pi z-8\pi^2 \sum_{\mu=1}^{\infty} \frac{\mu q^{2\mu}}{1-q^{2\mu}} \cos 2\mu\pi z. \quad (5.11\text{–}14)$$

Now we expand in a neighbourhood of the origin in terms of powers of z. By virtue of (5.3–4) we have

$$4\omega^2 \wp(2\omega z) = \frac{1}{z^2} + \sum_{\nu=1}^{\infty} c_{2\nu}\, 2^{2\nu+2}\, \omega^{2\nu+2}\, z^{2\nu}.$$

Differentiating the series for ctn z, represented by (2.17–21), we easily deduce

$$\pi^2 \csc^2 \pi z = \frac{1}{z^2} + \sum_{\nu=0}^{\infty} (2\nu+1) \frac{B_{2\nu+2}}{(2\nu+2)!}\, 2^{2\nu+2}\, \pi^{2\nu+2}\, z^{2\nu}.$$

Taking account of (1.10–8) we may write the last term of (5.11–14) as

$$-8\pi^2 \sum_{\mu=1}^{\infty} \frac{\mu q^{2\mu}}{1-q^{2\mu}} \cos 2\mu\pi z = -\sum_{\nu=0}^{\infty} 2^{2\nu+3} \pi^{2\nu+2} (-1)^{\nu} \sum_{\mu=1}^{\infty} \frac{\mu^{2\nu+1} q^{2\mu}}{1-q^{2\mu}} \frac{z^{2\nu}}{(2\nu)!}.$$

Inserting these series into (5.11–14) we find by comparing equal powers of z

$$4\eta\omega = \tfrac{1}{3}\pi^2-8\pi^2 \sum_{\nu=1}^{\infty} \frac{\nu q^{2\nu}}{1-q^{2\nu}} \quad (5.11\text{–}15)$$

and for $n = 1, 2, 3, \ldots,$

$$c_{2n} = \left(\frac{\pi}{\omega}\right)^{2n+2} \left\{(2n+1) \frac{B_{2n+2}}{(2n+2)!} - \frac{2(-1)^n}{(2n)!} \sum_{\nu=1}^{\infty} \frac{\nu^{2n+1} q^{2\nu}}{1-q^{2\nu}}\right\}. \quad (5.11\text{–}16)$$

In particular, by virtue of (5.4–2),

$$g_2 = \left(\frac{\pi}{\omega}\right)^4 \left\{\frac{1}{12} + 20 \sum_{\nu=1}^{\infty} \frac{\nu^3 q^{2\nu}}{1-q^{2\nu}}\right\}, \quad g_3 = \left(\frac{\pi}{\omega}\right)^6 \left\{\frac{1}{216} - \frac{7}{3} \sum_{\nu=1}^{\infty} \frac{\nu^5 q^{2\nu}}{1-q^{2\nu}}\right\}. \quad (5.11\text{–}17)$$

5.11.3 – Expressions for e_1, e_2, e_3

We wish to conclude our considerations by deriving expressions for e_1, e_2, e_3 in terms of q. Consulting the conversion formulas (5.8–27) and (5.8–28) we readily find

$$4\omega^2 \wp(2\omega z+\omega_\alpha) = -4\eta\omega - \frac{d}{dz} \frac{\vartheta'_{\alpha+1}(z)}{\vartheta_{\alpha+1}(z)}, \quad \alpha = 1, 2, 3,$$

whence, on performing the differentiation

$$4\omega^2 \wp(2\omega z+\omega) = -4\eta\omega+\pi^2 \sec^2 \pi z-8\pi^2 \sum_{\nu=1}^{\infty} \frac{(-1)^\nu \nu q^{2\nu}}{1-q^{2\nu}} \cos 2\nu\pi z,$$

$$4\omega^2 \wp(2\omega z+\omega+\omega') = -4\eta\omega-8\pi^2 \sum_{\nu=1}^{\infty} \frac{(-1)^\nu \nu q^\nu}{1-q^{2\nu}} \cos 2\nu\pi z, \qquad (5.11\text{–}18)$$

$$4\omega^2 \wp(2\omega z+\omega') = -4\eta\omega-8\pi^2 \sum_{\nu=1}^{\infty} \frac{\nu q^\nu}{1-q^{2\nu}} \cos 2\nu\pi z.$$

Inserting $z = 0$, we successively have

$$\begin{aligned} 4\omega^2 e_1 &= -4\eta\omega-\pi^2+8\pi^2 \sum_{\nu=1}^{\infty} \frac{(-1)^\nu \nu q^{2\nu}}{1-q^{2\nu}}, \\ 4\omega^2 e_2 &= -4\eta\omega \qquad -8\pi^2 \sum_{\nu=1}^{\infty} \frac{(-1)^\nu \nu q^\nu}{1-q^{2\nu}}, \qquad (5.11\text{–}19) \\ 4\omega^2 e_3 &= -4\eta\omega \qquad -8\pi^2 \sum_{\nu=1}^{\infty} \frac{\nu q^\nu}{1-q^{2\nu}}. \end{aligned}$$

5.12 – The pe function with real invariants

5.12.1 – The possible cases

In practical applications frequently occur pe functions whose invariants g_2 and g_3 are real. We wish to show that then all coefficients in the expansion (5.3–4) are real. This may be done by deriving a recurrence relation between these coefficients.

Differentiating both members of (5.4–3) we get

$$\wp''(z) = 6\wp^2(z)-\tfrac{1}{2}g_2 = 6\wp^2(z)-10c_2.$$

Hence

$$\frac{6}{z^4}+\sum_{\nu=1}^{\infty} 2\nu(2\nu-1)c_{2\nu}z^{2\nu-2} = -10c_2+6\left(\frac{1}{z^2}+\sum_{\nu=1}^{\infty} c_{2\nu}z^{2\nu}\right)^2$$

$$= -10c_2+6\left(\frac{1}{z^4}+2\sum_{\nu=1}^{\infty} c_{2\nu}z^{2\nu-2}+\sum_{\lambda=1}^{\infty}\sum_{\mu=1}^{\infty} c_{2\lambda}c_{2\mu}z^{2(\lambda+\mu)}\right).$$

Equating coefficients of z^{2n-2}, supposing $n > 2$, we readily find

$$2n(2n-1)c_{2n} = 12c_{2n}+6\sum_{\lambda+\mu=n-1} c_{2\lambda}c_{2\mu},$$

whence

$$(n-2)(2n+3)c_{2n} = 3\sum_{\lambda+\mu=n-1} c_{2\lambda}c_{2\mu}. \qquad (5.12\text{–}1)$$

By virtue of this relation we can successively express $c_6, c_8, \ldots$ rationally in terms of c_2, c_4, and hence also in terms of g_2, g_3.

A function of this nature assumes real values for real values of z. More generally

$$\wp(\bar{z}) = \overline{\wp(z)}. \qquad (5.12\text{–}2)$$

An easy consequence is:

If w is a period then also its conjugate complex value $\bar{w}$ is a period.

It follows that the lattice-points determine a network of rectangles whose sides are parallel to the real and imaginary axes respectively.

Since the sum of two conjugate periods is real and the difference is purely imaginary, we see that in the case under consideration the pe functions have real and purely imaginary periods.

Now two cases occur:

(i) One of the primitive periods is real, the other is purely imaginary. In this case the fundamental period-parallelogram is a rectangle whose sides are parallel to the real and imaginary axis respectively, (fig. 5.12–1).

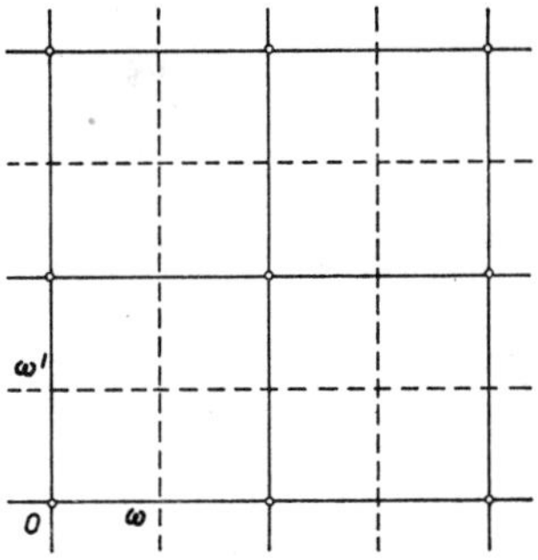

Fig. 5.12–1. Periods of $\wp(z)$ in case (i)

(ii) A set of primitive periods is made up of a pair of conjugate complex numbers. The fundamental period-parallelogram is a rhomb, whose diagonals are parallel to the real and imaginary axis, (fig. 5.12–2).

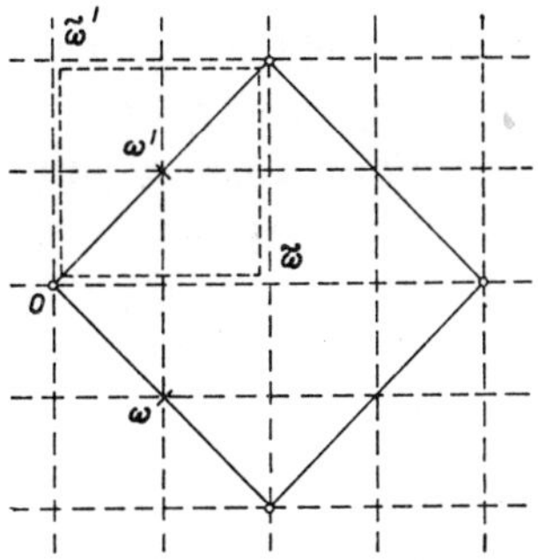

Fig. 5.12–2. Periods of $\wp(z)$ in case (ii)

Conversely, when the primitive periods are of the type described in (i) and (ii) then the coefficients in the expansion (5.3–4) of $\wp(z)$

are necessarily real. In fact, since the set of lattice-points is symmetric with respect to the real axis and the terms of the sums (5.3–5) defining these coefficients assume conjugate complex values in lattice-points which are situated symmetrically with respect to the real axis, we can combine the terms in pairs, contributing real values.

Examples of particular interest are the following. Let $\omega' = i\omega$, ω being positive, i.e., the fundamental period-parallelogram is a square. Then $g_3 = 0$. In fact

$$\sum{}' \frac{1}{(n+n'i)^6} = -\sum{}' \frac{1}{(n'-ni)^6} = -\sum{}' \frac{1}{(n+n'i)^6}, \tag{5.12–3}$$

for the numbers n', $-n$ run through the same pairs as n, n'.

Another example is provided by $2\omega = a\varrho^{-1}$, $2\omega' = a\varrho$ where $a > 0$ and $\varrho = \exp(2\pi i/3)$. In this case $g_2 = 0$. In fact

$$\begin{aligned} \sum{}' \frac{1}{(n\varrho^{-1}+n'\varrho)^4} &= \sum{}' \frac{1}{(n\varrho^2+n'\varrho)^4} = \frac{1}{\varrho}\sum{}' \frac{1}{(n\varrho+n')^4} \\ &= \frac{1}{\varrho}\sum{}' \frac{1}{\{(n-n')\varrho-n'\varrho^2\}^4} \\ &= \frac{1}{\varrho}\sum{}' \frac{1}{\{-n'\varrho^{-1}+(n-n')\varrho\}^4} = \frac{1}{\varrho}\sum{}' \frac{1}{(n\varrho^{-1}+n'\varrho)^4}, \end{aligned} \tag{5.12–4}$$

since the numbers $-n'$, $n-n'$ run through the same pairs of values as n, n'.

5.12.2 – The sign of the discriminant

The two cases discussed above are also characterized by the sign of the discriminant (5.4–11):

(i) If ω is real and ω' purely imaginary then $e_1 = \wp(\omega)$ and $e_3 = \wp(\omega')$ are real. Hence $e_2 = -(e_1+e_3)$.

The discriminant is positive when a pair of primitive periods consists of a real and a purely imaginary number.

(ii) If ω and ω' are conjugate complex, then $\omega+\omega'$ is real and so $e_2 = \wp(\omega+\omega')$. Since e_1 and e_3 are different and conjugate complex they are not real.

The discriminant is negative when a pair of primitive periods consists of two conjugate complex numbers.

5.12.3 – The points where the pe function is real

Next we wish to determine all points in the complex plane where $\wp(z)$ assumes real values. It is, of course, sufficient to study the behaviour in a fundamental period-parallelogram.

(i) When the discriminant is positive we shall prove that $\wp(z)$ assumes real values along the perimeter of the rectangle $0, \omega, \omega+\omega'$, ω'. As a consequence of the periodicity and the property to be even the function is real on the boundary and two median lines of the fundamental period-parallelogram.

It is plain that $\wp(z)$ is real between 0 and ω. When $z \to 0$ along the real axis then $\wp(z) \to +\infty$, while $\wp(z) = e_1$, for $z = \omega$. Hence $\wp(z) = c$ with $c > e_1$ has a solution between 0 and ω and, on account of the periodicity and the property to be even, also between ω and 2ω. Since $\wp(z)$ is of order two there is therefore only one solution between 0 and ω. Thus we see that the function is monotonously decreasing from $+\infty$ to e_1, when z varies from 0 to ω. An important consequence is:

The number e_1 is the largest root of the equation

$$4z^3 - g_2 z - g_3 = 0. \tag{5.12–5}$$

On the other hand $\wp(z)$ is also real on the imaginary axis and $\wp(z) \to -\infty$ as $z \to 0$ along this axis. By the same argument as used above we see that $\wp(z)$ is monotonously increasing from $-\infty$ to e_3 when z varies from 0 to ω' along the imaginary axis. Hence:

The number e_3 is the smallest root of the equation (5.12–5). Taking account of (5.4–4) we have

$$e_1 > e_2 > e_3, \qquad e_1 > 0, \qquad e_3 < 0. \tag{5.12–6}$$

The values of $\wp(z)$ at the points of the remaining sides of the rectangle under consideration are also real, for on the right vertical side we have $z+\bar{z} = 2\omega$. Hence $\overline{\wp(z)} = \wp(\bar{z}) = \wp(-z) = \wp(z)$.

On the upper horizontal side we have $\bar{z}+2\omega' = z$, hence $\overline{\wp(z)} = \wp(\bar{z}) = \wp(z)$. It is easily seen that on the right vertical side $\wp(z)$ assumes all real values between e_1 and e_2, each only once, and on the upper horizontal side each value between e_2 and e_3.

The equation $\wp(z) = c$, where c is real, cannot have a solution in the interior of the parallelogram, for then the equation would have more than two roots in the fundamental period-parallelogram.

Summing up we see that, if we traverse the rectangle $0, \omega, \omega+\omega'$, ω' in the counter-clockwise sense, the function $\wp(z)$ decreases monotonously from $+\infty$ to $-\infty$, (fig. 5.12–3).

(ii) A similar situation occurs in the case of a negative discriminant. It is convenient to introduce the numbers, (fig. 5.12–2),

$$\tilde{\omega} = \omega+\omega', \qquad \tilde{\omega}' = -\omega+\omega'. \tag{5.12–7}$$

By a similar reasoning as that above we find, when z traverses

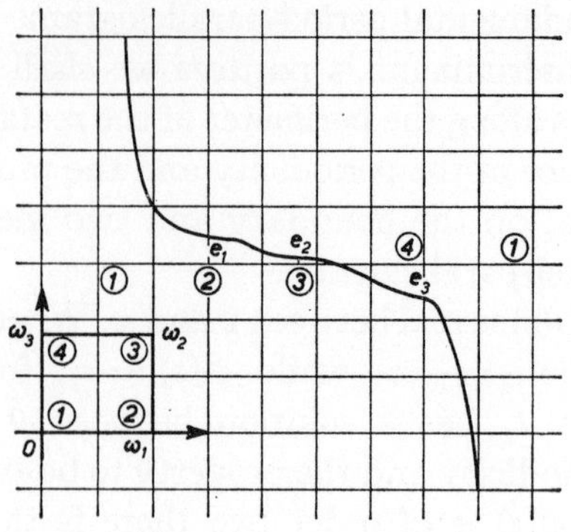

Fig. 5.12–3. Values of $\wp(z)$ on the sides of the period-parallelogram in case (i)

the rectangle 0, $\tilde{\omega}$, $\tilde{\omega}+\tilde{\omega}'$, $\tilde{\omega}'$ in the counter-clockwise sense, the function $\wp(z)$ decreases monotonously from $+\infty$ to e_2 when z varies from 0 to $\tilde{\omega}$ and from e_2 to $-\infty$ when z varies from $\tilde{\omega}$ to $\tilde{\omega}+\tilde{\omega}'$ along the vertical line. Then it starts again with the value $+\infty$ and arrives with the value e_2 at $\tilde{\omega}'$, while it tends to $-\infty$ when z varies from $\tilde{\omega}'$ to 0 along the vertical line, (fig. 5.12–4). Inside the rectangle the values of $\wp(z)$ are complex.

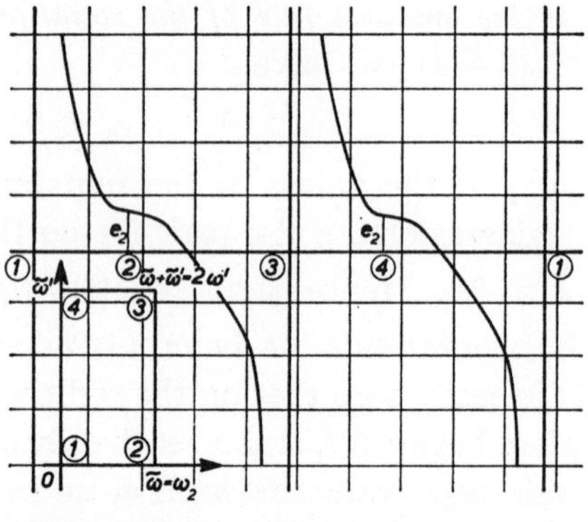

Fig. 5.12–4. Values of $\wp(z)$ on the sides of the rectangle 0, $\tilde{\omega}$, $\tilde{\omega}+\tilde{\omega}'$, $\tilde{\omega}'$ in the case (ii)

In both cases we can say that $\wp(z)$ assumes real values at the points of a set of equidistant horizontal and vertical lines. In the first case these are the lines through the lattice points and the lines midway between them. In the second case they are the lines through the lattice-points only.

5.12.4 – The sign of Im e_1 and Im e_3 when Δ is negative

Finally we wish to discuss the sign of Im e_1 in the case (ii). It is evident that Im $e_3 = -$ Im e_1.

We insert $a = \frac{1}{2}\tilde{\omega}$, $b = -\frac{1}{2}\tilde{\omega}'$ into the addition theorem (5.5–3) written in the form

$$\wp(a+b) = -\wp(a)-\wp(b)+\frac{\wp'^2(a)+\wp'^2(b)-2\wp'(a)\wp'(b)}{4\{\wp(a)-\wp(b)\}^2}.$$

Now a is real and b is purely imaginary. Since $\wp(z)$ is decreasing between 0 and $\tilde{\omega}$ we have $\wp'(a) < 0$. Further it follows from the expansion (5.3–11) of $\wp'(z)$ that $\wp'(b)$ is purely imaginary. Hence the sign of $\operatorname{Im} e_1 = \operatorname{Im} \wp(a+b)$ is the sign of $-\wp'(a)\wp'(b)/i$.

When z is near to zero on the imaginary axis $i\wp'(z)$ is negative and since there are no zeros of $\wp'(z)$ between 0 and $\tilde{\omega}'$ we conclude that also $i\wp'(b)$ is negative. Thus we proved:

The sign of Im e_1 *is positive, the sign of* Im e_3 *is negative, provided the discriminant is negative.*

5.13 – The periods represented as integrals

5.13.1 – Weierstrass's elliptic integral

Suppose that the real variable x varies in the interval $0 < x \leqq \omega$, when $\Delta > 0$, and in the interval $0 < x \leqq \tilde{\omega}$ when $\Delta < 0$. In these intervals $\wp(x)$ is monotonously decreasing, i.e., $\wp'(x) < 0$. On the other hand $4\wp^3(x)-g_2\wp(x)-g_3 > 0$. Hence the differential equation (5.4–3) may be written as

$$\wp'(x) = -\sqrt{4\wp^3(x)-g_2\wp(x)-g_3}. \tag{5.13–1}$$

Accordingly, supposing $u \geqq e_1$ when $\Delta > 0$, $u \geqq e_2$ when $\Delta < 0$, the equation

$$u = \wp(x) \tag{5.13–2}$$

defines the variable x as a function of u,

$$x = f(u) \tag{5.13–3}$$

which vanishes for $u \to \infty$. The derivative is

$$\frac{dx}{du} = \frac{-1}{\sqrt{4u^3-g_2u-g_3}} \tag{5.13–4}$$

and so we see that *the inverse function of* $\wp(x)$ *in the given intervals is represented by Weierstrass's integral*

$$\boxed{x = \int_u^\infty \frac{dt}{\sqrt{4t^3-g_2t-g_3}}} \tag{5.13–5}$$

where $u \geqq e_1$ when $\Delta > 0$, $u \geqq e_2$ when $\Delta < 0$.

Next we suppose that ix varies along the imaginary axis from

0 to ω', or from 0 to $\tilde{\omega}'$, according as $\Delta > 0$ or $\Delta < 0$.

From the definition of the pe function we easily deduce

$$\wp(z|\omega, \omega') = -\wp(-iz|-i\omega', i\omega) = -\wp\left(\frac{z}{i}\,\middle|\, -i\omega', -i\omega\right). \qquad (5.13\text{–}6)$$

Hence the function $\wp(ix|\omega, \omega')$ behaves like the function $-\wp(x|-i\omega', -i\omega)$. The invariants of this function are evidently g_2, $-g_3$, and $-e_1$, $-e_2$, $-e_3$ are the roots of the equation

$$4z^3 - g_2 z + g_3 = 0 \qquad (5.13\text{–}7)$$

where now $-e_3$ is the largest root when $\Delta > 0$.

By virtue of the previous result the equation

$$u = \wp(ix) \qquad (5.13\text{–}8)$$

defines the inverse function

$$x = \int_{-u}^{\infty} \frac{dt}{\sqrt{4t^3 - g_2 t + g_3}}.$$

5.13.2 – Expressions for the periods

The results obtained above enable us to write down the expression for the periods as definite integrals.

(i) When $\Delta > 0$ we evidently have for the semi-periods

$$\omega = \int_{e_1}^{\infty} \frac{dt}{\sqrt{4t^3 - g_2 t - g_3}}, \quad \frac{\omega'}{i} = \int_{-e_3}^{\infty} \frac{dt}{\sqrt{4t^3 - g_2 t + g_3}}. \qquad (5.13\text{–}9)$$

(ii) We similarly have when $\Delta < 0$

$$\tilde{\omega} = \int_{e_2}^{\infty} \frac{dt}{\sqrt{4t^3 - g_2 t - g_3}}, \quad \frac{\tilde{\omega}'}{i} = \int_{-e_2}^{\infty} \frac{dt}{\sqrt{4t^3 - g_2 t + g_3}}. \qquad (5.13\text{–}10)$$

5.13.3 – Legendre's complete elliptic integral of the first kind

For the discussion of the integrals representing the half-periods it will be convenient to bring them into another form. We have to consider the cases $\Delta > 0$ and $\Delta < 0$ separately.

(i) $\Delta > 0$. Writing the first integral (5.13–9) as

$$\omega = \int_{e_1}^{\infty} \frac{dt}{2\sqrt{(t-e_1)(t-e_2)(t-e_3)}} \qquad (5.13\text{–}11)$$

we find by putting

$$t = e_3 + g^2/t'^2$$

and omitting afterwards the prime

$$\omega = \int_0^{g/\sqrt{e_1-e_3}} \frac{dt}{g\sqrt{\left(1-\frac{e_1-e_3}{g^2}t^2\right)\left(1-\frac{e_2-e_3}{g^2}t^2\right)}}.$$

Now let

$$g^2 = e_1-e_3, \quad k^2 = \frac{e_2-e_3}{e_1-e_3}, \quad g > 0, \quad k > 0. \tag{5.13–12}$$

Then we get the following expression

$$\boxed{\omega g = \int_0^1 \frac{dt}{\sqrt{(1-t^2)(1-k^2t^2)}}.} \tag{5.13–13}$$

This integral is known as *Legendre's complete elliptic integral of the first kind.* The number g is called the *multiplicator* and k is the *modulus*. According to (5.12–6) the number k^2 satisfies the inequality

$$0 < k^2 < 1.$$

In a similar way we can transform the second integral (5.13–9) writing it in the form

$$\frac{\omega'}{i} = \int_{-e_3}^{\infty} \frac{dt}{2\sqrt{(t+e_1)(t+e_2)(t+e_3)}}. \tag{5.13–14}$$

Now we perform the substitution

$$t = -e_1+g^2/t'^2$$

and we find after omitting the prime

$$\frac{\omega'}{i} = \int_0^{g/\sqrt{e_1-e_3}} \frac{dt}{g\sqrt{\left(1-\frac{e_1-e_2}{g^2}t^2\right)\left(1-\frac{e_2-e_3}{g^2}t^2\right)}}.$$

Again let

$$g^2 = e_1-e_3, \quad k'^2 = \frac{e_1-e_2}{e_1-e_3}, \quad g > 0, \quad k' > 0. \tag{5.13–15}$$

We then find

$$\boxed{\frac{\omega' g}{i} = \int_0^1 \frac{dt}{\sqrt{(1-t^2)(1-k'^2t^2)}}.} \tag{5.13–16}$$

The number g has the same value as in (5.13–13). But k has been replaced by k'. The moduli k and k' are said to be *complementary.* The relation between k and k' is expressed by

$$k^2+k'^2 = 1. \tag{5.13–17}$$

By taking $t = \sin\theta$ the integrals appear in the trigonometric form

$$\omega g = \int_0^{\frac{1}{2}\pi} \frac{d\theta}{\sqrt{1-k^2\sin^2\theta}}, \quad \frac{\omega' g}{i} = \int_0^{\frac{1}{2}\pi} \frac{d\theta}{\sqrt{1-k'^2\sin^2\theta}}. \tag{5.13–18}$$

(ii) Writing the first integral (5.13–10) in a form exhibiting the numbers e_1, e_2, e_3 like (5.13–11), where now e_1 and e_3 are conjugate complex, we find by the substitution

$$t'^2 = t - e_2$$

and omitting afterwards the prime

$$\tilde{\omega} = \int_0^{\infty} \frac{dt}{\sqrt{(t^2+e_2-e_1)\,(t^2+e_2-e_3)}}.$$

Since $e_2 - e_3$ and $e_2 - e_1$ are conjugate complex and $\operatorname{Im}(e_2-e_3) > 0$ as has been proved in section 5.12.4, we may write

$$e_2 - e_3 = r(\cos\psi + i\sin\psi),$$
$$e_2 - e_1 = r(\cos\psi - i\sin\psi),$$

where $r > 0$ and $0 < \psi < \pi$. The polynomial in the denominator becomes

$$t^4 + 2t^2 r\cos\psi + r^2 = (t^2+r)^2 - 4t^2 r\sin^2\tfrac{1}{2}\psi.$$

Now we introduce a new variable u by $u\sqrt{r} = t$ and a number $\tilde{k}$ being equal to

$$\tilde{k} = \sin\tfrac{1}{2}\psi. \tag{5.13–19}$$

We then have

$$\tilde{\omega}\sqrt{r} = \int_0^{\infty} \frac{du}{\sqrt{(u^2+1)^2 - 4\tilde{k}^2u^2}}. \tag{5.13–20}$$

The second integral (5.13–10) may be treated in a similar manner. Next we perform the substitution

$$t'^2 = t + e_2$$

and introduce the number

$$\tilde{k}' = \cos\tfrac{1}{2}\psi. \tag{5.13–21}$$

We get

$$\frac{\tilde{\omega}'\sqrt{r}}{i} = \int_0^{\infty} \frac{du}{\sqrt{(u^2+1)^2 - 4\tilde{k}'^2u^2}}. \tag{5.13–22}$$

Writing $\int_0^{\infty}$ as $\int_0^1 + \int_1^{\infty}$ we see by taking $u' = 1/u$ in the second term that $\int_0^1 = \int_1^{\infty}$. Hence

$$\tilde{\omega}\sqrt{r} = 2\int_0^1 \frac{du}{\sqrt{(u^2+1)^2-4\tilde{k}^2u^2}}, \qquad \frac{\tilde{\omega}'\sqrt{r}}{i} = 2\int_0^1 \frac{du}{\sqrt{(u^2+1)^2-4\tilde{k}'^2u^2}}. \tag{5.13–23}$$

Finally we put

$$\sin\theta = \frac{2u}{u^2+1}$$

and so we obtain the trigonometric forms

$$\boxed{\tilde{\omega}\sqrt{r} = \int_0^{\frac{1}{2}\pi} \frac{d\theta}{\sqrt{1-\tilde{k}^2\sin^2\theta}}, \qquad \frac{\tilde{\omega}'\sqrt{r}}{i} = \int_0^{\frac{1}{2}\pi} \frac{d\theta}{\sqrt{1-\tilde{k}'^2\sin^2\theta}}.} \tag{5.13–24}$$

5.13.4 – Existence of a pe function with prescribed invariants

The previous results enable us to solve a fundamental problem in the theory of the pe function. Representing the right-hand sides of (5.4–2) by $g_2(\omega, \omega')$, $g_3(\omega, \omega')$ we may ask whether it is possible to determine the numbers ω and ω' in such a way that

$$g_2(\omega, \omega') = g_2, \qquad g_3(\omega, \omega') = g_3,$$

where g_2 and g_3 have prescribed real values. A necessary condition is that the discriminant $g_2^3-27g_3^2$ should be different from zero. This condition is, however, also sufficient.

(i) First we consider the case $\Delta > 0$. The ratio

$$\frac{\tau}{i} = \frac{\omega'}{i\omega} = \int_0^{\frac{1}{2}\pi} \frac{d\theta}{\sqrt{1-k'^2\sin^2\theta}} \Bigg/ \int_0^{\frac{1}{2}\pi} \frac{d\theta}{\sqrt{1-k^2\sin^2\theta}} \tag{5.13–25}$$

is monotonously and continuously decreasing from $+\infty$ to 0 when k^2 varies from 0 to 1. In fact, the integral

$$\int_0^\theta \frac{d\theta}{\sqrt{1-\sin^2\theta}} = \int_0^\theta \frac{d\theta}{\cos\theta} = \log\tan\left(\tfrac{1}{2}\theta+\tfrac{1}{4}\pi\right)$$

is divergent as $\theta \to \frac{1}{2}\pi$. Hence to a given value of τ corresponds a uniquely determined value of k^2.

Now e_1, e_2, e_3 are uniquely determined by g^2, k^2 and the relation $e_1+e_2+e_3 = 0$. Given g_2 and g_3 we can find e_1, e_2, e_3 as roots of the equation (5.12–5). Then we calculate g^2, k^2 and k'^2 by (5.13–12), (5.13–15). Next we determine ω and ω' by (5.13–18) and construct a pe function associated with the periods 2ω, $2\omega'$. Since k^2 is uniquely determined by ω'/ω g is also fixed by (5.13–18). This means that the numbers e_1, e_2, e_3 associated with the pe function are precisely the roots of (5.12–5) and hence the invariants of the pe function are the given numbers g_2, g_3. It is plain that the argument fails when $\Delta = 0$, for then either $g = 0$ or one of the numbers k^2, k'^2 is zero.

(ii) In the case $\Delta < 0$ we proceed in a similar way. From the given numbers g_2 and g_3 we calculate $\tilde{\omega}$, $\tilde{\omega}'$ and as in (i) we verify that $\tilde{k}$ is uniquely determined by the ratio $\tilde{\omega}'/\tilde{\omega}$. Conversely e_1, e_2, e_3 are determined by r and ψ, hence by r and $\tilde{k}$ on account of

$$\cos\psi = \tilde{k}'^2 - \tilde{k}^2, \qquad \sin\psi = 2\tilde{k}\tilde{k}', \qquad 0 < \psi < \pi.$$

Thus we have established the important result:

It is always possible to construct a pe function having prescribed real invariants, provided the discriminant is different from zero.

The case where the discriminant is zero does not cause any difficulty, for then the pe function is degenerated, as we pointed out in section 5.4.4.

The general problem, where g_2 and g_3 have complex values, is more difficult and will be deferred to vol. II.

5.14 – The Jacobian elliptic functions

5.14.1 – Legendre's elliptic integral of the first kind

When $0 < k^2 < 1$ the integral

$$\int_0^\varphi \frac{d\theta}{\sqrt{1-k^2\sin^2\theta}} \tag{5.14–1}$$

is a monotonously and continuously increasing differentiable function of φ. In fact, the integrand is always $\geqq 1$. Denoting this integral, which is called *Legendre's elliptic integral of the first kind*, by $F(k, \varphi)$, the equation

$$z = F(k, \varphi) \tag{5.14–2}$$

where z is assumed to be real, defines φ as a function of z. This function has been called by Jacobi the *amplitude* of z and is denoted by

$$\varphi = \operatorname{am}(z, k). \tag{5.14–3}$$

The value of $F(k, \varphi)$ which corresponds to $\varphi = \frac{1}{2}\pi$ is denoted by K. Hence K is *the complete integral*

$$\mathsf{K} = \int_0^{\frac{1}{2}\pi} \frac{d\theta}{\sqrt{1-k^2\sin^2\theta}}. \tag{5.14–4}$$

When it is not necessary to exhibit the dependence on k we briefly write $\operatorname{am} z$ instead of $\operatorname{am}(z, k)$.

The function $\operatorname{am} z$ is quasi-periodic. This is expressed by

$$\operatorname{am}(z+2\mathsf{K}) = \operatorname{am} z + \pi. \tag{5.14–5}$$

In fact, it is easily verified that

$$F(k, \pi) = 2F(k, \tfrac{1}{2}\pi)$$

and so

$$F(k, \varphi+\pi) = F(k, \pi)+F(k, \varphi) = 2\mathsf{K}+F(k, \varphi).$$

For $k \to 0$ the function am z degenerates into z. In fig. 5.14–1 a graph is reproduced of the function am z.

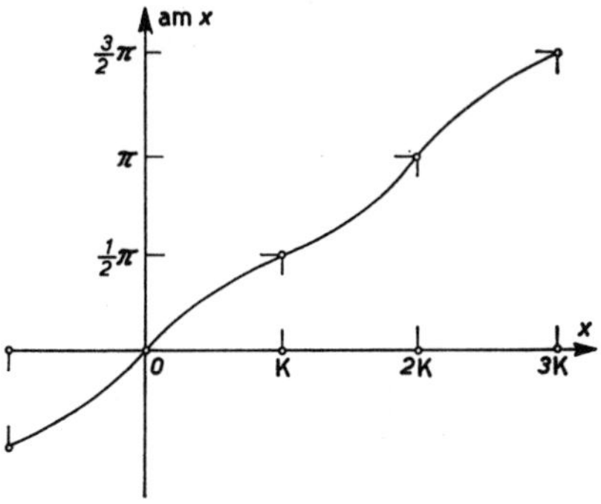

Fig. 5.14–1. The function am x ($k^2 = 0{,}75$, $k = 2{,}157$)

Since

$$\frac{d\varphi}{dz} = \sqrt{1-k^2 \sin^2\varphi} \tag{5.14–6}$$

the function am z is convex upwards in the interval $0 \leqq z \leqq \mathsf{K}$ and convex downwards in the interval $\mathsf{K} \leqq z \leqq 2\mathsf{K}$.

5.14.2 – Elementary definition of the Jacobian functions

Jacobi introduced further the functions sinus amplitudinis and cosinus amplitudinis

$$\boxed{\operatorname{sn} z = \sin \operatorname{am} z, \qquad \operatorname{cn} z = \cos \operatorname{am} z.} \tag{5.14–7}$$

These functions are evidently periodic, the period being 4K. The zeros of sn z are at the points $2n\mathsf{K}$, the zeros of cn z at the points $(2n+1)\mathsf{K}$, $n = 0, \pm 1, \pm 2, \ldots$. Since am z is an odd function, the function sn z is also odd, whereas cn z is even.

The Jacobian functions satisfy the functional relation

$$\boxed{\operatorname{cn}^2 z+\operatorname{sn}^2 z = 1.} \tag{5.14–8}$$

The derivative of am z is denoted by dn z (delta amplitudinis z)

$$\boxed{\operatorname{dn} z = \operatorname{am}' z.} \tag{5.14–9}$$

This function is always positive, for am z is a strictly increasing function. From (5.14–6) we easily deduce the functional relation

$$\boxed{\mathrm{dn}^2 z + k^2\,\mathrm{sn}^2 z = 1.} \tag{5.14–10}$$

The function dn z being equal to

$$\mathrm{dn}\, z = \sqrt{1-k^2\,\mathrm{sn}^2 z} \tag{5.14–11}$$

is also periodic, its period being, however, 2K. Graphs of the functions are reproduced in fig. 5.14–2.

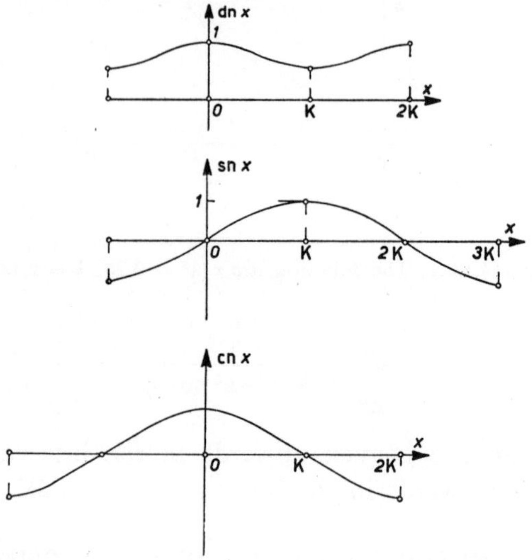

Fig. 5.14–2. The elliptic functions of Jacobi with real period

The derivatives are easily found. We successively have

$$\boxed{\begin{aligned} \mathrm{sn}'\, z &= \mathrm{cn}\, z\, \mathrm{dn}\, z, \\ \mathrm{cn}'\, z &= -\mathrm{sn}\, z\, \mathrm{dn}\, z, \\ \mathrm{dn}'\, z &= -k^2\, \mathrm{sn}\, z\, \mathrm{cn}\, z. \end{aligned}} \tag{5.14–12}$$

The last formula may be obtained by differentiating both members of (5.14–10).

5.14.3 – DEGENERATIONS

We wish to investigate the degenerations as $k \to 0$ and $k \to 1$. In the first case we have for $k = 0$

$$\mathrm{am}\, z = z, \quad \mathrm{sn}\, z = \sin z, \quad \mathrm{cn}\, z = \cos z, \quad \mathrm{dn}\, z = 1, \quad \mathsf{K} = \tfrac{1}{2}\pi.$$

In the second case the relation between z and φ is expressed by

$$z = \int_0^{\varphi} \frac{d\theta}{\cos\theta} = -\log\tan(\tfrac{1}{4}\pi - \tfrac{1}{2}\varphi).$$

Hence

$$\tan\tfrac{1}{2}\varphi = \frac{e^z - 1}{e^z + 1} = \tanh\tfrac{1}{2}z,$$

$$\sin\varphi = \frac{2\tan\frac{1}{2}\varphi}{1 + \tan^2\frac{1}{2}\varphi} = \tanh z, \quad \cos\varphi = \frac{1 - \tan^2\frac{1}{2}\varphi}{1 + \tan^2\frac{1}{2}\varphi} = \frac{1}{\cosh z}$$

or, when $k = 1$,

$$\operatorname{sn} z = \tanh z, \quad \operatorname{cn} z = \operatorname{dn} z = \frac{1}{\cosh z}.$$

The periodicity has disappeared, since $\mathsf{K} \to \infty$ as $k \to 1$.

5.14.4 – General definition of the Jacobian functions

Next we shall try to define the Jacobian functions for complex values of z. This may be done by using the Weierstrassian pe function. We know that it is always possible to find a pe function such that k and g, defined in section 5.13.3, have prescribed values, provided $0 < k^2 < 1$, $\Delta > 0$.

Performing the substitution

$$t = e_3 + \frac{g^2}{\sin^2\theta}$$

we find as in section 5.13.3

$$z = \int_u^{\infty} \frac{dt}{\sqrt{4t^3 - g_2 t - g_3}} = \frac{1}{g}\int_0^{\varphi} \frac{d\theta}{\sqrt{1 - k^2\sin^2\theta}}, \tag{5.14–13}$$

with

$$u = e_3 + \frac{g^2}{\sin^2\varphi}. \tag{5.14–14}$$

Now

$$\varphi = \operatorname{am} gz$$

and (5.14–14) may be read as

$$\wp(z) = e_3 + \frac{g^2}{\operatorname{sn}^2 gz} \tag{5.14–15}$$

and in the interval $0 \leq z \leq 2\mathsf{K}$ we have

$$\operatorname{sn} gz = \frac{g}{\sqrt{\wp(z) - e_3}}. \tag{5.14–16}$$

In the same interval we have on account of (5.14–8) and (5.14–10)

$$\text{cn}\, gz = \frac{\sqrt{\wp(z) - e_1}}{\sqrt{\wp(z) - e_3}}, \tag{5.14–17}$$

$$\text{dn}\, gz = \frac{\sqrt{\wp(z) - e_2}}{\sqrt{\wp(z) - e_3}}. \tag{5.14–18}$$

In section 5.7.2. we saw that the expressions on the right also have a meaning for complex values of z. Given a set of periods 2ω, $2\omega'$ such that $\tau = \omega'/\omega$ has a positive imaginary component we may introduce the Jacobian functions as

$$\boxed{\text{sn}\, z = \frac{g}{\sqrt{\wp(z|g) - e_3}}, \quad \text{cn}\, z = \frac{\sqrt{\wp(z|g) - e_1}}{\sqrt{\wp(z|g) - e_3}}, \quad \text{dn}\, z = \frac{\sqrt{\wp(z|g) - e_2}}{\sqrt{\wp(z|g) - e_3}}.} \tag{5.14–19}$$

An alternative representation is

$$\text{sn}\, z = \frac{g\sigma(z/g)}{\sigma_3(z/g)}, \quad \text{cn}\, z = \frac{\sigma_1(z/g)}{\sigma_3(z/g)}, \quad \text{dn}\, z = \frac{\sigma_2(z/g)}{\sigma_3(z/g)}. \tag{5.14–20}$$

5.14.5 – Relations of homogeneity

It might seem that the Jacobian functions depend on ω and ω' separately. Actually *they depend only on the ratio* $\tau = \omega'/\omega$. This follows from the relations of homogeneity which may easily be derived from the defining expansions

$$\wp(\lambda z|\lambda\omega, \lambda\omega') = \lambda^{-2}\wp(z|\omega, \omega'), \tag{5.14–21}$$

$$\zeta(\lambda z|\lambda\omega, \lambda\omega') = \lambda^{-1}\zeta(z|\omega, \omega'). \tag{5.14–22}$$

Hence

$$\eta_\alpha(\lambda\omega, \lambda\omega') = \lambda^{-1}\eta_\alpha(\omega, \omega'), \quad \alpha = 1, 2, 3. \tag{5.14–23}$$

Further

$$\sigma(\lambda z|\lambda\omega, \lambda\omega') = \lambda\sigma(z|\omega, \omega'), \tag{5.14–24}$$

but, according to (5.14–22),

$$\sigma_\alpha(\lambda z|\lambda\omega, \lambda\omega') = \sigma_\alpha(z|\omega, \omega'), \quad \alpha = 1, 2, 3, \tag{5.14–25}$$

and so

$$g(\lambda\omega, \lambda\omega') = \lambda^{-1}g(\omega, \omega') \tag{5.14–26}$$

whence

$$g(\lambda\omega, \lambda\omega')\,\sigma(\lambda z|\lambda\omega, \lambda\omega') = g(\omega, \omega')\,\sigma(z|\omega, \omega'). \tag{5.14–27}$$

All functions occurring in the numerator and the denominator of the expressions defining the Jacobian functions have therefore the fundamental property of being homogeneous of degree 0, expressed by

$$f(\lambda z|\lambda\omega, \lambda\omega') = f(z|\omega, \omega'). \tag{5.14–28}$$

As a consequence we have

$$f\left(\frac{z}{g(\lambda\omega,\lambda\omega')}\middle|\lambda\omega,\lambda\omega'\right)=f\left(\frac{\lambda z}{g(\omega,\omega')}\middle|\lambda\omega,\lambda\omega'\right)=f\left(\frac{z}{g(\omega,\omega')}\middle|\omega,\omega'\right),$$

and this proves the assertion.

5.14.6 – The periods

Introducing the numbers

$$\mathsf{K} = g\omega, \qquad i\mathsf{K}' = g\omega' \tag{5.14–29}$$

which actually depend on τ only, we deduce from the quasi-periodic properties of the sigma functions

$$\begin{aligned} &\operatorname{sn}(z+2\mathsf{K}) = -\operatorname{sn} z, \ \operatorname{cn}(z+2\mathsf{K}) = -\operatorname{cn} z, \ \operatorname{dn}(z+2\mathsf{K}) = \operatorname{dn} z, \\ &\operatorname{sn}(z+2i\mathsf{K}') = \operatorname{sn} z, \ \operatorname{cn}(z+2i\mathsf{K}') = -\operatorname{cn} z, \ \operatorname{dn}(z+2i\mathsf{K}') = -\operatorname{dn} z. \end{aligned} \tag{5.14–30}$$

The function sn z *is an odd function.* Its zeros are congruent to $z = 0$ and $z = 2\mathsf{K}$. *The function* cn z *is an even function.* Its zeros are congruent to $z = \mathsf{K}$ and $z = 3\mathsf{K}$. *The function* dn z *is also an even function.* Its zeros are congruent to $z = \mathsf{K}+i\mathsf{K}'$ and $\mathsf{K}+3i\mathsf{K}'$.

All functions have the same poles represented by $2n\mathsf{K}+(2n'+1)i\mathsf{K}'$, (fig. 5.14–3). The poles are simple and the order of all functions is two.

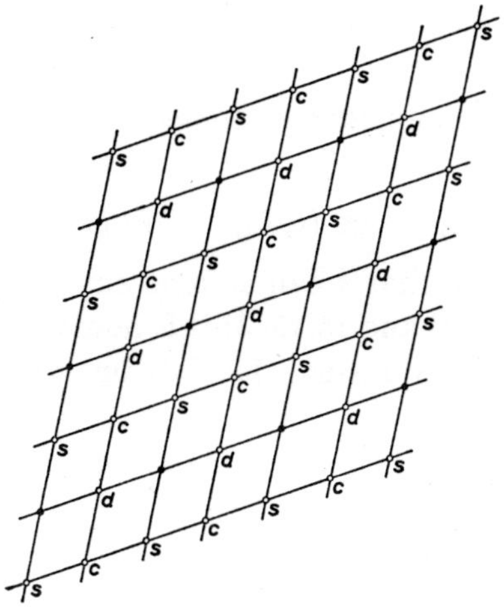

Fig. 5.14–3. Poles (black dots) and zeros of the elliptic functions of Jacobi

Taking account of (5.14–30), it is now clear that sn z is doubly-periodic with periods $4\mathsf{K}$, $2i\mathsf{K}'$, that dn z is doubly-periodic with periods 2K, $4i$K', while cn z is doubly-periodic with periods **4K**, 2K+$2i$K'.

5.15 – Fourier expansions of the Jacobian functions

5.15.1 – The effect of Jacobi's imaginary transformation

It is evident that the transformation

$$\tau' = -\frac{1}{\tau}$$

induces the transformation

$$e_1' = e_3, \qquad e_2' = e_2, \qquad e_3' = e_1, \tag{5.15–1}$$

for ω is replaced by ω' and ω' by $-\omega$. Hence, according to (5.7–6)

$$g' = \sqrt{e_1'-e_3'} = \sqrt{e_3-e_1} = \frac{1}{i}\sqrt{e_1-e_3} = \frac{g}{i}, \tag{5.15–2}$$

and

$$\begin{aligned} \sqrt{\wp(z/g')-e_1'} &= \sqrt{\wp(iz/g)-e_3}, \\ \sqrt{\wp(z/g')-e_2'} &= \sqrt{\wp(iz/g)-e_2}, \\ \sqrt{\wp(z/g)-e_3'} &= \sqrt{\wp(iz/g)-e_1}. \end{aligned} \tag{5.15–3}$$

Now we introduce the *modulus* k and *complementary modulus* k' by

$$k = \frac{\sqrt{e_2-e_3}}{\sqrt{e_1-e_3}}, \quad k' = \frac{\sqrt{e_2'-e_3'}}{\sqrt{e_1'-e_3'}} = \frac{\sqrt{e_1-e_2}}{\sqrt{e_1-e_3}}. \tag{5.15–4}$$

The moduli k, k' are uniquely determined by τ. It is customary to exhibit the dependence of the Jacobian functions on τ by writing

$$\text{sn}\,(z, k), \qquad \text{cn}\,(z, k), \qquad \text{dn}\,(z, k),$$

but that does not mean that k can assume any preassigned value.

On account of (5.15–2) and (5.15–3) it is now very easy to verify the following formulas expressing Jacobi's imaginary transformation of his functions:

$$\boxed{\begin{aligned} \text{sn}\,(iz, k) &= i\,\frac{\text{sn}\,(z, k')}{\text{cn}\,(z, k')}, \\ \text{cn}\,(iz, k) &= \frac{1}{\text{cn}\,(z, k')}, \\ \text{dn}\,(iz, k) &= \frac{\text{dn}\,(z, k')}{\text{cn}\,(z, k')}. \end{aligned}} \tag{5.15–5}$$

5.15.2 – The Jacobian functions as theta quotients

The same formulas can also directly be obtained from the transformation formulas for the theta functions (5.10–9). First we have to express the Jacobian functions in terms of the theta functions.

By virtue of (5.10–2) we evidently have

$$k = \frac{\vartheta_2^2(0)}{\vartheta_3^2(0)}, \qquad k' = \frac{\vartheta_4^2(0)}{\vartheta_3^2(0)}. \tag{5.15–6}$$

Hence the relation (5.10–3) is equivalent to

$$k^2+k'^2 = 1. \tag{5.15–7}$$

Now we define

$$\sqrt{k} = \frac{\vartheta_2(0)}{\vartheta_3(0)}, \qquad \sqrt{k'} = \frac{\vartheta_4(0)}{\vartheta_3(0)}. \tag{5.15–8}$$

Finally we observe that, according to (5.10–2),

$$\mathsf{K} = \omega g = \tfrac{1}{2}\pi\,\vartheta_3^2(0) \tag{5.15–9}$$

while K' appears from K by applying Jacobi's transformation.

From (5.8–22) and (5.14–19) we now easily deduce, taking account of (5.10–2) and (5.9–14),

$$\boxed{\begin{aligned} \operatorname{sn} z &= \frac{1}{\sqrt{k}}\,\frac{\vartheta_1(z/2\mathsf{K})}{\vartheta_4(z/2\mathsf{K})}, \\ \operatorname{cn} z &= \frac{\sqrt{k'}}{\sqrt{k}}\,\frac{\vartheta_2(z/2\mathsf{K})}{\vartheta_4(z/2\mathsf{K})}, \\ \operatorname{dn} z &= \sqrt{k'}\,\frac{\vartheta_3(z/2\mathsf{K})}{\vartheta_4(z/2\mathsf{K})}. \end{aligned}} \tag{5.15–10}$$

It is now immediately seen how the transformation formulas (5.15–5) follow from (5.10–9).

The expansions (5.15–10) are important from a theoretical as well as from a practical point of view, for the theta functions are rapidly convergent and they can serve for numerical computations.

It is possible to determine from the first principles the properties of the four theta functions and thence to deduce the whole theory of Jacobi's elliptic functions independent of the theory of the pe function, when we define them as quotients of the theta functions.

5.15.3 – Evaluation of the residues

It is now easy to determine the residue of the Jacobian functions at the poles. First we list some particular values.

The definition (5.14–19) yields at once

$$\mathrm{sn}\,(\mathsf{K}, k) = 1, \quad \mathrm{cn}\,(\mathsf{K}, k) = 0, \quad \mathrm{dn}\,(\mathsf{K}, k) = k'. \qquad (5.15\text{–}11)$$

Hence also

$$\mathrm{sn}\,(\mathsf{K}', k') = 1, \quad \mathrm{cn}\,(\mathsf{K}', k') = 0, \quad \mathrm{dn}\,(\mathsf{K}', k') = k. \qquad (5.15\text{–}12)$$

Next we verify that the equations (5.14–8), (5.14–10) and (5.14–12) hold also in the complex case.

Indeed, the functional equations are a direct consequence of (5.6–20). By virtue of the third formula of (5.6–24) we have

$$\frac{d}{dz}\frac{g\sigma(z/g)}{\sigma_3(z/g)} = \frac{\sigma_1(z/g)}{\sigma_3(z/g)}\,\frac{\sigma_2(z/g)}{\sigma_3(z/g)}.$$

Hence the first formula (5.14–12) is proved and by differentiating the functional equations we obtain the remaining formulas of (5.14–12).

The residue of $\mathrm{sn}\,(z, k)$ at $z = i\mathsf{K}'$ is

$$\lim_{z\to i\mathsf{K}'} (z-i\mathsf{K}')\,\mathrm{sn}\,(z, k) = i \lim_{z\to \mathsf{K}'} (z-\mathsf{K}')\,\mathrm{sn}\,(iz, k)$$

$$= -i \lim_{z\to \mathsf{K}'} (z-\mathsf{K}')\frac{\mathrm{sn}\,(z, k')}{\mathrm{cn}\,(z, k')} = \frac{\mathrm{sn}\,(\mathsf{K}', k')}{\mathrm{cn}'\,(\mathsf{K}', k')} = \frac{1}{\mathrm{dn}\,(\mathsf{K}', k')} = \frac{1}{k}.$$

The residue of the function $\mathrm{sn}\, z$ *at the pole* $z = i\mathsf{K}'$ *is* $1/k$. In a similar way we find:

The residue of the function $\mathrm{cn}\, z$ *at the pole* $z = i\mathsf{K}'$ *is* $-i/k$.

The residue of the function $\mathrm{dn}\, z$ *at the pole* $z = i\mathsf{K}'$ *is* $-i$.

These residues are the same at all poles congruent to $i\mathsf{K}'$, whereas they have the opposite values at the other poles.

5.15.4 – Fourier expansions

As an application of the results obtained in section 5.15.3 we shall determine Fourier expansions for the Jacobian functions.

The function $\mathrm{sn}\, 2\mathsf{K}z$ is periodic with period 2. It is holomorphic in the region

$$|\mathrm{Im}\, z| < \tfrac{1}{2}\,\mathrm{Im}\,\tau, \qquad (5.15\text{–}13)$$

for its poles are congruent to $z = \frac{1}{2}\tau$, $z = -1+\frac{1}{2}\tau$. According to the remark at the end of section 2.23.2 we may expand $\mathrm{sn}\, 2\mathsf{K}z$ as

$$\mathrm{sn}\, 2\mathsf{K}z = \sum_{\nu=-\infty}^{\infty} A_\nu \exp \nu\pi i z \qquad (5.15\text{–}14)$$

where the coefficients are given by the formula

$$A_n = \tfrac{1}{2}\int_{-1}^{1} \mathrm{sn}\, 2\mathsf{K}x \exp\,(-n\pi i x)dx. \qquad (5.15\text{–}15)$$

To evaluate this integral consider the integral

$$\int_C \operatorname{sn} 2K\zeta \exp(-n\pi i\zeta)d\zeta, \tag{5.15–16}$$

taken around the parallelogram whose vertices are $+1$, -1, τ, $-2+\tau$.

The poles of the integrand inside the contour are at $z = \frac{1}{2}\tau$ and $z = -1+\frac{1}{2}\tau$ with residues

$$\frac{1}{k}\frac{1}{2K}\exp(-\tfrac{1}{2}ni\pi\tau), \quad -\frac{1}{k}\frac{1}{2K}\exp(-\tfrac{1}{2}ni\pi\tau+ni\pi),$$

where the factor $1/2K$ has to be inserted because we are dealing with the function $\operatorname{sn} 2Kz$, instead of $\operatorname{sn} z$. Hence the integral (5.15–16) is equal to

$$\frac{\pi i}{Kk} q^{-\frac{1}{2}n}\{1-(-1)^n\}. \tag{5.15–17}$$

From the periodic properties of $\operatorname{sn} 2Kz$ and $\exp(-ni\pi z)$ we see that the integrals along the left and right side of the parallelogram cancel. Hence (5.15–16) is equal to

$$\int_{-1}^{1} \operatorname{sn} 2K\zeta \exp(-n\pi i\zeta)d\zeta - \int_{-2+\tau}^{\tau} \operatorname{sn} 2K\zeta \exp(-n\pi i\zeta)d\zeta.$$

Writing $\zeta-1+\tau$ for ζ in the second integral, we get

$$\{1+(-1)^n q^{-n}\}\int_{-1}^{1} \operatorname{sn} 2Kx \exp(-n\pi ix)dx = \frac{\pi i}{Kk} q^{-\frac{1}{2}n}\{1-(-1)^n\}.$$

Hence, when n is even, the integral vanishes. But when n is odd, we find, writing $2n+1$ for n,

$$A_{2n+1} = \frac{\pi i}{Kk}\,\frac{q^{-n-\frac{1}{2}}}{1-q^{-(2n+1)}} = -\frac{\pi i}{Kk}\,\frac{q^{n+\frac{1}{2}}}{1-q^{2n+1}}$$

and

$$A_{-(2n+1)} = \frac{\pi i}{Kk}\,\frac{q^{n+\frac{1}{2}}}{1-q^{2n+1}}.$$

Thus we obtain

$$\boxed{\operatorname{sn} 2Kz = \frac{2\pi}{Kk}\sum_{\nu=0}^{\infty}\frac{q^{\nu+\frac{1}{2}}}{1-q^{2\nu+1}}\sin(2\nu+1)\pi z.} \tag{5.15–18}$$

In exactly the same way we may find

$$\boxed{\operatorname{cn} 2Kz = \frac{2\pi}{Kk}\sum_{\nu=0}^{\infty}\frac{q^{\nu+\frac{1}{2}}}{1+q^{2\nu+1}}\cos(2\nu+1)\pi z} \tag{5.15–19}$$

and

$$\boxed{\operatorname{dn} 2\mathsf{K}z = \frac{\pi}{2\mathsf{K}} + \frac{2\pi}{\mathsf{K}} \sum_{\nu=0}^{\infty} \frac{q^\nu}{1+q^{2\nu}} \cos 2\nu\pi z.} \qquad (5.15\text{–}20)$$

The last formula enables us to obtain an expansion of the function am z defined as

$$\boxed{\operatorname{am} z = \int_0^z \operatorname{dn} t\, dt.} \qquad (5.15\text{–}21)$$

This function is holomorphic in the strip $|\operatorname{Im} z/2\mathsf{K}| < \frac{1}{2} \operatorname{Im} \tau$. Hence the function am $2\mathsf{K}z$ is holomorphic in the strip (5.15–13). By performing integration term-by-term, which is legitimate in our case, we obtain

$$\boxed{\operatorname{am} 2\mathsf{K}z = \pi z + \sum_{\nu=1}^{\infty} \frac{2q^\nu}{\nu(1+q^{2\nu})} \sin 2\nu\pi z.} \qquad (5.15\text{–}22)$$

It is possible to define sin am z and cos am z throughout the entire z-plane. In fact, since the residues of dn z at the poles are $\pm i$, the integrals

$$\int_{C_1} \operatorname{dn} t\, \mathrm{dt} \quad \text{and} \quad \int_{C_2} \operatorname{dn} t\, dt,$$

where C_1 and C_2 are two curves connecting 0 and z, differ by a multiple of 2π and hence they give the same value to the functions mentioned above, which coincide with sn z and cn z respectively.

5.16 – Addition theorems

5.16.1 – Addition theorems of the Jacobian functions

The circumstance that the Jacobian functions have the same poles makes it easy to derive addition theorems.

The functions

$$f(z) = \operatorname{sn} z \operatorname{sn}(z+b), \quad g(z) = \operatorname{cn} z \operatorname{cn}(z+b), \quad h(z) = \operatorname{dn} z \operatorname{dn}(z+b) \qquad (5.16\text{–}1)$$

where b is a given number are elliptic functions with periods $2\mathsf{K}$, $2i\mathsf{K}'$ and of order two. Their poles are congruent to $i\mathsf{K}'$ and $-b+i\mathsf{K}'$. Hence the functions

$$g(z)+Af(z), \qquad h(z)+Bf(z)$$

are constants, when we determine A and B in such a fashion that they have no pole at $z = i\mathsf{K}'$. By inserting $z = 0$ we see that these constant values are cn b and dn b respectively. Hence we have the relations

$$\text{cn}\, z\, \text{cn}\,(z+b)+A\, \text{sn}\, z\, \text{sn}\,(z+b) = \text{cn}\, b,$$
$$\text{dn}\, z\, \text{dn}\,(z+b)+B\, \text{sn}\, z\, \text{sn}\,(z+b) = \text{dn}\, b.$$

Differentiating these equations and putting $z = 0$ we easily find $A = \text{dn}\, b$, $B = k^2\, \text{cn}\, b$. Thus

$$\text{cn}\, z\, \text{cn}\,(z+b)+ \text{sn}\, z\, \text{sn}\,(z+b)\, \text{dn}\, b = \text{cn}\, b, \qquad (5.16\text{–}2)$$
$$\text{dn}\, z\, \text{dn}\,(z+b)+k^2\, \text{sn}\, z\, \text{sn}\,(z+b)\, \text{cn}\, b = \text{dn}\, b. \qquad (5.16\text{–}3)$$

Now we take $z = -a$, whereas $a+b$ is written instead of b. Putting also $z = a$ in (5.16–2), we obtain the following ***preliminary addition theorems***:

$$\text{cn}\,(a+b) = \text{cn}\, a\, \text{cn}\, b - \text{sn}\, a\, \text{sn}\, b\, \text{dn}\,(a+b), \qquad (5.16\text{–}4)$$
$$\text{dn}\,(a+b) = \text{dn}\, a\, \text{dn}\, b - k^2\, \text{sn}\, a\, \text{sn}\, b\, \text{cn}\,(a+b), \qquad (5.16\text{–}5)$$
$$\text{cn}\, b = \text{cn}\, a\, \text{cn}\,(a+b) + \text{sn}\, a\, \text{sn}\,(a+b)\, \text{dn}\, b. \qquad (5.16\text{–}6)$$

Solving the equations (5.16–4) and (5.15–5) for cn $(a+b)$, dn $(a+b)$ and inserting the expression thus obtained for cn $(a+b)$ into (5.16–6) we finally have

$$\boxed{\begin{aligned} \text{sn}\,(a+b) &= \frac{\text{sn}\, a\, \text{cn}\, b\, \text{dn}\, b + \text{sn}\, b\, \text{cn}\, a\, \text{dn}\, a}{1-k^2\, \text{sn}^2 a\, \text{sn}^2 b}, \\ \text{cn}\,(a+b) &= \frac{\text{cn}\, a\, \text{cn}\, b - \text{sn}\, a\, \text{sn}\, b\, \text{dn}\, a\, \text{dn}\, b}{1-k^2\, \text{sn}^2 a\, \text{sn}^2 b}, \\ \text{dn}\,(a+b) &= \frac{\text{dn}\, a\, \text{dn}\, b - k^2\, \text{sn}\, a\, \text{sn}\, b\, \text{cn}\, a\, \text{cn}\, b}{1-k^2\, \text{sn}^2 a\, \text{sn}^2 b}. \end{aligned}} \qquad (5.16\text{–}7)$$

5.16.2 – Addition of a half period

Making use of the values (5.15–11) we find on applying the addition theorems

$$\text{sn}\,(z+\mathsf{K}) = \frac{\text{cn}\, z}{\text{dn}\, z}, \quad \text{cn}\,(z+\mathsf{K}) = -k'\frac{\text{sn}\, z}{\text{dn}\, z}, \quad \text{dn}\,(z+\mathsf{K}) = \frac{k'}{\text{dn}\, z}. \qquad (5.16\text{–}8)$$

Further it follows easily from the definition of the Jacobian functions

$$\text{sn}\,(\mathsf{K}+i\mathsf{K}') = \frac{1}{k}, \quad \text{cn}\,(\mathsf{K}+i\mathsf{K}') = -i\frac{k'}{k}, \quad \text{dn}\,(\mathsf{K}+i\mathsf{K}') = 0. \qquad (5.16\text{–}9)$$

Hence

$$\begin{aligned} \text{sn}\,(z+\mathsf{K}+i\mathsf{K}') &= \frac{1}{k}\frac{\text{dn}z}{\text{cn}z}, \quad \text{cn}\,(z+\mathsf{K}+i\mathsf{K}') \\ &= -\frac{ik'}{k}\frac{1}{\text{cn}\, z}, \quad \text{dn}\,(z+\mathsf{K}+i\mathsf{K}') = ik'\frac{\text{sn}\, z}{\text{cn}\, z}. \end{aligned} \qquad (5.16\text{–}10)$$

From (5.16–8) and (5.16–10) we now easily deduce

$$\operatorname{sn}(z+i\mathsf{K}') = \frac{1}{k}\frac{1}{\operatorname{sn} z}, \quad \operatorname{cn}(z+i\mathsf{K}') = \frac{-i}{k}\frac{\operatorname{dn} z}{\operatorname{sn} z}, \quad \operatorname{dn}(z+i\mathsf{K}') = -i\frac{\operatorname{cn} z}{\operatorname{sn} z}. \tag{5.16–11}$$

5.16.3 – Addition theorem for Legendre's integral of the first kind

The first formula (5.16–7) solves a famous problem due to Euler. It is well known that if z is chosen in such a fashion that

$$\int_0^x \frac{dt}{\sqrt{1-t^2}} + \int_0^y \frac{dt}{\sqrt{1-t^2}} = \int_0^z \frac{dt}{\sqrt{1-t^2}}, \tag{5.16–12}$$

then z can be expressed algebraically in terms of x and y:

$$z = x\sqrt{1-y^2}+y\sqrt{1-x^2}, \tag{5.16–13}$$

where x, y and z are assumed to be real. This is actually the addition theorem for the function arcsine.

The proof is simple. In fact, if we write $t = \sin\theta$ we have

$$\int_0^\varphi d\theta + \int_0^\psi d\theta = \int_0^\chi d\theta,$$

or

$$\varphi+\psi = \chi,$$

where

$$x = \sin\varphi, \qquad y = \sin\psi, \qquad z = \sin\chi. \tag{5.16–14}$$

The addition theorem for the sine yields at once the relation (5.6–13).

By a bold generalization Euler solved the analogous problem for Legendre's integrals of the first kind. The result is

If

$$\int_0^x \frac{dt}{\sqrt{(1-t^2)(1-k^2t^2)}} + \int_0^y \frac{dt}{\sqrt{(1-t^2)(1-k^2t^2)}} = \int_0^z \frac{dt}{\sqrt{(1-t^2)(1-k^2t^2)}}, \tag{5.16–15}$$

then

$$z = \frac{x\sqrt{(1-y^2)(1-k^2y^2)}+y\sqrt{(1-x^2)(1-k^2x^2)}}{1-k^2x^2y^2}. \tag{5.16–16}$$

This might be called the addition theorem of Legendre's integral of the first kind.

We assume x, y, z to be real and $0 < k^2 < 1$. Let $t = \sin\theta$. Then, if again

$$x = \sin \varphi, \qquad y = \sin \psi, \qquad z = \sin \chi,$$

the relation (5.6–15) is equivalent to

$$\boxed{F(k, \varphi) + F(k, \psi) = F(k, \chi).} \tag{5.16–17}$$

By putting

$$a = \int_0^x \frac{dt}{\sqrt{(1-t^2)(1-k^2t^2)}} = \int_0^\varphi \frac{d\theta}{\sqrt{1-k^2 \sin^2 \theta}}$$
$$= F(k, \varphi), \quad b = F(k, \psi), \quad c = F(k, \chi)$$

we evidently have

$$a+b = c$$

and

$$x = \operatorname{sn} a, \qquad y = \operatorname{sn} b, \qquad z = \operatorname{sn} c. \tag{5.16–18}$$

The desired formula (5.16–16) now follows at once from the first formula (5.16–7).

Another result is due to Legendre. It is customary to write

$$\Delta\theta = \sqrt{1-k^2 \sin^2 \theta}. \tag{5.16–19}$$

Now (5.16–4) may be written in the form

$$\boxed{\cos \chi = \cos \varphi \cos \psi - \sin \varphi \sin \psi \, \Delta\chi} \tag{5.16–20}$$

and (5.16–5) appears as

$$\boxed{\Delta\chi - \Delta\varphi \, \Delta\psi = -k^2 \sin \varphi \sin \psi \cos \chi.} \tag{5.16–21}$$

These relations hold, provided (5.16–17) is satisfied.

5.16.4 – An elementary approach to the addition theorems

A very simple relation may be obtained when we write (5.16–6) as

$$\cos \psi = \cos \varphi \cos \chi + \sin \varphi \sin \chi \, \Delta\psi$$

and insert the value (5.16–20) for $\cos \chi$. An easy computation leads to

$$\sin \varphi \cos \psi + \cos \varphi \sin \psi \, \Delta\chi = \sin \chi \, \Delta\psi$$

and, interchanging φ and ψ,

$$\sin \psi \cos \varphi + \cos \psi \sin \varphi \, \Delta\chi = \sin \chi \, \Delta\varphi.$$

Hence by adding and subtracting corresponding members

$$\frac{\Delta\varphi + \Delta\psi}{\sin(\varphi+\psi)} = \frac{\Delta\chi + 1}{\sin \chi}, \qquad \frac{\Delta\varphi - \Delta\psi}{\sin(\varphi-\psi)} = \frac{\Delta\chi - 1}{\sin \chi}. \tag{5.16–22}$$

Now we observe that these equations can also be obtained in an elementary way. Assuming χ constant and the variables φ and ψ connected by (5.16–17) we find by differentiation

$$\frac{d\varphi}{\Delta\varphi}+\frac{d\psi}{\Delta\psi}=0. \tag{5.16–23}$$

By a straightforward computation it may be verified that then also

$$d\,\frac{\Delta\varphi+\Delta\psi}{\sin\,(\varphi+\psi)}=0, \qquad d\,\frac{\Delta\varphi-\Delta\psi}{\sin\,(\varphi-\psi)}=0.$$

Hence the functions on the left of the equations (5.16–22) are constant and this constant may be determined by taking $\varphi=\chi$, $\psi=0$.

The equations (5.16–22) are interesting in themselves, for they provide a means to obtain the addition theorems in a purely elementary way, provided we consider only the real functions defined in section 5.14.2. In fact, (5.16–22) is equivalent to

$$\frac{\mathrm{dn}\,\mathrm{a}+\mathrm{dn}\,b}{\mathrm{sn}\,a\,\mathrm{cn}\,b+\mathrm{cn}\,a\,\mathrm{sn}\,b}=\frac{\mathrm{dn}\,(a+b)+1}{\mathrm{sn}\,(a+b)},$$

$$\frac{\mathrm{dn}\,a-\mathrm{dn}\,b}{\mathrm{sn}\,a\,\mathrm{cn}\,b-\mathrm{cn}\,a\,\mathrm{sn}\,b}=\frac{\mathrm{dn}\,(a+b)-1}{\mathrm{sn}\,(a+b)}.$$

We may solve for sn $(a+b)$ and dn $(a+b)$. A rather lengthy computation yields the first and the third formula (5.16–7). The second may be found by observing that

$$\mathrm{cn}^2(a+b)=1-\mathrm{sn}^2\,(a+b).$$

5.16.5 – Geometric interpretation

We conclude our considerations by showing how (5.16–20) and (5.16–21) may be interpreted geometrically.

The study of the elliptic functions, or more correctly the elliptic integrals, arose from the problem of rectifying the arc of an ellips. This is the reason why the functions studied in this chapter are called elliptic, for they are intimately related to the integrals occurring in this problem.

An ellipse with semi-axis a and b may be represented in a system of rectangular co-ordinates by the equation

$$\frac{x^2}{a^2}+\frac{y^2}{b^2}=1 \tag{5.16–24}$$

and parametrically by

$$x=a\sin\theta, \qquad y=b\cos\theta \tag{5.16–25}$$

where θ denotes the angle between the positive y-axis and the line through (x, y) issuing from the origin, (fig. 5.16–1), reckoned positively in the clockwise sense.

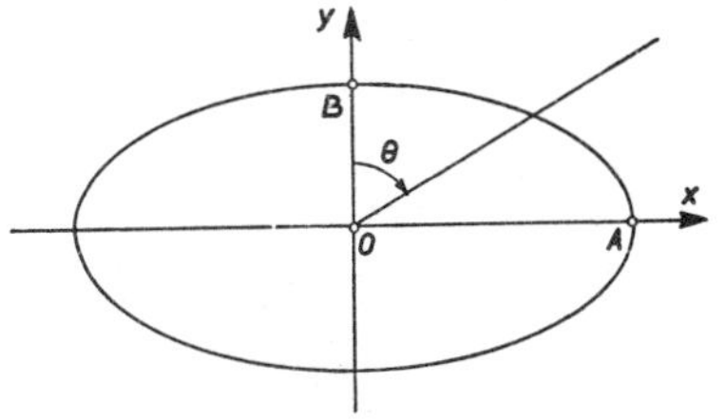

Fig. 5.16–1. The ellipse (5.16–24)

If P corresponds to an angle φ, we find, B denoting the upper vertex of the ellipse:

$$\text{arc } BP = \int_0^{\varphi} \sqrt{a^2 \cos^2\theta + b^2 \sin^2\theta}\, d\theta = a \int_0^{\varphi} \sqrt{1-k^2 \sin^2\theta}\, d\theta,$$

where

$$k = \frac{\sqrt{a^2-b^2}}{a}$$

represents the excentricity of the ellipse. The integral

$$\boxed{E(k, \varphi) = \int_0^{\varphi} \Delta\theta\, d\theta} \qquad (5.16\text{–}26)$$

is *Legendre's elliptic integral of the second kind.* Hence

$$\text{arc } BP = aE(k, \varphi). \qquad (5.16\text{–}27)$$

The quarter of the perimeter of the ellipse is given by

$$a\mathsf{E} = a \int_0^{\frac{1}{2}\pi} \Delta\theta\, d\theta \qquad (5.16\text{–}28)$$

where

$$\mathsf{E} = E(k, \tfrac{1}{2}\pi)$$

is *Legendre's complete elliptic integral of the second kind.*

Now we turn to the relation (5.16–21). Since (5.16–17) may also be written in the form

$$F(k, -\chi)+F(k, \psi) = F(k, -\varphi)$$

we have besides (5.16–21)

$$\Delta\varphi-\Delta\psi\,\Delta\chi = k^2 \sin\psi \cos\varphi \sin\chi, \qquad (5.16\text{–}29)$$

and, interchanging φ and ψ,

$$\Delta\psi - \Delta\varphi\,\Delta\chi = k^2 \sin\varphi \cos\psi \sin\chi. \qquad (5.16\text{–}30)$$

Multiplying the first equation by $d\varphi$ and the second by $d\psi$, we find by adding corresponding members, assuming χ constant, and φ and ψ related by (5.16–17),

$$\Delta\varphi\,d\varphi + \Delta\psi\,d\psi - \Delta\varphi\,\Delta\psi\,\Delta\chi\left(\frac{d\varphi}{\Delta\varphi} + \frac{d\psi}{\Delta\psi}\right) = k^2\,d(\sin\varphi \sin\psi \sin\chi).$$

Taking account of (5.16–23) and integrating we get

$$E(k, \varphi) + E(k, \psi) = C + k^2 \sin\varphi \sin\psi \sin\chi,$$

where C is a constant. This constant may be evaluated by taking $\varphi = \chi$, $\psi = 0$. Hence $C = E(k, \chi)$ and thus

$$\boxed{E(k, \chi) = E(k, \varphi) + E(k, \psi) - k^2 \sin\varphi \sin\psi \sin\chi.} \qquad (5.16\text{–}31)$$

This relation is often called the addition theorem for the integral of the second kind. Geometrically it expresses a statement about arcs of an ellipse. In particular we may take $\chi = \frac{1}{2}\pi$. Then (5.16–20) yields

$$\operatorname{ctn}\varphi \operatorname{ctn}\psi = \Delta(\tfrac{1}{2}\pi) = \sqrt{1-k^2},$$

or

$$\operatorname{ctn}\varphi \operatorname{ctn}\psi = \frac{b}{a}. \qquad (5.16\text{–}32)$$

Under this condition we find from (5.16–20), when P corresponds to φ and Q to ψ and A denotes the right vertex of the ellipse,

$$\text{arc } BP + \text{arc } BQ - \text{arc } BA = ak^2 \sin\varphi \sin\psi. \qquad (5.16\text{–}33)$$

This result is known as *Fagnano's theorem*. It states that the sum of the two arcs BP and BQ minus a quadrant of the ellips can be rectified algebraically in terms of the semi-axes of the ellipse.

Finally we observe that P and Q may coincide in *Fagnano's point* F characterized by

$$\operatorname{ctn}^2\varphi = \frac{b}{a},$$

or

$$\sin^2\varphi = \frac{a}{a+b}.$$

Then (5.16–32) becomes

$$\text{arc } BF - \text{arc } AF = a-b. \qquad (5.16\text{–}34)$$

5.17 – Legendre's elliptic integral of the second kind

5.17.1 – Definition

If we make the substitution $\operatorname{sn} t = \sin \theta$ in Legendre's integral of the second kind (5.16–26) we find that it becomes

$$E(k, \operatorname{am} x) = \int_0^x \operatorname{dn}^2 t \, dt. \tag{5.17–1}$$

It is customary to write $E(k, x)$ in place of $E(k, \operatorname{am} x)$.

The expression on the right of (5.17–1) also has, however, a meaning in the complex domain. We may, therefore, introduce the function

$$\boxed{E(k, z) = \int_0^z \operatorname{dn}^2 t \, dt,} \tag{5.17–2}$$

it being supposed that the path of integration does not pass through any pole of the integrand. When it is unnecessary to exhibit the dependence on the modulus k we shall denote the function more briefly by $E(z)$.

The function $E(z)$ is meromorphic throughout the entire z-plane, its poles being at the poles of $\operatorname{dn} z$, *and the residues are always* $+1$.

To prove this we observe that the meromorphic part of $\operatorname{dn} z$ at a pole a is $\pm i/(z-a)$, as has been proved in section 5.15.3. Hence $\operatorname{dn}^2 z$ is an elliptic function with periods $2\mathsf{K}$, $2i\mathsf{K}'$ and the residues at its poles are zero. As a consequence from Cauchy's residue theorem the integral on the right of (5.17–2) is independent of the path of integration and is evidently regular at every point which is not a pole of the integrand. The meromorphic part of $E(z)$ at any pole $z = a$ is found to be $1/(z-a)$, for the meromorphic part of $\operatorname{dn}^2 z$ is $1/(z-a)^2$. This proves the assertion.

From the definition follows at once:

The function $E(z)$ is an odd function

$$E(-z) = -E(z). \tag{5.17–3}$$

Since the sum of the residues at any set of poles can never be zero the function $E(z)$ is not elliptic.

It should be noticed that the above substitution applied to Legendre's integral of the first kind leads to the trivial result

$$F(k, \operatorname{am} x) = x, \tag{5.17–4}$$

i.e., the function z is the natural extension into the complex domain. The function $\operatorname{am} z$ has already been defined in (5.15–21).

5.17.2 – Legendre's relation

It is convenient to express $\mathrm{dn}^2 t$ in terms of the pe function. Then $E(z)$ may be written as

$$E(z) = \int_0^z \frac{\wp(t/g)-e_2}{\wp(t/g)-e_3}\,dt = \int_0^z \left(1-\frac{e_2-e_3}{\wp(t/g)-e_3}\right) dt,$$

whence, by virtue of (5.5–7),

$$E(z) = \int_0^z \left(1-\frac{\wp(t/g+\omega')-e_3}{e_1-e_3}\right) dt = \frac{1}{g}\int_0^{z/g} \{e_1-\wp(t+\omega')\}dt.$$

Performing the integration we find

$$E(z) = \frac{e_1 z}{g^2}+\frac{1}{g}\left\{\zeta\left(\frac{z}{g}+\omega'\right)-\zeta(\omega')\right\}. \tag{5.17–5}$$

Inserting in this equation $z = \mathsf{K} = g\omega$ and observing that $\zeta(\omega') = \eta'$, $\zeta(\omega+\omega') = \eta+\eta'$ we get

$$\mathsf{E} = \frac{e_1 \mathsf{K}}{g^2}+\frac{\eta}{g}, \tag{5.17–6}$$

where $\mathsf{E} = E(k, \mathsf{K})$. Now we apply Jacobi's imaginary transformation. Introducing the number $\mathsf{E}' = E(k', \mathsf{K}')$, we readily find

$$\mathsf{E}' = \frac{-e_3 \mathsf{K}'}{g^2}+\frac{\eta' i}{g}. \tag{5.17–7}$$

Multiplying both members of the first equation by $\mathsf{K}' = -ig\omega'$ and those of (5.17–7) by $\mathsf{K} = \omega g$, we find by adding, taking account of (5.5–19),

$$\boxed{\mathsf{K}\mathsf{E}'+\mathsf{K}'\mathsf{E} = \mathsf{K}\mathsf{K}'+\tfrac{1}{2}\pi.} \tag{5.17–8}$$

This is the original *relation of Legendre* which historically preceded (5.5–19).

5.17.3 – Quasi-periodicity

From the property (5.5–10) of quasi-periodicity of the zeta function we readily obtain from (5.17–5)

$$E(z+2\mathsf{K}) = E(z)+2\left(\frac{e_1 \mathsf{K}}{g^2}+\frac{\eta}{g}\right),$$

$$E(z+2i\mathsf{K}') = E(z)+2i\left(\frac{e_1 \mathsf{K}'}{g^2}-i\frac{\eta'}{g}\right) = E(z)+2i\left(\frac{e_3 \mathsf{K}'}{g^2}-i\frac{\eta'}{g}\right)+2i\,\mathsf{K}'$$

and so, by virtue of (5.17–6) and (5.17–7),

$$E(z+2\mathsf{K}) = E(z)+2\mathsf{E}, \quad E(z+2i\,\mathsf{K}') = E(z)+2i(\mathsf{K}'-\mathsf{E}'). \tag{5.17–9}$$

5.17.4 – Effect of Jacobi's imaginary transformation

We already made use of Jacobi's imaginary transformation in a special case. To find the effect of this transformation on the function $E(z)$, we write

$$E(k, iz) = \int_0^{iz} \mathrm{dn}^2(t, k)dt = i\int_0^{z} \mathrm{dn}^2(it, k)dt = i\int_0^{z} \frac{\mathrm{dn}^2(t, k')}{\mathrm{cn}^2(t, k')}dt,$$

where we have applied the third formula (5.15–5). Hence

$$E(k, iz)+iE(k', iz) = i\int_0^{z} \left(\frac{\mathrm{dn}^2(t, k')}{\mathrm{cn}^2(t, k')} + \mathrm{dn}^2(t, k')\right) dt. \qquad (5.17\text{–}10)$$

In order to guess the value of the integral on the right we observe that for $k' = 0$ it degenerates into

$$\int_0^{z} (\sec^2 t+1)dt = \tan z + z.$$

On the other hand the integrand has poles at the poles of dn z and at the zeros of cn z. Since, moreover, the integral vanishes at $z = 0$, it is natural to presume

$$\int_0^{z} \left(\frac{\mathrm{dn}^2 t}{\mathrm{cn}^2 t} + \mathrm{dn}^2 t\right)dt = \frac{\mathrm{sn}\, z\, \mathrm{dn}\, z}{\mathrm{cn}\, z} + z. \qquad (5.17\text{–}11)$$

By formal differentiation it is easily verified that this answer is correct. Hence, (5.17–10) leads to the formula

$$E(k, iz) = i\left(\frac{\mathrm{sn}\,(z, k')\,\mathrm{dn}\,(z, k')}{\mathrm{cn}\,(z, k')} + z - E(k', z)\right). \qquad (5.17\text{–}12)$$

5.17.5 – Addition theorem

The addition theorem for the function $E(z)$ may be derived by observing that the function

$$f(z) = E(z)+E(b)-E(z+b)$$

is an elliptic function with periods $2\mathrm{K}$, $2i\mathrm{K}'$. Its poles are congruent to $i\mathrm{K}'$, $-b+i\mathrm{K}'$, and its zeros to $z = 0$, $z = -b$. The function sn z sn $(z+b)$ has, however, exactly the same zeros and poles. By the wellknown arguments we conclude that

$$f(z) = C\, \mathrm{sn}\, z\, \mathrm{sn}\,(z+b),$$

where C is a constant. By differentiation we have

$$\mathrm{dn}^2 z - \mathrm{dn}^2(z+b) = C\{\mathrm{cn}\, z\, \mathrm{dn}\, z\, \mathrm{sn}\,(z+b) + \mathrm{sn}\, z\, \mathrm{cn}\,(z+b)\, \mathrm{dn}\,(z+b)\}$$

whence, by inserting $z = 0$,

$$C = k^2 \operatorname{sn} b.$$

This leads to the formula

$$\boxed{E(a+b) = E(a)+E(b)-k^2 \operatorname{sn} a \operatorname{sn} b \operatorname{sn}(a+b),} \tag{5.17–13}$$

which is evidently the extension of (5.16–30) to the complex domain.

5.17.6 – The Jacobian zeta function

For some purposes it is desirable to have a function which is of the same general character as $E(z)$, but is simply-periodic. Such a function is Jacobi's zeta function $\operatorname{zn} z$ defined by the equation

$$\boxed{\operatorname{zn} z = E(z) - \frac{\mathsf{E}}{\mathsf{K}} z.} \tag{5.17–14}$$

It is easily verified from (5.17–9) and (5.17–8) that

$$\boxed{\operatorname{zn}(z+2\mathsf{K}) = \operatorname{zn} z, \quad \operatorname{zn}(z+2i\mathsf{K}') = \operatorname{zn} z - \frac{\pi i}{\mathsf{K}}.} \tag{5.17–15}$$

On the other hand the function

$$\frac{\vartheta_4'(z)}{\vartheta_4(z)} \tag{5.17–16}$$

possesses the same property of quasi-periodicity as $2\mathsf{K} \operatorname{zn} 2\mathsf{K}z$. Indeed, by differentiating logarithmically the last equation of (5.8–25) we find

$$\frac{\vartheta_4'(z+\tau)}{\vartheta_4(z+\tau)} = \frac{\vartheta_4'(z)}{\vartheta_4(z)} - 2\pi i.$$

Since the zeros of $\vartheta_4(z)$ are simple, the residues at the poles of $\vartheta_4'(z)/\vartheta_4(z)$ are unity. As a consequence the function

$$2\mathsf{K} \operatorname{zn} 2\mathsf{K}z - \frac{\vartheta_4'(z)}{\vartheta_4(z)}$$

is doubly-periodic with no poles, for the zeros of $\vartheta_4(z)$ are just the poles of $\operatorname{zn} 2\mathsf{K}z$. Hence the function is a constant, this constant being zero, for the function vanishes at $z = 0$. In fact $\operatorname{zn} 0 = 0$, $\vartheta_4'(0) = 0$. We thus established the equality

$$\boxed{\operatorname{zn} 2\mathsf{K}z = \frac{1}{2\mathsf{K}} \frac{\vartheta_4'(z)}{\vartheta_4(z)}.} \tag{5.17–17}$$

The expansion (5.11–12) yields at once the Fourier expansion of the Jacobian zeta function

$$\boxed{\operatorname{zn} 2\mathsf{K}z = \frac{2\pi}{\mathsf{K}} \sum_{\nu=1}^{\infty} \frac{q^{\nu}}{1-q^{2\nu}} \sin 2\nu\pi z,} \tag{5.17–18}$$

valid throughout the strip $|\operatorname{Im} z| < \frac{1}{2} \operatorname{Im} \tau$.

Writing Legendre's relation (5.17–8) in the form

$$\frac{\mathsf{E}'}{\mathsf{K}'} + \frac{\mathsf{E}}{\mathsf{K}} = 1 + \frac{\pi}{2\mathsf{K}\mathsf{K}'}$$

we may conclude that the effect of Jacobi's imaginary transformation on his zeta function is expressed by

$$\operatorname{zn}(iz, k) = i\left(\frac{\operatorname{sn}(z, k')\operatorname{dn}(z, k')}{\operatorname{cn}(z, k')} - \frac{\pi z}{2\mathsf{K}\mathsf{K}'} - \operatorname{zn}(z, k')\right). \tag{5.17–19}$$

The addition theorem of $\operatorname{zn} z$ has the same form as that of $E(z)$, viz.

$$\boxed{\operatorname{zn}(a+b) = \operatorname{zn} a + \operatorname{zn} b - k^2 \operatorname{sn} a \operatorname{sn} b \operatorname{sn}(a+b).} \tag{5.17–20}$$

Chapter 6

INTEGRAL FUNCTIONS OF FINITE ORDER

6.1 – The genus of an integral function

6.1.1 – The factorization of an integral function

Weierstrass's factorization theorem considered in section **4.4.1** states that every integral function can be represented as

$$f(z) = z^m P(z) \exp Q(z) \tag{6.1–1}$$

where m is an integer $\geqq 0$, $P(z)$ a canonical product and $Q(z)$ an integral function.

The class of integral functions is very extensive and more precise statements can only be made when we introduce suitable restrictions.

In the first place we shall assume that the canonical product $P(z)$ is of rank k. We recall the definition: k is the smallest non-negative integer for which the series

$$\sum_{\nu=1}^{\infty} r_\nu^{-(k+1)} \tag{6.1–2}$$

is convergent; as usual the numbers $r_1, r_2, \ldots$ denote the moduli of the zeros of the function not coinciding with $z = 0$, arranged in order of non-decreasing values, $0 < r_1 \leqq r_2 \leqq \ldots$.

6.1.2 – Exponent of convergence

When $P(z)$ is of finite rank k, the set of non-negative numbers such that the series

$$\sum_{\nu=1}^{\infty} r_\nu^{-\alpha} \tag{6.1–3}$$

is convergent is not an empty set; it has the property that $\alpha' > \alpha$ belongs to the set whenever α is an element of the set. Moreover, it contains no negative numbers by definition. Hence there must be a greatest lower bound ϱ_c, called the *exponent of convergence* of the zeros. In the case that there is a finite number of zeros the exponent of convergence is zero.

The number ϱ_c plays an important part in the theory of integral functions. An alternative definition is:

The series

$$\sum_{\nu=1}^{\infty} r_\nu^{-(\varrho_c+\varepsilon)} \tag{6.1–4}$$

is always convergent, whereas the series

$$\sum_{\nu=1}^{\infty} r_\nu^{-(\varrho_c-\varepsilon)} \tag{6.1–5}$$

is always divergent, ε *being an arbitrary positive number.*

It is plain that

$$k \leqq \varrho_c \leqq k+1 \tag{6.1–6}$$

k being the rank of the corresponding canonical product. When ϱ_c is not an integer the rank k is uniquely determined as the number $[\varrho_c]$. If ϱ_c is a positive integer then $k = \varrho_c-1$ or $k = \varrho_c$ according as the series

$$\sum_{\nu=1}^{\infty} r_\nu^{-\varrho_c}$$

is convergent or not, while $k = 0$ when $\varrho_c = 0$. In the case that ϱ_c is not an integer this number gives more information than the rank.

6.1.3 – Case of the exponent of convergence being zero

Suppose $\varrho_c = 0$. This means that the series

$$\sum_{\nu=1}^{\infty} r_\nu^{-\varepsilon} \tag{6.1–7}$$

is convergent, irrespective of the value of the positive number ε. Since the terms of the series (6.1–7) are all positive and monotonously decreasing we may conclude that

$$n r_n^{-\varepsilon} \to 0$$

as $n \to \infty$, and this implies the existence of a number n_0 depending only on ε such that

$$n r_n^{-\varepsilon} < 1$$

or

$$r_n > n^{1/\varepsilon}$$

provided that $n > n_0$. An equivalent statement is

$$\frac{\log r_n}{\log n} > A, \tag{6.1–8}$$

A being an arbitrary positive number. Conversely, let (6.1–8) be satisfied for all sufficiently large values of n. Then to a given $\varepsilon > 0$ there is an n_0 such that

$$\frac{\log r_n}{\log n} > 1+\frac{1}{\varepsilon},$$

for all values of $n > n_0$. Hence

$$r_n^{-\varepsilon} < n^{-(1+\varepsilon)}$$

and it follows that the series (6.1–7) is convergent.

Summing up we have:

A necessary and sufficient condition that the exponent of convergence of the zeros of an integral function should be equal to zero is expressed by

$$\lim_{n\to\infty} \frac{\log r_n}{\log n} = \infty. \tag{6.1–9}$$

For instance, if $r_n = r^n$, $r > 1$, then

$$\frac{\log r_n}{\log n} = \frac{n}{\log n} \log r \to \infty, \quad \text{as } n \to \infty.$$

6.1.4 – Case of the exponent of convergence being positive

Next we consider the case $\varrho_c > 0$. The convergent series

$$\sum_{\nu=1}^{\infty} r_\nu^{-(\varrho_c+\tau)}, \qquad \tau > 0,$$

has monotonously decreasing terms and therefore

$$n r_n^{-(\varrho_c+\tau)} \to 0$$

as $n \to \infty$, i.e., there is a number n_0 such that

$$n r_n^{-(\varrho_c+\tau)} < 1$$

or

$$r_n > n^{\frac{1}{\varrho_c+\tau}},$$

provided that $n > n_0$. If ε is a given positive number we may select τ in such a manner that

$$\frac{1}{\varrho_c+\tau} - \left(\frac{1}{\varrho_c} - \varepsilon\right) = \varepsilon - \frac{\tau}{\varrho_c(\varrho_c+\tau)} > 0.$$

As a consequence we have

$$r_n > n^{\frac{1}{\varrho_c}-\varepsilon}$$

or

$$\frac{\log r_n}{\log n} > \frac{1}{\varrho_c} - \varepsilon \tag{6.1–10}$$

for all sufficiently large values of n. Again, the series

$$\sum_{\nu=1}^{\infty} r_\nu^{-(\varrho_c-\tau)}$$

is divergent, whereas the series

$$\sum_{\nu=1}^{\infty} \nu^{-(1+\tau)}$$

is convergent. It follows that there are infinitely many numbers n such that

$$r_n^{-(\varrho_c-\tau)} > n^{-(1+\tau)}$$

or

$$r_n < n^{\frac{1+\tau}{\varrho_c-\tau}}.$$

Given $\varepsilon > 0$ it is possible to select τ in such a manner that

$$\frac{1}{\varrho_c}+\varepsilon-\frac{1+\tau}{\varrho_c-\tau} = \varepsilon-\frac{\tau(\varrho_c+1)}{\varrho_c(\varrho_c-\tau)} > 0.$$

Hence the inequality

$$r_n < n^{\frac{1}{\varrho_c}+\varepsilon}$$

or

$$\frac{\log r_n}{\log n} < \frac{1}{\varrho_c}+\varepsilon \tag{6.1–11}$$

is satisfied for an infinity of numbers n. Combining (6.1–10) and (6.1–11) we conclude:

If the exponent of convergence is positive it is uniquely determined by

$$\boxed{\frac{1}{\varrho_c} = \liminf_{n\to\infty} \frac{\log r_n}{\log n}.} \tag{6.1–12}$$

This formula reduces to (6.1–9) when $\varrho_c = 0$.

6.1.5 – Illustrative example

The following example is instructive. Let

$$r_n = n^{\alpha} \log^{\beta} n, \qquad \alpha > 0, \quad \beta > 0.$$

Then

$$\frac{\log r_n}{\log n} = \alpha + \frac{\beta \log\log n}{\log n} \to \alpha, \quad \text{as } n \to \infty$$

and thus we have

$$\varrho_c = \frac{1}{\alpha}.$$

The series

$$\sum_{\nu=1}^{\infty} r_\nu^{-\varrho_c} = \sum_{\nu=1}^{\infty} \frac{1}{\nu \log^{\beta/\alpha} \nu}$$

is convergent if $\beta > \alpha$, and divergent if $\beta \leqq \alpha$. In fact, for $n > 2$ we have

$$\int_n^{n+1} \frac{dx}{x \log^h x} < \frac{1}{n \log^h n} < \int_{n-1}^{n} \frac{dx}{x \log^h x}, \qquad h > 0,$$

whence

$$\int_3^{n+1} \frac{dx}{x \log^h x} < \sum_{\nu=3}^{n} \frac{1}{\nu \log^h \nu} < \int_2^{n} \frac{dx}{x \log^h x}.$$

But

$$\int \frac{dx}{x \log^h x} = \begin{cases} \log \log x \quad \text{when } h = 1, \quad x > 1, \\ \dfrac{1}{1-h} \log^{1-h} x, \quad \text{when } h \neq 1, \; x > 0, \end{cases}$$

and the truth of the statement follows.

6.1.6 – Genus and exponential degree

The second restriction will be that the function $Q(z)$ occurring in (6.1–1) is a polynomial. Let q be the degree of the polynomial if it does not vanish identically. If this should be the case we put $q = 0$.

Laguerre observed that in many problems the largest of the numbers q and k is decisive. He introduced the number

$$p = \max\,(q, k), \tag{6.1–13}$$

the *genus* of the integral function. It is uniquely determined by the function, for, theoretically, we know the zeros and hence the exponent of convergence. Then the canonical product is uniquely determined and thus also the exponential factor. The number q is called the *exponential degree* of the integral function.

If $P(z)$ is not of finite rank or $Q(z)$ is not a polynomial the function is said to be of *infinite genus*. Only functions of finite genus will concern us in the sequel.

It is an easy matter to give examples of functions with a prescribed genus. Thus, for instance, $\exp z$ is of genus 1, $\exp z^2$ of genus 2, etc. A polynomial

$$c_0 + c_1 z + \ldots + c_n z^n = c_0 \left(1 - \frac{z}{a_1}\right) \ldots \left(1 - \frac{z}{a_n}\right), \quad c_0 \neq 0,$$

is of genus 0. Conversely, the actual determination of the genus of a given integral function is not always easy. The following proposition is trivial.

The genus of a canonical product is equal to its rank.

The representation

$$f(z) = z^m \prod_{\nu=1}^{\infty} E\left(\frac{z}{a_\nu}; k\right) \cdot \exp Q(z) \tag{6.1–14}$$

is not unique if k does not designate the rank of the canonical product. Assume $q > k$. Then

$$\left| \sum_{\nu=1}^{\infty} \left\{ \sum_{\varkappa=k+1}^{q} \frac{1}{\varkappa} \left(\frac{z}{a_\nu}\right)^{\varkappa} \right\} \right| = \left| \sum_{\varkappa=k+1}^{q} \sum_{\nu=1}^{\infty} \frac{1}{\varkappa} \left(\frac{z}{a_\nu}\right)^{\varkappa} \right| \leqq \sum_{\varkappa=k+1}^{q} \frac{|z|^{\varkappa}}{\varkappa} \sum_{\nu=1}^{\infty} \frac{1}{r_\nu^{\varkappa}},$$

and since $\sum_{\nu=1}^{\infty} r_\nu^{-\varkappa}$ is convergent for $\varkappa \geqq k+1$ (k being at least equal to the rank) the infinite product

$$\prod_{\nu=1}^{\infty} \exp \left\{ \sum_{\varkappa=k+1}^{q} \frac{1}{\varkappa} \left(\frac{z}{a_\nu}\right)^{\varkappa} \right\}$$

is unconditionally convergent and (6.1–15) can be written in the form

$$f(z) = z^m P_1(z) \exp Q_1(z) \tag{6.1–15}$$

with

$$P_1(z) = \prod_{\nu=1}^{\infty} E\left(\frac{z}{a_\nu}, q\right)$$

and

$$Q_1(z) = Q(z) - \sum_{\varkappa=k+1}^{q} \frac{z^{\varkappa}}{\varkappa} \sum_{\nu=1}^{\infty} \frac{1}{a_\nu^{\varkappa}}.$$

Hence $Q(z)$ can be replaced by a polynomial of degree not exceeding q. To evaluate the genus we must suppose that $f(z)$ has been written in the form (6.1–15) where k is the rank of the canonical product. We already pointed out that this representation is unique. On the other hand:

Every integral function of genus $\leqq p$ can be put into the form

$$f(z) = z^m \prod_{\nu=1}^{\infty} E\left(\frac{z}{a_\nu}, p\right) \exp Q(z), \tag{6.1–16}$$

where the degree of the polynomial $Q(z)$ does not exceed p.

6.2 – The theorems of Laguerre

6.2.1 – Laguerre's first theorem

The presence of an exponential factor in the decomposition of an integral function of finite genus makes it essentially distinct from a polynomial. Only in the case of genus $p = 0$ it is to be expected that there is some similarity with polynomials. Actually the wellknown theorem stating that if $f(z)$ is a polynomial with all its zeros real then also the derivative $f'(z)$ has the same property, can be extended to integral functions of genus not exceeding unity.

If $f(z)$ is a non-constant integral function of genus 0 or 1, real for real z and with real zeros only, then the zeros of $f'(z)$ are also real and between any two consecutive zeros of $f(z)$ there is precisely one zero of $f'(z)$.

Referring to the last theorem of the previous section we state that *a function of genus 0 or 1 can always be represented as*

$$f(z) = z^m e^{az+b} \prod_{\nu=1}^{\infty} \left(1 - \frac{z}{a_\nu}\right) e^{\frac{z}{a_\nu}}, \tag{6.2–1}$$

m being an integer $\geqq 0$. Since the zeros $a_1, a_2, \ldots$ are real the factor e^{az+b} must be real for all real values of z, and this is only possible if a is real.

Differentiating (6.2–1) logarithmically we obtain

$$\frac{f'(z)}{f(z)} = \frac{m}{z} + a + \sum_{\nu=1}^{\infty} \left(\frac{1}{z-a_\nu} + \frac{1}{a_\nu}\right), \tag{6.2–2}$$

and if $z = x+iy$

$$\operatorname{Im} \frac{f'(z)}{f(z)} = -iy \left(\frac{m}{x^2+y^2} + \sum_{\nu=1}^{\infty} \frac{1}{(x-a_\nu)^2+y^2}\right). \tag{6.2–3}$$

The expression on the right is zero for $y = 0$ only. Hence $f'(z)$ cannot be zero except on the real axis.

Again the function

$$\frac{d}{dz}\left(\frac{f'(z)}{f(z)}\right) = -\frac{m}{z^2} - \sum_{\nu=1}^{\infty} \frac{1}{(z-a_\nu)^2} \tag{6.2–4}$$

is real and negative for real values of z. Hence $f'(z)/f(z)$ decreases steadily from $+\infty$ to $-\infty$ as z increases through real values between two consecutive zeros of $f(z)$ and so it vanishes just once between these zeros.

6.2.2 – Laguerre's second theorem

The previous theorem ceases to be true for functions of genus $p \geqq 2$. Thus, for instance, the function

$$f(z) = (z+1) \exp z^2$$

is of genus 2 and has only one real zero, whereas the function

$$f'(z) = (2z^2+2z+1) \exp z^2$$

has two complex zeros. The situation is clarified by the following theorem.

If $f(z)$ is a non-constant integral function of genus p, real for real z, all the zeros of which are real, then the function $f'(z)$ has at most p non-real zeros.

This theorem throws light on the fact that the derivative of a function which is real for real z and is of genus 0 or 1 cannot have non-real zeros, for complex zeros always occur in pairs. Hence there cannot be such zeros when $p \leqq 1$.

Let

$$f(z) = z^m P(z) \exp Q(z), \tag{6.2–5}$$

$Q(z)$ being a polynomial of degree not exceeding p, and

$$P(z) = \prod_{\nu=1}^{\infty} \left(1 - \frac{z}{a_\nu}\right) \exp\left\{\frac{z}{a_\nu} + \frac{1}{2}\left(\frac{z}{a_\nu}\right)^2 + \ldots + \frac{1}{p}\left(\frac{z}{a_\nu}\right)^p\right\}.$$

It is evident that

$$f(z) = \lim_{n\to\infty} f_n(z) = \lim_{n\to\infty} z^m P_n(z) \exp Q_n(z)$$

with

$$f_n(z) = z^m P_n(z) \exp Q_n(z)$$

and

$$P_n(z) = \prod_{\nu=1}^{n} \left(1 - \frac{z}{a_\nu}\right), \quad Q_n(z) = Q(z) + \sum_{\nu=1}^{n} \left\{\frac{z}{a_\nu} + \frac{1}{2}\left(\frac{z}{a_\nu}\right)^2 + \ldots + \frac{1}{p}\left(\frac{z}{a_\nu}\right)^p\right\}.$$

We observe that the sequence

$$f_1(z), f_2(z), \ldots$$

tends uniformly to $f(z)$ in any bounded set of the z-plane. Hence, in accordance with the theorems of section 2.20.1 we also have

$$f'(z) = \lim_{n\to\infty} f_n'(z).$$

The polynomial $P_n(z)$ has the zeros $a_1, \ldots, a_n$. Hence the equation

$$f_n'(z) = 0$$

possesses at least $m+n-1$ real roots (multiple roots being repeated) by Rolle's theorem. Now

$$f_n'(z) = \{mz^{m-1} P_n(z) + z^m Q_n'(z) P_n(z) + z^m P_n'(z)\} \exp Q_n(z).$$

The degree of the polynomial between brackets on the right is $m+n+p-1$ at most and since there are already at least $m+n-1$ real zeros, there cannot be more than p complex zeros. By Hurwitz's theorem of section 3.11.1 the zeros of $f'(z)$ are the finite limits of the zeros of $f_n'(z)$ and the theorem is proved.

6.3 – Poincaré's theorems

6.3.1 – Poincaré's first theorem

The important results obtained by the French school concerning the rate of increase of integral functions in relation to the genus and the coefficients of the Cauchy-Taylor expansion originate from theorems due to Poincaré.

The *first theorem of Poincaré* states:

If $f(z)$ is an integral function of genus p and if α is an arbitrary positive number then

$$|f(z)| < e^{\alpha r^{p+1}} \tag{6.3–1}$$

for all sufficiently large values of $r = |z|$.

The theorem states roughly that an integral function of finite genus cannot increase arbitrarily rapidly.

Let

$$f(z) = z^m \prod_{\nu=1}^{\infty} E\left(\frac{z}{a_\nu}, p\right) \exp Q(z),$$

where $Q(z)$ either vanishes identically or is a polynomial of degree not exceeding p. We choose a number β such that $0 < \beta < \alpha$.

First we observe that we can find a positive constant A such that

$$\log |E(z; p)| < Ar^{p+1} \tag{6.3–2}$$

for all values of z. In fact, when $|z| < \frac{1}{2}$ we have by virtue of (4.3–8)

$$\log |E(z; p)| = \operatorname{Re} \log E(z; p) \leqq |\log E(z, p)| \leqq 2r^{p+1}.$$

On the other hand it is easy to see that

$$\exp Br^{-(p+1)}E(z; p),$$

where B denotes an arbitrary positive number, tends to zero as $z \to \infty$. This means that there is a number R such that

$$\log |E(z; p)| < Br^{p+1},$$

provided that $r > R$. Let, finally, M denote the maximum of the modulus of the function $E(z; p)$ in the closed domain $\frac{1}{2} \leqq |z| \leqq R$. It is possible to choose the constant C in such a way that

$$\log M < C(\tfrac{1}{2})^{p+1} \leqq Cr^{p+1}.$$

It follows that (6.3–2) is valid for a constant A that exceeds the numbers 2, B and C.

Since the series $\sum_{\nu=1}^{\infty} r_\nu^{-(p+1)}$ is convergent we can find a positive integer N such that

$$\sum_{\nu=N+1}^{\infty} r_\nu^{-(p+1)} < \frac{\alpha-\beta}{A}.$$

Hence

$$\sum_{\nu=N+1}^{\infty} \log \left| E\left(\frac{z}{a_\nu}; p\right) \right| < A \sum_{\nu=N+1}^{\infty} \left(\frac{r}{r_\nu}\right)^{p+1} < (\alpha-\beta)r^{p+1}. \quad (6.3\text{–}3)$$

Since (6.3–2) is valid for an arbitrarily small number A whenever r is sufficiently large, we may infer that

$$\sum_{\nu=1}^{N} \log \left| E\left(\frac{z}{a_\nu}; p\right) \right| < \tfrac{1}{2}\beta r^{p+1},$$

whenever r is large enough. But also

$$m \log |z| + |\varphi(z)| < \tfrac{1}{2}\beta r^{p+1}$$

for all sufficiently large values of r, for $\varphi(z)$ is either identically zero or a polynomial of degree not exceeding p. As a consequence we have that for all sufficiently large values of r the expression

$$\log \left| z^m \prod_{\nu=1}^{N} E\left(\frac{z}{a_\nu}; p\right) \exp Q(z) \right|$$

is less than βr^{p+1}, and this result combines with (6.3–3) to

$$\log |f(z)| < \alpha r^{p+1}$$

for all sufficiently large values of r. This completes the proof.

Let $M(r)$ denote, as usual, the maximum modulus of $|f(z)|$ for $|z| = r$. Then for all sufficiently large values of r

$$M(r) < e^{\alpha r^{p+1}}. \quad (6.3\text{–}4)$$

This may be expressed by saying that *the order of infinity of* $M(r)$ *is less than the order of infinity of the function* $\exp \alpha z^{p+1}$, α *being any positive number.*

6.3.2 – POINCARÉ'S SECOND THEOREM

We now may ask what can be concluded from the previous result when we take into consideration the coefficients of the Taylor expansion of $f(z)$. The answer is included in the *second theorem of Poincaré*:

If

$$f(z) = c_0 + c_1 z + c_2 z^2 + \dots \quad (6.3\text{–}5)$$

is an integral function of genus p, *then*

$$\lim_{n\to\infty} (n!)^{\frac{1}{p+1}} c_n = 0. \quad (6.3\text{–}6)$$

By Cauchy's inequality (2.18–2) we have

$$|c_n| \leqq \frac{M(r)}{r^n}.$$

Hence, if α is a positive number,

$$|c_n| < \frac{e^{\alpha r^{p+1}}}{r^n}$$

for all sufficiently large values of r. We take

$$r = n^{\frac{1}{p+1}} \beta,$$

β being a suitably chosen constant. Then for all sufficiently large values of n we have

$$(n^n)^{\frac{1}{p+1}} |c_n| < \frac{e^{\alpha n \beta^{p+1}}}{\beta^n} = \left(\frac{e^{\alpha \beta^{p+1}}}{\beta}\right)^n.$$

We are still free in the choice of α and β. We shall take $\beta > e$ and α such that $\alpha \beta^{p+1} = 1$. Then

$$(n^n)^{\frac{1}{p+1}} |c_n| < \left(\frac{e}{\beta}\right)^n < \varepsilon$$

for all sufficiently large values of n, ε being a given positive number, and *a fortiori*

$$(n!)^{\frac{1}{p+1}} |c_n| < \varepsilon.$$

This concludes the proof of the assertion.

In particular, when $f(z)$ is a function of genus 0 we have from a certain value of n upwards

$$|c_n| < \frac{1}{n!}.$$

6.4 – The order of an integral function

6.4.1 – Definition

Let us take $\alpha = 1$ in the Poincaré's first theorem of the previous section. Then $M(r)$ satisfies the inequality

$$M(r) < e^{r^{p+1}}$$

for all sufficiently large values of r. This fact leads to the concept of order.

An integral function is said to be of *finite order* if there exists a positive constant A such that

$$M(r) < e^{r^A} \tag{6.4–1}$$

or

$$|f(z)| < e^{r^A}, \qquad |z| = r, \tag{6.4–2}$$

uniformly for all sufficiently large values of r. On account of the maximum modulus principle of section 2.13.2 the second inequality holds also for $|z| \leqq r$.

If there exists no such constant A the function is said to be of *infinite order*. In this section only functions of finite order will concern us.

An equivalent statement of the definition of finite order is the following:

An integral function $f(z)$ is of finite order if there exists a constant A such that

$$|f(z)| = O(e^{r^A}). \qquad (6.4\text{–}3)$$

The meaning is that there exists a constant B such that

$$|f(z)| < Be^{r^A}$$

for all sufficiently large values of r. Hence also

$$|f(z)| < e^{r^{A_1}}, \qquad A_1 > A.$$

If the set of numbers A for which (6.4–1) is satisfied is not an empty set then every $A_1 > A$ belongs to the set whenever A is an element of the set. On the other hand, if we exclude the trivial case of $f(z)$ being a constant, negative numbers A do not belong to the set on account of Liouville's theorem of section 2.12.1. Hence the set admits a non-negative greatest lower bound. This number ϱ is called the *order* of the function. We put $\varrho = \infty$ when $f(z)$ is of infinite order.

6.4.2 – Evaluation of the order

It is plain that *the order of a function $f(z)$ of finite genus p does not exceed $p+1$.*

Let ϱ be the (finite) order of an integral function $f(z)$. Then, according to the definition

$$M(r) < e^{r^{\varrho+\varepsilon}} \qquad (6.4\text{–}4)$$

for all sufficiently large values of r, ε being an arbitrary positive number. On the other hand we can find arbitrarily large values of r such that

$$M(r) > e^{r^{\varrho-\varepsilon}}. \qquad (6.4\text{–}5)$$

The two inequalities (6.4–4) and (6.4–5) combine into the statement:

The order ϱ of an integral function is uniquely characterized by

$$\boxed{\varrho = \limsup_{r\to\infty} \frac{\log\log M(r)}{\log r}.} \tag{6.4–6}$$

6.4.3 – Illustrative examples

We wish to illustrate the notion of order in a few examples. Let

$$f(z) = \exp e^z.$$

Then

$$|\exp e^z| = \exp \operatorname{Re} e^z = \exp (e^r \cos \theta) \leqq \exp e^r, \text{ when } z = re^{i\theta}.$$

Hence

$$M(r) = \exp e^r$$

and

$$\frac{\log\log M(r)}{\log r} = \frac{r}{\log r} \to \infty, \quad \text{as } r \to \infty.$$

The function $\exp e^z$ is of infinite order.

On the other hand the function $\exp z$ is of order 1. In fact,

$$|\exp z| = \exp \operatorname{Re} z = \exp (r \cos \theta) \leqq e^r$$

means that

$$M(r) = e^r,$$

while

$$\frac{\log\log M(r)}{\log r} = \frac{\log r}{\log r} = 1.$$

A polynomial

$$f(z) = c_0 + c_1 z + \ldots + c_n z^n$$

is of zero order. In fact,

$$|f(z)| \leqq \left(\frac{|c_0|}{r^n} + \ldots + |c_n|\right) r^n < A r^n$$

for all sufficiently large values of r and

$$\frac{\log\log M(r)}{\log r} \leqq \frac{\log\log A + \log n + \log\log r}{\log r} \to 0$$

as $r \to \infty$.

An important result is expressed by the theorem:

The function

$$\exp Q(z), \tag{6.4–7}$$

where $Q(z)$ is a polynomial of degree q, is of order q.

Let

$$Q(z) = b_0 + b_1 z + \ldots + b_q z^q.$$

By putting $z = re^{i\theta}$ we have

$$\operatorname{Re} Q(z) = \beta_0+\beta_1(\theta)r+\ldots+\beta_q(\theta)r^q$$

where

$$\beta_k(\theta) = \operatorname{Re} b_k e^{ik\theta}, \quad k = 0, \ldots, q.$$

If β denotes the maximum of all $\beta_k(\theta)$ for $-\pi \leqq \theta \leqq \pi$ then

$$\operatorname{Re} Q(z) \leqq \beta(1+B)r^q < r^{q+\varepsilon}$$

for all sufficiently large values of r, $B \geqq 1/r+1/r^2+\ldots+1/r^q$ denoting a constant independent of r, and being less than 1. Also

$$\operatorname{Re} Q(z) \geqq \beta(1-B)r^q > r^{q-\varepsilon}$$

for an infinite set of arbitrarily large values of r. Since $|\exp Q(z)| = \exp \operatorname{Re} Q(z)$ the assertion follows.

Of course the order is not necessarily an integral number. Thus, for instance, the function

$$f(z) = \cosh \sqrt{z} = \tfrac{1}{2}(e^{\sqrt{z}}+e^{-\sqrt{z}}) = \sum_{\nu=1}^{\infty} \frac{z^\nu}{(2\nu)!}$$

is an integral function of order $\frac{1}{2}$. In fact,

$$|f(z)| < \tfrac{1}{2}(e^{\sqrt{r}}+e^{\sqrt{r}}) = e^{\sqrt{r}} < e^{r^{\frac{1}{2}+\varepsilon}}$$

for all sufficiently large values of r. And for $z = r > 0$ we also have

$$|f(z)| = \tfrac{1}{2}(e^{\sqrt{r}}+e^{-\sqrt{r}}) > e^{r^{\frac{1}{2}-\varepsilon}},$$

i.e., $M(r) > e^{r^{\frac{1}{2}-\varepsilon}}$ for infinitely many arbitrarily large values of r.

6.4.4 – Order of a sum

The sum

$$f(z) = f_1(z)+f_2(z)$$

of two integral functions $f_1(z)$ and $f_2(z)$ of order ϱ_1, ϱ_2 respectively is of order $\varrho = \max(\varrho_1, \varrho_2)$ at most and exactly of order ϱ if $\varrho_1 \neq \varrho_2$.

Let $M_1(r)$, $M_2(r)$ denote the maximum moduli of $f_1(z)$, $f_2(z)$ respectively for $|z| = r$. Then

$$M(r) \leqq M_1(r)+M_2(r) < e^{r^{\varrho_1+\frac{1}{2}\varepsilon}}+e^{r^{\varrho_2+\frac{1}{2}\varepsilon}} \leqq 2e^{r^{\varrho+\frac{1}{2}\varepsilon}} < e^{r^{\varrho+\varepsilon}}$$

for all sufficiently large values of r. Hence the order of $f(z)$ does not exceed ϱ.

Assume now $\varrho_1 > \varrho_2$ and take ε such that $\varrho_1-\varepsilon > \varrho_2$. Then there is a set of arbitrarily large values of r such that

$$M(r) \geqq M_1(r)-M_2(r) > e^{r^{\varrho_1-\frac{1}{2}\varepsilon}}-e^{r^{\varrho_2+\frac{1}{2}\varepsilon}}$$
$$= e^{r^{\varrho_1-\frac{1}{2}\varepsilon}}(1-e^{r^{\varrho_2+\frac{1}{2}\varepsilon}-r^{\varrho_1-\frac{1}{2}\varepsilon}}) > \tfrac{1}{2}e^{r^{\varrho_1-\frac{1}{2}\varepsilon}} > e^{r^{\varrho_1-\varepsilon}}.$$

As a corollary of this theorem *the addition of a function of lower order does not affect the order of a given function.*

6.4.5 – ORDER OF A PRODUCT

The product

$$f(z) = f_1(z) f_2(z)$$

of two integral functions $f_1(z)$ *and* $f_2(z)$ *of orders* ϱ_1, ϱ_2 *respectively is of order* $\varrho = \max(\varrho_1, \varrho_2)$ *at most.*

In fact,

$$M(r) \leqq M_1(r) M_2(r) < e^{r^{\varrho_1+\frac{1}{2}\varepsilon}+r^{\varrho_2+\frac{1}{2}\varepsilon}} \leqq e^{2r^{\varrho+\frac{1}{2}\varepsilon}} < e^{r^{\varrho+\varepsilon}}$$

for all sufficiently large values of r.

The reader might expect that the order is exactly ϱ if $\varrho_1 \neq \varrho_2$. This statement is true, but the proof is not quite so simple as in the previous case. The difficulty arises from the fact that it is not easy to set a lower bound for $M(r)$ in the product case. The proof will be completed in section 6.9.4.

6.4.6 – ORDER OF THE DERIVATIVE

The derived function $f'(z)$ *is of the same order as* $f(z)$.

Since $f(z)$ and $f(z) - f(0)$ have the same order we may assume $f(0) = 0$. Let $M_1(r)$ be the maximum modulus of $f'(z)$ on $|z| = r$. Integrating along a straight path from 0 to z we have

$$f(z) = \int_0^z f'(\zeta) d\zeta$$

hence

$$M(r) \leqq r M_1(r). \tag{6.4–8}$$

Let C denote a circle around the point z with radius $R - r > 0$. Then by virtue of (2.9–9)

$$f'(z) = \frac{1}{2\pi i} \int_C \frac{f(\zeta)}{(\zeta - z)^2} d\zeta,$$

and it follows, if we take for z such a value that $f'(z) = M_1(r)$,

$$M_1(r) \leqq \frac{M(R)}{R - r}. \tag{6.4–9}$$

Taking $R = 2r$ we finally have

$$M(r) \leqq r M_1(r) \leqq M(2r). \tag{6.4–10}$$

For all sufficiently large values of r we have

$$\log M_1(r) \leqq \log r + \log M_1(r) \leqq \log M(2r) < (2r)^{\varrho+\frac{1}{2}\varepsilon} < r^{\varrho+\varepsilon}$$

and for infinitely many arbitrarily large values of r

$$\log M_1(r) \geqq \log M(r) - \log r > r^{\varrho-\frac{1}{2}\varepsilon} - \log r > r^{\varrho-\varepsilon}.$$

An alternative proof of this theorem will be given in section 6.6.4.

6.5 – Integral functions with a finite number of zeros

6.5.1 – Order of a function with a finite number of zeros

Let $f(z)$ be an integral function of order ϱ having only a finite number of zeros. We may represent such a function by

$$f(z) = p(z) \exp Q(z) \tag{6.5–1}$$

where $p(z)$ is a polynomial and $Q(z)$ an integral function. In the first place we wish to prove that $Q(z)$ is also a polynomial. Now

$$\exp Q(z) = \frac{f(z)}{c_n(z-a_1) \ldots (z-a_n)},$$

$a_1, \ldots, a_n$ denoting the zeros of $p(z)$. For all sufficiently large values of r we have

$$\max_{|z|=r} |\exp Q(z)| < \frac{e^{r^{\varrho+\varepsilon}}}{1} = e^{r^{\varrho+\varepsilon}}.$$

Hence the order of $\exp Q(z)$ does not exceed ϱ. It cannot be less than ϱ for on account of the theorem of section **6.4.5** the order of $f(z)$ would be less than ϱ.

Let $A(r)$ denote the maximum of the real part of $Q(z)$ on $|z| = r$, i.e.,

$$\max_{|z|=r} |\exp Q(z)| = e^{A(r)}.$$

But since $\exp Q(z)$ is of order ϱ we have

$$A(r) < r^{\varrho+\varepsilon}$$

for all sufficiently large values of r. It follows from the theorem of section **2.19.2** that $Q(z)$ is a polynomial of degree not exceeding ϱ, since ε may be chosen as small as we please. In section **6.4.3** we proved that the order of $\exp Q(z)$ is equal to the degree of $Q(z)$. Hence the degree of $Q(z)$ is exactly ϱ and ϱ is an integer. The result may be stated as follows:

If $f(z)$ is an integral function of order ϱ with only a finite number of zeros, then ϱ is an integer and

$$f(z) = p(z) \exp Q(z), \tag{6.5–2}$$

$p(z)$ and $Q(z)$ being polynomials, the latter of degree ϱ.

6.5.2 – Existence of infinitely many zeros

An immediate consequence of the previous theorem is:

An integral function whose order is not an integer possesses infinitely many zeros.

When the order is an integer it is not always easy to decide whether there are infinitely many zeros. But in some cases the problem can be reduced to the previous theorem.

Consider, for instance, the function $\cos z$. It is a function of order 1. But the function is even and, therefore, also $\cos \sqrt{z}$ is an integral function, the latter being of order $\frac{1}{2}$. This leads to the conclusion that $\cos z$ has infinitely many zeros. Reasoning along the same lines we also see that the function $\sin z$ has an infinity of zeros, since $z \sin z$ is even and of order 1.

6.5.3 – Illustrative example

In other cases special devices can facilitate the solution. We wish to prove that the equation

$$e^{\lambda z} = p(z), \qquad \lambda > 0,$$

$p(z)$ being a polynomial that does not vanish identically, has an infinity of roots. If not, we should have

$$e^{\lambda z} - p(z) = f(z) e^{az},$$

$f(z)$ being a polynomial. Differentiating logarithmically we obtain

$$\frac{\lambda e^{\lambda z} - p'}{e^{\lambda z} - p} = \frac{f'}{f} + a,$$

and $e^{\lambda z}$ would be a rational function.

6.6 – The order of a function related to the coefficients of its Taylor expansion

6.6.1 – A necessary condition for the function to be of finite order

Let

$$f(z) = \sum_{\nu=0}^{\infty} c_\nu z^\nu \tag{6.6–1}$$

be an integral function of finite order ϱ. If $\lambda > \varrho$ the inequality

$$M(r) < e^{r^\lambda}$$

is satisfied for all sufficiently large values of r. Hence, by Cauchy's inequality (2.18–1)

$$|c_n| < e^{r^\lambda} r^{-n} = \varphi(r),$$

say. The derivative of the right-hand side with respect to r is

$$\varphi'(r) = e^{r^\lambda} r^{-(n+1)} (\lambda r^\lambda - n)$$

and for

$$r^\lambda = \frac{n}{\lambda} \tag{6.6–2}$$

this function attains a minimum, since the derivative is negative for smaller values of r and positive for greater values of r than that determined by (6.6–2). And so for sufficiently large n

$$|c_n| < \left(\frac{e\lambda}{n}\right)^{\frac{n}{\lambda}}$$

or

$$\frac{\log(1/|c_n|)}{n \log n} > \frac{1}{\lambda} - \frac{\log(e\lambda)}{\lambda \log n}.$$

It follows that

$$\mu = \liminf_{n\to\infty} \frac{\log(1/|c_n|)}{n \log n} > 0 \tag{6.6–3}$$

is a necessary condition for $f(z)$ to be an integral function of finite order.

By the Cauchy-Hadamard test (1.6–5) we have

$$\lim_{n\to\infty} \sqrt[n]{|c_n|} = 0$$

when (6.6–1) represents an integral function. Hence, given a number ε between 0 and 1, we find that

$$\frac{1}{|c_n|} > \left(\frac{1}{\varepsilon}\right)^n > 1$$

for all sufficiently large n. Hence μ cannot be negative. This and the previous result combine into the statement:

The integral function $f(z)$ is of infinite order when $\mu = 0$. Conversely, $\mu = 0$ does not imply that $f(z)$ is an integral function. A counter-example will be given in section 6.6.3.

6.6.2 – Evaluation of the order from the Taylor expansion

We now inquire what can be concluded about a function given by its Taylor expansion (6.6–1) when μ is finite and positive. Given $\varepsilon > 0$ and $\varepsilon < \mu$ we can find an integer n_0 such that

$$\frac{\log(1/|c_n|)}{n \log n} > \mu - \varepsilon,$$

i.e.,

$$\sqrt[n]{|c_n|} < \frac{1}{n^{\mu-\varepsilon}} \tag{6.6–4}$$

provided that $n > n_0$. It follows that $f(z)$ *is an integral function.*

Suppose $|z| = r > 1$. By virtue of (6.6–4) we have

$$|f(z)| < Ar^{n_0} + \sum_{\nu=n_0+1}^{\infty} \left(\frac{r}{\nu^{\mu-\varepsilon}}\right)^{\nu}, \tag{6.6–5}$$

where A is a constant. Now we choose an integer N such that

$$N^{\mu-\varepsilon} \leqq 2r < (N+1)^{\mu-\varepsilon},$$

i.e.,

$$N = [(2r)^{\frac{1}{\mu-\varepsilon}}].$$

When r is sufficiently large then $N > n_0$.

Now

$$\sum_{\nu=n_0+1}^{\infty} \left(\frac{r}{\nu^{\mu-\varepsilon}}\right)^{\nu} < \sum_{\nu=n_0+1}^{N} \left(\frac{r}{\nu^{r-\varepsilon}}\right)^{\nu} + \sum_{\nu=N+1}^{\infty} \left(\frac{r}{\nu^{\mu-\varepsilon}}\right)^{\nu}.$$

The last sum on the right-hand side can easily be estimated. In fact,

$$\sum_{\nu=N+1}^{\infty} \left(\frac{r}{\nu^{\mu-\varepsilon}}\right)^{\nu} < \sum_{\nu=N+1}^{\infty} \left(\frac{r}{(N+1)^{\mu-\varepsilon}}\right)^{\nu} < \sum_{\nu=N+1}^{\infty} (\tfrac{1}{2})^{\nu} < 1. \tag{6.6–6}$$

For the first sum on the right-hand side we obtain

$$\sum_{\nu=n_0+1}^{N} \left(\frac{r}{\nu^{\mu-\varepsilon}}\right)^{\nu} = \sum_{\nu=n_0+1}^{N} e^{\nu \log r} \left(\frac{1}{\nu^{\mu-\varepsilon}}\right)^{\nu} \leqq e^{(2r)^{\frac{1}{\mu-\varepsilon}} \log r} \sum_{\nu=n_0+1}^{N} \left(\frac{1}{\nu^{\mu-\varepsilon}}\right)^{\nu},$$

or

$$\sum_{\nu=n_0+1}^{N} \left(\frac{r}{\nu^{\mu-\varepsilon}}\right)^{\nu} < Be^{(2r)^{\frac{1}{\mu-\varepsilon}} \log r}, \tag{6.6–7}$$

B being a constant independent of r. Combining the estimates (6.6–6) and (6.6–7) we find that

$$|f(z)| < e^{2(2r)^{\frac{1}{\mu-\varepsilon}} \log r}$$

for all sufficiently large values of r. It follows that

$$\limsup_{r\to\infty} \frac{\log \log M(r)}{\log r} \leqq \lim_{r\to\infty} \frac{\log 2 + \dfrac{1}{\mu-\varepsilon} \log 2r + \log \log r}{\log r} = \frac{1}{\mu-\varepsilon}.$$

Hence, taking account of (6.4–6)

$$\varrho \leqq \frac{1}{\mu}, \tag{6.6–8}$$

since ε can be chosen as small as we please.

On account of (6.6–2) we have $\mu \geqq 1/\lambda$, where λ is an arbitrary number $> \varrho$. Hence also $\mu \geqq 1/\varrho$ or

$$\varrho \geqq \frac{1}{\mu}. \tag{6.6–9}$$

Combining (6.6–8) and (6.6–9) we find

$$\varrho = \frac{1}{\mu}. \tag{6.6–10}$$

When $\mu = \infty$ we may repeat the first part of the proof by taking λ instead of $\mu - \varepsilon$, λ denoting any positive number. We then find $\varrho \leqq 1/\lambda$, i.e., $\varrho = 0$.

Our considerations lead to the following theorem.

A necessary and sufficient condition that a function

$$f(z) = \sum_{\nu=0}^{\infty} c_\nu z^\nu$$

should be an integral function of finite order ϱ *is expressed by*

$$\boxed{\frac{1}{\varrho} = \liminf_{n\to\infty} \frac{\log (1/|c_n|)}{n \log n}.} \tag{6.6–11}$$

6.6.3 – Illustrative examples

By applying the previous test it is at once evident that the function

$$f(z) = \sum_{\nu=1}^{\infty} \frac{z^\nu}{\nu^{\alpha\nu}}, \qquad \alpha > 0,$$

is an integral function of order $1/\alpha$. This example illustrates the fact that $\mu = 0$ (i.e., $\alpha = 0$) does not imply that the function is actually an integral function.

The function

$$f(z) = \sum_{\nu=0}^{\infty} \frac{z^\nu}{(\nu!)^\alpha}, \qquad \alpha > 0,$$

is an integral function of order $1/\alpha$. In fact, by Stirling's theorem of section 4.7.4

$$\frac{\log (1/|c_n|)}{n \log n} = \frac{\alpha \log n!}{n \log n} = \alpha \frac{(n+\frac{1}{2}) \log n - n + \log \sqrt{2\pi} + \mu(n)}{n \log n} \to \alpha$$

as $n \to \infty$.

Similarly, if m is an integer > 0, the function

$$f(z) = \sum_{\nu=0}^{\infty} (-1)^\nu \frac{z^\nu}{(m\nu)!}$$

is of order $1/m$. This function reduces to $\cos \sqrt{z}$ when $m = 2$.

6.6.4 – Alternative proof of theorem 6.4.6

The theorem of section 6.6.2 yields an alternative proof for the theorem of section 6.4.6 which asserts that the derivative of an integral function of finite order ϱ is also of order ϱ.

In fact,

$$f'(z) = \sum_{\nu=0}^{\infty} \nu c_\nu z^{\nu-1}$$

and

$$\liminf_{n\to\infty} \frac{\log (1/(n+1)|c_{n+1}|)}{n \log n} = \frac{1}{\varrho}$$

since

$$\frac{\log (1/(n+1)|c_{n+1}|)}{n \log n}$$

$$= -\frac{\log (n+1)}{n \log n} + \frac{\log (1/|c_{n+1}|)}{(n+1) \log (n+1)} \cdot \frac{(n+1) \log (n+1)}{n \log n},$$

and the result follows.

6.7 – Hadamard's first theorem

6.7.1 – Estimate of the number of zeros

The function $n(r)$, where $n(r)$ denotes the number of zeros of $f(z)$ with modulus not exceeding r, is a non-decreasing function of r and constant in intervals. From (3.9–11) we deduce

$$\int_0^r \frac{n(x)}{x}\, dx \leqq \log M(r) - \log |f(0)| \tag{6.7–1}$$

under the assumption that $f(0) \neq 0$. This formula enables us to prove:

If $f(z)$ is an integral function of order ϱ then

$$n(r) = O(r^{\varrho+\varepsilon}), \tag{6.7–2}$$

ε being an arbitrary positive number.

Without loss of generality we may assume that $f(0) \neq 0$, for there are only a finite number of zeros at $z = 0$ and $z^{-m} f(z)$ is also an integral function with the same order as $f(z)$, when $m > 0$, m being the order of multiplicity of the zero at $z = 0$.

Since $n(x)$ is a non-decreasing function we have

$$\int_0^{2r} \frac{n(x)}{x}\, dx \geqq \int_r^{2r} \frac{n(x)}{x}\, dx \geqq n(r) \int_r^{2r} \frac{dx}{x} = n(r) \log 2,$$

whence

$$n(r) \leqq \frac{1}{\log 2} \int_0^{2r} \frac{n(x)}{x}\, dx. \tag{6.7–3}$$

On the other hand, ϱ being the order of the function, the inequality

$$\log M(2r) < (2r)^{\varrho+\frac{1}{3}\varepsilon} < r^{\varrho+\frac{2}{3}\varepsilon}$$

holds for all sufficiently large values of r, and hence by (6.7–1)

$$\int_0^{2r} \frac{n(x)}{x}\, dx \leqq r^{\varrho+\frac{2}{3}\varepsilon} - \log |f(0)| < 2r^{\varrho+\frac{2}{3}\varepsilon} < r^{\varrho+\varepsilon}. \qquad (6.7\text{–}4)$$

Combining this result with (6.7–3), the assertion (6.7–2) turns out to be true.

The theorem states, roughly, that the higher the order of a function is, the more zeros it may have in a given region.

6.7.2 – A lemma

If $r_1, r_2, \ldots,$ are the moduli of the non-vanishing zeros of an integral function of order ϱ, arranged in order of non-decreasing magnitude, the series

$$\sum_{\nu=1}^{\infty} r_\nu^{-(\varrho+\varepsilon)} \qquad (6.7\text{–}5)$$

is convergent, irrespective of the value of the positive constant ε.

Let η denote a number between 0 and ε. There exists a constant A such that

$$n(r) < Ar^{\varrho+\eta}$$

for all sufficiently large values of r. Putting $r = r_n$ this gives

$$n = n(r_n) < Ar_n^{\varrho+\eta}$$

for all values of n which are large enough. Hence

$$r_n^{-(\varrho+\varepsilon)} < Bn^{-\frac{\varrho+\varepsilon}{\varrho+\eta}},$$

B being another constant.

The series

$$\sum_{\nu=1}^{\infty} \nu^{-\frac{\varrho+\varepsilon}{\varrho+\eta}}$$

is convergent since $\dfrac{\varrho+\varepsilon}{\varrho+\eta} > 1$. This proves the theorem.

6.7.3 – Hadamard's first theorem

The previous theorem states that

$$\sum_{\nu=1}^{\infty} r_\nu^{-\alpha} \qquad (6.7\text{–}6)$$

is convergent for $\alpha > \varrho$. Hence the greatest lower bound ϱ_c of these numbers α cannot exceed ϱ. This result is known as *Hadamard's first theorem*:

The exponent of convergence ϱ_c of the zeros of an integral function does not exceed the order ϱ of the function i.e.,

$$\boxed{\varrho_c \leqq \varrho.} \tag{6.7–7}$$

6.8 – Hadamard's second theorem

6.8.1 – Borel's theorem

A theorem due to Borel states:

The order of a canonical product of finite rank k is equal to the exponent of convergence ϱ_c of its zeros.

By Hadamard's first theorem of section 6.7.3 we have $\varrho_c \leqq \varrho$; it remains to prove that $\varrho_c \geqq \varrho$.

Consider

$$P(z) = \prod_{\nu=1}^{\infty} E\left(\frac{z}{a_\nu}; k\right), \tag{6.8–1}$$

k denoting the rank of the canonical product. Then

$$\log |P(z)| = \sum_{r_\nu \leqq 2r} \log \left| E\left(\frac{z}{a_\nu}; k\right)\right| + \sum_{r_\nu > 2r} \log \left| E\left(\frac{z}{a_\nu}; k\right)\right|. \tag{6.8–2}$$

By virtue of (4.3–8) we have

$$\sum_{r_\nu > 2r} \log \left| E\left(\frac{z}{a_\nu}; k\right)\right| < A \sum_{r_\nu > 2r} \left(\frac{r}{r_\nu}\right)^{k+1} = A r^{k+1} \sum_{r_\nu > 2r} \frac{1}{r_\nu^{k+1}}. \tag{6.8–3}$$

Suppose $\varrho_c < k+1$. We may take ε such that $\varrho_c + \varepsilon < k+1$. Then

$$r^{k+1} \sum_{r_\nu > 2r} \frac{1}{r_\nu^{k+1}} = r^{k+1} \sum_{r_\nu > 2r} r_\nu^{\varrho_c+\varepsilon-(k+1)} \frac{1}{r_\nu^{\varrho_c+\varepsilon}}$$

$$< r^{k+1} (2r)^{\varrho_c+\varepsilon-(k+1)} \sum_{r_\nu > 2r} \frac{1}{r_\nu^{\varrho_c+\varepsilon}} < r^{\varrho_c+\varepsilon}\, 2^{\varrho_c+\varepsilon-(k+1)} \sum_{r_\nu > 2r} \frac{1}{r_\nu^{\varrho_c+\varepsilon}},$$

and on account of the convergence of the ultimate series there exists a constant A_1 such that

$$\sum_{r_\nu > 2r} \log \left| E\left(\frac{z}{a_\nu}; k\right)\right| < A_1 r^{\varrho_c+\varepsilon}. \tag{6.8–4}$$

If it is not true that $\varrho_c < k+1$, then $\varrho_c = k+1$. In this case it is at once evident from (6.8–3) that (6.8–4) holds, for the inequality is already valid for $\varepsilon = 0$. If $|z| \geqq \frac{1}{2}$ and $k > 0$ then

$$\log|E(z;k)| \leqq |z|^k\left(\frac{\log\,(1+|z|)}{|z|^k}+\frac{1}{|z|^{k-1}}+\ldots+\frac{1}{k}\right) < A|z|^k$$

where A denotes a constant independent of z and $\varepsilon > 0$. The result is still true when $k = 0$.

Since $\varrho_c \geqq k$ we have

$$\sum_{r_\nu \leqq 2r} \log\left|E\left(\frac{z}{a_\nu}; k\right)\right| < A \sum_{r_\nu \leqq 2r}\left(\frac{r}{r_\nu}\right)^k = Ar^k \sum_{r_\nu \leqq 2r} \frac{r_\nu^{\varrho_c+\varepsilon-k}}{r_\nu^{\varrho_c+\varepsilon}}$$

$$\leqq A\,2^{\varrho_c+\varepsilon-k}\,r^{\varrho_c+\varepsilon} \sum_{r_\nu \leqq 2r} \frac{1}{r_\nu^{\varrho_c+\varepsilon}},$$

whence

$$\sum_{r_\nu \leqq 2r} \log\left|E\left(\frac{z}{a_\nu}; k\right)\right| < A_2 r^{\varrho_c+\varepsilon}, \tag{6.8–5}$$

A_2 denoting a constant independent of r. Combining (6.8–4) and (6.8–5) we deduce that

$$\log|P(z)| = O(r^{\varrho_c+\varepsilon}) \tag{6.8–6}$$

and this implies $\varrho \leqq \varrho_c$.

6.8.2 – Hadamard's second theorem

Since $P(z)$ vanishes at its zeros $a_1, a_2, \ldots$ we cannot expect that we can set a lower bound for $|P(z)|$ quite as simply as an upper bound. To overcome this difficulty we describe a circle

$$|z-a_n| = r_n^{-h}$$

about each zero $z = a_n$ for which $r_n > 1$, h being a real number greater than ϱ, the order of $P(z)$. The number $2\sum_{\nu=1}^{\infty} r_\nu^{-h}$ being finite, the intervals between $r_n - r_n^{-h}$ and $r_n + r_n^{-h}$ on the real axis do not cover the whole positive real axis, (fig. 6.8–1). Hence there exist infinitely many circles about the origin, whose radius r is arbitrarily large and which are in the region $\mathfrak{R}$ excluded from the small circles about the zeros.

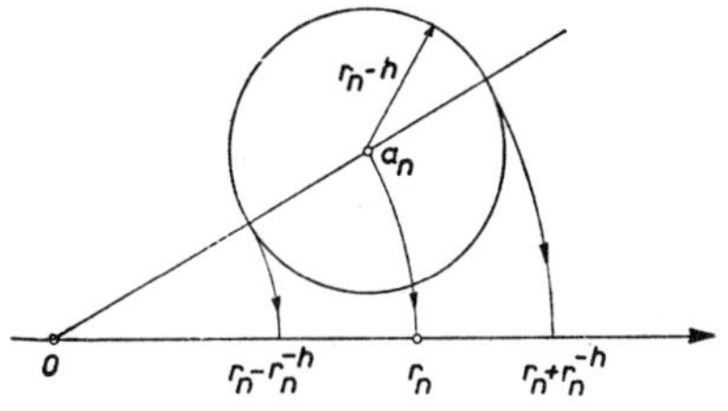

Fig. 6.8–1. Hadamard's second theorem

After these preliminaries we may state *Hadamard's second theorem*: *If about each zero $z = a_n$, $|a_n| > 1$, we describe a circle of radius r_n^{-h}, where h is greater than the order ϱ of the canonical product $P(z)$ then in the region $\mathfrak{R}$ excluded from these circles the estimate*

$$|P(z)| > e^{-r^{\varrho+\varepsilon}} \tag{6.8–7}$$

is valid on infinitely many circles of arbitrarily large radius.

We proceed as in section 6.8.1:

$$\log |P(z)| \geqq \sum_{r_\nu \leqq 2r} \log \left| 1 - \frac{z}{a_\nu} \right| - \sum_{r_\nu \leqq 2r} \left| \frac{z}{a_\nu} + \frac{1}{2}\left(\frac{z}{a_\nu}\right)^2 + \ldots + \frac{1}{k}\left(\frac{z}{a_\nu}\right)^k \right|$$
$$- \sum_{r_\nu > 2r} \log \left| E\left(\frac{z}{a_\nu}; k\right) \right|,$$

k being the rank of the canonical product. If $r_n \leqq 2r$ we have

$$\left| \frac{z}{a_n} + \frac{1}{2}\left(\frac{z}{a_n}\right)^2 + \ldots + \frac{1}{k}\left(\frac{z}{a_n}\right)^k \right| \leqq \left(\frac{r}{r_n}\right)^k \left(\frac{1}{k} + \frac{1}{k-1} \left|\frac{a_n}{z}\right| + \ldots + \left|\frac{a_n}{z}\right|^{k-1} \right)$$
$$\leqq \left(\frac{r}{r_n}\right)^k \left(\frac{1}{k} + \frac{2}{k-1} + \ldots + \frac{2^{k-1}}{1} \right) \leqq B \left(\frac{r}{r_n}\right)^k,$$

B being a constant independent of r. It follows that

$$\sum_{r_\nu \leqq 2r} \left| \frac{z}{a_\nu} + \frac{1}{2}\left(\frac{z}{a_\nu}\right)^2 + \ldots + \frac{1}{k}\left(\frac{z}{a_\nu}\right)^k \right| \leqq B \sum_{r_\nu \leqq 2r} \left(\frac{r}{r_\nu}\right)^k$$
$$= B \cdot 2^{\varrho+\frac{1}{2}\varepsilon-k} r^{\varrho+\frac{1}{2}\varepsilon} \sum_{r_\nu \leqq 2r} \frac{1}{(2r)^{\varrho+\frac{1}{2}\varepsilon-k} r_\nu^k} \leqq B \cdot 2^{\varrho+\frac{1}{2}\varepsilon-k} r^{\varrho+\frac{1}{2}\varepsilon} \sum_{r_\nu \leqq 2r} \frac{1}{r_\nu^{\varrho+\frac{1}{2}\varepsilon}} < A_1 r^{\varrho+\frac{1}{2}\varepsilon},$$

A_1 being a constant independent of r. When $k = 0$ this part of the proof can be omitted.

If z lies outside any circle $|z-a_n| = r_n^{-h}$ and $r_n \leqq 2r$ then

$$\left| 1 - \frac{z}{a_n} \right| > r_n^{-1-h} \geqq (2r)^{-1-h}.$$

Hence, taking account of (6.7–2), replacing ε by $\frac{1}{2}\varepsilon$

$$\sum_{1 \leqq r_\nu \leqq 2r} \log \left| 1 - \frac{z}{a_\nu} \right| \geqq -(1+h)\, n(2r) \log 2r > -A_2 r^{\varrho+\frac{1}{2}\varepsilon} \log 2r,$$

A_2 being a constant independent of r, provided r is sufficiently large. Finally we have on account of (6.7–7) and (6.8–4), replacing ε by $\frac{1}{2}\varepsilon$,

$$\sum_{r_\nu > 2r} \log \left| E\left(\frac{z}{a_\nu}; k\right) \right| < A_3 r^{\varrho+\frac{1}{2}\varepsilon},$$

A_3 being independent of r. Hence

$$\log |P(z)| > \sum_{r_\nu<1} \log \left|1-\frac{z}{a_\nu}\right| - A_1 r^{\varrho+\frac{1}{2}\varepsilon} - A_2 r^{\varrho+\frac{1}{2}\varepsilon} \log 2r - A_3 r^{\varrho+\frac{1}{2}\varepsilon}.$$

Since for $r > 2$

$$\sum_{r_\nu<1} \log \left|1-\frac{z}{a_\nu}\right| \geqq \sum_{r_\nu<1} \log \left(\frac{r}{r_\nu}-1\right) > \log 1 = 0$$

we have for all sufficiently large r associated with circles $|z| = r$ in $\mathfrak{R}$ the estimate

$$\log |P(z)| > -r^{\varrho+\varepsilon}$$

and this is equivalent to (6.8–7).

6.9 – Hadamard's factorization theorem

6.9.1 – Statement and proof of the theorem

We already pointed out in section 6.4.5 that the order of a product of two integral functions of finite order does not exceed the order of either of the factors. Hence the function

$$f(z) = z^m P(z) \exp Q(z), \tag{6.9–1}$$

where $P(z)$ is a canonical product of order ϱ_c and $Q(z)$ a polynomial of degree q, is an integral function of order not exceeding max (ϱ_c, q). *Hadamard's factorization theorem* states that the converse is also true, that is to say:

If $f(z)$ is an integral function of order ϱ, then the decomposition (6.9–1) *is valid, where $P(z)$ is a canonical product of rank $\leqq \varrho$ and $Q(z)$ a polynomial of degree $\leqq \varrho$.*

From Weierstrass's factorization theorem of section 4.4.1 it follows that a factorization (6.9–1) is always possible, $Q(z)$ denoting an integral function. Let ϱ_c be the exponent of convergence of the zeros of $f(z)$. Then by Hadamard's first theorem (6.7.3) $\varrho_c \leqq \varrho$. This means, however, by Borel's theorem (6.8.1) that the order of $P(z)$ is ϱ_c. Hadamard's second theorem (6.8–1) states that there is an infinity of circles of arbitrarily large radius on which the inequality

$$|P(z)| > e^{-r^{\varrho_c+\frac{1}{2}\varepsilon}} \geqq e^{-r^{\varrho+\frac{1}{2}\varepsilon}}$$

is satisfied, ε being arbitrary and positive. But since $f(z)$ is of order ϱ the inequality

$$|f(z)| < e^{r^{\varrho+\frac{1}{2}\varepsilon}}$$

holds for all sufficiently large values of r. And so

$$|\exp Q(z)| < e^{2r^{\varrho+\frac{1}{2}\varepsilon}} < e^{r^{\varrho+\varepsilon}}$$

on circles of arbitrarily large radius. By virtue of the theorem of section 2.9.12 the function $Q(z)$ is a polynomial of degree ϱ at most. This completes the proof.

6.9.2 – An illustrative example

Hadamard's factorization theorem plays an important part in the theory of integral functions of finite order. It is a precious tool in theoretical considerations, but also in concrete examples it is of great value. We wish to illustrate its significance in an elementary example which we encountered already many times.

It is easy to show that the integral function

$$f(z) = \frac{\sin \pi\sqrt{z}}{\pi\sqrt{z}} = 1 - \frac{\pi^2 z}{3!} + \frac{\pi^4 z^2}{5!} - \dots$$

is of order $\frac{1}{2}$. The zeros are $z = 1, 4, 9, \dots$ and we, therefore, have

$$f(z) = \exp Q(z) \prod_{\nu=1}^{\infty} \left(1 - \frac{z}{\nu^2}\right).$$

But $Q(z)$ must be a constant, since the degree of the polynomial does not exceed $\frac{1}{2}$. Moreover $f(0) = 1$. This leads at once to the formula

$$\sin \pi z = \pi z \prod_{\nu=1}^{\infty} \left(1 - \frac{z^2}{\nu^2}\right).$$

6.9.3 – Expression of the order in terms of the exponent of convergence and the exponential degree

Since $q \leqq \varrho$ and $\varrho_c \leqq \varrho$ we have

$$\varrho \geqq \max(\varrho_c, q).$$

But on account of the theorem of 6.4.5 we also have

$$\varrho \leqq \max(\varrho_c, q).$$

Hence

$$\boxed{\varrho = \max(\varrho_c, q),} \qquad (6.9\text{–}2)$$

ϱ_c being the exponent of convergence of the zeros and q the exponential degree of $f(z)$.

We may add the following remark:

If the order ϱ of an integral function is not an integer then the exponent of convergence of the zeros is equal to ϱ.

In fact, it follows from (6.9–2) that $\varrho = \varrho_c$ when ϱ is not an integer, for q is an integer.

6.9.4 – COMPLETION OF THE THEOREM 6.4.5

The previous result enables us to complete the theorem of section 6.4.5 In fact, let

$$f_1(z) = z^{m_1} P_1(z) \exp Q_1(z),$$
$$f_2(z) = z^{m_2} P_2(z) \exp Q_2(z).$$

We assume that neither $f_1(z)$ nor $f_2(z)$ vanishes identically. Then

$$f_1(z) f_2(z) = z^{m_1+m_2} P_1(z) P_2(z) \exp \{Q_1(z)+Q_2(z)\}.$$

Let ϱ_1 be the order of $f_1(z)$ and ϱ_2 that of $f_2(z)$ and assume $\varrho_1 > \varrho_2$. If the first canonical product is of order ϱ_1, then the same holds for $P_1(z)P_2(z)$, for ϱ_1 is at the same time the exponent of convergence of the zeros. The degree of the polynomial $Q_1(z)+Q_2(z)$ cannot exceed ϱ_1. Hence the product $f_1(z)f_2(z)$ is of order ϱ_1. If $P_1(z)$ is of order $< \varrho_1$, then $Q_1(z)$ is of degree ϱ_1 as is $Q_1(z)+Q_2(z)$, since the degree of $Q_2(z)$ is $< \varrho_1$. Also in this case the order of $f_1(z)f_2(z)$ is equal to ϱ_1. Hence:

The order of $f_1(z) f_2(z)$ is exactly equal to $\varrho = \max(\varrho_1, \varrho_2)$ when $\varrho_1 \neq \varrho_2$.

6.9.5 – GENUS AND ORDER

We conclude this section by listing the various cases which may be presented by an integral function of integral order as regards its genus. If $\varrho_c = \varrho$ then either $k = \varrho$, $q = \varrho$ or $k = \varrho$, $q < \varrho$ or $k = \varrho-1$, $q = \varrho$ or $k = \varrho-1$, $q < \varrho$, k being the rank of the corresponding canonical product. In these cases the genus is equal to ϱ except in the last case, where it is $\varrho-1$. When $\varrho_c < \varrho$ then necessarily $k < \varrho$ and $q = \varrho$, hence the genus is ϱ. We thus have:

When the order ϱ of an integral function is an integer then the genus is equal to the order, except when the rank of the canonical product occurring in Hadamard's decomposition is $\varrho-1$ and $q < \varrho$; then the genus is $\varrho-1$.

6.10 – The Borel-Caratheodory theorem

6.10.1 – STATEMENT AND PROOF OF THE THEOREM

There is an alternative proof of Hadamard's factorization theorem due to Landau based on an estimate of the maximum modulus by an expression involving the maximum of the real part of $f(z)$ on the circumference $|z| = r$ and the absolute value of the function at the origin.

The *Borel-Caratheodory theorem* states:

Let $f(z)$ be holomorphic in a region that contains all points $|z| \leqq R$ and let $M(r)$ and $A(r)$ denote the maximum of $|f(z)|$ and of Re $f(z)$ *respectively on the circumference $|z| = r$. Then for $0 < r < R$:*

$$\boxed{M(r) \leqq \frac{2r}{R-r} A(R) + \frac{R+r}{R-r} |f(0)|.} \tag{6.10–1}$$

The statement is trivial in the case that $f(z)$ is a constant. From now on we therefore assume $f(z)$ not to be a constant. In the first place let $f(0) = 0$. When $r > 0$ we have $A(r) > A(0) = 0$, since $A(r)$ is an increasing function (2.14.2). Consider the function

$$g(z) = \frac{f(z)}{2A(R) - f(z)}. \tag{6.10–2}$$

Obviously $g(z)$ is regular at every point of the disc $|z| \leqq R$, while $g(0) = 0$. If we put $f(z) = u + iv$, we have

$$|g(z)|^2 = \frac{u^2+v^2}{(2A(R)-u)^2+v^2}. \tag{6.10–3}$$

Also

$$(2A(R)-u)^2 \geqq u^2$$

since

$$4A(R)(A(R)-u) \geqq 0.$$

Hence

$$|g(z)| \leqq 1.$$

From Schwarz's lemma (2.21–2) we conclude that even

$$|g(z)| \leqq \frac{r}{R}, \qquad |z| = r. \tag{6.10–4}$$

Now (6.10–2) leads to

$$f(z) = \frac{2A(R)g(z)}{1+g(z)}$$

whence, taking account of (6.10–4),

$$|f(z)| \leqq \frac{2A(R)|g(z)|}{1-r/R} \leqq \frac{2rA(R)}{R-r}$$

and the truth of (6.10–1) follows.

If $f(0) \neq 0$ we may apply the foregoing result to the function $f(z) - f(0)$ and we get

$$|f(z) - f(0)| \leqq \frac{2r}{R-r} \max_{|z|=R} (\text{Re}\,(f(z) - f(0))).$$

Hence

$$|f(z)|-|f(0)| \leqq |f(z)-f(0)| \leqq \frac{2r}{R-r}(A(R)+|f(0)|),$$

and the desired result follows.

6.10.2 – A LEMMA

The estimate (6.10–1) implies in the case $A(R) \geqq 0$ that

$$M(r) \leqq \frac{R+r}{R-r}(A(R)+|f(0)|) \tag{6.10–5}$$

and, *a fortiori*,

$$M(r) \leqq \frac{2^2 R}{R-r}(A(R)+|f(0)|). \tag{6.10–6}$$

We wish to prove that this estimate can be generalized for the mth derivative of $f(z)$ in the following fashion:

$$\boxed{\max_{|z|=r} |f^{(m)}(z)| \leqq \frac{2^{m+2} m! R}{(R-r)^{m+1}}(A(R)+|f(0)|).} \tag{6.10–7}$$

Let C denote a circle about the point z with radius $\frac{1}{2}(R-r)$. If ζ varies on C, we have

$$|\zeta| \leqq |z|+|\zeta-z| = r+\tfrac{1}{2}(R-r) = \tfrac{1}{2}(R+r).$$

By virtue of (6.10–5) we have for ζ on C:

$$\max |f(\zeta)| \leqq M(\tfrac{1}{2}R+\tfrac{1}{2}r) \leqq \frac{R+\frac{1}{2}R+\frac{1}{2}r}{R-\frac{1}{2}R-\frac{1}{2}r}(A(R)+|f(0)|)$$
$$< \frac{4R}{R-r}(A(R)+|f(0)|),$$

and according to the formula (2.9–9) for the mth derivative of $f(z)$ we have, taking account of Darboux's inequality (2.4–17),

$$|f^{(m)}(\zeta)| \leqq \frac{m!}{2\pi} \frac{4R(A(R)+|f(0)|)}{R-r} \cdot \frac{2^{m+1}}{(R-r)^{m+1}} \cdot \tfrac{1}{2} \cdot 2\pi(R-r)$$

and the desired formula easily follows.

6.10.3 – LANDAU'S PROOF OF HADAMARD'S FACTORIZATION THEOREM

The previous theorem enables us to give an independent proof of Hadamard's factorization theorem. Without loss of generality we may assume $f(0) \neq 0$. By Weierstrass's theorem we have

$$f(z) = \exp Q(z) \cdot \prod_{\nu=1}^{\infty}\left(1-\frac{z}{a_\nu}\right)\exp\left\{\frac{z}{a_\nu}+\frac{1}{2}\left(\frac{z}{a_\nu}\right)^2+\dots+\frac{1}{k}\left(\frac{z}{a_\nu}\right)^k\right\}. \tag{6.10–8}$$

It remains to prove that $Q(z)$ is a polynomial. Put $m = [\varrho]$, ϱ being the order of $f(z)$. By Hadamard's first theorem $\varrho_c \leqq \varrho$ and hence $k \leqq m$, k being the rank of the canonical product. By logarithmic differentiation we obtain

$$\frac{f'(z)}{f(z)} = Q'(z) + \sum_{\nu=1}^{\infty}\left(-\frac{1}{a_\nu - z} + \frac{1}{a_\nu} + \frac{z}{a_\nu^2} + \ldots + \frac{z^{k-1}}{a_\nu^k}\right) \tag{6.10–9}$$

and since the series on the right converges uniformly in every bounded and closed set within a region from which the zeros of $f(z)$ are deleted, the process of term-by-term differentiation is justified. Effecting this process m times we get

$$\frac{d^m}{dz^m}\frac{f'(z)}{f(z)} = Q^{(m+1)}(z) - \sum_{\nu=1}^{\infty}\frac{m!}{(a_\nu - z)^{m+1}}, \tag{6.10–10}$$

and we have only to prove that $Q^{(m+1)}(z) = 0$ identically.

Let $R > 0$ and consider the function

$$g_R(z) = \frac{f(z)}{f(0)} \prod_{|a_\nu| \leqq R}\left(1 - \frac{z}{a_\nu}\right)^{-1}. \tag{6.10–11}$$

Whenever $|z| = 2R$ and $|a_n| \leqq R$, we have

$$\left|1 - \frac{z}{a_n}\right| \geqq \left|\frac{z}{a_n}\right| - 1 \geqq \frac{2R}{R} - 1 = 1,$$

whence

$$|g_R(z)| \leqq \frac{|f(z)|}{|f(0)|}, \quad |z| = 2R.$$

We recall that $f(z)$ is an integral function of order ϱ and therefore

$$|g_R(z)| \leqq e^{(2R)^{\varrho+\varepsilon}}, \quad |z| \leqq 2R \tag{6.10–12}$$

for all sufficiently large values of R. Put

$$h_R(z) = \log g_R(z).$$

Then $h_R(z)$ is regular at every point of the set $|z| \leqq R$, and

$$\operatorname{Re} h_R(z) = \log |g_R(z)| \leqq (2R)^{\varrho+\varepsilon} \tag{6.10–13}$$

for all sufficiently large values of R.

The next step will be the application of the Borel-Caratheodory theorem. We find, observing that $h_R(0) = 0$,

$$|h_R^{(m+1)}(z)| \leqq \frac{2^{m+3}(m+1)!\,R}{(R-r)^{m+2}}(2R)^{\varrho+\varepsilon}.$$

For $|z| = \frac{1}{2}R$ this yields

$$|h_R^{(m+1)}(z)| \leqq K R^{\varrho+\varepsilon-(m+1)}, \tag{6.10–14}$$

K being a constant independent of R. By the maximum modulus principle this inequality is also true for $|z| \leqq \frac{1}{2}R$.

Now we take $\varepsilon > 0$ so small that $\varrho+\varepsilon < m+1$. This is possible, since $\varrho < m+1$. Then the expression on the right of (6.10–14) tends to zero as $R \to \infty$, i.e.,

$$\lim_{R\to\infty} |h_R^{(m+1)}(z)| = 0. \tag{6.10–15}$$

Differentiating (6.10–11) logarithmically we get

$$\frac{g_R'(z)}{g_R(z)} = \frac{f'(z)}{f(z)} + \sum_{|a_\nu| \leqq R} \frac{1}{a_\nu - z}$$

whence

$$h_R^{(m+1)}(z) = \frac{d^m}{dz^m} \frac{f'(z)}{f(z)} + \sum_{|a_\nu| \leqq R} \frac{m!}{(a_\nu - z)^{m+1}},$$

and from (6.10–10) we deduce

$$Q^{(m+1)}(z) = h_R^{(m+1)}(z) + \sum_{|a_\nu| > R} \frac{m!}{(a_\nu - z)^{m+1}}. \tag{6.10–16}$$

Assuming $|z| \leqq \frac{1}{2}R$ we have for $|a_n| > R$

$$|a_n - z| = |a_n| \left| 1 - \frac{z}{a_n} \right| \geqq |a_n| \left(1 - \frac{\frac{1}{2}R}{R}\right) = \tfrac{1}{2}|a_n|.$$

Hence

$$\sum_{|a_\nu| > R} \frac{m!}{|a_\nu - z|^{m+1}} \leqq 2^{m+1} m! \sum_{|a_\nu| > R} \frac{1}{|a_\nu|^{m+1}},$$

and since the latter series is convergent we find

$$\lim_{R\to\infty} \left(\sum_{|a_\nu| > R} \frac{m!}{|a_\nu - z|^{m+1}} \right) = 0. \tag{6.10–17}$$

By (6.10–16) and (6.10–17) we may therefore infer that

$$Q^{(m+1)}(z) = 0, \tag{6.10–18}$$

identically in z. This proves that $Q(z)$ is a polynomial of degree not exceeding m.

6.11 – Picard's theorem for integral functions of finite order

6.11.1 – Statement and proof of the theorem

Picard's theorem for integral functions states:

An integral function which is not a constant takes every value, with one possible exception, at least once.

The proof of this theorem for general integral functions is not easy, but it is rather simple when we restrict ourselves to the case of integral functions of finite order. The general case will be considered in Vol. II.

Suppose that there are two different numbers a and b such that the equations

$$f(z) = a, \qquad f(z) = b \tag{6.11–1}$$

have no roots. The function $f(z)-a$, being a function with no zeros, can be represented as

$$f(z)-a = \exp Q(z),$$

$Q(z)$ being a polynomial. Since the equation

$$\exp Q(z) = b-a$$

has no roots, there are also no roots for the equation

$$Q(z) = \log (b-a).$$

But in view of the fundamental theorem of algebra $Q(z)$ is a constant, as is $f(z)$.

6.11.2 – The a-points of a function

We may generalize the concept of zeros in the following way: A point z_0 is called an *a-point* if the function $f(z)$ takes the value a at $z = z_0$, i.e., when z_0 is a zero of $f(z)-a$.

It is plain that a function of non-integral order has always an infinity of a-points, a being a given number, since the orders of $f(z)$ and $f(z)-a$ are the same. Also a function of zero order which does not reduce to a polynomial has an infinity of a-points, since $f(z)-a$ is a polynomial for every a or for none.

If $f(z)$ is of positive integral order there may be exceptions. Thus, for instance, the set of a-points of the function $\exp z$ is empty when $a = 0$. By Picard's theorem there is one exception at most.

6.11.3 – Exceptional values

A value a with the property that the set of a-points of the function $f(z)$ is empty will be called *exceptional P*. But an a-point can also be exceptional in a wider sense. Given an integral function of order ϱ it may happen that the set of a-points is either empty (case of Picard's theorem), or contains a finite number of a-points, or contains an infinity of points whose exponent of convergence is less than ϱ. In these latter two cases the value a is said to be *exceptional B* (where B stands for Borel). Thus the function $e^z \cos \sqrt{z}$ is of order 1, but the zeros $z = \frac{1}{4}(2n+1)^2\pi^2$, $n = 0, \pm 1, \pm 2, \ldots$ have the exponent of convergence equal to $\frac{1}{2}$.

It is plain that a value exceptional P is also a value exceptional B, but the converse is not true.

6.11.4 – Borel's theorem

Borel discovered a theorem which may be considered as an analogue of Picard's theorem.

If the function $f(z)$ is of finite order then the exponent of convergence of the a-points is equal to the order, except possibly for one value of a.

Let a be an exceptional value B. By Hadamard's decomposition we have

$$f(z)-a = z^{m_1} P_1(z) \exp Q_1(z), \tag{6.11–2}$$

where $Q_1(z)$ is a polynomial of degree q and $P_1(z)$ a canonical product. By hypothesis the exponent of convergence of the zeros of $P_1(z)$ is less than ϱ. Hence $q = \varrho$, i.e., the order must be an integer.

If $b \neq a$ is also exceptional B we similarly have

$$f(z)-b = z^{m_2} P_2(z) \exp Q_2(z), \tag{6.11–3}$$

$Q_2(z)$ being also a polynomial of degree $q = \varrho$. By subtracting we find from (6.11–2) and (6.11–3)

$$b-a = z^{m_1} P_1(z) \exp Q_1(z) - z^{m_2} P_2(z) \exp Q_2(z) \tag{6.11–4}$$

or

$$z^{m_1} P_1(z) \exp \{Q_1(z)-Q_2(z)\} = z^{m_2} P_2(z) + (b-a) \exp \{-Q_2(z)\}$$

and since $Q_2(z)$ is of degree ϱ the function on the right is of order ϱ. As a consequence the polynomial $Q_1(z)-Q_2(z)$ is of degree ϱ. Differentiating (6.11–4) we obtain

$$\begin{aligned}&\{m_1 z^{m_1-1} P_1(z) + z^{m_1} Q_1'(z) P_1(z) + z^{m_1} P_1'(z)\} \exp Q_1(z)\\ &= \{m_2 z^{m_2-1} P_2(z) + z^{m_2} Q_2'(z) P_2(z) + z^{m_2} P_2'(z)\} \exp Q_2(z),\end{aligned} \tag{6.11–5}$$

and since the orders of $P_1'(z)$ and $P_2'(z)$ are the same as those of $P_1(z)$ and $P_2(z)$ respectively (6.4–6), i.e., less than ϱ, we may put

$$\begin{aligned}m_1 z^{m_1-1} P_1(z) + z^{m_1} Q_1'(z) P_1(z) + z^{m_1} P_1'(z) &= z^{m_3} P_3(z) \exp Q_3(z),\\ m_2 z^{m_2-1} P_2(z) + z^{m_2} Q_2'(z) P_2(z) + z^{m_2} P_2'(z) &= z^{m_4} P_4(z) \exp Q_4(z),\end{aligned}$$

where $Q_3(z)$ and $Q_4(z)$ are polynomials of degree $\varrho - 1$ at most, and $P_3(z)$ and $P_4(z)$ are canonical products of order $< \varrho$. Hence (6.11–5) may be rewritten in the form

$$z^{m_3} P_3(z) \exp \{Q_1(z)+Q_3(z)\} = z^{m_4} P_4(z) \exp \{Q_2(z)+Q_4(z)\},$$

and since Hadamard's decomposition is unique we have, neglecting multiples of $2\pi i$,

$$Q_1(z)+Q_3(z) = Q_2(z)+Q_4(z)$$

or

$$Q_1(z)-Q_2(z) = Q_4(z)-Q_3(z).$$

But now we have obtained a contradiction, since the polynomial on the left is exactly of degree ϱ and the polynomial on the right is of degree $< \varrho$. It is, therefore, impossible that a function of finite order admits more than one value exceptional B.

6.12 – The theorem of Phragmén

6.12.1 – Phragmén's principle

The modulus of the function $\exp z$ is $\exp(r\cos\theta)$, if we put $z = re^{i\theta}$. If we let $z \to \infty$ along a half-line $\arg z = \theta = \text{const.}$ the rate of increase of the modulus is different according as $|\theta| < \frac{1}{2}\pi$ or $|\theta| \geqq \frac{1}{2}\pi$, (fig. 6.12–1). In the first case the modulus increases beyond every positive value, whereas in the second case the modulus remains bounded.

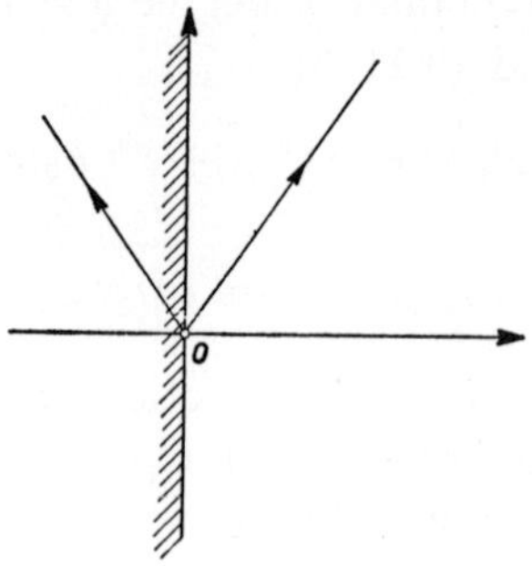

Fig. 6.12–1. Asymptotic behaviour of the exponential function

As we shall see presently the rate of increase of an integral function for various directions depends on the order. The theory is based on a central principle due to Phragmén which generalizes the maximum modulus theorem.

Let the function $f(z)$ be continuous on the closure $\overline{\mathfrak{R}}$ of a region $\mathfrak{R}$ between two straight half-lines making an angle π/α, $\alpha \geqq \frac{1}{2}$ at the origin and outside a circle $|z| = r_0 \geqq 0$. If $f(z)$ is holomorphic throughout $\mathfrak{R}$ and bounded on the boundary of the region and if throughout the region

$$|f(z)| < e^{r^\beta} \tag{6.12–1}$$

for all sufficiently large values of r, where $\beta < \alpha$, then actually the function is bounded in $\mathfrak{R}$.

Without loss of generality we may assume that the region is symmetric with respect to the real axis, i.e., the two sides of the angular region are given by $\theta = \pm\frac{1}{2}\pi/\alpha$.

Consider the function

$$F(z) = e^{-\varepsilon z^\eta} f(z) \tag{6.12–2}$$

where $\beta < \eta < \alpha$ and $\varepsilon > 0$. Then

$$|F(z)| = e^{-\varepsilon r^\eta \cos \eta\theta} |f(z)|. \tag{6.12–3}$$

On the lines $\theta = \pm\frac{1}{2}\pi/\alpha$ the function $\cos \eta\theta$ is positive, since $\eta < \alpha$. Hence on the boundary of $\mathfrak{R}$

$$|F(z)| \leqq |f(z)| \leqq M,$$

M being a constant. On the arc $|\theta| \leqq \frac{1}{2}\pi/\alpha$ of the circle $|z| = R > r_0$ we have

$$\begin{aligned} |F(z)| &\leqq e^{-\varepsilon R^\eta \cos \frac{1}{2}\pi(\eta/\alpha)} |f(z)| < e^{R^\beta - \varepsilon R^\eta \cos \frac{1}{2}\pi(\eta/\alpha)} \\ &= e^{R^\eta (R^{\beta-\eta} - \varepsilon \cos \frac{1}{2}\pi(\eta/\alpha))} \end{aligned}$$

as $R \to \infty$, since $\eta > \beta$ and $\varepsilon \cos \frac{1}{2}\pi(\eta/\alpha) > 0$. As a consequence

$$|F(z)| \leqq M \tag{6.12–4}$$

on the arc $|z| = R$ within the angle for R exceeding a certain value. By the maximum modulus theorem the inequality (6.12–4) holds throughout the set $|\theta| \leqq \frac{1}{2}\pi/\alpha$, $r_0 \leqq r \leqq R$ and since R is arbitrary we have by virtue of (6.12–3)

$$|f(z)| \leqq M e^{\varepsilon r^\eta \cos \eta\theta} \leqq M e^{\varepsilon r^\eta}.$$

Letting $\varepsilon \to 0$ we obtain the desired result.

6.12.2 – Asymptotic behaviour of an integral function

Consider an integral function of order ϱ which is assumed to be bounded in the exterior and on the sides of the angle $|\theta| < \varphi \leqq \pi$, (fig. 6.12–2), hence for all values of θ satisfying $\varphi \leqq |\theta| \leqq \pi$. If $\varrho < \pi/2\varphi$ we can apply Phragmén's theorem in the closure of the region $|\theta| < \varphi$ by taking for β a number between ϱ and $\alpha = \pi/2\varphi$ because $\varphi = \pi/2\alpha$ and $\alpha \geqq \frac{1}{2}$. Since $\beta > \varrho$ it follows from the definition of order that (6.12–1) is satisfied for all sufficiently large values of r. Hence the function is also bounded for $|\theta| \leqq \varphi$ and by Liouville's theorem the function is a constant. This result leads to a contradiction when $\varrho \geqq \frac{1}{2}$ and $\varphi < \pi/2\varrho$. Hence:

An integral function of order $\varrho \geqq \frac{1}{2}$ cannot be uniformly bounded in the exterior and on the sides of an angle of width smaller than π/ϱ.

If $\varrho < \frac{1}{2}$ we can take $\varphi = \pi$. The previous reasoning is still applicable and we find:

A non-constant function of order $\varrho < \frac{1}{2}$ cannot be uniformly bounded on any half-line issuing from the origin.

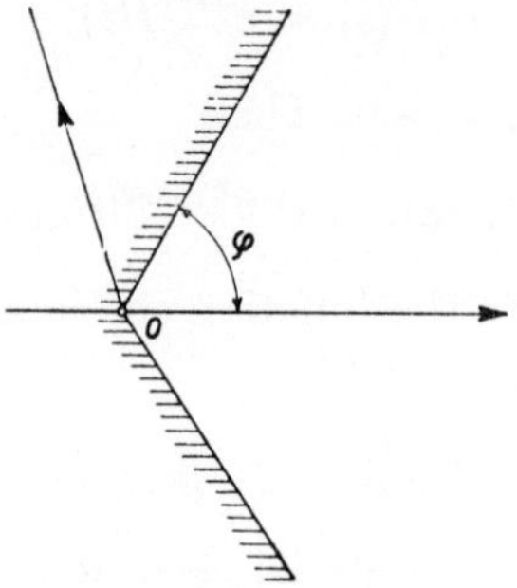

Fig. 6.12–2. Asymptotic behaviour of an arbitrary integral function of finite order

It is not possible to ameliorate the conditions in these theorems as we shall illustrate in the example of the next section. Already for the case $\varrho = \frac{1}{2}$ we can give an elementary example of a function which is bounded on a half-line, viz., $\cos \sqrt{z}$, this function being actually of order $\frac{1}{2}$. For positive real values of z we have $|\cos \sqrt{z}| \leqq 1$.

6.12.3 – Behaviour of the minimum modulus

If $f(z)$ is an integral function of order $\varrho < \frac{1}{2}$ there is a sequence of values of z tending to infinity through which the minimum modulus tends to infinity, provided that the function is not constant.

Hadamard's factorization of the function is

$$f(z) = z^m \prod_{\nu=1}^{\infty} \left(1 - \frac{z}{a_\nu}\right).$$

Consider the function

$$g(z) = z^m \prod_{\nu=1}^{\infty} \left(1 + \frac{z}{r_\nu}\right).$$

Since

$$\left|1 - \frac{z}{a_n}\right| \geqq \left|1 - \frac{r}{r_n}\right|, \qquad n = 1, 2, \ldots,$$

we have

$$m(r) \geqq g(-r).$$

Now $g(z)$ is an integral function of the same order as $f(z)$ and, therefore, $g(-r)$ is unbounded by the previous theorem.

6.13 – Mittag-Leffler's function

6.13.1 – Definition

The considerations of the previous section may be illustrated in an impressive way in an example due to Mittag-Leffler. He discovered the following function:

$$E_{\alpha}(z) = \sum_{\nu=0}^{\infty} \frac{z^{\nu}}{\Gamma(1+\alpha\nu)}, \qquad (6.13\text{–}1)$$

where α denotes a real or complex parameter. Only real positive values of α will concern us in the sequel.

Mittag-Leffler's function (6.13–1) *is an integral function of order* $1/\alpha$.

On applying Stirling's theorem we find that

$$\frac{\log \Gamma(1+n\alpha)}{n \log n} = \frac{(n\alpha+\frac{1}{2}) \log n\alpha - n\alpha + \log \sqrt{2\pi} + \mu(n\alpha)}{n \log n} \to \alpha$$

as $n \to \infty$, and the truth of the statement follows from the theorem of section 6.6.2.

For $\alpha = 1$ the function reduces to the exponential function and for $\alpha = 2$ to the function $\cosh \sqrt{z}$.

6.13.2 – Representation of the function as an integral

The study of the function (6.13–1) will be facilitated on applying Hankel's representation (4.7–35) of the gamma function

$$\frac{1}{\Gamma(s)} = \frac{1}{2\pi i} \int_{L(a)} e^{t} t^{-s} \, dt, \qquad (6.13\text{–}2)$$

the path $L(a)$ being defined as in section 4.7.6. For our purpose it will be desirable to give the path a shape as shown in fig. 6.13–1.

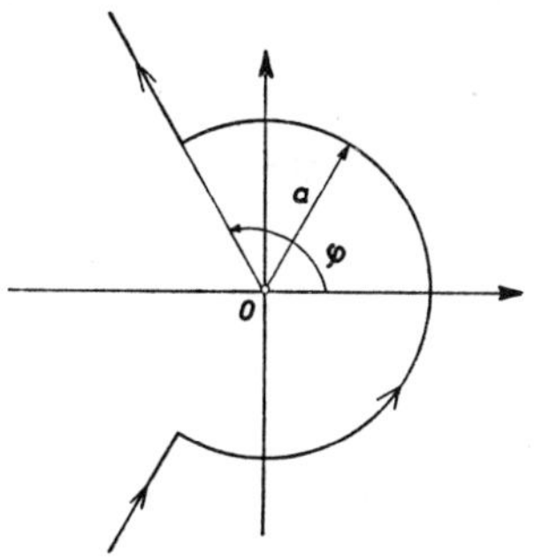

Fig. 6.13–1. Reshaping of Hankels' contour

This path $L(a, \varphi)$ consists of two half-lines $\arg t = \varphi$, $\arg t = -\varphi$, $\frac{1}{2}\pi < \varphi < \pi$, with $|t| \geqq a > 0$, and of the arc $|t| = a$, $|\arg t| \leqq \varphi$ the path being traversed in such a sense that the origin is at the left. As regards the part of the path above the real axis we observe that the integral taken along an arc $|t| = R > a$, $\varphi \leqq \theta = \arg t \leqq \pi$ is

$$i \int_{\pi}^{\varphi} e^{Re^{i\theta}} (Re^{i\theta})^{-s} Re^{i\theta} \, d\theta$$

and that the modulus tends to zero like $e^{R \cos \varphi} R^{1-\mathrm{Re}\, s}$ as $R \to \infty$.

The integral taken along the contour consisting of two arcs of radius R and a respectively, $\varphi \leqq \arg t \leqq \theta \leqq \pi$ and the two segments joining the corresponding extremities of these arcs, (fig. 6.13–2), is equal to zero. This may be proved either as in section

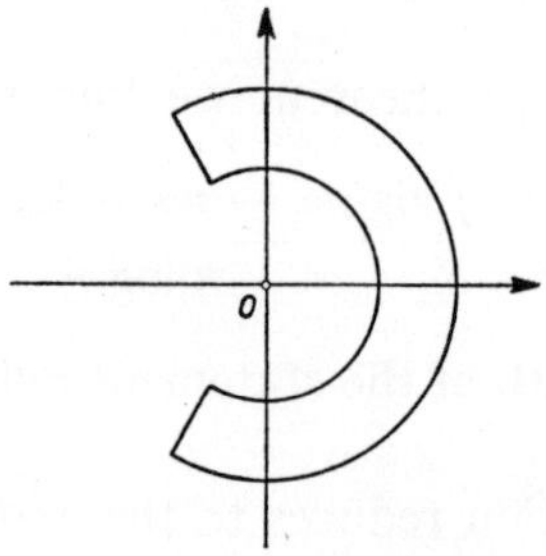

Fig. 6.13–2. Enlargement of the circular part of the path in fig. 6.13–1

4.7.6 on replacing t by t^2, or also by observing that this contour can be imbedded in a simply connected region where the integrand is a holomorphic function. Observing that the same reasoning is valid for the part below the real axis we find that Hankel's integral may be written in the form

$$\frac{1}{\Gamma(s)} = \frac{1}{2\pi i} \int_{L(a, \varphi)} e^t t^{-s} \, dt, \quad \tfrac{1}{2}\pi < \varphi < \pi, \quad a > 0. \qquad (6.13\text{–}3)$$

The last result enables us to represent Mittag-Leffler's function as a loop-integral. In fact

$$E_\alpha(z) = \sum_{\nu=0}^{\infty} \frac{z^\nu}{2\pi i} \int_{L(a, \varphi)} e^t t^{-\alpha\nu - 1} \, dt = \frac{1}{2\pi i} \int_{L(a, \varphi)} \frac{e^t}{t} \sum_{\nu=0}^{\infty} \left(\frac{z}{t^\alpha}\right)^\nu dt$$

or

$$\boxed{E_\alpha(z) = \frac{1}{2\pi i} \int_{L(a, \varphi)} \frac{e^t t^{\alpha - 1}}{t^\alpha - z} \, dt,} \qquad (6.13\text{–}4)$$

the reversal of the order of integration and summation being easily justified. The transformation of the series into an integral assumes that $|z|$ is sufficiently small. But the result is always true on account of the identity principle, for we may take a such that z lies on the left of the path of integration and that $t^\alpha \neq z$ on this path by suitable choice of φ.

6.13.3 – Asymptotic behaviour of Mittag-Leffler's function

We consider two positions of $L(a, \varphi)$. In the first we take $a = 1$, in the second a will be greater than $(2r)^{1/\alpha}$, $|z| = r$. It is our aim to investigate the behaviour of $E_\alpha(z)$ for large $|z|$ and, therefore, we may assume $|z| > 1$. It is plain that all zeros of $t^\alpha - z$ lie to the left of the second loop. By the residue theorem

$$E_\alpha(z) = E(z) + \sum_k R_k, \tag{6.13–5}$$

where

$$E(z) = \frac{1}{2\pi i}\int_{L(1,\varphi)} \frac{e^t t^{\alpha-1}}{t^\alpha - z}\,dt, \tag{6.13–6}$$

and the R_k are the residues of the integrand at the poles, if any, which lie between $L(1, \varphi)$ and $L(a, \varphi)$. If φ is so chosen that no pole lies on $L(1, \varphi)$ and is sufficiently near $\frac{1}{2}\pi$ then these poles are

$$t = r^{1/\alpha} e^{i(\theta+2k\pi)/\alpha}, \quad \theta = \arg z, \tag{6.13–7}$$

where k runs through integers satisfying

$$-\tfrac{1}{2}\alpha\pi \leqq \theta + 2k\pi \leqq \tfrac{1}{2}\alpha\pi \tag{6.13–8}$$

and, according to (3.3–8),

$$R_k = \frac{1}{\alpha} e^{r^{1/\alpha} e^{i(\theta+2k\pi)/\alpha}} \tag{6.13–9}$$

First we wish to prove that

$$|zE(z)|$$

remains bounded when z tends to infinity along a ray issuing from the origin. To this end we remark that the rectilinear parts of L can be chosen in such a fashion that the points $z^{1/\alpha}$, where z moves along a ray as mentioned above, do not lie on it. As a consequence the expression $|t^\alpha/z - 1|$ has a positive lower bound m when t and z move along their own paths. Now

$$zE(z) = \frac{1}{2\pi i}\int_L \frac{e^t t^{\alpha-1}}{t^\alpha/z - 1}\,dt, \tag{6.13–10}$$

and it is clear that the modulus of the expression on the right is dominated by the modulus of

$$\frac{1}{2\pi i m}\int_L e^t t^{\alpha-1}\,dt = \frac{1}{m\Gamma(1-\alpha)}.$$

This proves the assertion.

We wish to consider the cases $0 < \alpha < 2$, $\alpha = 2$, only.

Case (i). If $0 < \alpha < 2$ and $\frac{1}{2}\alpha\pi < |\theta| \leqq \pi$ then there is no k satisfying (6.13–8). The function $E_\alpha(z)$ coincides with $E(z)$. If $|\theta| \leqq \frac{1}{2}\alpha\pi$ then only $k = 0$ satisfies (6.13–8). Summing up we have for $0 < \alpha < 2$

$$\lim_{z\to\infty} E_\alpha(z) = 0, \quad \tfrac{1}{2}\alpha\pi < |\arg z| \leqq \pi \tag{6.13–11}$$

and

$$\lim_{z\to\infty} \alpha e^{-z^{1/\alpha}} E_\alpha(z) = 1, \quad |\arg z| \leqq \tfrac{1}{2}\alpha\pi. \tag{6.13–12}$$

On the lines $\arg z = \pm\frac{1}{2}\alpha\pi$ we have

$$\lim_{r\to\infty} \alpha(\cos r^{1/\alpha} \mp i \sin r^{1/\alpha})^{-1} E_\alpha(z) = 1 \tag{6.13–13}$$

and hence $|E_\alpha(z)|$ remains bounded and tends to $1/\alpha$.

Case (ii). The case $\alpha = 2$ offers no difficulty, since

$$E_2(z) = \cosh\sqrt{z}$$

and it is evident that (6.13–12) is also valid in this case, provided $\theta \neq \pi$. On the negative real axis $\cosh\sqrt{z} = \cos\sqrt{r}$ and hence the function is bounded along this half-line.

6.13.4 – The Lindelöf-Phragmén diagram

If $f(z)$ is an integral function of order ϱ then on a certain line $\arg z = \theta =$ constant the inequality

$$\log|f(re^{i\theta})| < r^{\varrho+\varepsilon} \tag{6.13–14}$$

holds for all sufficiently large values of r. It may occur that we can find a constant A such that

$$\log|f(re^{i\theta})| < Ar^{\varrho} \tag{6.13–15}$$

for all sufficiently large values of r. If so, then there is a greatest lower bound $h(\theta)$ of the set of these numbers A which, of course, depends on θ. It is defined by

$$\boxed{h(\theta) = \limsup_{r\to\infty} \frac{\log|f(re^{i\theta})|}{r^{\varrho}}} \tag{6.13–16}$$

and referred to as the *Lindelöf-Phragmén function* corresponding to the given integral function $f(z)$. It measures the rate of increase of the integral function in a given direction. It may be pictured in a polar diagram which we shall call the *Lindelöf-Phragmén diagram* of the integral function.

It is an easy matter to find such diagrams in the case of Mittag-Leffler's function.

When $0 < \alpha < 2$ and $|\theta| \leqq \frac{1}{2}\alpha\pi$ the function $zE_\alpha(z)$ is bounded. Hence $h(\theta)$ is zero for these directions. In the other directions the function $E_\alpha(z)$ behaves like $\exp z^{1/\alpha}$ and $h(\theta) = \cos(\theta/\alpha)$.

In fig. 6.13–3 the diagrams have been plotted when $\alpha = \frac{1}{2}, 1, 2$ respectively. When $\alpha = 1$ the diagram is a circle.

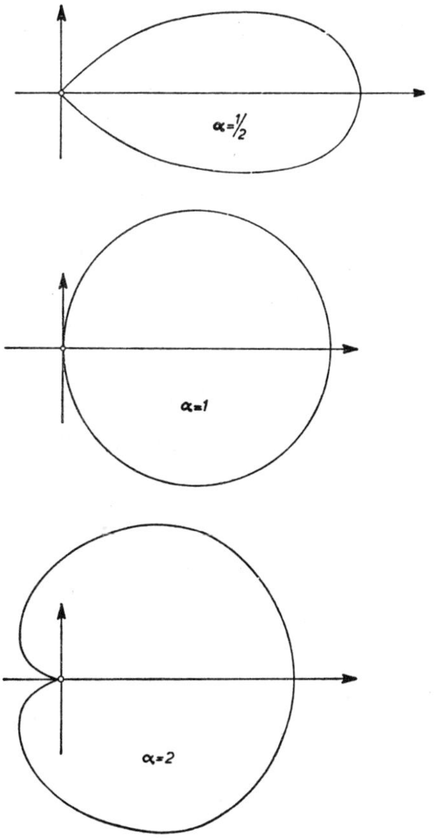

Fig. 6.13–3. Lindelöf-Phragmén diagrams for Mittag-Leffler's function for the cases $\alpha = \frac{1}{2}$, $\alpha = 1$, $\alpha = 2$.

Chapter 7

DIRICHLET SERIES
THE ZETA FUNCTION OF RIEMANN
THE LAPLACE INTEGRAL

7.1 – Dirichlet series. Absolute convergence

7.1.1 – Definition of a Dirichlet series

By a *general Dirichlet series* is understood a series of the form

$$\sum_{\nu=0}^{\infty} a_\nu e^{-\lambda_\nu s} \tag{7.1–1}$$

where $\lambda_0, \lambda_1, \ldots$ is a sequence of real numbers, increasing monotonically beyond any preassigned positive bound,

$$\lambda_0 < \lambda_1 < \ldots \to \infty.$$

The variable s is a complex variable and $a_0, a_1, \ldots$ is a sequence of complex numbers. They are called the *coefficients* of the series. In most cases we shall assume $\lambda_0 \geqq 0$, but sometimes it is desirable to admit a finite number of terms with $\lambda_n < 0$. The sequence $\lambda_0, \lambda_1, \ldots$ is termed the *type* of the series.

A very important type is characterized by $\lambda_n = \log n$, $a_0 = 0$. A series of the form

$$\sum_{\nu=1}^{\infty} a_\nu \nu^{-s} = \frac{a_1}{1^s} + \frac{a_2}{2^s} + \ldots \tag{7.1–2}$$

is called an *ordinary Dirichlet series*. A particular case of utmost importance is the series

$$\zeta(s) = \sum_{\nu=1}^{\infty} \nu^{-s}, \tag{7.1–3}$$

representing the *zeta function of Riemann*.

As a matter of fact we are only interested in the cases where the series possesses a region of convergence and it will be our task to study the functions defined by the sum.

In many respects the theory of Dirichlet series is more complicated than that of power series. In the latter case the circles of convergence and of absolute convergence coincide. In the theory of Dirichlet series the word "circle" must be replaced by "half-plane", but the corresponding half-planes may be different.

7.1.2 – Absolute convergence

Things are quite simple when we are concerned with absolute convergence. The Dirichlet series (7.1–1) is called *absolutely convergent,* when the series

$$\sum_{\nu=0}^{\infty} |a_\nu e^{-\lambda_\nu s}| \tag{7.1–4}$$

is convergent. We shall prove the theorem:

If a Dirichlet series (7.1–1) *is absolutely convergent at* $s = s_0$ *it is also absolutely convergent at* s, *when* $\operatorname{Re} s \geqq \operatorname{Re} s_0$.

In fact, if ε is a positive number, there is a number n_0 such that

$$\sum_{\nu=m}^{n} \left|a_\nu e^{-\lambda_\nu s_0}\right| < \varepsilon$$

provided that $m > n > n_0$. Hence

$$\sum_{\nu=n}^{m} \left|a_\nu e^{-\lambda_\nu s}\right| = \sum_{\nu=n}^{m} \left|a_\nu e^{-\lambda_\nu s_0} e^{-\lambda(s-s_0)}\right| \tag{7.1–5}$$

$$= \sum_{\nu=n}^{m} \left|a_\nu e^{-\lambda_\nu s_0}\right| e^{-\lambda_\nu \operatorname{Re}(s-s_0)} \leqq \sum_{\nu=n}^{m} \left|a_\nu e^{-\lambda_\nu s_0}\right| e^{-\lambda_n \operatorname{Re}(s-s_0)} < \varepsilon,$$

whenever $n > n_0$. This proves the assertion.

7.1.3 – Abscissa of absolute convergence

It follows that when the series (7.1–1) is not absolutely convergent at $s = s_0$ it is not absolutely convergent at s, with $\operatorname{Re} s \leqq \operatorname{Re} s_0$. We can divide the values $\operatorname{Re} s_0$ into two classes, the first class containing those for which the series is absolutely convergent as soon as $\operatorname{Re} s \geqq \operatorname{Re} s_0$, and the second class containing the other values of $\operatorname{Re} s_0$. When none of these classes is empty then, by the above theorem, every member of the first class is not smaller than any member of the second class. By well-known arguments there exists a number σ_a such that the series is absolutely convergent if $\operatorname{Re} s > \sigma_a$ and not absolutely convergent if $\operatorname{Re} s < \sigma_a$. It is convenient to take $\sigma_a = -\infty$ if the series is absolutely convergent everywhere in the plane, and $\sigma_a = +\infty$ when the series is nowhere absolutely convergent.

The number σ_a is called the *abscissa of absolute convergence.* The line $\operatorname{Re} s = \sigma_a$ is the boundary of a half-plane containing all points to the right of this line, the half-plane of absolute convergence. The line may or may not belong to the half-plane of absolute convergence. In the latter case none of its points are points of absolute convergence. Otherwise stated: *The half-plane of absolute convergence is either open or closed.*

In the proof of the theorem of section 7.1.2 we obtained an estimate (7.1–5) independent of s. Hence:

If the series (7.1–1) *is absolutely convergent at* $s = s_0$ *it is uniformly convergent in the half-plane* $\operatorname{Re} s \geqq \operatorname{Re} s_0$.

7.1.4 – Illustrative examples

The previous considerations may be illustrated in some simple examples. The series

$$\sum_{\nu=1}^{\infty} \nu^{-s} \tag{7.1–6}$$

is absolutely convergent for $\operatorname{Re} s > 1$ and divergent for $\operatorname{Re} s \leqq 1$. In fact, we have

$$\int_{n-1}^{n} \frac{dx}{x^\sigma} \geqq \frac{1}{n^\sigma} \geqq \int_{n}^{n+1} \frac{dx}{x^\sigma}, \quad \sigma = \operatorname{Re} s \geqq 1,$$

whence

$$\int_{1}^{n} \frac{dx}{x^\sigma} \geqq \sum_{\nu=2}^{n} \nu^{-\sigma} \geqq \int_{2}^{n+1} \frac{dx}{x^\sigma},$$

and the truth of the assertion follows by observing that

$$\int_{1}^{x} \frac{dx}{x^\sigma} = \begin{cases} \log x, & \text{when } \sigma = 1 \\ \dfrac{1}{1-\sigma}(x^{1-\sigma}-1), & \text{when } \sigma > 1. \end{cases}$$

As a consequence $\sigma_a = 1$, but the line $\operatorname{Re} s = 1$ does not belong to the half-plane of absolute convergence.

Next we consider the series

$$\sum_{\nu=1}^{\infty} \nu^{-s} \log^{-2} \nu \tag{7.1–7}$$

and let $0 < \sigma = \operatorname{Re} s < 1$. Then

$$\sum_{\nu=2}^{n} \nu^{-\sigma} \log^{-2} \nu > \log^{-2} n \sum_{\nu=2}^{n} \nu^{-\sigma} > \frac{n^{1-\sigma}-2^{1-\sigma}}{\log^2 n}.$$

The sum on the left tends to ∞ as $n \to \infty$ and so the series is divergent for $\sigma < 1$. On the other hand, when $\sigma \geqq 1$ we have

$$\sum_{\nu=3}^{n} \nu^{-\sigma} \log^{-2} \nu \leqq \sum_{\nu=3}^{n} \frac{1}{\nu \log^2 \nu} \leqq \sum_{\nu=2}^{n-1} \int_{\nu}^{\nu+1} \frac{dx}{x \log^2 x} = \int_{2}^{n} \frac{dx}{x \log^2 x}$$
$$= \frac{1}{\log 2} - \frac{1}{\log n} < \frac{1}{\log 2}.$$

We find the result $\sigma_a = 1$ and the line $\operatorname{Re} s = 1$ belongs to the half-plane of absolute convergence.

7.2 Simple convergence

7.2.1 – Abscissa of simple convergence

The situation regarding convergence is almost just as simple as in the case of absolute convergence, but the proofs are more intricate. A first result in this direction has been obtained by Jensen. He proved the theorem:

If the Dirichlet series (7.1–1) *is convergent at* $s = s_0$, *then it is also convergent for any value of* s *with* $\operatorname{Re} s > \operatorname{Re} s_0$.

Admitting for the present the truth of this statement we can also define an *abscissa of simple convergence* σ_c, such that the series is convergent for $\operatorname{Re} s > \sigma_c$ and divergent for $\operatorname{Re} s < \sigma_c$. Concerning the convergence of the series on the line $\operatorname{Re} s = \sigma_c$ various cases are possible as in the case of power series.

It should be noticed that in contrast with power series the numbers σ_a and σ_c need not be the same. In any case

$$\sigma_c \leqq \sigma_a. \tag{7.2–1}$$

In fact,

$$\Big|\sum_{\nu=n}^{m} a_\nu e^{-\lambda_\nu s}\Big| \leqq \sum_{\nu=n}^{m} |a_\nu| e^{-\lambda_\nu \operatorname{Re} s}.$$

In general there will be a strip between the lines of convergence and absolute convergence throughout which the series is convergent, but not absolutely convergent. The strip may vanish (if $\sigma_c = \sigma_a$) or comprise the entire plane ($\sigma_c = -\infty$, $\sigma_a = +\infty$). We already encountered examples of the first situation (for the coefficients were all positive). An example of the second case is the following. The series

$$\sum_{\nu=2}^{\infty} (-1)^\nu \nu^{-\frac{1}{2}} \log^{-s} \nu = \sum_{\nu=2}^{\infty} (-1)^\nu \nu^{-\frac{1}{2}} e^{-s \log\log \nu}$$

is convergent for all values of s, but never absolutely convergent. The proof is quite simple. If s is a real number the series is alternating, its terms (taken absolutely) tending monotonically to zero. By an elementary test (Leibniz's test) the series is convergent. On the other hand, the series

$$\sum_{\nu=2}^{\infty} \nu^{-\frac{1}{2}} \log^{-s} \nu$$

is always divergent. We have only to investigate the case $s = \sigma \geqq 0$ and the argument runs as in the example (7.1–7).

7.2.2 – Cahen's theorem

Jensen's theorem is included in a less elementary theorem due to Cahen.

If a Dirichlet series (7.1–1) is convergent for $s = s_0$ it is uniformly convergent throughout the angular area defined by

$$|\arg (s-s_0)| \leqq \vartheta \tag{7.2–2}$$

where ϑ is any fixed positive number $< \frac{1}{2}\pi$, (fig. 7.2–1).

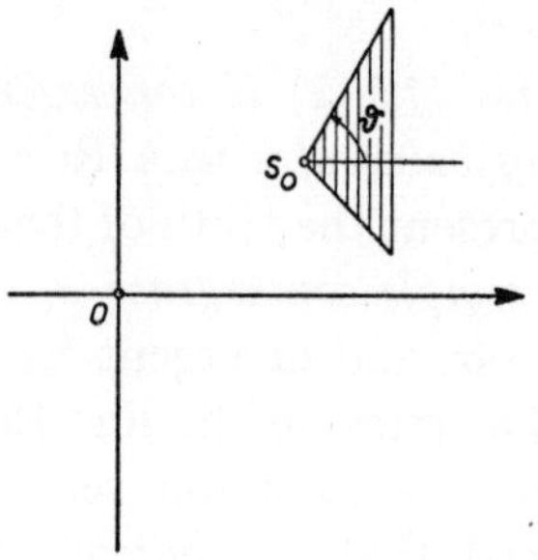

Fig. 7.2–1. Domain of uniform convergence

The main tool in the proof will be Abel's method of summation by parts, already discussed in section 1.8.2. We suppose that the series

$$\sum_{\nu=0}^{\infty} a_\nu e^{-\lambda_\nu s_0} \tag{7.2–3}$$

is convergent. We put

$$R_n = \sum_{\nu=n+1}^{\infty} a_\nu e^{-\lambda_\nu s_0}, \qquad n = 0, 1, 2, \ldots, \tag{7.2–4}$$

and we write, assuming $m > n > 1$,

$$\sum_{\nu=n}^{m} a_\nu e^{-\lambda_\nu s} = \sum_{\nu=n}^{m} a_\nu e^{-\lambda_\nu s_0} e^{-\lambda_\nu (s-s_0)} = \sum_{\nu=n}^{m} (R_{\nu-1}-R_\nu) e^{-\lambda_\nu (s-s_0)}$$

$$= R_{n-1} e^{-\lambda_n (s-s_0)} - R_m e^{-\lambda_m (s-s_0)} + \sum_{\nu=n}^{m-1} R_\nu (e^{-\lambda_{\nu+1}(s-s_0)} - e^{-\lambda_\nu (s-s_0)})$$

$$= R_{n-1} e^{-\lambda_n (s-s_0)} - R_m e^{-\lambda_m (s-s_0)} - \sum_{\nu=n}^{m-1} R_\nu (s-s_0) \int_{\lambda_\nu}^{\lambda_{\nu+1}} e^{-t(s-s_0)}\, dt.$$

If $\operatorname{Re}(s-s_0) \geqq 0$, then $e^{-\lambda_n \operatorname{Re}(s-s_0)} \leqq 1$ for all sufficiently large n. Let ε be a given positive number. For all sufficiently large values of n the numbers (7.2–4) are numerically smaller than ε. For those values of n we have

$$\left| \sum_{\nu=n}^{m-1} R_\nu \int_{\lambda_\nu}^{\lambda_{\nu+1}} e^{-t(s-s_0)}\, dt \right| < \varepsilon \int_{\lambda_n}^{\lambda_m} e^{-t \operatorname{Re}(s-s_0)}\, dt < \varepsilon \int_{\lambda_n}^{\infty} e^{-t \operatorname{Re}(s-s_0)}\, dt$$

$$= \frac{\varepsilon}{\operatorname{Re}(s-s_0)} e^{-\lambda_n \operatorname{Re}(s-s_0)} \leqq \frac{\varepsilon}{\operatorname{Re}(s-s_0)}.$$

Hence

$$\left|\sum_{\nu=n}^{m} a_\nu e^{-\lambda_\nu s}\right| < \varepsilon\left(2+\frac{|s-s_0|}{\operatorname{Re}(s-s_0)}\right) \leqq \varepsilon(2+\sec\vartheta), \qquad (7.2\text{–}5)$$

since

$$\frac{|s-s_0|}{\operatorname{Re}(s-s_0)} \leqq \sec\vartheta,$$

the estimate (7.2–5) being valid for all sufficiently large n, $m > n$ and $\operatorname{Re}(s-s_0) > 0$. Since the last member of (7.2–5) is independent of s the truth of the statement follows.

7.2.3 – Asymptotic behaviour

The following theorem can easily be deduced from Cahen's theorem.

If a Dirichlet series (7.1–1) *with* $\lambda_0 > 0$ *is convergent at* $s = s_0$ *its sum tends uniformly to zero as* $s \to \infty$ *in the area* (7.2–2).

We may write

$$\sum_{\nu=0}^{\infty} a_\nu e^{-\lambda_\nu s} = \sum_{\nu=0}^{n} a_\nu e^{-\lambda_\nu s} + \sum_{\nu=n+1}^{\infty} a_\nu e^{-\lambda_\nu s}.$$

Let ε denote a positive number. Taking account of the uniform convergence of the series we can take n so large that

$$\left|\sum_{\nu=n+1}^{\infty} a_\nu e^{-\lambda_\nu s}\right| < \tfrac{1}{2}\varepsilon$$

for all s in the area (7.2–2). Moreover, it is possible to find a real number σ such that

$$\left|\sum_{\nu=0}^{n} a_\nu e^{-\lambda_\nu s}\right| < \tfrac{1}{2}\varepsilon$$

whenever $\operatorname{Re} s > \sigma$. Hence

$$\left|\sum_{\nu=0}^{\infty} a_\nu e^{-\lambda_\nu s}\right| < \varepsilon$$

for s in the area and $\operatorname{Re} s > \sigma$.

A simple corollary is:

If a Dirichlet series (7.1–1) *is convergent at* $s = s_0$ *then its sum is bounded in the area* (7.2–2) *for any* $\vartheta < \frac{1}{2}\pi$.

7.2.4 – The Dirichlet series representing a holomorphic function

Finally we have:

In the half-plane of simple convergence the sum $\varphi(s)$ *of the Dirichlet function* (7.1–1) *is a holomorphic function.*

We can draw an angle of the type considered in Cahen's theorem its vertex being a point sufficiently near the line of convergence Re $s = \sigma_c$ and including any given and bounded set to the right of this line. Hence the series is uniformly convergent throughout such a set and since all terms are integral functions, the assertion follows from Weierstrass's theorem of section 2.20.3.

A direct consequence of this theorem is an analogue of Abel's theorem for power series of section 1.8.3.

If the Dirichlet series (7.1.–1) *is convergent for* $s = s_0$ *then the sum* $\varphi(s)$ *tends to* $\varphi(s_0)$ *as* $s \to s_0$ *along any path which lies in an angular area defined by* (7.2–2).

It is plain that it gives only any information beyond that what is given by the previous theorem when s_0 lies on the line of simple convergence.

7.3 – Formulas for the abscissa of convergence

7.3.1 – Statement and proof of the formulas

We wish to derive a formula for the abscissa of convergence in terms of the coefficients and the exponents of a Dirichlet series. The situation is not quite so simple as in the case of the Cauchy-Hadamard formula (1.6–11) for the radius of convergence of a power series. The formula takes slightly different forms according to whether $\sigma_c \geqq 0$ or $\sigma_c < 0$.

The abscissa of simple convergence of the Dirichlet series (7.1–1) *is given by*

$$\boxed{\sigma_c = \limsup_{n\to\infty} \frac{\log \left|\sum_{\nu=0}^{n} a_\nu\right|}{\lambda_n}} \qquad (7.3\text{–}1)$$

if $\sigma_c > 0$ *and by*

$$\boxed{\sigma_c = \limsup_{n\to\infty} \frac{\log \left|\sum_{\nu=n}^{\infty} a_\nu\right|}{\lambda_n}} \qquad (7.3\text{–}2)$$

if $\sigma_c < 0$.

Let

$$A_n = \sum_{\nu=0}^{n} a_\nu \qquad (7.3\text{–}3)$$

and

$$\alpha = \limsup_{n\to\infty} \frac{\log |A_n|}{\lambda_n}. \tag{7.3–4}$$

If A_n does not tend to zero there is a positive number p such that $\log |A_n| > -p$ for an infinity of values of n. Hence among the numbers $-p/\lambda_n$ there are infinitely many as near to zero as we want and this implies $\alpha \geqq 0$. We suppose further that $\alpha < +\infty$. We shall prove that the series (7.1–1) is convergent for $s = \sigma$ when $\sigma > \alpha$. Let ε be a number such that $\sigma - \varepsilon > \alpha$. The equation (7.3–4) implies that we can find a number n_0 such that

$$\frac{\log |A_n|}{\lambda_n} < \sigma - \varepsilon$$

or

$$|A_n| < e^{\lambda_n(\sigma-\varepsilon)} \tag{7.3–5}$$

provided that $n > n_0$. By Abel's method of summation by parts we find

$$\begin{aligned}\sum_{\nu=0}^{n} a_\nu e^{-\lambda_\nu \sigma} &= A_0 e^{-\lambda_0 \sigma} + \sum_{\nu=1}^{n} (A_\nu - A_{\nu-1}) e^{-\lambda_\nu \sigma} \\ &= \sum_{\nu=0}^{n-1} A_\nu (e^{-\lambda_\nu \sigma} - e^{-\lambda_{\nu+1}\sigma}) + A_n e^{-\lambda_n \sigma} \\ &= \sum_{\nu=0}^{n-1} A_\nu \sigma \int_{\lambda_\nu}^{\lambda_{\nu+1}} e^{-\sigma t}\, dt + A_n e^{-\lambda_n \sigma}.\end{aligned}$$

Taking account of (7.3–5) we have

$$|A_n e^{-\lambda_n \sigma}| < e^{-\lambda_n \varepsilon}.$$

Hence the last term on the right tends to zero as $n \to \infty$. It remains to establish the convergence of the series

$$\sum_{\nu=0}^{\infty} A_\nu \int_{\lambda_\nu}^{\lambda_{\nu+1}} e^{-\sigma t}\, dt.$$

We have

$$\left|A_n \int_{\lambda_n}^{\lambda_{n+1}} e^{-\sigma t}\, dt\right| \leqq \int_{\lambda_n}^{\lambda_{n+1}} e^{-\varepsilon t}\, dt,$$

provided that $n > n_0$. The series

$$\sum_{\nu=0}^{\infty} \int_{\lambda_\nu}^{\lambda_{\nu+1}} e^{-\varepsilon t}\, dt$$

is convergent, its sum being

$$\int_{\lambda_0}^{\infty} e^{-\varepsilon t}\, dt = \frac{1}{\varepsilon} e^{-\varepsilon \lambda_0}.$$

This proves the assertion.

The foregoing considerations lead to the result

$$\sigma_c \leqq \alpha. \tag{7.3–6}$$

Next we take a *positive* number $\sigma > \sigma_c$. Put

$$b_n = a_n e^{-\lambda_n \sigma}, \qquad n = 0, 1, 2, \ldots,$$

and

$$B_n = \sum_{\nu=0}^{n} b_\nu. \tag{7.3–7}$$

Since the Dirichlet series (7.1–1) is convergent for $s = \sigma$ the numbers B_n are bounded:

$$|B_n| \leqq B.$$

By summation by parts we find

$$A_n = \sum_{\nu=0}^{n} a_\nu = \sum_{\nu=0}^{n} b_\nu e^{\lambda_\nu \sigma} = B_0 e^{\lambda_0 \sigma} + \sum_{\nu=1}^{n} (B_\nu - B_{\nu-1}) e^{\lambda_\nu \sigma}$$

$$= \sum_{\nu=0}^{n-1} B_\nu (e^{\lambda_\nu \sigma} - e^{\lambda_{\nu+1} \sigma}) + B_n e^{\lambda_n \sigma} = -\sum_{\nu=0}^{n-1} B_\nu \sigma \int_{\lambda_\nu}^{\lambda_{\nu+1}} e^{\sigma t}\, dt + B_n e^{\lambda_n \sigma},$$

and, since σ is positive,

$$|A_n| \leqq B\sigma \sum_{\nu=0}^{n-1} \int_{\lambda_\nu}^{\lambda_{\nu+1}} e^{\sigma t}\, dt + B e^{\lambda_n \sigma} \leqq B\sigma \int_{\lambda_0}^{\lambda_n} e^{\sigma t}\, dt + B e^{\lambda_n \sigma},$$

whence

$$|A_n| \leqq 2B e^{\lambda_n \sigma}. \tag{7.3–8}$$

This inequality is equivalent to

$$\frac{\log |A_n|}{\lambda_n} < \frac{\log 2B}{\lambda_n} + \sigma$$

and so $\alpha \leqq \sigma$. If $\sigma_c < 0$ then σ can be any positive number. If $\sigma_c \geqq 0$ then $\sigma > \sigma_c$. In all cases

$$\alpha \leqq \max(\sigma_c, 0). \tag{7.3–9}$$

In the case that $\sigma_c > 0$ it is clear that A_n does not tend to zero. Hence (7.3–9) and (7.3–6) combine into (7.3–1).

Hitherto we excluded the case $\alpha = +\infty$. But the argument shows that the assumption, that only one of the numbers σ_c, α is finite, leads to a contradiction. Analyzing the proof it appears that (7.3–1) is also valid for $\sigma_c = 0$, provided A_n does not tend to zero as $n \to \infty$.

Now we suppose $\sigma_c < 0$. Then the series $\sum_{\nu=0}^{\infty} a_\nu$ is convergent. Let

$$R_n = \sum_{\nu=n+1}^{\infty} a_\nu \tag{7.3–10}$$

and

$$\beta = \limsup_{n\to\infty} \frac{\log |R_{n-1}|}{\lambda_n}. \tag{7.3–11}$$

Proceeding along the same lines as above we easily deduce that the series (7.1–1) is convergent for $s = \sigma > \beta$, hence

$$\sigma_c \leqq \beta. \tag{7.3–12}$$

Let now

$$\sigma_c < \sigma < 0.$$

Then

$$R_{n-1} = \sum_{\nu=n}^{\infty} a_\nu = \sum_{\nu=n}^{\infty} b_\nu e^{\lambda_\nu \sigma} = \sum_{\nu=n}^{\infty} (B_\nu - B_{\nu-1}) e^{\lambda_\nu \sigma}$$

$$= \sum_{\nu=n}^{\infty} B_\nu (e^{\lambda_\nu \sigma} - e^{\lambda_{\nu+1}\sigma}) - B_{n-1} e^{\lambda_n \sigma} = -\sum_{\nu=n}^{\infty} B_\nu \sigma \int_{\lambda_\nu}^{\lambda_{\nu+1}} e^{\sigma t}\, dt - B_{n-1} e^{\lambda_n \sigma}.$$

Remembering that $\sigma < 0$ we deduce

$$|R_{n-1}| \leqq -B\sigma \sum_{\nu=n}^{\infty} \int_{\lambda_\nu}^{\lambda_{\nu+1}} e^{\sigma t}\, dt + B e^{\lambda_n \sigma},$$

whence

$$|R_{n-1}| \leqq 2B e^{\lambda_n \sigma}. \tag{7.3–13}$$

As a consequence we have

$$\frac{\log |R_{n-1}|}{\lambda_n} \leqq \frac{\log 2B}{\lambda_n} + \sigma$$

and so $\beta \leqq \sigma$. Since σ can be any negative number $> \sigma_c$ we have

$$\beta \leqq \sigma_c. \tag{7.3–14}$$

The inequalities (7.3–12) and (7.3–14) combine into (7.3–2).

7.3.2 – The breadth of the strip of conditional convergence

We already pointed out that the abscissa of simple convergence σ_c and the abscissa of absolute convergence σ_a are not necessarily the same. For a given series we can derive an estimate of the breadth of the strip of conditional convergence.

The breadth $\sigma_a - \sigma_c$ *of the strip of conditional convergence of the Dirichlet series* (7.5.1) *satisfies the inequality*

$$\boxed{\sigma_a - \sigma_c \leqq \limsup_{n\to\infty} \frac{\log n}{\lambda_n}.} \tag{7.3–15}$$

Let λ denote the value of the right hand member of (7.3–15). When $\lambda = \infty$ the theorem is obvious. Suppose that λ is a finite number. Evidently $\lambda \geqq 0$. The theorem is proved if we can establish the following statement. When the series (7.1–1) is convergent for the real number $s = \sigma$ it is absolutely convergent for $s = \sigma+\lambda+\varepsilon$, where ε is any positive number. By hypothesis $a_n e^{-\lambda_n \sigma}$ tends to zero as $n \to \infty$. Hence for sufficiently large values of n

$$|a_n| e^{-\lambda_n \sigma} < 1 .$$

and

$$|a_n| e^{-\lambda_n(\sigma+\lambda+\varepsilon)} = |a_n| e^{-\lambda_n \sigma} e^{-\lambda_n(\lambda+\varepsilon)} < e^{-\lambda_n(\lambda+\varepsilon)}.$$

For sufficiently large values of n we also have

$$\frac{\log n}{\lambda_n} < \lambda + \tfrac{1}{2}\varepsilon$$

or

$$\lambda_n > \frac{\log n}{\lambda+\frac{1}{2}\varepsilon}.$$

Hence

$$|a_n| e^{-\lambda_n(\sigma+\lambda+\varepsilon)} < n^{-(\lambda+\varepsilon)/(\lambda+\frac{1}{2}\varepsilon)},$$

and since $(\lambda+\varepsilon)/(\lambda+\frac{1}{2}\varepsilon) > 1$ the series under consideration is dominated by a convergent series. This completes the proof.

In the case of an ordinary Dirichlet series we have $\lambda_n = \log n$ and the breadth of the strip does not exceed unity.

The abscissas of convergence coincide when

$$\frac{\log n}{\lambda_n} \to 0 \tag{7.3–16}$$

as $n \to \infty$. In this case it is not difficult to show (proceeding by a method similar to that used in the proof of the first theorem of this section) that

$$\sigma_a = \sigma_c = \limsup_{n\to\infty} \frac{\log |a_n|}{\lambda_n}. \tag{7.3–17}$$

This formula may be considered as the analogue of the Cauchy-Hadamard formula for the radius of convergence of power series.

7.4 – The representation of a Dirichlet series by an infinite integral

7.4.1 – Statement and proof of the representation

Let the Dirichlet series

$$\sum_{\nu=0}^{\infty} a_\nu e^{-\lambda_\nu s} \tag{7.4–1}$$

be convergent for some value of s with $\text{Re}\, s > 0$. We introduce new numbers μ_n by putting

$$\mu_n = e^{\lambda_n}, \qquad n = 0, 1, 2, \ldots. \tag{7.4–2}$$

Taking the Euler integral

$$\Gamma(s) = \int_0^\infty e^{-t} t^{s-1}\, dt, \qquad \text{Re}\, s > 0$$

as a starting point, we readily find

$$\Gamma(s) = \int_0^\infty e^{-\mu_n t} (\mu_n t)^{s-1} d(\mu_n t) = \mu_n^s \int_0^\infty e^{-\mu_n t} t^{s-1}\, dt,$$

whence

$$\Gamma(s) e^{-\lambda_n s} = \Gamma(s) \mu_n^{-s} = \int_0^\infty e^{-\mu_n t} t^{s-1}\, dt. \tag{7.4–3}$$

This leads to the conjecture

$$\boxed{\Gamma(s) \sum_{\nu=0}^\infty a_\nu e^{-\lambda_\nu s} = \int_0^\infty \sum_{\nu=0}^\infty a_\nu e^{-\mu_\nu t} t^{s-1}\, dt.} \tag{7.4–4}$$

In the first place we wish to prove that the abscissa of convergence of the series

$$\sum_{\nu=0}^\infty a_\nu e^{-\mu_\nu t} \tag{7.4–5}$$

occurring in the integrand of (7.4–4) is not positive. For in the contrary case we should have on account of (7.3–1)

$$0 < \limsup_{n\to\infty} \frac{\log \left|\sum_{\nu=0}^n a_\nu\right|}{\mu_n} = \limsup_{n\to\infty} \frac{\log \left|\sum_{\nu=0}^n a_\nu\right|}{\lambda_n} \cdot \frac{\log \mu_n}{\mu_n} = 0,$$

since $\log \mu_n$ increases more slowly than μ_n as $n \to \infty$.

After these preliminaries we proceed to establish the validity of the equation (7.4–4). Since the series (7.4–5) is uniformly convergent for $0 < \varepsilon \leqq t \leqq \omega$ the process of term-by-term integration is justified over the interval from ε to ω:

$$\int_\varepsilon^\omega \left(\sum_{\nu=0}^\infty a_\nu e^{-\mu_\nu t}\right) t^{s-1}\, dt = \sum_{\nu=0}^\infty \int_\varepsilon^\omega a_\nu e^{-\mu_\nu t} t^{s-1}\, dt.$$

It remains to establish the convergence of the integral on the left as $\varepsilon \to 0$ and $\omega \to \infty$, for the validity of (7.4–4) follows then at once from (7.4–3).

Assuming that the series (7.4–1) is convergent for all s satisfying $\text{Re}\, s > \sigma \geqq 0$, we find when t is positive and δ denotes an arbitrary positive number:

$$\sum_{\nu=0}^{\infty} a_\nu e^{-\mu_\nu t} = \sum_{\nu=0}^{\infty} a_\nu e^{-\lambda_\nu(\sigma+\delta)} \mu_\nu^{\sigma+\delta} e^{-\mu_\nu t}$$

$$= \sum_{\nu=0}^{\infty} (s_\nu - s_{\nu-1}) \mu_\nu^{\sigma+\delta} e^{-\mu_\nu t},$$

where

$$s_n = \sum_{\nu=0}^{n} a_\nu e^{-\lambda_\nu(\sigma+\delta)}, \quad s_{-1} = 0.$$

By summation by parts we arrive at

$$\sum_{\nu=0}^{\infty} a_\nu e^{-\mu_\nu t} = \sum_{\nu=0}^{\infty} s_\nu (e^{-\mu_\nu t} \mu_\nu^{\sigma+\delta} - e^{-\mu_{\nu+1} t} \mu_{\nu+1}^{\sigma+\delta}).$$

By hypothesis s_n tends to a limit as $n \to \infty$. Hence we can find a number C such that $|s_n| < C$ for all $n \geqq 0$. Next we wish to prove that the series

$$\sum_{\nu=0}^{\infty} (e^{-\mu_\nu t} \mu_\nu^{\sigma+\delta} - e^{-\mu_{\nu+1} t} \mu_{\nu+1}^{\sigma+\delta})$$

is absolutely convergent. This follows from

$$\sum_{\nu=0}^{\infty} |e^{-\mu_\nu t} \mu_\nu^{\sigma+\delta} - e^{-\mu_{\nu+1} t} \mu_{\nu+1}^{\sigma+\delta}| = \sum_{\nu=1}^{\infty} \left| \int_{\mu_\nu}^{\mu_{\nu+1}} d(e^{-ut} u^{\sigma+\delta}) \right|$$

$$= \sum_{\nu=0}^{\infty} \left| (\sigma+\delta) \int_{\mu_\nu}^{\mu_{\nu+1}} e^{-ut} u^{\sigma+\delta-1} du \right.$$

$$\left. + t \int_{\mu_\nu}^{\mu_{\nu+1}} e^{-ut} u^{\sigma+\delta} du \right|$$

$$< \sum_{\nu=0}^{\infty} (\sigma+\delta) \int_{\mu_\nu}^{\mu_{\nu+1}} e^{-ut} u^{\sigma+\delta-1} du$$

$$+ t \int_{\mu_\nu}^{\mu_{\nu+1}} e^{-ut} u^{\sigma+\delta} du$$

$$= (\sigma+\delta) \int_{\mu_0}^{\infty} e^{-ut} u^{\sigma+\delta-1} du + t \int_{\mu_0}^{\infty} e^{-ut} u^{\sigma+\delta} du.$$

This proves the absolute convergence of the series under consideration. Continuing the proof we make use of the fact that μ_0 is essentially positive. If λ is a positive number we have

$$\int_{\mu_0}^{\infty} e^{-ut} u^{\lambda-1} du < e^{-\frac{1}{2}\mu_0 t} \int_{\mu_0}^{\infty} e^{-\frac{1}{2}ut} u^{\lambda-1} du$$

$$< e^{-\frac{1}{2}\mu_0 t} \int_{0}^{\infty} e^{-\frac{1}{2}ut} u^{\lambda-1} du = 2^\lambda t^{-\lambda} e^{-\frac{1}{2}\mu_0 t} \Gamma(\lambda).$$

Hence we may infer that

$$\sum_{\nu=0}^{\infty} |e^{-\mu_\nu t}\mu_\nu^{\sigma+\delta} - e^{-\mu_{\nu+1}}\mu_{\nu+1}^{\sigma+\delta}| < e^{-\frac{1}{2}\mu_0 t}\{2^{\sigma+\delta}t^{-(\sigma+\delta)}(\sigma+\delta)\Gamma(\sigma+\delta)$$
$$+ 2^{\sigma+\delta+1}t^{-(\sigma+\delta)}\Gamma(\sigma+\delta+1)\}$$
$$= 3\cdot 2^{\sigma+\delta}e^{-\frac{1}{2}\mu_0 t}t^{-(\sigma+\delta)}\Gamma(\sigma+\delta+1).$$

Thus we arrive at the result

$$\left|\sum_{\nu=0}^{\infty} a_\nu e^{-\mu_\nu t}\right| < 3\cdot 2^{\sigma+\delta}C\Gamma(\sigma+\delta+1)e^{-\frac{1}{2}\mu_0 t}t^{-(\sigma+\delta)},$$

whence, if $\operatorname{Re} s > \sigma+\delta$,

$$\left|\int_{\varepsilon}^{\infty}\left(\sum_{\nu=0}^{\infty} a_\nu e^{-\mu_\nu t}\right)t^{s-1}\,dt\right| < C_1\int_0^{\infty} e^{-\frac{1}{2}\mu_0 t}t^{\operatorname{Re} s-(\sigma+\delta)-1}\,dt,$$

where C_1 denotes an appropriate constant.

Hence we can make $\varepsilon \to 0$ and $\omega \to \infty$ and it follows that

$$\int_0^{\infty}\left(\sum_{\nu=0}^{\infty} a_\nu e^{-\mu_\nu t}\right)t^{s-1}\,dt$$

has a meaning, viz.

$$\sum_{\nu=0}^{\infty}\int_0^{\infty} a_\nu e^{-\mu_\nu t}t^{s-1}\,dt = \Gamma(s)\sum_{\nu=0}^{\infty} a_\nu e^{-\lambda_\nu s}.$$

7.4.2 – Application to the Riemann zeta function

The formula (7.4–4) is a precious tool for the study of particular series. As a first example we consider the series

$$\zeta(s) = \sum_{\nu=1}^{\infty} \nu^{-s}, \qquad \operatorname{Re} s > 1. \tag{7.4–6}$$

In this case $\lambda_n = \log n$, $\mu_n = n$, $a_n = 1$, $n = 1, 2, \ldots$. Hence

$$\sum_{\nu=1}^{\infty} a_\nu e^{-\mu_\nu t} = \sum_{\nu=1}^{\infty} e^{-\nu t} = \frac{e^{-t}}{1-e^{-t}} = \frac{1}{e^t-1},$$

and we thus find Riemann's expression for the zeta function as an integral

$$\boxed{\zeta(s)\Gamma(s) = \int_0^{\infty}\frac{t^{s-1}}{e^t-1}\,dt,} \qquad \operatorname{Re} s > 1. \tag{7.4–7}$$

The remarkable similarity between the integral on the right and the Euler integral for the gamma function should be noticed. The representation (7.4–7) has been the starting point for classical investigations in the theory of the zeta function.

The zeta function is a specialization of a more general function involving a parameter w, which is usually taken as a positive number not exceeding unity, viz. the *generalized zeta function*

$$\zeta(z, w) = \sum_{\nu=0}^{\infty} (\nu+w)^{-s}, \qquad 0 < w \leqq 1, \quad \operatorname{Re} s > 1. \qquad (7.4\text{–}8)$$

For $w = 1$ this function reduces to the ordinary zeta function. In the case under consideration we have $\lambda_n = \log(n+w)$, $\mu_n = n+w$, $n = 0, 1, 2, \ldots$, and so

$$\boxed{\zeta(s, w)\Gamma(s) = \int_0^\infty \frac{e^{-wt}t^{s-1}}{1-e^{-t}}\,dt,} \qquad \operatorname{Re} s > 1, \quad 0 < w \leqq 1. \qquad (7.4\text{–}9)$$

Another function of some interest is *Appell's function*

$$\varphi(s, z) = \sum_{\nu=1}^{\infty} z^\nu \nu^{-s}, \qquad |z| \leqq 1, \quad \operatorname{Re} s > 1. \qquad (7.4\text{–}10)$$

We readily find

$$\varphi(s, z)\Gamma(s) = \int_0^\infty \frac{zt^{s-1}}{e^t - z}\,dt, \qquad \operatorname{Re} s > 1, \quad |z| \leqq 1. \qquad (7.4\text{–}11)$$

This equation reduces to (7.4–7) for $z = 1$.

7.5 – The functional equation of the zeta function

7.5.1 – First proof of the functional equation

The function $\zeta(s)$ has been defined by its Dirichlet series (7.1–3) which has a meaning only in the region $\operatorname{Re} s > 1$, and we have next to inquire whether this function can be continued beyond this region, i.e., if there exists a function defined in a larger region that coincides with the sum of the series in $\operatorname{Re} s > 1$. The problem can be solved by means of a remarkable functional equation for $\zeta(s)$ discovered by Riemann.

Our starting point will be (7.4–7). When $\operatorname{Re} s > 1$ it may be written in the form

$$\zeta(s)\Gamma(s) = \int_0^1 \left(\frac{1}{e^t-1} - \frac{1}{t}\right) t^{s-1}\,dt + \frac{1}{s-1} + \int_1^\infty \frac{t^{s-1}\,dt}{e^t-1}. \qquad (7.5\text{–}1)$$

The integrals are holomorphic as regards s in the larger region $\operatorname{Re} s > 0$. In fact, the factor of t^{s-1} in the first integral is bounded as $t \to 0$ and the substitution $t = 1/u$ transforms this integral into one of a type considered in section 2.20.5. Hence (7.5–1) may be considered as a definition of $\zeta(s)$ throughout the region $\operatorname{Re} s > 0$ except for $s = 1$, where the function on the right presents a simple pole with residue 1.

For $0 < \operatorname{Re} s < 1$ we have

$$\frac{1}{s-1} = -\int_1^\infty \frac{t^{s-1}}{t}\,dt.$$

Hence in this strip

$$\zeta(s)\Gamma(s) = \int_0^\infty \left(\frac{1}{e^t-1} - \frac{1}{t}\right) t^{s-1}\,dt, \qquad 0 < \operatorname{Re} s < 1.$$

Again

$$\zeta(s)\Gamma(s) = \int_0^1 \left(\frac{1}{e^t-1} - \frac{1}{t} + \frac{1}{2}\right) t^{s-1}\,dt - \frac{1}{2s} + \int_1^\infty \left(\frac{1}{e^t-1} - \frac{1}{t}\right) t^{s-1}\,dt \tag{7.5–2}$$

and the integrals on the right are holomorphic in the region $\operatorname{Re} s > -1$, since the factor of t^{s-1} in the first integral is $o(1)$ as $t \to 0$. Hence we can define $\zeta(s)$ in the region $1 > \operatorname{Re} s > -1$ by means of this formula, the point $s = 0$ giving no difficulty, for $s\Gamma(s) = \Gamma(s+1)$ is defined at $s = 0$.

If $-1 < \operatorname{Re} s < 0$ we have

$$\int_1^\infty \tfrac{1}{2} t^{s-1}\,dt = -\frac{1}{2s},$$

hence

$$\zeta(s)\Gamma(s) = \int_0^\infty \left(\frac{1}{e^t-1} - \frac{1}{t} + \frac{1}{2}\right) t^{s-1}\,dt, \quad -1 < \operatorname{Re} s < 0. \tag{7.5–3}$$

The integral on the right presents a striking similarity with the expression (4.9–21) of Binet's function $\mu(s)$. It is, therefore, natural to effect the same transformations as in section 4.9.5 and we may write

$$\begin{aligned}\zeta(s)\Gamma(s) &= \int_0^\infty 2\sum_{\nu=1}^\infty \frac{1}{t^2+4\nu^2\pi^2}\, t^s\,dt = 2\sum_{\nu=1}^\infty \int_0^\infty \frac{t^s}{t^2+4\nu^2\pi^2}\,dt \\ &= 2\sum_{\nu=1}^\infty (2\nu\pi)^{s-1} \int_0^\infty \frac{t^s}{t^2+1}\,dt, \qquad -1 < \operatorname{Re} s < 0,\end{aligned} \tag{7.5–4}$$

the reversal of the order of integration and summation being justified by similar arguments.

Consulting (3.6–30), (3.6–31) and (3.6–34) we find

$$\begin{aligned}2\int_0^\infty \frac{t^s}{t^2+1}\,dt &= \int_0^\infty \frac{u^{\frac{1}{2}(s-1)}}{u+1}\,du = \int_0^\infty \frac{u^{\frac{1}{2}(s+1)-1}}{u+1}\,du \\ &= B(\tfrac{1}{2}+\tfrac{1}{2}s, \tfrac{1}{2}-\tfrac{1}{2}s) = \Gamma(\tfrac{1}{2}+\tfrac{1}{2}s)\Gamma(\tfrac{1}{2}-\tfrac{1}{2}s) \\ &= \pi \csc \tfrac{1}{2}\pi(1-s) = \pi \sec \tfrac{1}{2}\pi s.\end{aligned}$$

Again, by the theorem of the complementary arguments of the gamma function

$$\frac{1}{\Gamma(s)} = \frac{\sin \pi s}{\pi} \Gamma(1-s) = \frac{2 \sin \frac{1}{2}\pi s \cos \frac{1}{2}\pi s}{\pi} \Gamma(1-s).$$

This leads to the famous *functional equation of the zeta function*

$$\boxed{\zeta(s) = 2(2\pi)^{s-1} \Gamma(1-s)\zeta(1-s) \sin \tfrac{1}{2}\pi s.} \tag{7.5–5}$$

This is valid primarily for $-1 < \operatorname{Re} s < 0$. But the function on the right is holomorphic in the region $\operatorname{Re} s < 0$. It, therefore, provides a definition of $\zeta(s)$ over the whole s-plane and there are no other singularities than at $s = 1$, where the function $\zeta(s)$ has a simple pole. Replacing s by $1-s$ we obtain an alternative form of the functional equation

$$\zeta(1-s) = 2(2\pi)^{-s}\zeta(s)\Gamma(s) \cos \tfrac{1}{2}\pi s, \tag{7.5–6}$$

which for many problems is more convenient.

7.5.2 – Second proof of the functional equation

There is an alternative approach to the theory of the zeta function which is based on the properties of the function

$$\vartheta(t) = \sum_{\nu=-\infty}^{\infty} e^{-\nu^2 \pi t}, \qquad t > 0, \tag{7.5–7}$$

which we already encountered in section 2.23.5. It is natural to relate this function to the theory of Dirichlet series. In fact, if we put

$$\omega(t) = \sum_{\nu=1}^{\infty} e^{-\nu^2 \pi t}, \qquad t > 0, \tag{7.5–8}$$

we evidently have

$$\omega(t) = \tfrac{1}{2}\vartheta(t) - \tfrac{1}{2}, \tag{7.5–9}$$

and on applying (7.4–4) we get

$$\pi^s \int_0^\infty \omega(t) t^{s-1}\, dt = \Gamma(s) \sum_{\nu=1}^{\infty} e^{-2s \log \nu} = \Gamma(s)\zeta(2s).$$

Replacing s by $\frac{1}{2}s$,

$$\pi^{-\frac{1}{2}s}\zeta(s)\Gamma(\tfrac{1}{2}s) = \int_0^\infty \omega(t) t^{\frac{1}{2}s-1} dt = \int_0^1 \omega(t) t^{\frac{1}{2}s-1} dt + \int_1^\infty \omega(t) t^{\frac{1}{2}s-1} dt, \tag{7.5–10}$$

this formula being valid whenever $\operatorname{Re} s > 1$. From the functional equation (2.23–29) of the theta function we derive

$$\omega(t) = \frac{1}{\sqrt{t}}\,\omega\!\left(\frac{1}{t}\right) - \frac{1}{2} + \frac{1}{2\sqrt{t}}, \qquad t > 0. \tag{7.5–11}$$

Hence

$$\int_0^1 \omega(t) t^{\frac{1}{2}s-1}\,dt = \int_0^1 \omega\left(\frac{1}{t}\right) t^{\frac{1}{2}s-3/2}\,dt - \frac{1}{s} + \frac{1}{s-1}$$

or

$$\int_0^1 \omega(t) t^{\frac{1}{2}s-1}\,dt = \int_1^\infty \omega(t) t^{\frac{1}{2}(1-s)-1}\,dt + \frac{1}{s(s-1)}. \tag{7.5–12}$$

Combining this result with (7.5–10) we obtain the formula

$$\pi^{-\frac{1}{2}s}\zeta(s)\,\Gamma(\tfrac{1}{2}s) - \frac{1}{s(s-1)} = \int_1^\infty \omega(t)\,(t^{\frac{1}{2}s-1} + t^{\frac{1}{2}(1-s)-1})dt. \tag{7.5–13}$$

Now we have achieved our end. For it is easy to prove that the integral on the right is an integral function of s. In fact, if $\sigma_1 \leqq \operatorname{Re} s \leqq \sigma_2$ and $t \geqq 1$ then

$$|t^{\frac{1}{2}s-1} + t^{\frac{1}{2}(1-s)-1}| \leqq t^{\frac{1}{2}(\sigma_2-1)} + t^{\frac{1}{2}(1-\sigma_1)-1}$$

and

$$\omega(t) < e^{-\pi t} + \sum_{\nu=2}^{\infty} e^{-\nu\pi t}\,\frac{1}{e^{\pi t}-1}.$$

Hence the conditions of section 2.20.5 are satisfied and the truth of the assertion follows at once. Accordingly (7.5–13) may be used to define $\zeta(s)$ throughout the whole s-plane.

Introducing the function

$$\boxed{\xi(s) = s(s-1)\pi^{-\frac{1}{2}s}\zeta(s)\,\Gamma(\tfrac{1}{2}s)} \tag{7.5–14}$$

we evidently have on account of (7.5–13)

$$\boxed{\xi(s) = \xi(1-s).} \tag{7.5–15}$$

We shall verify that this equation is equivalent to the functional equation (7.5–6). The proof is based on the duplication formula (4.6–26) and the theorem of the complementary arguments (4.6–13) of the gamma function. Taking account of these theorems we have

$$\Gamma(\tfrac{1}{2}s)\,\Gamma(\tfrac{1}{2}s+\tfrac{1}{2}) = 2\sqrt{\pi}\,2^{-s}\,\Gamma(s)$$

and

$$\Gamma(\tfrac{1}{2}-\tfrac{1}{2}s)\Gamma(\tfrac{1}{2}+\tfrac{1}{2}s) = \pi \sec \tfrac{1}{2}\pi s.$$

Hence

$$\frac{\Gamma(\tfrac{1}{2}s)}{\Gamma(\tfrac{1}{2}-\tfrac{1}{2}s)} = \pi^{-\frac{1}{2}}\,2^{1-s}\,\Gamma(s)\cos\tfrac{1}{2}\pi s,$$

and the remaining part of the verification is a trivial matter.

7.6 – Euler's infinite product

7.6.1 – Euler's product

The zeta function of Riemann has been extensively studied for the sake of the theory of prime numbers. The analytic theory of prime numbers takes its origin from a remarkable identity due to Euler, viz.,

$$\boxed{\frac{1}{\zeta(s)} = \prod_p (1-p^{-s}),} \qquad \operatorname{Re} s > 1, \tag{7.6–1}$$

where p runs through all primes. The infinite product is absolutely convergent when $\operatorname{Re} s > 1$; for so is

$$\sum_p |p^{-s}| = \sum_p p^{-\operatorname{Re} s},$$

this being merely a selection of terms from the series $\sum_{\nu=1}^{\infty} \nu^{-\operatorname{Re} s}$. If we expand the reciprocal of the factor involving p^{-s} in terms of powers of p^{-s}, we obtain

$$\prod_p (1+p^{-s}+p^{-2s}+\ldots) \tag{7.6–2}$$

and on multiplying formally, we obtain the series for the zeta function since each integer n can be expressed as a product of prime powers in just one way. A rigorous proof may be constructed as follows. Take the product (7.6–1) for the primes $p = 2, 3, \ldots, P$. Effecting the multiplication, the general term resulting is of the type

$$2^{-\alpha_2 s} 3^{-\alpha_3 s} \ldots P^{-\alpha_P s} = n^{-s},$$

where

$$n = 2^{\alpha_2} 3^{\alpha_3} \ldots P^{\alpha_P}, \qquad \alpha_2 \geqq 0, \quad \alpha_3 \geqq 0, \ldots, \alpha_P \geqq 0.$$

A number n will occur if and only if it has no prime factors greater than P, and once only. Hence

$$\prod_{p \leqq P} \frac{1}{1-p^{-s}} = \sum_{(P)} \nu^{-s}, \tag{7.6–3}$$

the summation on the right extending over numbers formed from the primes up to P. As a by-product we find:

There are infinitely many prime numbers.

For in the contrary case the series on the right of (7.6–3) should converge for $s = 1$, since we could form all integers from the primes up to a certain prime P. But actually the series $\sum_{\nu=1}^{\infty} \nu^{-1}$ is divergent.

The difference

$$\prod_{p \leq P} \frac{1}{1-p^{-s}} - \sum_{(P)} \nu^{-s}$$

is a sum of terms of the form n^{-s}, n being an integer $> P$. It tends to zero as $P \to \infty$ and thus we obtain the desired result.

An easy consequence of (7.6–1) is:

The zeta function has no zeros to the right of the line $\operatorname{Re} s = 1$.

7.6.2 – Series for the reciprocal and the logarithmic derivative of the zeta function

Euler's theorem can be expressed in various ways which all throw light on the intimate relation between the zeta function and the sequence of primes.

Carrying out the multiplication on the right-hand side of (7.6–1) we obtain

$$\boxed{\frac{1}{\zeta(s)} = \sum_{\nu=1}^{\infty} \mu(\nu)\nu^{-s},} \qquad \operatorname{Re} s > 1, \tag{7.6–4}$$

where $\mu(1) = 1$, $\mu(n) = (-1)^k$, if n is the product of k different primes, and $\mu(n) = 0$, if n contains any factor to a power higher than the first. The process may be justified just as in the previous part of this section.

The function $\mu(n)$ is known as the *Möbius function*. It is only defined for positive integers and, of course, stands in no relation to Binet's function $\mu(z)$.

Differentiating (7.6–1) logarithmically, we get for $\operatorname{Re} s > 1$,

$$\frac{\zeta'(s)}{\zeta(s)} = -\sum_{p} \frac{\log p}{p^s} \frac{1}{1-p^{-s}} = -\sum_{p} \left(\log p \sum_{\nu=1}^{\infty} p^{-\nu s}\right)$$

or

$$\boxed{\frac{\zeta'(s)}{\zeta(s)} = -\sum_{\nu=2}^{\infty} \Lambda(\nu)\nu^{-s},} \qquad \operatorname{Re} s > 1, \tag{7.6–5}$$

where $\Lambda(n) = \log p$, if n is a power of p, and $\Lambda(n) = 0$ otherwise.

7.6.3 – The series of the reciprocals of the prime numbers

The series formed from the reciprocals of the prime numbers is divergent, i.e.,

$$\sum_{p} \frac{1}{p} = \frac{1}{2} + \frac{1}{3} + \frac{1}{5} + \frac{1}{7} + \frac{1}{11} + \ldots = \infty. \tag{7.6–6}$$

Let n denote an integer formed from the prime numbers up to P.

If the series (7.6–6) should be convergent then also the product $\prod_{p}(1-p^{-1})$ and so the series $\sum_{\nu=1}^{\infty}\nu^{-1}$, since

$$\frac{1}{\prod_{p}(1-p^{-1})} > \frac{1}{\prod_{p\leq P}(1-p^{-1})} = \sum_{(P)}\nu^{-1}.$$

This, however, is an absurdity.

7.7 – Some properties of the zeta function

7.7.1 – The pole of the zeta function

In section 7.5.2 we introduced the function

$$\xi(s) = 1+s(s-1)\int_{1}^{\infty}\omega(t)\,(t^{\frac{1}{2}s-1}+t^{\frac{1}{2}(1-s)-1})dt. \tag{7.7–1}$$

According to the remarks made in section 7.5.2 about the integral involved, we have:

The function $\xi(s)$ is an integral function.

On the other hand we may write (7.5–14) in the form

$$\zeta(s) = \frac{\pi^{\frac{1}{2}s}}{2(s-1)}\,\frac{\xi(s)}{\Gamma(\frac{1}{2}s+1)} \tag{7.7–2}$$

and since the reciprocal of the gamma function is also an integral function, we may infer that:

The function $\zeta(s)$ is a meromorphic function having only a pole at $s = 1$.

It follows from (7.7–1) that $\xi(1) = 1$. Hence

$$\lim_{s\to 1}(s-1)\zeta(s) = \frac{\sqrt{\pi}}{2\Gamma(\frac{3}{2})} = \frac{\sqrt{\pi}}{\Gamma(\frac{1}{2})} = 1,$$

that is:

The residue of the zeta function at its pole is unity. More precisely stated:

The function

$$\zeta(s)-\frac{1}{s-1} \tag{7.7–3}$$

is an integral function.

Since also $\xi(0) = 1$, we find at once from (7.7–2)

$$\zeta(0) = -\tfrac{1}{2}. \tag{7.7–4}$$

7.7.2 – The real zeros

The problem of the determination of all zeros of $\zeta(s)$ is extremely difficult and has not yet been solved in its full extent. The determination of the real zeros is, however, almost trivial.

According to the last theorem of section 7.6.1 we have $\zeta(s) \neq 0$, whenever $\operatorname{Re} s > 1$. It follows from the functional equation (7.5–6) that the only negative zeros of $\zeta(1-s)$ are those of $\cos \frac{1}{2}\pi s$ with the same order of multiplicity. Hence $\zeta(1-s) = 0$ if s is a positive odd integer and, consequently,

$$\zeta(-2m) = 0, \qquad m = 1, 2, 3, \ldots. \tag{7.7–5}$$

Next we shall prove that the negative even integers are the only real zeros of the zeta function. We already found $\zeta(0) \neq 0$ while $s = 1$ is a pole. It remains to prove:

The function $\zeta(s)$ *does not vanish within the range* $0 < s < 1$.

This can be done by taking the series

$$\sum_{\nu=1}^{\infty} (-1)^{\nu+1}\nu^{-s} = 1 - \frac{1}{2^s} + \frac{1}{3^s} - \frac{1}{4^s} + \ldots \tag{7.7–6}$$

as a starting point. An elementary calculation yields

$$\sum_{\nu=1}^{\infty} (-1)^{\nu+1}\nu^{-s} = \sum_{\nu=0}^{\infty} (2\nu+1)^{-s} - \sum_{\nu=1}^{\infty} (2\nu)^{-s} = \sum_{\nu=1}^{\infty} \nu^{-s} - 2\sum_{\nu=1}^{\infty} (2\nu)^{-s}$$

or

$$\sum_{\nu=1}^{\infty} (-1)^{\nu+1}\nu^{-s} = (1-2^{1-s})\,\zeta(s). \tag{7.7–7}$$

The proof is valid for $\operatorname{Re} s > 1$. But by Leibniz's test the series on the left is convergent for $s > 0$ and hence for $\operatorname{Re} s > 0$.

If s is real and $0 < s < 1$ then

$$\sum_{\nu=1}^{\infty} (-1)^{\nu+1}\nu^{-s} = \left(1 - \frac{1}{2^s}\right) + \left(\frac{1}{3^s} - \frac{1}{4^s}\right) + \ldots > 0,$$

and, therefore, $\zeta(s) < 0$ within the range $0 < s < 1$.

7.7.3 – Values of the zeta function at particular points

It is easy to write down the values of $\zeta(s)$ for positive even integral values and for all negative odd integral values of s. Equation (3.7–20) may be read as

$$\boxed{\zeta(2n) = \tfrac{1}{2}(2\pi)^{2n}\frac{B_{2n}}{(2n)!},} \qquad n = 1, 2, \ldots. \tag{7.7–8}$$

Corresponding simple expressions for $\zeta(2n+1)$ are not known. Inserting (7.7–8) in the functional equation, we get

$$\boxed{\zeta(1-2n) = (-1)^n \frac{B_{2n}}{2n},} \qquad n = 1, 2, \ldots. \qquad (7.7\text{–}9)$$

The formula (7.4–7) can also be written as

$$\zeta(s) = \frac{(2\pi)^s}{\Gamma(s)} \int_0^\infty \frac{t^{s-1}\,dt}{e^{2\pi t}-1}. \qquad (7.7\text{–}10)$$

Inserting (7.7–8) we readily obtain the representation of the Bernoulli numbers by an infinite integral, viz.,

$$B_{2n} = 4n \int_0^\infty \frac{t^{2n-1}}{e^{2\pi t}-1}\,dt \qquad (7.7\text{–}11)$$

a result that we already encountered as formula (4.8–38).

7.7.4 – The non-real zeros

We conclude this section by establishing the theorem:

The zeta function has no zeros on the line Re $s = 1$.

Then, by virtue of the functional equation, it also has no zeros on the line Re $s = 0$.

Since $\zeta(s)$ is holomorphic throughout the region Re $s > 1$ and does not vanish in this region, the function (7.6–5)

$$\eta(s) = \frac{\zeta'(s)}{\zeta(s)} = -\sum_{\nu=1}^{\infty} \Lambda(\nu)\nu^{-s}$$

is holomorphic in the same region. Now

$$\lim_{s\to s_0} (s-s_0)\,\eta(s)$$

is always an integer, being positive when s_0 is a zero of $\zeta(s)$, negative when s_0 is a pole and zero otherwise. Hence we may turn our attention to the evaluation of

$$\lim_{\varepsilon\to 0} \operatorname{Re} \varepsilon\eta(s_0+\varepsilon).$$

It is easily seen that

$$\operatorname{Re} \eta(1+\varepsilon+it) = -\sum_{\nu=1}^{\infty} \Lambda(\nu)\nu^{-(1+\varepsilon)} \cos(t \log \nu), \qquad \varepsilon > 0,$$

and from

$$0 \leqq (1+\cos\varphi)^2 = 1+2\cos\varphi + \cos^2\varphi = \tfrac{1}{2}(3+4\cos\varphi + \cos 2\varphi)$$

we deduce:

$$\begin{aligned} &3 \operatorname{Re} \eta(1+\varepsilon)+4 \operatorname{Re} \eta(1+\varepsilon+it)+\operatorname{Re} \eta(1+\varepsilon+2it) \\ &= -\sum_{\nu=1}^{\infty} \Lambda(\nu)\nu^{-(1+\varepsilon)}\{(3+4\cos(t\log\nu)+\cos(2t\log\nu)\} \leqq 0. \end{aligned} \qquad (7.7\text{–}12)$$

When ε tends to zero the expression $\varepsilon \operatorname{Re} \eta(1+\varepsilon) = \varepsilon\eta(1+\varepsilon)$ tends to -1, since $s = 1$ is a simple pole of $\zeta(s)$, whereas $\varepsilon\eta(1+\varepsilon+it)$ tends to zero if $1+it$ is not a zero of $\zeta(s)$, and a positive integer if this number is a zero. If $1+it$ should be a zero of $\zeta(s)$ we should have

$$\lim_{\varepsilon\to 0} \varepsilon\{3 \operatorname{Re}\eta(1+\varepsilon)+4 \operatorname{Re}\eta(1+\varepsilon+it)+\operatorname{Re}\eta(1+\varepsilon+2it)\} \geqq -3+4=1,$$

contrary to (7.7–12). This proves the assertion.

Our conclusion will be the following:

The non-real zeros of the zeta function are all within the strip $0 < \operatorname{Re} s < 1$.

They are in conjugate pairs since $\zeta(s)$ is real on the real axis; and if s is a zero, so is $1-s$ by the functional equation and hence so is $1-\bar{s}$. Consequently the zeros either lie on the line $\operatorname{Re} s = \frac{1}{2}$ or occur in pairs symmetrically about this line.

The real zeros of the zeta function are called the *trivial zeros.* The strip $0 < \operatorname{Re} s < 1$ is termed the *critical strip* and the line $\operatorname{Re} s = \frac{1}{2}$ the *critical line,* (fig. 7.7–1).

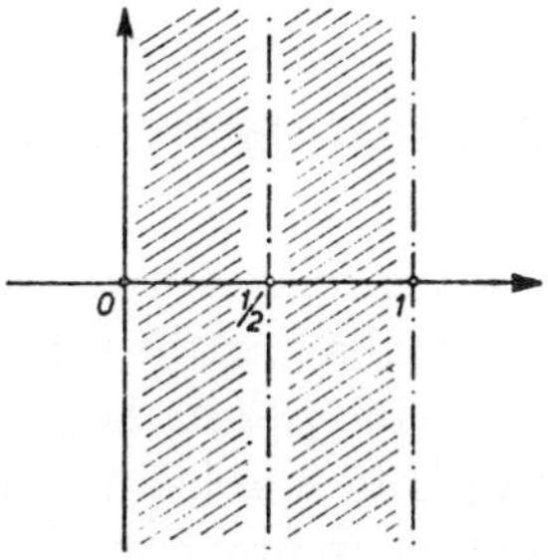

Fig. 7.7–1. The critical strip and the critical line

It was conjectured by Riemann that all the non-trivial zeros of $\zeta(s)$ are on the critical line. This conjecture has never been either proved or disproved.

In this direction the following main results deserve mention:

(i) Hardy's theorem:

There are infinitely many zeros on the critical line.

(ii) Von Mangoldt's first theorem:

If $2N(T)$ *denotes the number of zeros having ordinates between* T *and* $-T$ *then*

$$N(T+1)-N(T) = O(\log T).$$

(iii) Von Mangoldt's second theorem:

$$N(T) = \frac{1}{2\pi} T \log T - \frac{1+2\pi}{2\pi} T + O(\log T).$$

(iv) The Bohr-Landau theorem:

If $M(T)$ denotes the number of zeros within the strip

$$\tfrac{1}{2}-\delta < \operatorname{Re} s < \tfrac{1}{2}+\delta,$$

$\delta > 0$ and arbitrary, and whose ordinates are between $-T$ and $+T$ then

$$\lim_{T\to\infty} \frac{M(T)}{2N(T)} = 1.$$

This can be expressed by saying that almost all zeros lie within an arbitrary narrow strip containing the critical line.

By modern methods of calculation the position of a large number of zeros has been determined and it is found that they lie exactly on the critical line. Naturally the Riemann conjecture cannot be proved by calculation, but, if it is false, it could be disproved by the discovery of an exception.

7.8 – The existence of zeros in the critical strip

7.8.1 – The order of the function $\xi(s)$

The function

$$\xi(s) = s(s-1)\pi^{-\frac{1}{2}s}\zeta(s)\Gamma(\tfrac{1}{2}s) \tag{7.8–1}$$

has no real zeros.

In fact, $\xi(0) = \xi(1) = 1$ as follows from (7.7–1), and the zeros of $\zeta(s)$ lie at the poles of $\Gamma(\frac{1}{2}s)$, having the same order of multiplicity. Hence, the non-trivial zeros of $\zeta(s)$ are the zeros of $\xi(s)$ and we have attained the end when we can establish the existence of an infinity of zeros of $\xi(s)$, when we wish to prove that the zeta function has an infinity of non-trivial zeros.

In section 7.7.1 we already pointed out that $\xi(s)$ is an integral function. The main difficulty consists in the determination of its order. To this end we derive an alternative integral representation for the zeta function.

By Abel's summation by parts we find

$$\begin{aligned}\sum_{\nu=1}^{n} \nu^{-s} &= \sum_{\nu=1}^{n} \frac{\nu-(\nu-1)}{\nu^s} = \sum_{\nu=1}^{n-1} \nu\left(\frac{1}{\nu^s}-\frac{1}{(\nu+1)^s}\right)+\frac{n}{n^s}\\ &= \sum_{\nu=1}^{n-1} \nu s\int_{\nu}^{\nu+1}\frac{du}{u^{s+1}}+\frac{1}{n^{s-1}} = s\sum_{\nu=1}^{n-1}\int_{\nu}^{\nu+1}\frac{[u]}{u^{s+1}}\,du+\frac{1}{n^{s-1}},\end{aligned} \tag{7.8–2}$$

u being a real variable. Hence, assuming $\operatorname{Re} s > 1$ and letting $n \to \infty$,

$$\zeta(s) = s\int_{1}^{\infty}\frac{[u]}{u^{s+1}}\,du. \tag{7.8–3}$$

We also have

$$\frac{1}{s-1} = \int_1^\infty \frac{u}{u^{s+1}}\,du. \qquad 7.\ -4)$$

Hence

$$\boxed{\zeta(s) = \frac{s}{s-1} + s\int_1^\infty \frac{[u]-u}{u^{s+1}}\,du.} \qquad (7.8\text{–}5)$$

The integral on the right is uniformly convergent when $0 < \sigma_1 \leqq \operatorname{Re} s \leqq \sigma_2$, and since $|[u]-u| < 1$, it represents a function which is holomorphic throughout the region $\operatorname{Re} s > 0$ (2.20.5). Hence (7.8–5) is valid in this region.

When $\operatorname{Re} s \geqq \frac{1}{2}$ and $|s| > 2$, it follows from (7.8–5)

$$|\zeta(s)| \leqq \frac{|s|}{|s-1|} + |s|\int_1^\infty \frac{[u]-u}{u^{\operatorname{Re} s+1}}\,du < |s| + |s|\int_1^\infty \frac{du}{u^{3/2}} = O(|s|).$$

Under the same assumptions, putting $\sigma = \operatorname{Re} s$,

$$\begin{aligned}|\Gamma(s)| &\leqq \int_0^\infty e^{-u}u^{\sigma-1}du < \int_0^1 e^{-u}u^{-\frac{1}{2}}du + \int_1^\infty e^{-u}u^{[\sigma]}du = O(1) + \int_0^\infty e^{-u}u^{[\sigma]}du \\ &= O(1) + [\sigma]! \leqq O(1) + [\sigma]^{[\sigma]} \leqq O(1) + [|s|]^{[|s|]} \leqq O(1) + |s|^{|s|} \\ &= O(1) + e^{|s|\log|s|} = O(e^{|s|^{1+\varepsilon}}),\end{aligned}$$

ε being any positive number. Since $\pi^{-\frac{1}{2}s}$ is an integral function of order 1, we infer from (7.8–1) that

$$\xi(s) = O(e^{|s|^{1+\varepsilon}}), \qquad (7.8\text{–}6)$$

whenever $\operatorname{Re} s \geqq \frac{1}{2}$. But since $\xi(s) = \xi(1-s)$ the estimate (7.8–6) holds throughout the s-plane. We may conclude that $\xi(s)$ is of order 1 at most.

Next we take s real and > 2. Then

$$\begin{aligned}\xi(s) &= 2(s-1)\pi^{-\frac{1}{2}s}\zeta(s)\Gamma(\tfrac{1}{2}s+1) > 2\Gamma(\tfrac{1}{2}s+1) = 2\int_0^\infty e^{-u}u^{\frac{1}{2}s}du \\ &> 2\int_s^\infty e^{-u}u^{\frac{1}{2}s}du > 2s^{\frac{1}{2}s}\int_s^\infty e^{-u}du = 2s^{\frac{1}{2}s}e^{-s} = e^{\frac{1}{2}s\log s - s + \log 2}.\end{aligned}$$

If $\varepsilon > 0$ is arbitrary then for large s

$$\tfrac{1}{2}\log s - 1 + \frac{1}{s}\log 2 > s^{-\varepsilon}.$$

Hence

$$\xi(s) > e^{s^{1-\varepsilon}} \qquad (7.8\text{–}7)$$

for large real values of s. Combining (7.8–6) and (7.8–7) we have:

The function $\xi(s)$ is exactly of order unity.

7.8.2 – The existence of non-real zeros of the zeta function

Now we consider the function

$$f(z) = \xi(\tfrac{1}{2}+z). \tag{7.8–8}$$

This function is, of course, also an integral function of order 1, but since $\xi(s) = \xi(1-s)$, we have

$$f(z) = f(-z),$$

i.e., the function $f(z)$ is even. As a consequence $f(\sqrt{z})$ is an integral function of order $\frac{1}{2}$ and by the theorem of section 6.5.2 there are infinitely many zeros. We thus proved:

The zeta function has an infinity of non-trivial zeros.

7.9 – The generalized zeta function

7.9.1 – The Euler sum formula

The method used in section 7.8.1 to obtain an integral for the zeta function can be put into a more general form.

Let $f(x)$ denote a real or a complex function of the real variable with a continuous derivative. We wish to evaluate the sum

$$\sum_{\nu=a}^{b} f(\nu), \tag{7.9–1}$$

a and b being integers and $a < b$. By Abel's method of partial summation we get

$$\sum_{\nu=a}^{b} f(\nu) = \sum_{\nu=a}^{b} \{\nu-(\nu-1)\}f(\nu) = \sum_{\nu=a}^{b-1} \nu\{f(\nu)-f(\nu+1)\}+bf(b)-(a-1)f(a)$$

$$= -\sum_{\nu=a}^{b-1} \nu \int_{\nu}^{\nu+1} f'(u)du+bf(b)-af(a)+f(a)$$

or

$$\sum_{\nu=a}^{b} f(\nu) = -\int_{a}^{b} [u]f'(u)du+bf(b)-af(a)+f(a). \tag{7.9–2}$$

Next we eliminate $bf(b)-af(a)$ by observing that

$$\int_{a}^{b} uf'(u)du = bf(b)-af(a)-\int_{a}^{b} f(u)du. \tag{7.9–3}$$

Hence

$$\sum_{\nu=a}^{b} f(\nu) = f(a)+\int_{a}^{b} f(u)du+\int_{a}^{b} (u-[u])f'(u)du. \tag{7.9–4}$$

It is often desirable to introduce the function

$$\mathsf{P}_1(u) = u-[u]-\tfrac{1}{2}$$

which we already encountered in section 4.9.1. Then (7.9–4) may be written in the form

$$\boxed{\sum_{\nu=a}^{b} f(\nu) = \tfrac{1}{2}f(a)+\tfrac{1}{2}f(b)+\int_a^b f(u)du+\int_a^b \mathsf{P}_1(u)f'(u)du.} \tag{7.9–5}$$

This is the *Euler sum formula* in its simplest form. More general expressions will be derived in the next chapter.

7.9.2 – Representation of the generalized zeta function as an integral

The sum formula (7.9–5) enables us to obtain an expression of the generalized zeta function (7.4–8) as an integral, similar to that obtained in section 7.8.1 for the ordinary zeta function.

Take $a = 0$, $b = n$, $f(x) = (x+w)^{-s}$. Then

$$\sum_{\nu=0}^{n} (\nu+w)^{-s} = \tfrac{1}{2}w^{-s}+\tfrac{1}{2}(n+w)^{-s}+\frac{1}{s-1}\{w^{-s+1}-(n+w)^{-s+1}\}+$$
$$-s\int_0^n \frac{\mathsf{P}_1(u)}{(u+w)^{s+1}}du.$$

Assuming $0 < w \leqq 1$ and $\operatorname{Re} s > 1$, we can make $n \to \infty$. We find

$$\boxed{\zeta(s, w) = \tfrac{1}{2}w^{-s}+\frac{1}{s-1}w^{-s+1}-s\int_0^\infty \frac{\mathsf{P}_1(u)}{(u+w)^{s+1}}du.} \tag{7.9–6}$$

Reasoning along the same lines as in section 4.9.1 we can easily prove that the integral on the right of (7.9–6) is convergent for $\operatorname{Re} s > -1$ and represents a holomorphic function throughout this half-plane. Hence $\zeta(s, w)$ is a meromorphic function throughout this region, having a simple pole at $s = 1$.

By putting $s = 0$ we get

$$\zeta(0, w) = \tfrac{1}{2}-w, \tag{7.9–7}$$

a result that reduces to (7.7–4) for $w = 1$.

7.9.3 – The value of the derivative of the generalized zeta function at the origin

An interesting problem is the evaluation of $\zeta'(0, w)$. Differentiating both members of (7.9–6) with regard to s and putting $s = 0$, we readily obtain

$$\zeta'(0, w) = (w-\tfrac{1}{2})\log w-w-\int_0^\infty \frac{\mathsf{P}_1(u)}{u+w}du. \tag{7.9–8}$$

But in section 4.9.1 we found

$$-\int_0^\infty \frac{P_1(u)}{u+w}\,du = \mu(w) = \log\Gamma(w+1)-(w+\tfrac{1}{2})\log w + w - \log\sqrt{2\pi}.$$

Hence

$$\zeta'(0, w) = \log\Gamma(w) - \log\sqrt{2\pi}. \qquad (7.9\text{–}9)$$

In particular

$$\zeta'(0) = -\log\sqrt{2\pi}. \qquad (7.9\text{–}10)$$

7.9.4 – The behaviour of the generalized zeta function at its pole

The equation (7.9–6) can be put into the form

$$\zeta(s, w) = \frac{1}{s-1} + \tfrac{1}{2}w^{-s} + \frac{1}{s-1}(w^{1-s}-1) - s\int_0^\infty \frac{P_1(u)}{(u+w)^{s+1}}\,du, \qquad (7.9\text{–}11)$$

and letting $s \to 1$ we find

$$\lim_{s\to 1}\left(\zeta(s, w) - \frac{1}{s-1}\right) = \frac{1}{2w} - \log w - \int_0^\infty \frac{P_1(u)}{(u+w)^2}\,du. \qquad (7.9\text{–}12)$$

Taking account of (4.9–4) and (4.9–7) we have

$$\int_0^1 (u-\tfrac{1}{2})\Psi(z+u)\,du = -\int_0^\infty \frac{P_1(u)}{u+z}\,du. \qquad (7.9\text{–}13)$$

Differentiating with respect to z, we get

$$\int_0^1 (u-\tfrac{1}{2})\Psi'(z+u)\,du = \int_0^\infty \frac{P_1(u)}{(u+z)^2}\,du \qquad (7.9\text{–}14)$$

whence, on integrating by parts,

$$\tfrac{1}{2}\Psi(z+1) + \tfrac{1}{2}\Psi(z) - \int_0^1 \Psi(z+u)\,du = \int_0^\infty \frac{P_1(u)}{(u+z)^2}\,du \qquad (7.9\text{–}15)$$

or else, taking account of (4.8–4) and (4.8–18),

$$\Psi(z) + \frac{1}{2z} - \log z = \int_0^\infty \frac{P_1(u)}{(u+z)^2}\,du. \qquad (7.9\text{–}16)$$

Putting $z = w$ and inserting the value of the integral on the right into (7.9–12) we finally have

$$\lim_{s\to 1}\left(\zeta(s, w) - \frac{1}{s-1}\right) = -\Psi(w). \qquad (7.9\text{–}17)$$

In particular, by virtue of (4.8–3),

$$\lim_{s\to 1}\left(\zeta(s) - \frac{1}{s-1}\right) = \gamma, \qquad (7.9\text{–}18)$$

γ being Euler's constant.

7.9.5 – Alternative proof of Stirling's theorem

The fundamental properties of the generalized zeta function enable us to give an alternative proof of Stirling's theorem.

In the Euler sum formula we take $a = 0$, $b = w$, $f(x) = (x+z)^{-1}$, z being in the principal region $z+|z| \neq 0$. We have

$$\sum_{\nu=0}^{n} (z+\nu)^{-1} = \frac{1}{2}\,\frac{1}{z} + \frac{1}{2}\,\frac{1}{z+n} + \log(z+n) - \log z - \int_0^n \frac{P_1(u)}{(u+z)^2}\,du.$$

Also, z being real,

$$\sum_{\nu=1}^{n} \log\left(1+\frac{1}{z+\nu}\right) = \sum_{\nu=0}^{n} \{\log(z+\nu+1) - \log(z+\nu)\}$$
$$= \log(z+n+1) - \log z,$$

whence

$$\sum_{\nu=0}^{n} \left\{\frac{1}{z+\nu} - \log\left(1+\frac{1}{z+\nu}\right)\right\}$$
$$= \frac{1}{2z} + \frac{1}{2}\,\frac{1}{z+n} - \log\left(1+\frac{1}{z+n}\right) - \int_0^n \frac{P_1(u)}{(u+z)^2}\,du.$$

Letting $n \to \infty$ and taking account of (4.8–14) we readily find

$$\log z - \Psi(z) = \frac{1}{2z} - \int_0^\infty \frac{P_1(u)}{(u+z)^2}\,du \qquad (7.9\text{–}19)$$

and by the identity principle this result holds when z varies throughout the principal region.

We now integrate along a linear path from 1 to z. The result is

$$z\log z - z + 1 - \log\Gamma(z) = \tfrac{1}{2}\log z - \int_0^\infty \frac{P_1(u)}{u+1}\,du + \int_0^\infty \frac{P_1(u)}{u+z}\,du \qquad (7.9\text{–}20)$$

or

$$\log\Gamma(z) = (z-\tfrac{1}{2})\log z - z + 1 + \int_0^\infty \frac{P_1(u)}{u+1}\,du - \int_0^\infty \frac{P_1(u)}{u+z}\,du. \qquad (7.9\text{–}21)$$

In particular, when $z = \frac{1}{2}$, by (4.6–14)

$$\log\sqrt{\pi} = \tfrac{1}{2} + \int_0^\infty \frac{P_1(u)}{u+1}\,du - \int_0^\infty \frac{P_1(u)}{u+\frac{1}{2}}\,du. \qquad (7.9\text{–}22)$$

The last integral can be evaluated on applying the following device. From the corresponding Dirichlet series we easily deduce the identity

$$\zeta(s, \tfrac{1}{2}) = (2^s - 1)\zeta(s) \qquad (7.9\text{–}23)$$

this formula also being valid for $\operatorname{Re} s > -1$, since both members are meromorphic in this region. By differentiating and putting $s = 0$ we get in view of (7.7–4)

$$\zeta'(0, \tfrac{1}{2}) = \zeta(0) \log 2 = -\tfrac{1}{2} \log 2. \qquad (7.9\text{–}24)$$

Inserting $w = \frac{1}{2}$ into (7.9–8) we obtain

$$\tfrac{1}{2} \log 2 = \tfrac{1}{2} + \int_0^\infty \frac{P_1(u)}{u+\frac{1}{2}} du. \qquad (7.9\text{–}25)$$

Hence (7.9–22) yields

$$\int_0^\infty \frac{P_1(u)}{u+1} du = -1 + \log \sqrt{2\pi}. \qquad (7.9\text{–}26)$$

Accordingly we may write (7.9–21) in the form

$$\log \Gamma(z) = (z-\tfrac{1}{2}) \log z - z + \log \sqrt{2\pi} - \int_0^\infty \frac{P_1(u)}{u+z} du, \quad (7.9\text{–}27)$$

whence by (4.9–7)

$$\mu(z) = -\int_0^\infty \frac{P_1(u)}{u+z} du = \log \Gamma(z+1) - (z+\tfrac{1}{2}) \log z + z - \log \sqrt{2\pi}, \qquad (7.9\text{–}28)$$

the desired result.

7.10 – The representation of the generalized zeta function by a loop integral

7.10.1 – Deduction of the representation

The generalized zeta function may be studied by a method which is similar to that of the study of the gamma function by means of the Hankel integral.

The starting point will be the integral

$$\Gamma(s)\zeta(s, w) = \int_0^\infty \frac{e^{-wt} t^{s-1}}{1-e^{-t}} dt, \qquad \text{Re}\, s > 1, \qquad (7.10\text{–}1)$$

already derived in section 7.4.2. Now we consider the integral

$$F(s) = \int_{L(a)} \frac{e^{wt} t^{s-1}}{1-e^t} dt, \qquad (7.10\text{–}2)$$

taken along the same loop as described in section 4.7.6, (fig 4.7–1).

The integrand is single-valued in the t-plane cut along the negative real axis (origin included). When $0 < a < 2\pi$ the integrand has no poles inside the circular part of the loop.

Reasoning along the same lines as in section 4.7.6 we find that $F(s)$ does not depend on a, provided that a is less than 2π. We may evaluate $F(s)$ by taking $a = 0$ (fig. 7.20–2). On the upper part of the path of integration we have

$$t^{s-1} = (ue^{\pi i})^{s-1} = -u^{s-1}e^{\pi is},$$

u being real and $\geqq 0$. On the lower part

$$t^{s-1} = (ue^{-\pi i})^{s-1} = -u^{s-1}e^{-\pi is}.$$

Hence, still assuming $\operatorname{Re} s > 1$ and taking account of (7.10–1),

$$F(s) = \int_0^\infty \frac{e^{-\pi is}e^{-wu}u^{s-1}}{1-e^{-u}}du + \int_0^\infty \frac{e^{\pi is}e^{-wu}u^{s-1}}{1-e^{-u}}du$$

$$= (e^{\pi is}-e^{-\pi is})\int_0^\infty \frac{e^{-wu}u^{s-1}}{1-e^{-u}}du = 2i\sin\pi s\,\Gamma(s)\,\zeta(s, w)$$

and by virtue of the theorem of the complementary arguments of the gamma function

$$\zeta(s, w) = \frac{1}{2i\sin\pi s\cdot\Gamma(s)}F(s) = \frac{\Gamma(1-s)}{2\pi i}F(s). \quad (7.10\text{–}3)$$

The result is

$$\boxed{\zeta(s, w) = \frac{\Gamma(1-s)}{2\pi i}\int_{L(a)} \frac{e^{wt}t^{s-1}}{1-e^t}dt,} \qquad 0 \leqq a < 2\pi. \quad (7.10\text{–}4)$$

This formula yields a definition of $\zeta(s, w)$ throughout the entire s-plane except for $s = 1$. In fact, it is apparent from (7.10–4) that the only possible singularities of $\zeta(s, w)$ are at the poles of $\Gamma(1-s)$, i.e., at the points $s = 1, 2, 3, \ldots$ and, with the exception of these points, the integral affords a representation of $\zeta(s, w)$ valid over the entire plane. But we also know that $\zeta(s, w)$ is holomorphic in the region $\operatorname{Re} s > 1$. Hence all poles of $\Gamma(1-s)$ except $s = 1$ are compensated by zeros of the integral.

The point $s = 1$ is actually a pole of $\zeta(s, w)$, for writing $s = 1$ in the integral we obtain

$$\frac{1}{2\pi i}\int_{L(0)} \frac{e^{wt}}{1-e^t}dt \quad (7.10\text{–}5)$$

and this is the residue of the integrand, this residue being -1.

7.10.2 – Hurwitz's theorem

The singular points of the integrand apart from $t = 0$ are $t = 2n\pi i$, $t = -2n\pi i$, $n = 1, 2, \ldots$, these points being simple poles. Now consider a loop whose circular part is a circle of radius $a_n = (2n+1)\pi$. By the same reasoning as in section 4.7.6 it is easily established that

$$\frac{1}{2\pi i}\int_{L(a_n)} \frac{e^{wt}t^{s-1}}{1-e^t}dt - \frac{1}{2\pi i}\int_{L(0)} \frac{e^{wt}t^{s-1}}{1-e^t}dt = \sum_{\nu=1}^{n}(R_\nu + R_{-\nu}) \quad (7.10\text{–}6)$$

where R_k denotes the residue of the integrand at $t = 2k\pi i$ and R_{-k} the residue at $t = -2k\pi i$, $k = 1, \ldots, n$.

According to section 3.3.4 we have

$$R_n = \frac{(2n\pi i)^{s-1} e^{2n\pi i w}}{-e^{2n\pi i}} = (2n\pi)^{s-1} i\, e^{(\frac{1}{2}s+2nw)\pi i},$$

$$R_{-n} = \frac{(-2n\pi i)^{s-1} e^{-2n\pi i w}}{-e^{-2n\pi i}} = -(2n\pi)^{s-1} i\, e^{-(\frac{1}{2}s+2nw)\pi i}.$$

Hence

$$R_n + R_{-n} = (2n\pi)^{s-1}\, 2 \sin(\tfrac{1}{2}s + 2nw)\pi$$
$$= \frac{2}{(2\pi)^{1-s}} \left(\sin \tfrac{1}{2}\pi s \frac{\cos 2n\pi w}{n^{1-s}} + \cos \tfrac{1}{2}\pi s \frac{\sin 2n\pi w}{n^{1-s}} \right). \tag{7.10–7}$$

Since $0 < w \leqq 1$, we can find a number A independent of n, such that on the circle $|z| = a_n$, putting $\sigma = \operatorname{Re} s$,

$$\left| \frac{e^{wt} t^{s-1}}{1 - e^t} \right| < \{(2n+1)\pi\}^{\sigma-1} \frac{|e^{(w-1)t}|}{|e^{-t} - 1|} |e^{(s-1)\cos t}| < \{(2n+1)\pi\}^{\sigma-1} Ae.$$

In fact, the values of e^{-t} on that circle do not come arbitrarily near to 1. Hence the absolute value of the integral along this circle is less than $2\pi\{(2n+1)\pi\}^{\sigma}A$, *and if we assume* $\sigma < 0$, this number tends to zero as $n \to \infty$.

From (7.10–4), (7.10–6) and (7.10–7) we now may infer that

$$\boxed{\zeta(s, w) = \frac{2\Gamma(1-s)}{(2\pi)^{1-s}} \left(\sin \tfrac{1}{2}\pi s \sum_{\nu=1}^{\infty} \frac{\cos 2\nu\pi w}{\nu^{1-s}} + \cos \tfrac{1}{2}\pi s \sum_{\nu=1}^{\infty} \frac{\sin 2\nu\pi w}{\nu^{1-s}} \right),} \tag{7.10–8}$$

provided that $\operatorname{Re} s < 0$. This result is due to Hurwitz.

If $w = 1$ then (7.10–8) reduces to

$$\zeta(s) = \frac{2\Gamma(1-s)\zeta(1-s)}{(2\pi)^{1-s}} \sin \tfrac{1}{2}\pi s$$

or else

$$\zeta(1-s) = \frac{\pi}{(2\pi)^s} \frac{\zeta(s)}{\Gamma(1-s) \sin \frac{1}{2}\pi s} = \frac{2}{(2\pi)^s} \zeta(s)\Gamma(s) \cos \tfrac{1}{2}\pi s,$$

i.e., the functional equation of the ordinary zeta function.

7.11 – Perron's formula

7.11.1 – Statement of Perron's theorem

Given the sum $f(z)$ of a power series $\sum_{\nu=0}^{\infty} c_\nu z^\nu$ it is possible to express every coefficient of the series by means of a contour integral involving the function $f(z)$, as has been pointed out in section 2.16.1. It is our aim to derive an analogous theorem in the theory of Dirichlet series, due to Kronecker and Cahen and rigorously proved by Perron.

Let us assume that the series

$$\sum_{\nu=0}^{\infty} a_\nu e^{-\lambda_\nu s} \tag{7.11–1}$$

is convergent for $\operatorname{Re} s > \sigma_c$ and denote its sum by $\varphi(s)$. Let c denote a real number exceeding $\max(0, \sigma_c)$. We recall the formula (3.6–18) of the discontinuous factor:

$$\frac{1}{2\pi i}\int_{c-i\infty}^{c+i\infty} \frac{e^{st}}{s} ds = \begin{cases} 1 \text{ when } t > 0, \\ \frac{1}{2} \text{ when } t = 0, \\ 0 \text{ when } t < 0, \end{cases} \tag{7.11–2}$$

the integral being a principal value.

Leaving for a moment the path of rigorous analysis we might proceed in the following way. We evaluate the function

$$a(t) = \frac{1}{2\pi i}\int_{c-i\infty}^{c+i\infty} \varphi(s)\frac{e^{st}}{s} dt \tag{7.11–3}$$

on applying term-by-term integration. We then obtain

$$a(t) = \sum_{\nu=0}^{\infty} a_\nu \frac{1}{2\pi i}\int_{c-i\infty}^{c+i\infty} \frac{e^{(t-\lambda_\nu)s}}{s} ds.$$

Hence, if $\lambda_0 > 0$ and $0 \leqq t < \lambda_0$, we have $a(t) = 0$; if $\lambda_n < t < \lambda_{n+1}$ we have $a(t) = \sum_{\nu=0}^{n} a_\nu$ and if $t = \lambda_n$, we have $a(t) = \sum_{\nu=0}^{n-1} a_\nu + \frac{1}{2}a_n$. In particular $a(\lambda_0) = \frac{1}{2}a_0$.

These considerations lead to the conjecture:

If $c > \max(0, \sigma_c)$, *then*

$$\frac{1}{2\pi i}\int_{c-i\infty}^{c+i\infty} \varphi(s)\frac{e^{st}}{s} ds = a(t) \tag{7.11–4}$$

with

$$a(t) = \begin{cases} \sum_{\nu=0}^{n} a_\nu \text{ when } \lambda_n < t < \lambda_{n+1}, \\ \sum_{\nu=0}^{n-1} a_\nu + \frac{1}{2}a_n \text{ when } t = \lambda_n, \\ 0 \text{ when } 0 \leqq t < \lambda_0 \text{ and } \lambda_0 > 0, \end{cases} \tag{7.11–5}$$

the integral being understood as a principal value.

This is the *Kronecker-Cahen-Perron theorem.*

7.11.2 – A LEMMA

The following lemma enables us to give a rigorous proof of the theorem of the previous section.

Let the series (7.11–1) *be convergent for* $s = \alpha$, α *being real. Then, if* $s = \sigma + i\omega$,

$$|\varphi(s)| = o(|\mathrm{Im}\, s|) \tag{7.11–6}$$

uniformly for $\sigma \geqq \alpha + \varepsilon > \alpha$.

This lemma expresses the fact that the function $\varphi(s)$ does not increase very rapidly on a line $\mathrm{Re}\, s =$ constant lying in the half-plane of convergence.

Without loss of generality we may assume $\alpha = 0$. For if $\sigma_c > 0$ we can shift the origin in the s-plane along the real axis on multiplying the series by a suitable power of e. Let

$$A_n = \sum_{\nu=0}^{n} a_\nu.$$

Assuming $0 < m < n$, we have

$$\sum_{\nu=0}^{n} a_\nu e^{-\lambda_\nu s} = \sum_{\nu=0}^{m-1} a_\nu e^{-\lambda_\nu s} + \sum_{\nu=m}^{n} (A_\nu - A_{\nu-1}) e^{-\lambda_\nu s}$$

$$= \sum_{\nu=0}^{m-1} a_\nu e^{-\lambda_\nu s} - A_{m-1} e^{-\lambda_m s} + \sum_{\nu=m}^{n-1} A_\nu (e^{-\lambda_\nu s} - e^{-\lambda_{\nu+1} s}) + A_n e^{-\lambda_n s}.$$

Since $\sum_{\nu=0}^{\infty} a_\nu$ is convergent, by hypothesis, the numbers A_n are bounded. Letting $n \to \infty$ we obtain

$$\varphi(s) = \sum_{\nu=0}^{m-1} a_\nu e^{-\lambda_\nu s} - A_{m-1} e^{-\lambda_m s} + \sum_{\nu=m}^{\infty} A_\nu (e^{-\lambda_\nu s} - e^{-\lambda_{\nu+1} s}).$$

Taking account of

$$|e^{-\lambda_n s} - e^{-\lambda_{n+1} s}| = |s| \left| \int_{\lambda_n}^{\lambda_{n+1}} e^{-st}\, dt \right| \leqq |s| \int_{\lambda_n}^{\lambda_{n+1}} e^{-\sigma t}\, dt = \frac{|s|}{\sigma} (e^{-\lambda_n \sigma} - e^{-\lambda_{n+1} \sigma})$$

we find, A being a suitable constant,

$$|\varphi(s)| < A \left\{ \sum_{\nu=0}^{m-1} e^{-\lambda_\nu \sigma} + e^{-\lambda_m \sigma} + \frac{|s|}{\sigma} \sum_{\nu=m}^{\infty} (e^{-\lambda_\nu \sigma} - e^{-\lambda_{\nu+1} \sigma}) \right\}$$

$$< A \left(\sum_{\nu=0}^{m} e^{-\lambda_\nu \sigma} + \frac{|s|}{\sigma} e^{-\lambda_m \sigma} \right).$$

Because of the fact that $e^{-\lambda_n \sigma} \leqq 1$ the first term of the last expression is $O(m)$. The second term does not exceed

$$A + \frac{A}{\sigma} |\mathrm{Im}\, s| e^{-\lambda_m \sigma}.$$

Taking $m = [\log |\text{Im } s|]$, the desired result follows, since

$$\frac{[\log |\text{Im } s|]}{|\text{Im } s|} \leqq \frac{\log |\text{Im } s|}{|\text{Im } s|} \to 0$$

as $\text{Im } s \to \infty$.

7.11.3 – Proof of Perron's theorem

Now we proceed to prove the theorem of section 7.11.1. First we consider the case $\lambda_n < t < \lambda_{n+1}$. We introduce the function

$$f(s) = e^{ts}(\varphi(s) - \sum_{\nu=0}^{n} a_\nu e^{-\lambda_\nu s}) = \sum_{\nu=n+1}^{\infty} a_\nu e^{(t-\lambda_\nu)s} = \sum_{\nu=0}^{\infty} b_\nu e^{-\mu_\nu s} \qquad (7.11\text{–}7)$$

with $b_\nu = a_{n+\nu+1}$, $\mu_\nu = \lambda_{n+\nu+1} - t$. Hence $\mu_0 > 0$. It is sufficient to show that

$$\int_{c-i\infty}^{c+i\infty} \frac{f(s)}{s} ds = 0.$$

We apply Cauchy's theorem to the rectangle whose vertices are $c \pm iT$, $\omega \pm iT$, $\omega > c$, $T > 0$ (fig. 7.11–1). Since $f(s)/s$ is holo-

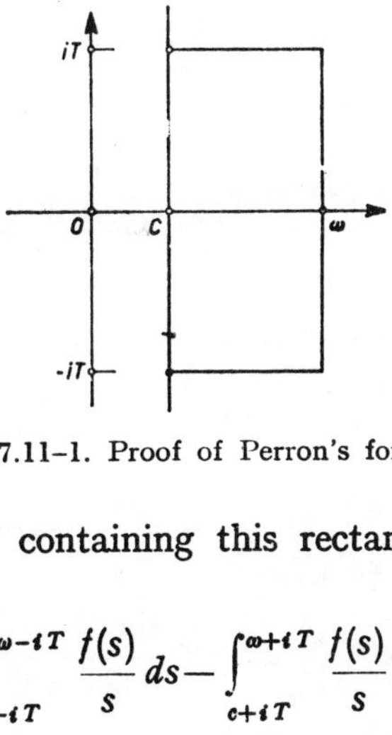

Fig. 7.11–1. Proof of Perron's formula

morphic in a region containing this rectangle, we immediately obtain

$$\int_{c-iT}^{c+iT} \frac{f(s)}{s} ds = \int_{c-iT}^{\omega-iT} \frac{f(s)}{s} ds - \int_{c+iT}^{\omega+iT} \frac{f(s)}{s} ds + \int_{\omega-iT}^{\omega+iT} \frac{f(s)}{s} ds.$$

Keeping T fixed we let $\omega \to \infty$. By the second theorem of section 7.2.3 the function $|f(s)|$ in the last integral remains bounded. Hence this integral tends to zero and

$$\int_{c-iT}^{c+iT} \frac{f(s)}{s} ds = \int_{c-iT}^{\infty-iT} \frac{f(s)}{s} ds - \int_{c+iT}^{\infty+iT} \frac{f(s)}{s} ds \qquad (7.11\text{–}8)$$

provided that the two integrals on the right are convergent. Now we may write

$$f(s) = e^{-\mu_0 s} g(s)$$

and by the lemma stated above we can choose T in such a way that

$$|g(s)| < \varepsilon T,$$

for $s = \sigma + iT$, $\sigma \geqq c$, and T sufficiently large. Hence the second integral on the right of (7.11–8) is convergent and

$$\left| \int_{c+iT}^{\infty+iT} \frac{f(s)}{s} ds \right| < \frac{\varepsilon T}{\sqrt{c^2+T^2}} \int_0^\infty e^{-\mu_0 t} dt < \frac{\varepsilon}{\mu_0}.$$

Thus the integral in question tends to zero as $T \to \infty$. A similar argument applies to the first integral on the right of (7.11–8). This proves the first part of the theorem of section 7.11.1. In almost the same way the other parts may be proved.

7.12 – A formula of Hadamard

7.12.1 – Hadamard's formula

Let σ_a be the abscissa of absolute convergence of the Dirichlet series

$$\varphi(s) = \sum_{\nu=0}^{\infty} a_\nu e^{-\lambda_\nu s}. \tag{7.12–1}$$

If $\sigma = \operatorname{Re} s > \sigma_a$, then

$$\lim_{T\to\infty} \frac{1}{2T} \int_{-iT}^{iT} e^{\lambda s} \varphi(s) ds = \begin{cases} a_n \text{ when } \lambda = \lambda_n, \\ 0, \text{ when } \lambda \text{ is different} \end{cases} \tag{7.12–2}$$

from all numbers λ_n.

Let $\lambda = \lambda_n$. Then, if $t = \operatorname{Im} s$,

$$\frac{1}{2T}\int_{-T}^{T} \varphi(s) e^{\lambda s} dt = \frac{1}{2T}\int_{-T}^{T} \left(\sum_{\nu=0}^{\infty} a_\nu e^{-\lambda_\nu s}\right) e^{\lambda s} dt = \frac{e^{\lambda\sigma}}{2T} \sum_{\nu=0}^{\infty} a_\nu e^{-\lambda_\nu \sigma} \int_{-T}^{T} e^{(\lambda-\lambda_\nu)it} dt$$

$$= a_n + \frac{e^{\lambda\sigma}}{2T} \sum_{\lambda_\nu \neq \lambda} a_\nu e^{-\lambda_\nu \sigma} \int_{-T}^{T} e^{(\lambda-\lambda_\nu)it} dt$$

$$= a_n + e^{\lambda\sigma} \sum_{\lambda_\nu \neq \lambda} a_\nu e^{-\lambda_\nu \sigma} \frac{\sin(\lambda-\lambda_\nu)T}{(\lambda-\lambda_\nu)T}.$$

The last series is uniformly convergent with respect to T and hence by making $T \to \infty$ we obtain the first part of (7.12–2). If λ is different from any λ_n the term a_n does not occur. The reasoning, however, remains the same.

Hadamard's formula (7.12–2) provides a necessary condition for a function to be expressible as the sum of a Dirichlet series. The condition is, however, not sufficient. An adequate answer to the question what sort of function can be represented by a Dirichlet series is not easily given. The study of the almost periodic functions, created by H. Bohr, answers to this question.

7.12.2 – The uniqueness theorem

A function $\varphi(s)$ can have at most one representation as a Dirichlet series of given type $\lambda_0, \lambda_1, \lambda_2, \ldots$, i.e.,

$$\sum_{\nu=0}^{\infty} a_\nu e^{-\lambda_\nu s} = \sum_{\nu=0}^{\infty} b_\nu e^{-\lambda_\nu s}$$

in any region of values of s entails $a_n = b_n$ for all values of n.

This assertion is a direct consequence of Hadamard's theorem of section 7.12.1.

An alternative proof arises from the theorem:

Suppose that the series

$$\varphi(s) = \sum_{\nu=0}^{\infty} a_\nu e^{-\lambda_\nu s} \tag{7.12–3}$$

is convergent for $s = 0$ and let $\mathfrak{K}$ denote the set

$$\operatorname{Re} s \geqq \delta > 0, \qquad |\arg s| \leqq \vartheta < \tfrac{1}{2}\pi.$$

Suppose further that $\varphi(s) = 0$ for an infinity of values of s lying in $\mathfrak{K}$. Then $a_n = 0$ for all values of n.

The function $\varphi(s)$ cannot have an infinity of zeros in a neighbourhood of any point of $\mathfrak{K}$, since according to section 7.2.4 the function $\varphi(s)$ is holomorphic in the half-plane $\operatorname{Re} s > 0$. Hence we can find an infinity of values s_k, such that $\varphi(s_k) = 0$, $\sigma_{k+1} > \sigma_k$, $\lim_{k\to\infty} \sigma_k = \infty$, $\sigma_k = \operatorname{Re} s_k$. Now

$$\psi(s) = e^{\lambda_0 s}\varphi(s) = a_0 + \sum_{\nu=1}^{\infty} a_\nu e^{-(\lambda_\nu-\lambda_0)s}$$

is convergent for $s = 0$ and so uniformly convergent in $\mathfrak{K}$ as has been proved in section 7.2.2. Hence $\psi(s) \to a_0$ when $s \to \infty$ along any path in $\mathfrak{K}$. This contradicts the fact that $\psi(s_k) = 0$, unless $a_0 = 0$. By repeating the argument we can complete the proof.

7.13 – Representation of the sum of a Dirichlet series as a Laplace integral

7.13.1 – An inverse of Perron's theorem

In section 7.4.1 we obtained a representation of the sum of a Dirichlet series as an infinite integral. We now wish to derive an alternative representation which brings us in contact with a remarkable type of integrals to be studied more closely in the subsequent sections of this chapter.

Let $\varphi(s)$ *denote the sum of the Dirichlet series*

$$\sum_{\nu=0}^{\infty} a_\nu e^{-\lambda_\nu s}, \qquad \operatorname{Re} s > \sigma_c,$$

and let $a(t)$ *denote the function* (7.11–5) *occurring in Perron's theorem. Then*

$$\varphi(s) = s\int_0^\infty e^{-st} a(t)dt, \tag{7.13–1}$$

when $\operatorname{Re} s > \max(\sigma_c, 0)$, *and*

$$\varphi(s)-\varphi(0) = s\int_0^\infty e^{-st}\{a(t)-\varphi(0)\}dt, \tag{7.13–2}$$

when $\operatorname{Re} s > \sigma_c$, $\sigma_c < 0$.

This theorem may be considered as an inverse of Perron's theorem.

We shall use the same notations as in the proof of the theorem of section 7.3.1. By summation by parts we find

$$\begin{aligned}\sum_{\nu=0}^{n} a_\nu e^{-\lambda_\nu s} &= A_n e^{-\lambda_n s} + \sum_{\nu=0}^{n-1} A_\nu (e^{-\lambda_\nu s} - e^{-\lambda_{\nu+1} s}) \\ &= A_n e^{-\lambda_n s} + s\sum_{\nu=0}^{n-1} A_\nu \int_{\lambda_\nu}^{\lambda_{\nu+1}} e^{-st}dt = A_n e^{-\lambda_n s} + s\int_0^{\lambda_n} e^{-st} a(t)dt.\end{aligned} \tag{7.13–3}$$

If $\operatorname{Re} s > \sigma_c$ the first member of (7.13–3) tends to $\varphi(s)$ as n increases beyond any bound. Hence the last member does likewise. Taking account of the estimate (7.3–8), assuming $\sigma > 0$, we have for $\operatorname{Re} s > \sigma$ that $A_n e^{-\lambda_n s} \to 0$ as $n \to \infty$. Hence

$$\lim_{n\to\infty} s\int_0^{\lambda_n} e^{-st} a(t)dt = \varphi(s). \tag{7.13–4}$$

Again by (7.3–8)

$$a(t) = O(e^{\sigma t}).$$

It follows that the integral

$$\int_0^\infty e^{-st} a(t)dt$$

is convergent for $\operatorname{Re} s > \max(\sigma_c, 0)$ and the left-hand side of (7.13–4) is equal to this integral.

$\varphi(0)$ exists when $\sigma_c < 0$. The integral in

$$\varphi(0) = s\int_0^\infty e^{-st}\varphi(0)dt \tag{7.13–5}$$

is convergent for $\operatorname{Re} s > 0$. Subtracting corresponding members of (7.13–1) and (7.13–5) we obtain (7.13–2).

There remains the case $\sigma_c < \operatorname{Re} s \leqq 0$. Instead of (7.13–3) we may write

$$\sum_{\nu=0}^{n} a_\nu e^{-\lambda_\nu s} = \{A_n - \varphi(0)\}e^{-\lambda_n s} + s\int_0^{\lambda_n} e^{-st}\{a(t)-\varphi(0)\}dt + \varphi(0).$$

But

$$R_n = \varphi(0) - A_n$$

and taking account of (7.3–13) we may proceed as above to complete the proof of (7.13–2).

7.13.2 – Illustrative examples

The function $a(t)$ is a step function with discontinuities at $t = \lambda_0, \lambda_1, \ldots$, its value at such a point λ_n being $\frac{1}{2}A(\lambda_n - 0) + \frac{1}{2}A(\lambda_n + 0)$. For the evaluation of the integrals in (7.13–1) and (7.13–2) the value of the function $a(t)$ at these points is irrelevant.

As an example we consider the series

$$\frac{1}{e^s - 1} = \sum_{\nu=1}^{\infty} e^{-\nu s}, \qquad \operatorname{Re} s > 0. \tag{7·13–6}$$

Evidently

$$a(t) = n, \qquad \text{when } n < t < n+1.$$

Hence we may represent the function $a(t)$ by $[t]$ and we find

$$\frac{1}{e^s - 1} = s\int_0^{\infty} e^{-st}[t]\,dt, \quad \operatorname{Re} s > 0. \tag{7.13–7}$$

A similar example is the following:

$$\log\frac{1}{1-e^{-s}} = \sum_{\nu=1}^{\infty}\frac{e^{-\nu s}}{\nu}, \qquad \operatorname{Re} s > 0, \tag{7.13–8}$$

. $a(t)$ may be represented by

$$a(t) = 1 + \frac{1}{2} + \ldots + \frac{1}{[t]}, \qquad t > 1.$$

Hence

$$\log\frac{1}{1-e^{-s}} = s\int_0^{\infty} e^{-st}\left(1 + \frac{1}{2} + \ldots + \frac{1}{[t]}\right)dt, \quad \operatorname{Re} s > 0. \tag{7.13–9}$$

Now we mention two examples provided by the zeta function of Riemann,

$$\zeta(s) = \sum_{\nu=1}^{\infty}\nu^{-s} = \sum_{\nu=1}^{\infty} e^{-s\log\nu}, \qquad \operatorname{Re} s > 1. \tag{7.13–10}$$

In this case

$$a(t) = n, \qquad \text{when } \log n < t < \log(n+1),$$

i.e., we m y take

$$a(t) = [e^t]$$

and we thus obtain

$$\zeta(s) = s\int_0^\infty e^{-st}[e^t]dt, \qquad \text{Re } s > 1. \tag{7.13-11}$$

The following example will be used in section 7.18.3. We wish to represent the function $\zeta'(s)/\zeta(s)$ as a Laplace integral. Our starting-point will be the Dirichlet series (7.6–5). We define

$$a(t) = \sum_{\nu=1}^{n} \Lambda(\nu) \tag{7.13–12}$$

for $\log n < t < \log (n+1)$, i.e., for $n < e^t < n+1$. Then, according to (7.13–1)

$$\sum_{\nu=1}^{n} \frac{\Lambda(\nu)}{\nu^s} = s\int_0^\infty e^{-st}a(t)dt, \qquad \text{Re } s > 1.$$

In the theory of prime numbers the function

$$\psi(x) = \sum_{\nu \leqq x} \Lambda(\nu), \qquad x \geqq 0, \tag{7.13–13}$$

plays an important part. It is plain that

$$a(t) = \psi(e^t).$$

Hence

$$\boxed{-\frac{\zeta'(s)}{\zeta(s)} = s\int_0^\infty e^{-st}\psi(e^t)dt,} \qquad \text{Re } s > 1, \tag{7.13–14}$$

the desired formula.

7.14 – The Laplace integral

7.14.1 – Convergence

In the previous section we encountered some examples of a remarkable type of integrals, the Laplace integrals. By a *Laplace integral* is understood an integral of the form

$$\int_0^\infty e^{-st}a(t)dt, \tag{7.14–1}$$

s being a complex and t a real variable.

There is a remarkable similarity between the properties of this integral and those of the Dirichlet series; in a certain sense the Laplace integral is a continuous analogue of a Dirichlet series.

The scope of the theory depends on the assumptions concerning the function $a(t)$. For our purpose it is sufficient to make the following assumptions:

(i) The function is defined for $t > 0$ and integrable in the Riemann sense in every finite interval $0 < a \leqq t \leqq b$.

(ii) The integral

$$\int_a^b a(t)dt$$

is absolutely convergent as regards the lower limit, i.e.,

$$\lim_{\delta \to 0} \int_\delta^\omega |a(t)|dt, \quad 0 < \delta < \omega \tag{7.14-2}$$

exists.

(iii) There is a number s_0 such that

$$\int_\delta^\infty e^{-s_0 t} a(t)dt$$

is convergent.

An easy consequence of these assumptions is:

The integral

$$\int_0^\infty e^{-s_0 t} a(t)dt \tag{7.14-3}$$

is also convergent as regards its lower limit.

In fact,

$$\left|\int_\delta^\omega e^{-s_0 t} a(t)dt\right| \leqq \int_\delta^\omega e^{-\mathrm{Re}\, s_0 t} |a(t)|dt \leqq \begin{cases} \int_\delta^\omega |a(t)|dt, & \text{when } \mathrm{Re}\, s_0 \geqq 0, \\ e^{-\omega\, \mathrm{Re}\, s_0} \int_\delta^\omega |a(t)|dt, & \text{when } \mathrm{Re}\, s_0 < 0, \end{cases}$$

and the assertion follows from assumption (ii).

7.14.2 – Absolute convergence

The integral (7.14–1) is called *absolutely convergent* when the integral

$$\int_0^\infty |e^{-st} a(t)|\, dt \tag{7.14-4}$$

is convergent.

If a Laplace integral (7.14–1) *is absolutely convergent at* $s = s_0$ *it is also absolutely convergent at* s, *when* $\mathrm{Re}\, s \geqq \mathrm{Re}\, s_0$.

With respect to the lower limit of the integral the theorem follows at once from the assumption (ii).

Let ε be a positive number. We can find a number t_0 such that

$$\int_x^\omega \left|e^{-s_0 t} a(t)\right| dt < \varepsilon,$$

provided that $t_0 < x < \omega$. Hence

$$\int_x^\infty |e^{-st} a(t)| dt = \int_x^\infty |e^{-s_0 t} e^{-(s-s_0)t} a(t)| dt$$
$$< e^{-\operatorname{Re}(s-s_0)x} \int_x^\infty |e^{-s_0 t} a(t)| dt < \varepsilon.$$

When the integral (7.14–1) is absolutely convergent for a certain value s_0 of s, but not convergent for all values of s, then there exists a number σ_a, *the abscissa of absolute convergence,* such that the integral is absolutely convergent if $\operatorname{Re} s > \sigma_a$ and not absolutely convergent if $\operatorname{Re} s < \sigma_a$. It is convenient to take $\sigma_a = -\infty$ when the integral is absolutely convergent anywhere, and $\sigma_a = +\infty$ when the integral is nowhere absolutely convergent. It is easily seen that *the half-plane of absolute convergence is either open or closed.*

7.14.3 – Uniform convergence

By examining the proof of the theorem of section 7.14.2 we conclude that the following proposition is also valid.

If the integral (7.14–1) *is absolutely convergent at* $s = s_0$ *it is uniformly convergent in the half-plane* $\operatorname{Re} s \geqq \operatorname{Re} s_0$.

Now we shall prove an analogue of Cahen's theorem of section 7.2.2.

If a Laplace integral is convergent for $s = s_0$ *it is uniformly convergent throughout any angular area defined by*

$$|\arg (s-s_0)| \leqq \vartheta < \tfrac{1}{2}\pi.$$

As regards the lower limit of the integral the situation is quite simple. In fact,

$$|e^{-st}| = e^{-t \operatorname{Re} s} \leqq e^{t|\operatorname{Re} s|}$$

and, assuming $\delta_1 < \delta_2$,

$$\left|\int_{\delta_1}^{\delta_2} e^{-st} a(t) dt\right| \leqq e^{\delta_2 |\operatorname{Re} s|} \int_{\delta_1}^{\delta_2} |a(t)| dt.$$

The expression on the right is arbitrarily small, whenever δ_1 and δ_2 are sufficiently small. As a consequence the integral is absolutely convergent as regards the lower limit to the right of any vertical line in the s-plane.

Next we turn to the case of the upper limit. The argument is quite the same as in the proof of Cahen's theorem. Instead of Abel's method of summation by parts we make use of integration by parts.

Suppose that the integral

$$\int_0^\infty e^{-s_0 t} a(t) dt$$

is convergent. Put

$$R(x) = \int_x^\infty e^{-s_0 t} a(t)dt.$$

Then

$$\int_x^\omega e^{-st} a(t)dt = \int_x^\omega e^{-s_0 t} e^{-(s-s_0)t} a(t)dt = -\int_x^\omega e^{-(s-s_0)t} dR(t)$$

$$= -e^{-(s-s_0)\omega} R(\omega) + e^{-(s-s_0)x} R(x) - (s-s_0)\int_x^\omega e^{-(s-s_0)t} R(t)dt.$$

If Re $(s-s_0) > 0$, then $e^{-t\,\mathrm{Re}(s-s_0)} \leqq 1$, since also $t \geqq 0$.

To a given positive number ε we can find a number x_0 such that $|R(x)| < \varepsilon$, provided that $x > x_0$. For these values of x we have, assuming $\omega > x$,

$$\left|\int_x^\omega e^{-(s-s_0)t} R(t)dt\right| < \varepsilon \int_x^\omega e^{-t\,\mathrm{Re}(s-s_0)}\, dt < \varepsilon \int_x^\infty e^{-t\,\mathrm{Re}(s-s_0)}\, dt$$

$$= \frac{\varepsilon}{\mathrm{Re}(s-s_0)} e^{-x\,\mathrm{Re}(s-s_0)} \leqq \frac{\varepsilon}{\mathrm{Re}(s-s_0)}.$$

Hence

$$\left|\int_x^\omega e^{-st} a(t)dt\right| < \varepsilon\left(2 + \frac{|s-s_0|}{\mathrm{Re}\,(s-s_0)}\right) \leqq \varepsilon(2+\sec\vartheta).$$

It is now easy to complete the proof as in section 7.2.2.

7.15 – Abscissa of convergence

7.15.1 – Abscissa of simple convergence

First we may assert:

If the integral (7.14–1) *is convergent for* $s = s_0$ *it is also convergent for any value of* s *with* Re $s >$ Re s_0.

This theorem enables us to define an *abscissa of simple convergence* σ_c perfectly analogous to the considerations of section 7.2.1. From

$$\left|\int_0^\infty e^{-st} a(t)dt\right| \leqq \int_0^\infty e^{-t\,\mathrm{Re}\,s} |a(t)| dt$$

follows

$$\sigma_c \leqq \sigma_a.$$

It may occur that $\sigma_c < \sigma_a$. This will be illustrated in the following example.

The function $a(t)$ is defined as e^t for $0 \leqq t < \log 2$, $-e^t$ for $\log 2 \leqq t < \log 3$, e^t for $\log 3 \leqq t < \log 4$, and so on. Evidently the integral $\int_0^\infty e^{-st}|a(t)|dt = \int_0^\infty e^{(1-s)t} dt$ is convergent for Re $s > 1$ and divergent for $s = 1$. Hence $\sigma_a = 1$. If $n \neq 1$ we have

$$I_n = \int\limits_{\log n}^{\log(n+1)} e^{-st} e^t \, dt = \int\limits_n^{n+1} u^{-s} du$$

and $u^{-s} \to 0$ as $u \to \infty$, provided that Re $s > 0$. Hence also $I_n \to 0$ as n increases beyond any bound, while for $s > 0$ $I_n > I_{n+1}$. The alternating series

$$\int\limits_0^\infty e^{-st} a(t) dt = I_1 - I_2 + I_3 - \ldots$$

is therefore convergent, whenever $s > 0$. When $s = 0$ the series is divergent, since all $I_n = 1$. Consequently $\sigma_c = 0$.

7.15.2 – Formulas for the abscissa of convergence

The analogue of the theorem of section 7.3.1 concerning the abscissa of convergence σ_c may be stated for integrals as follows:

The abscissa of simple convergence of the Laplace integral (7.14–1) *is given by*

$$\sigma_c = \limsup_{\omega \to \infty} \frac{\log \left| \int\limits_0^\omega a(t) dt \right|}{\omega} \tag{7.15–1}$$

if $\sigma_c > 0$ *and by*

$$\sigma_c = \limsup_{\omega \to \infty} \frac{\log \left| \int\limits_\omega^\infty a(t) dt \right|}{\omega} \tag{7.15–2}$$

if $\sigma_c < 0$.

The proof runs along the same lines as in section **7.3.1**. Instead of Abel's summation by parts we have to integrate by parts.

The Laplace integral occurring in the theorem of section **7.13.1** is certainly convergent in the half-plane of convergence of the Dirichlet series. But the abscissa of convergence of the integral can be smaller than that of the series. The formula (7.15–1) is also true for $\sigma_c = 0$, provided $\int\limits_0^\omega a(t) dt$ does not tend to zero as $\omega \to \infty$.

7.16 – Regularity

7.16.1 – The Laplace integral representing a holomorphic function

In section **7.2.4** we concluded from Cahen's theorem that the Dirichlet series represents a holomorphic function in its half-plane of simple convergence. The same can be asserted about the Laplace integral, but the proof is not so simple.

The function

$$\varphi(s) = \int_0^\infty e^{-st} a(t)dt \tag{7.16–1}$$

is holomorphic in the half-plane of simple convergence and every derivative is also a Laplace integral

$$\varphi^{(k)}(s) = (-1)^k \int_0^\infty e^{-st} t^k a(t)dt, \tag{7.16–2}$$

being convergent in the same half-plane at least.

In order to prove this statement we first consider the integral

$$f(s) = \int_a^b e^{-st} a(t)\,dt. \tag{7.16–3}$$

Because of the uniform convergence of the exponential series we have

$$f(s) = \sum_{\nu=0}^{\infty} (-1)^\nu \frac{s^\nu}{\nu!} \int_a^b t^\nu a(t)dt. \tag{7.16–4}$$

The series on the right converges uniformly as regards s in any bounded set and so its sum is an integral function. Term-by-term differentiation is permitted and we find

$$f^{(k)}(s) = \sum_{\nu=k}^{\infty} (-1)^\nu \frac{s^{\nu-k}}{(\nu-k)!} \int_a^b t^\nu a(t)dt = (-1)^k \int_a^b e^{-st} t^k a(t)dt. \tag{7.16–5}$$

Now let s_0 denote a point with $\mathrm{Re}\, s_0 > \sigma_c$. We can surround it by a circle which lies also in the half-plane of simple convergence of the integral. By virtue of the second theorem of section 7.14.3 the integral (7.16–1) converges uniformly in this circle. We take an arbitrary sequence

$$0 = t_0 < t_1 < t_2 < \ldots,$$

tending to infinity. Then the series

$$\varphi(s) = \sum_{\nu=0}^{\infty} \int_{t_\nu}^{t_{\nu+1}} e^{-st} a(t)dt$$

is also uniformly convergent in the circle and by Weierstrass's theorem of section 2.20.3 term-by-term differentiation is justified, since each term of the series is holomorphic within the circle. Hence

$$\varphi^{(k)}(s) = \sum_{\nu=0}^{\infty} (-1)^k \int_{t_\nu}^{t_{\nu+1}} e^{-st} t^k a(t)dt$$

and the truth of the statement easily follows.

7.16.2 – Abel's theorem

An easy consequence is *Abel's continuity theorem* which is the analogue for Laplace integrals of Abel's theorem stated in section 7.2.2.

If

$$\varphi(s) = \int_0^\infty e^{-st} a(t) dt$$

is convergent at $s = s_0$, *then* $\varphi(s)$ *tends to* $\varphi(s_0)$ *as* $s \to s_0$ *in the angular area* $|\arg(s-s_0)| \leqq \vartheta < \frac{1}{2}\pi$.

In fact, the integral is uniformly continuous throughout this area and hence to a given number $\varepsilon > 0$ we can find a number $\omega > 0$ such that

$$\left|\int_\omega^\infty e^{-st} a(t) dt\right| < \tfrac{1}{3}\varepsilon. \tag{7.16–6}$$

On account of the convergence of the integral at $s = s_0$ we can, moreover, take ω in such a way that also

$$\left|\int_\omega^\infty e^{-s_0 t} a(t) dt\right| < \tfrac{1}{3}\varepsilon. \tag{7.16–7}$$

Since $\int_0^\omega e^{-st} a(t) dt$ is holomorphic as regards s throughout the entire s-plane it is possible to find a number $\delta > 0$ such that

$$\left|\int_0^\omega e^{-st} a(t) dt - \int_0^\omega e^{-s_0 t} a(t) dt\right| < \tfrac{1}{3}\varepsilon \tag{7.16–8}$$

provided $|s-s_0| < \delta$. By the usual arguments we now find that $|\varphi(s)-\varphi(s_0)| < \varepsilon$, provided that $|s-s_0| < \delta$ and $|\arg(s-s_0)| \leqq \vartheta < \frac{1}{2}\pi$. This proves the assertion.

7.17 – Some remarkable integrals of the Laplace type

7.17.1 – The Laplace transformation

By means of the relation

$$\varphi(s) = \int_0^\infty e^{-st} a(t) dt \tag{7.17–1}$$

the function $a(t)$ is transformed into another function $\varphi(s)$. The process (7.17–1) is called a *Laplace transformation*. It plays an important role in pure as well as in applied mathematics. Extensive tables have been constructed containing particular functions $a(t)$ and their corresponding transforms. In this section we wish to consider some remarkable examples which are related to functions studied previously.

7.17.2 – First example

In section 7.13.2 we obtained (7.13–7)

$$s\int_0^\infty e^{-st}\,[t]\,dt = \frac{1}{e^s-1}, \qquad \operatorname{Re} s > 0. \qquad (7.17\text{–}2)$$

Taking account of the elementary results

$$\int_0^\infty e^{-st}\,dt = \frac{1}{s}, \qquad \operatorname{Re} s > 0, \qquad (7.17\text{–}3)$$

and

$$\int_0^\infty e^{-st}\,t\,dt = \frac{1}{s^2}, \qquad \operatorname{Re} s > 0, \qquad (7.17\text{–}4)$$

we easily find

$$\boxed{\left(\frac{1}{e^s-1}-\frac{1}{s}+\frac{1}{2}\right)\frac{1}{s} = -\int_0^\infty e^{-st}\,\mathsf{P}_1(t)\,dt,} \qquad \operatorname{Re} s > 0, \qquad (7.17\text{–}5)$$

where

$$\mathsf{P}_1(t) = t-[t]-\tfrac{1}{2}.$$

On the left of (7.17–5) appears the integrand occurring in Binet's integral (4.9–21)

$$\boxed{\mu(s) = \int_0^\infty e^{-st}\left(\frac{1}{e^t-1}-\frac{1}{t}+\frac{1}{2}\right)\frac{dt}{t}} \qquad \operatorname{Re} s > 0, \qquad (7.17\text{–}6)$$

another example of a Laplace integral.

7.17.3 – Second example

Starting with the expression (2.20–28) for the logarithm

$$\log s = \int_0^\infty \frac{e^{-t}-e^{-st}}{t}\,dt, \qquad \operatorname{Re} s > 0,$$

we immediately obtain

$$\boxed{\log\left(1+\frac{1}{s}\right) = \int_0^\infty e^{-st}\,(1-e^{-t})\,\frac{dt}{t},} \qquad \operatorname{Re} s > 0. \qquad (7.17\text{–}7)$$

7.17.4 – Third example

Another interesting example is found when we take (4.8–31) into account:

$$\Psi(s) = \int_0^\infty \left(\frac{e^{-t}}{t}-\frac{e^{-st}}{1-e^{-t}}\right)dt, \qquad \operatorname{Re} s > 0.$$

A simple calculation yields

$$\Psi(\tfrac{1}{2}s+1)-\Psi(\tfrac{1}{2}s+\tfrac{1}{2})=\int_0^\infty e^{-\frac{1}{2}st}\frac{e^{-\frac{1}{2}t}-e^{-t}}{1-e^{-t}}\,dt=\int_0^\infty e^{-\frac{1}{2}st}\frac{1}{e^{\frac{1}{2}t}+1}\,dt$$

and so

$$\boxed{\tfrac{1}{2}\Psi(\tfrac{1}{2}s+1)-\tfrac{1}{2}\Psi(\tfrac{1}{2}s+\tfrac{1}{2})=\int_0^\infty e^{-st}\frac{1}{e^{t}+1}\,dt,} \qquad (7.17\text{–}8)$$

this integral being convergent for $\operatorname{Re} s > -1$.

As a particular result we mention

$$\tfrac{1}{2}\Psi(1)-\tfrac{1}{2}\Psi(\tfrac{1}{2})=\int_0^\infty \frac{dt}{e^{t}+1}=-\int_0^\infty \frac{e^{-t}}{1+e^{-t}}dt=-\log(1+e^{-t})\Big|_0^\infty=\log 2$$

whence, according to (4.8–3),

$$\Psi(\tfrac{1}{2}) = -\gamma-2\log 2, \qquad (7.17\text{–}9)$$

γ being Euler's constant.

7.17.5 – Formulas deduced from the gamma function

In the formula

$$\Gamma(z)=\int_0^\infty e^{-u}u^{z-1}\,du, \qquad \operatorname{Re} z>0 \qquad (7.17\text{–}10)$$

we replace u by ts, assuming s to be positive. We get

$$\boxed{\Gamma(z)s^{-z}=\int_0^\infty e^{-st}t^{z-1}\,dt,} \qquad \operatorname{Re} z>0. \qquad (7.17\text{–}11)$$

This result also holds for complex values of s in the region $\operatorname{Re} s>0$, since both members of (7.17–10) are holomorphic in the region and coincide for real values of s. The argument bears on the identity principle of section 2.11.2. This device is also applicable in the following example.

Differentiating (7.17–10) we obtain

$$\Gamma'(z)=\int_0^\infty e^{-u}u^{z-1}\log u\,du, \qquad (7.17\text{–}12)$$

and performing the substitution $u=ts$, taking account of (7.17–11), we get

$$\Gamma'(z)=s^{z}\int_0^\infty e^{-st}t^{z-1}\log t\,dt+s^{z}\int_0^\infty e^{-st}t^{z-1}\log s\,dt$$

$$=s^{z}\int_0^\infty e^{-st}t^{z-1}\log t\,dt+\Gamma(z)\log s.$$

Hence

$$\{\Gamma'(z)-\Gamma(z)\log s\}s^{-z}=\int_0^\infty e^{-st}t^{z-1}\log t\,dt, \qquad \operatorname{Re} s>0. \tag{7.17–13}$$

In particular, taking $z = 1$,

$$-\gamma - \log s = s\int_0^\infty e^{-st}\log t\,dt. \tag{7.17–14}$$

In this formula we take $s = 1$. We then obtain a representation of Euler's constant as an integral, viz.,

$$\gamma = -\int_0^\infty e^{-t}\log t\,dt$$

or else, by putting $t = -\log u$,

$$\gamma = -\int_0^1 \log\log(1/u)\,du. \tag{7.17–15}$$

This formula is due to Malmstén.

7.18 – The prime number theorem

7.18.1 – Introduction

One of the most famous problems in the theory of numbers is the estimate of the function $\pi(x)$, denoting the number of prime numbers up to a given non-negative number x. Gauss already conjectured that for large values of x this number may be approximated by the simple expression $x/\log x$.

By the *prime number theorem* we understand the assertion

$$\lim_{x\to\infty}\frac{\pi(x)}{x/\log x}=1. \tag{7.18–1}$$

The proof of this theorem is difficult. The first rigorous proof has been given by Hadamard and De la Vallée-Poussin. The shortest proof is due to Landau.

The theorem is a consequence of certain properties of the Riemann zeta function. In recent years an elementary proof avoiding the advanced theory of the zeta function has been found by A. Selberg, but this proof is also very intricate. It is our aim to present the classical proof because of its undeniable beauty.

It is interesting to compare the assertion (7.18–1) with the evidence of the tables. The values of $\pi(x)$ for $x = 10^3$, $x = 10^6$, $x = 10^9$ are 168, 78498, 50847478 respectively. The values of $x/\log x$ to the nearest integer are 145, 72382, 48254942. The ratios are 1·16, 1·08, 1·05 approximately and show a tendency, though not a very rapid one, to unity.

7.18.2 – Deduction of the prime number theorem from the Hadamard-De La Vallée Poussin theorem

The problem can easily be reduced to the investigation of the function $\psi(x)$ introduced in section 7.13.2.

The main theorem, which is known as the *Hadamard-De la Vallée Poussin theorem*, is the assertion

$$\lim_{x\to\infty} \frac{\psi(x)}{x} = 1. \tag{7.18–2}$$

Before attacking this last problem we wish to show how the prime number theorem can be deduced from this assertion.

First we derive a trivial inequality about $\psi(x)$. If p is a fixed prime number, we have to consider the powers $p, p^2, \ldots, p^\alpha$, where $p^\alpha \leqq x$, i.e., $\alpha \log p \leqq \log x$. These powers contribute $\alpha \log p$ to $\psi(x)$. The largest number α satisfying the above inequality is

$$\left[\frac{\log x}{\log p}\right],$$

and so

$$\psi(x) = \sum_{p\leqq x} \left[\frac{\log x}{\log p}\right] \log p \leqq \sum_{p\leqq x} \frac{\log x}{\log p} \log p,$$

whence

$$\psi(x) \leqq \pi(x) \log x, \tag{7.18–3}$$

including

$$\psi(x) \leqq x \log x. \tag{7.18–4}$$

If $1 < \xi < x$ we have

$$\pi(x) - \pi(\xi) = \sum_{\xi<p\leqq x} 1 < \sum_{\xi<p\leqq x} \frac{\log p}{\log \xi}.$$

Hence, assuming $x > e$ and taking $\xi = x/\log^2 x$

$$1 \leqq \frac{\pi(x)\log x}{\psi(x)} < \frac{\pi(\xi)\log x + \sum\limits_{\xi<p\leqq x} \dfrac{\log p}{\log \xi} \log x}{\psi(x)}$$

$$\leqq \frac{\xi \log x}{\psi(x)} + \frac{\log x}{\log \xi} = \frac{x}{\psi(x)\log x} + \frac{\log x}{\log x - 2\log\log x}.$$

Anticipating the validity of (7.18–2) we see that the last expression tends to 1 as $x \to \infty$. Hence

$$\frac{\pi(x)\log x}{\psi(x)} \to 1$$

and (7.18–1) follows at once.

7.18.3 – Alternative statement of the Hadamard-De La Vallée Poussin theorem

The guiding principle in the proof of (7.18–2) is the deduction of the properties of $\psi(e^t)$ from the representation (7.13–14) of $\zeta'(s)/\zeta(s)$ as a Laplace integral. It will be more convenient to use the function

$$g(s) = -\frac{1}{s}\frac{\zeta'(s)}{\zeta(s)} - \frac{1}{s-1}, \tag{7.18–5}$$

this function being regular at every point s with $\operatorname{Re} s \geqq 1$. In fact, in the sections 7.6.1 and 7.7.4 we proved that all zeros of $\zeta(s)$ are to the left of the line $\operatorname{Re} s = 1$. Further $\zeta(s)$ has only a simple pole at $s = 1$ (7.7.1) and it follows from the theorem of section 3.8.1 that $\zeta'(s)/\zeta(s)$ possesses a pole at $s = 1$ with residue -1 and is regular everywhere else in the area $\operatorname{Re} s \geqq 1$. The assertion about $g(s)$ is now a trivial consequence.

Starting from (7.13–14) we easily find

$$g(s) = \int_0^\infty e^{-(s-1)t}(H(t)-1)dt, \qquad \operatorname{Re} s > 1, \tag{7.18–6}$$

with

$$H(t) = e^{-t}\psi(e^t), \tag{7.18–7}$$

and we shall have achieved our end when we have proved

$$\lim_{t\to\infty} H(t) = 1, \tag{7.18–8}$$

this assertion being equivalent to (7.18–2).

7.18.4 – Decisive step in the proof

Let $F(y)$ denote the function

$$F(y) = \tfrac{1}{2}(1-\tfrac{1}{2}|y|)e^{iuy},$$

all variables involved being real. This function is continuous in the range $-2 \leqq y \leqq 2$.

It is easy to prove that

$$\int_{-2}^{2} F(y)dy = \frac{\sin^2 u}{u^2}. \tag{7.18–9}$$

In fact, when $u \neq 0$ the integral on the left is equal to

$$\int_0^2 (1-\tfrac{1}{2}y)\cos uy\,dy = (1-\tfrac{1}{2}y)\frac{\sin uy}{u}\Big|_0^2 + \frac{1}{2u}\int_0^2 \sin uy\,dy$$
$$= \frac{1}{2u^2}(1-\cos 2u) = \frac{\sin^2 u}{u^2},$$

the result being also valid when $u = 0$.

Let $s = 1+\varepsilon+i\lambda y$, $\varepsilon > 0$, $\lambda > 0$. We consider the expression

$$\int_{-2}^{2} F(y)\,g(s)dy = \int_{-2}^{2} F(y)dy \int_0^\infty (H(t)-1)\,e^{-\varepsilon t}e^{-i\lambda y t}\,dt.$$

We may reverse the order of integration. In fact, by virtue of (7.18–4) we have

$$|H(t)-1| < 1+t, \qquad t > 0,$$

and by writing

$$\int_{-2}^{2}\int_0^\infty = \int_{-2}^{2}\int_0^\omega + \int_{-2}^{2}\int_\omega^\infty = \int_0^\omega\int_{-2}^{2} + \int_{-2}^{2}\int_\omega^\infty$$

we readily find the required result since $\int_\omega^\infty$ tends to zero as $\omega \to \infty$.

We thus obtain

$$\int_{-2}^{2} F(y)g(s)dy = \int_0^\infty (H(t)-1)e^{-\varepsilon t}\frac{\sin^2(u-\lambda t)}{(u-\lambda t)^2}\,dt, \qquad (7.18\text{–}10)$$

where we have utilized (7.18–9).

Letting $\varepsilon \to 0$ we find

$$\int_{-2}^{2} F(y)\,g(1+i\lambda y)\,dy = \int_0^\infty (H(t)-1)\,\frac{\sin^2(u-\lambda t)}{(u-\lambda t)^2}\,dt. \qquad (7.18\text{–}11)$$

This step will be justified in section 7.18.5. It will be more convenient to introduce the variable $v = u-\lambda t$. Then the integral on the right of (7.18–11) appears as

$$\frac{1}{\lambda}\int_{-\infty}^{u}\left(H\left(\frac{u-v}{\lambda}\right)-1\right)\frac{\sin^2 v}{v^2}\,dv,$$

and since the variable t is now available we can make the expression more flexible by writing λt instead of u. And so we may bring (7.18–11) into the form

$$\int_{-\infty}^{\lambda t}\left(H\left(t-\frac{v}{\lambda}\right)\right)\frac{\sin^2 v}{v^2}\,dv$$
$$= \tfrac{1}{2}\lambda\int_{-2}^{2} g(1+i\lambda y)(1-\tfrac{1}{2}|y|)e^{i\lambda y t}\,dy + \int_{-\infty}^{\lambda t}\frac{\sin^2 v}{v^2}\,dv. \qquad (7.18\text{–}12)$$

Since $f(y) = g(1+i\lambda y)(1-\tfrac{1}{2}|y|)$ has a bounded derivative in the range $-2 \leqq y \leqq 2$, this derivative having a jump at $y = 0$, we may integrate by parts and conclude that

$$\left| \int_{-2}^{2} f(y) e^{i\lambda_y t} dy \right| = \left| \frac{e^{i\lambda_y t}}{i\lambda t} f(y) \right|_{y=-2}^{2} - \int_{-2}^{2} \frac{e^{i\lambda_y t}}{i\lambda t} f'(y) dy \Bigg| < \frac{A}{t},$$

A being a suitable constant. Hence, letting $t \to \infty$ and taking account of (3.6–22), we deduce from (7.18–12)

$$\lim_{t\to\infty} \int_{-\infty}^{\lambda t} H\left(t - \frac{v}{\lambda}\right) \frac{\sin^2 v}{v^2} dv = \pi. \tag{7.18–13}$$

It will turn out that we now have done the decisive step.

7.18.5 – A lemma

Before continuing our proof we wish to justify the way in which we obtained (7.18–11). We need the following lemma.

Consider the Laplace integral

$$\varphi(s) = \int_0^\infty e^{-st} a(t) dt, \tag{7.18–14}$$

assumed to be convergent for $\operatorname{Re} s > 0$ and where $a(t)$ denotes a non-negative real function. We assert:

If $\varphi(s)$ tends to a limit l as $s \to 0$, then $\int_0^t a(u) du$ tends to the same limit as $t \to \infty$.

It is plain that also

$$\int_0^\infty e^{-st} e^{-nst} a(t) dt$$

tends to l as s tends to zero, n being a non-negative integer. As a consequence

$$\int_0^\infty e^{-st} p(e^{-st}) a(t) dt \to l \tag{7.18–15}$$

where $p(x)$ is any polynomial where $p(1) = 1$.

Now we consider a function $q(x)$ defined in the range $0 \leqq x \leqq 1$ as follows:

$$q(x) = \begin{cases} 0, & \text{when } 0 \leqq x < e^{-1}, \\ \dfrac{1}{x}, & \text{when } e^{-1} \leqq x. \end{cases}$$

We evidently have

$$\int_0^\infty e^{-st} q(e^{-st}) a(t) dt = \int_0^{1/s} a(t) dt. \tag{7.18–16}$$

It is easy to find two real polynomials $p_1(x)$, $p_2(x)$ such that

$p_1(x) \leqq q(x) \leqq p_2(x)$, $p_1(1) = q(1) = p_2(1) = 1$. We might take, for instance,

$$p_1(x) = \frac{\mathrm{e}x-1}{\mathrm{e}-1}, \qquad p_2(x) = -\mathrm{e}x+\mathrm{e}+1.$$

Because $a(t) \geqq 0$, we have

$$\int_0^\infty \mathrm{e}^{-st} p_1(\mathrm{e}^{-st}) a(t)dt \leqq \int_0^\infty \mathrm{e}^{-st} q(\mathrm{e}^{-st}) a(t)dt \leqq \int_0^\infty \mathrm{e}^{-st} p_2(\mathrm{e}^{-st}) a(t)dt.$$

Letting $s \to 0$ and taking account of (7.18–16) the desired result follows.

Now we are sufficiently prepared to complete the considerations of section 7.18.4. The integral on the left of (7.18–10) tends to a limit as $\varepsilon \to 0$, because $g(s)$ is regular on the line $\operatorname{Re} s = 1$, this limit being the expression on the left of (7.18–11). The integral

$$\int_0^\infty \mathrm{e}^{-\varepsilon t} \frac{\sin^2(u-\lambda t)}{(u-\lambda t)^2} dt$$

is convergent when $\varepsilon = 0$. On account of Abel's continuity theorem of section 7.16.2 it possesses a limit as $\varepsilon \to 0$, this limit being the integral which appears for $\varepsilon = 0$. By virtue of (7.18–10) the integral

$$\int_0^\infty \mathrm{e}^{-\varepsilon t} H(t) \frac{\sin^2(u-\lambda t)}{(u-\lambda t)^2} dt$$

also tends to a limit as $\varepsilon \to 0$. The factor of $\mathrm{e}^{-\varepsilon t}$ under the sign of integration is not negative and so we may apply the above lemma, stating that

$$\int_0^\infty H(t) \frac{\sin^2(u-\lambda t)}{(u-\lambda t)^2} dt$$

is convergent, its value being the limit of the previous integral as $\varepsilon \to 0$. Thus the proof of (7.18–11) is complete.

7.18.6 –. Completion of the proof

We proceed to complete the proof of (7.18–8). First we observe that $\mathrm{e}^t H(t) = \psi(\mathrm{e}^t)$ increases as t increases. Hence for $|v| < \sqrt{\lambda}$

$$H(t) < H\left(t+\frac{1}{\sqrt{\lambda}}-\frac{v}{\lambda}\right) \mathrm{e}^{\frac{1}{\sqrt{\lambda}}-\frac{v}{\lambda}} \leqq H\left(t+\frac{1}{\sqrt{\lambda}}-\frac{v}{\lambda}\right) \mathrm{e}^{\frac{2}{\sqrt{\lambda}}},$$

whence, by virtue of (7.18–13),

$$H(t)\int_{-\sqrt{\lambda}}^{\sqrt{\lambda}}\frac{\sin^2 v}{v^2}\,dv \leqq e^{\frac{2}{\sqrt{\lambda}}}\int_{-\sqrt{\lambda}}^{\sqrt{\lambda}} H\left(t+\frac{1}{\sqrt{\lambda}}-\frac{v}{\lambda}\right)\frac{\sin^2 v}{v^2}\,dv$$

$$\leqq e^{\frac{2}{\sqrt{\lambda}}}\int_{-\infty}^{\lambda\left(t+\frac{1}{\sqrt{\lambda}}\right)} H\left(t+\frac{1}{\sqrt{\lambda}}-\frac{v}{\lambda}\right)\frac{\sin^2 v}{v^2}\,dv \to e^{\frac{2}{\sqrt{\lambda}}}\pi,$$

as $t\to\infty$. Taking t sufficiently large we have

$$H(t)\int_{-\sqrt{\lambda}}^{\sqrt{\lambda}}\frac{\sin^2 v}{v^2}\,dv < e^{\frac{2}{\sqrt{\lambda}}}(1+\tfrac{1}{2}\varepsilon)\pi,$$

ε denoting a given positive number. When λ is beyond a sufficiently large number we also have

$$\frac{(1+\frac{1}{2}\varepsilon)e^{\frac{2}{\sqrt{\lambda}}}\pi}{\displaystyle\int_{-\sqrt{\lambda}}^{\sqrt{\lambda}}\frac{\sin^2 v}{v^2}\,dv} < 1+\varepsilon$$

and it follows that

$$H(t) < 1+\varepsilon. \tag{7.18–17}$$

For sufficiently large values of t we have $H(t) < 2$; as a consequence $H(t)$ is bounded for $t \geqq 0$. Accordingly, whenever t is large enough,

$$\int_{\sqrt{t}}^{\lambda\left(t-\frac{1}{\sqrt{\lambda}}\right)} H\left(t-\frac{1}{\sqrt{\lambda}}-\frac{v}{\lambda}\right)\frac{\sin^2 v}{v^2}\,dv < M\int_{\sqrt{t}}^{\lambda\left(t-\frac{1}{\sqrt{\lambda}}\right)}\frac{\sin^2 v}{v^2}\,dv,$$

the right-hand side tending to zero as $t\to\infty$, M being an upper bound for $H(t)$. Since on account of (7.18–13)

$$\lim_{t\to\infty}\int_{-\infty}^{\lambda\left(t-\frac{1}{\sqrt{\lambda}}\right)} H\left(t-\frac{1}{\sqrt{\lambda}}-\frac{v}{\lambda}\right)\frac{\sin^2 v}{v^2}\,dv = \pi,$$

we also have

$$\lim_{t\to\infty}\int_{-\infty}^{\sqrt{t}} H\left(t-\frac{1}{\sqrt{\lambda}}-\frac{v}{\lambda}\right)\frac{\sin^2 v}{v^2}\,dv = \pi.$$

Using again that $H(t) < 2$ when t is sufficiently large we evidently have

$$(1-\tfrac{1}{2}\varepsilon)\pi < \int_{-\infty}^{\sqrt{t}} H\left(t-\frac{1}{\sqrt{\lambda}}-\frac{v}{\lambda}\right)\frac{\sin^2 v}{v^2}\,dv$$

$$\leqq \int_{-\infty}^{-\sqrt{\lambda}}\frac{2}{v^2}\,dv+\int_{-\sqrt{\lambda}}^{\sqrt{\lambda}} H(t)e^{\frac{2}{\sqrt{\lambda}}}\frac{\sin^2 v}{v^2}\,dv+\int_{\sqrt{\lambda}}^{\infty}\frac{2}{v^2}\,dv \leqq \frac{4}{\sqrt{\lambda}}+H(t)e^{\frac{2}{\sqrt{\lambda}}}\pi.$$

Taking λ large enough we have

$$e^{-\frac{2}{\sqrt{\lambda}}}\left(1-\tfrac{1}{2}\varepsilon-\frac{4}{\pi\sqrt{\lambda}}\right)>1-\varepsilon$$

and so

$$H(t) > 1-\varepsilon, \qquad (7.18\text{–}18)$$

when t is large enough. The inequalities (7.18–17) and (7.18–18) are equivalent to the assertion (7.18–8) and thus the proof of the prime number theorem is complete.

7.19 – The incomplete gamma functions

7.19.1 – Definition

By the *incomplete gamma functions* or *Prym's functions* are understood the integrals

$$\boxed{P(s,z)=\int_0^s e^{-t}t^{z-1}\,dt,} \qquad \operatorname{Re} z>0, \qquad (7.19\text{–}1)$$

and

$$\boxed{Q(s,z)=\int_s^{\infty} e^{-t}t^{z-1}\,dt} \qquad (7.19\text{–}2)$$

where s varies in the region $s+|s| \neq 0$. The variable t is complex and in the second integral the path of integration consists of a curve connecting the points s and 1 and remaining in the region $s+|s| \neq 0$ followed by the infinite half-ray from 1 to $+\infty$, (fig. 7.19–1).

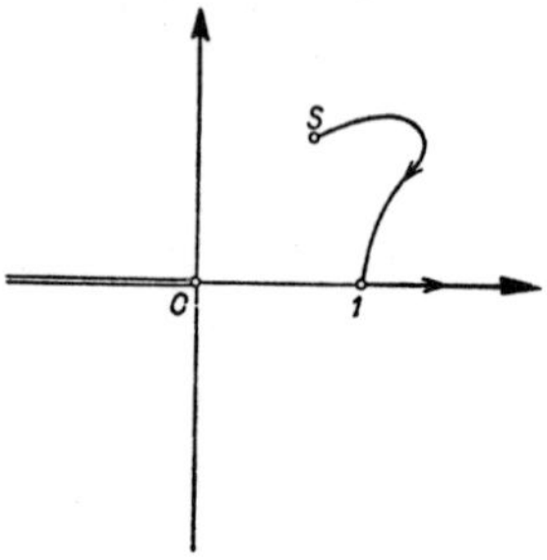

Fig. 7.19–1. Path of integration for the function $Q(s, z)$

It is easy to show that $Q(s, z)$ is an integral function as regards z and holomorphic as regards s in the region $s+|s| \neq 0$.

By virtue of Cauchy's integral theorem we have

$$\boxed{P(s,z)+Q(s,z)=\Gamma(z).} \qquad (7.19\text{–}3)$$

7.19.2 – Functional equation and decomposition

The incomplete gamma function $Q(s, z)$ has many properties which are obvious generalizations of the ordinary gamma function. Thus, for instance, on integrating by parts, the *functional equation*

$$\boxed{Q(s, z+1)-zQ(s, z) = e^{-s}s^z.} \qquad (7.19\text{–}4)$$

Expanding e^{-t} in its power series and performing term-by-term integration from 0 to s, we obtain

$$P(s, z) = s^z \sum_{\nu=0}^{\infty} \frac{(-1)^\nu s^\nu}{\nu!\,(z+\nu)}, \qquad (7.19\text{–}5)$$

whence

$$\boxed{Q(s, z) = \Gamma(z)-s^z \sum_{\nu=0}^{\infty} \frac{(-1)^\nu s^\nu}{\nu!\,(z+\nu)}.} \qquad (7.19\text{–}6)$$

This result generalizes Prym's decomposition (4.7–30) of the gamma function. The equation holds, provided that z is different from $0, -1, -2, \ldots$.

7.19.3 – The value of $Q(s, z)$ at $z = 0, -1, -2, \ldots$

In contrast with the gamma function the function $Q(s, z)$ still has a meaning for $z = 0, -1, -2, \ldots$.

Let us first consider the simplest case, viz., $z = 0$. We may write (7.19–6) in the form

$$Q(s, z) = \frac{\Gamma(z+1)-\Gamma(1)}{z} - \frac{s^z-1}{z} - s^z \sum_{\nu=1}^{\infty} \frac{(-1)^\nu s^\nu}{\nu!\,(z+\nu)},$$

and, letting $z \to 0$, we readily obtain

$$\boxed{Q(s, 0) = -\gamma - \log s - \sum_{\nu=1}^{\infty} \frac{(-1)^\nu s^\nu}{\nu!\,\nu},} \qquad (7.19\text{–}7)$$

γ being Euler's constant.

A similar method applies to the case $z = -n$, where n is a positive integer. We may write (7.19–6) in the form

$$Q(s, z) = \frac{1}{z(z+1)\ldots(z+n-1)} \frac{\Gamma(z+n+1)-\Gamma(1)}{z+n} - \frac{(-1)^n}{n!} \frac{s^{z+n}-1}{z+n}$$
$$+ \frac{1}{n!} \frac{1}{z+n} \left\{ \frac{n!}{z(z+1)\ldots(z+n-1)} - (-1)^n \right\} - s^z \sum_{\nu=0}^{\infty}{}' \frac{(-1)^\nu s^\nu}{\nu!\,(z+\nu)},$$

where the prime denotes that the term corresponding to $\nu = n$ is missing. Since the derivative of

$$\frac{n!}{z(z+1)\ldots(z+n-1)}$$

at $z = -n$ takes the value $1+\frac{1}{2}+\ldots+1/n$, we readily obtain

$$Q(s, -n) = \frac{(-1)^n}{n!}\left(-\gamma+1+\tfrac{1}{2}+\ldots+\frac{1}{n}-\log s\right) - \sum_{\nu=0}^{\infty}{}' \frac{(-1)^\nu s^{\nu-n}}{\nu!(\nu-n)}.$$

7.19.4 – Representation of $Q(s, z)$ as an integral

Replacing t by $st+s$, we find

$$Q(s, z) = s^z e^{-s}\int_0^\infty e^{-st}(1+t)^{z-1}\,dt$$

where now t is real and s positive. Hence

$$\boxed{s^{-z}e^{s}Q(s, z) = \int_0^\infty e^{-st}(1+t)^{z-1}\,dt,} \qquad \operatorname{Re} s > 0. \qquad (7.19\text{–}8)$$

In fact, the substitution is valid for positive values of s and since both members of (7.19–8) are holomorphic in the region $\operatorname{Re} s > 0$ the equation holds throughout this region.

7.19.5 – Mellin's integral

An alternative representation of $Q(s, z)$ as a Laplace integral is due to Mellin and can be obtained by first replacing z by $1-z$,

$$Q(s, 1-z) = \int_s^\infty e^{-t}t^{-z}\,dt. \qquad (7.19\text{–}9)$$

Recalling (7.17–11) in the form

$$t^{-z} = \frac{1}{\Gamma(z)}\int_0^\infty e^{-ut}u^{z-1}\,du, \qquad \operatorname{Re} z > 0, \qquad (7.19\text{–}10)$$

we evidently have

$$\Gamma(z)Q(s, 1-z) = \int_s^\infty e^{-t}\,dt\int_0^\infty e^{-ut}u^{z-1}\,du, \quad \operatorname{Re} z > 0. \qquad (7.19\text{–}11)$$

Reversing the order of integration we arrive at

$$\Gamma(z)Q(s, 1-z) = \int_0^\infty u^{z-1}\,du\int_s^\infty e^{-t(u+1)}\,dt = e^{-s}\int_0^\infty e^{-su}\frac{u^{z-1}}{1+u}\,du,$$

whence, replacing again z by $1-z$ and u by t,

$$\boxed{e^{s}\Gamma(1-z)Q(s,z) = \int_0^\infty e^{-st}\frac{t^{-z}}{1+t}\,dt,} \qquad \operatorname{Re} z<1,\ \operatorname{Re} s>0. \qquad (7.19\text{–}12)$$

We have to justify the reversal of the order of integration in (7.19–11). It is sufficient to suppose $s > 0$, $z > 0$. If $b > s$ we have

$$\int_s^b e^{-t}\,dt \int_0^\infty e^{-ut} u^{z-1}\,du = \int_s^b dt \int_0^\infty e^{-t(u+1)} u^{z-1}\,du$$

$$= \int_s^b dt \int_0^\omega e^{-t(u+1)} u^{z-1}\,du + \int_s^b dt \int_\omega^\infty e^{-t(1+u)} u^{z-1}\,du$$

$$= \int_0^\omega u^{z-1}\,du \int_s^b e^{-t(u+1)}\,dt + \int_s^b dt \int_\omega^\infty e^{-t(u+1)} u^{z-1}\,du.$$

But

$$\int_s^b dt \int_\omega^\infty e^{-t(u+1)} u^{z-1}\,du = \int_s^b e^{-t} t^{-z} Q(\omega t, z)\,dt$$

and this tends to zero as $\omega \to \infty$. Hence

$$\int_s^b e^{-t}\,dt \int_0^\infty e^{-ut} u^{z-1}\,du = \int_0^\infty u^{z-1}\,du \int_s^b e^{-t(u+1)}\,dt. \qquad (7.17\text{–}13)$$

Since the expression on the left has a limit as $b \to \infty$, the same is true for the expression on the right and the assertion follows.

7.19.6 – The exponential integral

Intimately related to the function $Q(s, 0)$ is the so-called *exponential integral,* defined as

$$\boxed{\mathrm{Ei}\, s = \int_{-\infty}^{s} \frac{e^t}{t}\,dt,} \qquad (7.19\text{–}14)$$

valid for all $s \neq 0$. The path of integration is shown in fig. 7.19–2.

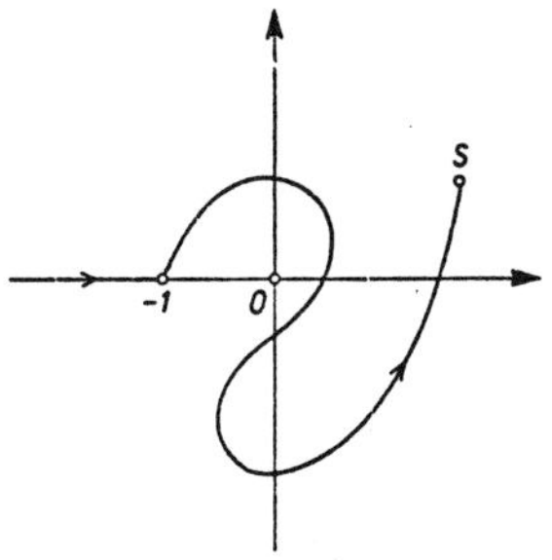

Fig. 7.19–2. Path of integration for the function Ei s

The curve connecting -1 and s may be arbitrary, provided that it avoids the origin. As a consequence *the exponential integral is infinitely many valued,* its period being $2\pi i$.

It is plain that Ei s possesses a branch taking real values for negative real values $-x$ of s. When $\operatorname{Im} s > 0$ we have $\log(-s) = \log s - \pi i$. Hence

$$-Q(-s, 0) = \gamma + \log s - \pi i + \sum_{\nu=1}^{\infty} \frac{s^\nu}{\nu!\,\nu} \quad \operatorname{Im} s > 0.$$

As a consequence we may write

$$\boxed{\operatorname{Ei} s = \gamma - \pi i + \operatorname{Log} s + \sum_{\nu=1}^{\infty} \frac{s^\nu}{\nu!\,\nu}} \tag{7.19–15}$$

where Log s is the general logarithm, introduced in section 1.11.2.

By replacing s by is we can divide the expression on the right of (7.19–15) into two parts, similar to Euler's decomposition of the exponential function

$$\operatorname{Ei} is = \operatorname{ci} s + i \operatorname{si} s \tag{7.19–16}$$

where

$$\operatorname{ci} s = \gamma + \operatorname{Log} s + \sum_{\nu=1}^{\infty} \frac{(-1)^\nu s^{2\nu}}{(2\nu)!\,2\nu} = \gamma + \operatorname{Log} s + \int_0^s \frac{\cos t - 1}{t}\, dt \tag{7.19–17}$$

and

$$\operatorname{si} s = -\tfrac{1}{2}\pi + \sum_{\nu=0}^{\infty} \frac{(-1)^\nu s^{2\nu+1}}{(2\nu+1)!\,(2\nu+1)} = -\tfrac{1}{2}\pi + \int_0^s \frac{\sin t}{t}\, dt \tag{7.19–18}$$

are the *cosine integral* and the *sine integral* respectively. The cosine integral is infinitely many-valued, whereas the sine integralis an integral function.

7.19.7 – The cosine integral and the sine integral

In view of (7.19–14) we may write

$$\operatorname{Ei} is = -\int_{-is}^{\infty} \frac{e^{-t}}{t}\, dt.$$

Here the path of integration connects the points $-is$ and 1 avoiding

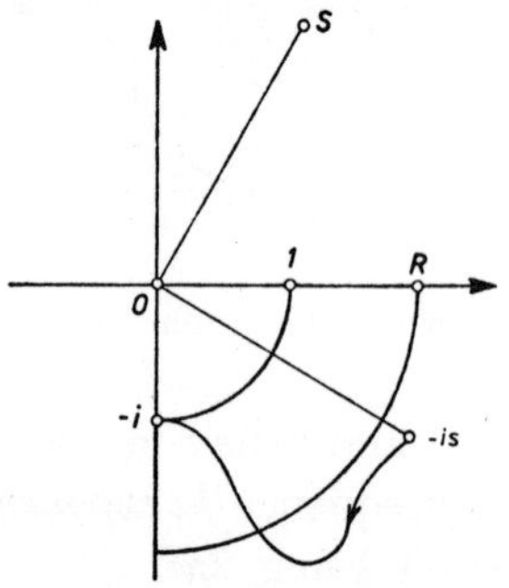

Fig. 7.19–3. Path of integration for the function Ei *is*

the origin and proceeds along the real axis from 1 to $+\infty$. We shall take a slightly more particular path issuing from $-is$ and going first to $-i$, then continuing along an arc of a circle from $-i$ to 1. The integral taken around the contour shown in fig. 7.19–3 consisting of two arcs of a circle of radius 1 and radius $R > 1$ respectively, completed by two segments on the real and the imaginary axis, is by Cauchy's integral theorem zero. On the other hand, the integral along the large circular arc is

$$i\int_0^{\frac{1}{2}\pi} e^{-Re^{i\theta}}\, d\theta$$

and tends to zero as $R \to \infty$. Hence we may replace the half-ray on the real axis from 1 to $+\infty$ by the half-ray from $-i$ to $-i\infty$ along the imaginary axis and so we have

$$\mathrm{Ei}\, is = -\int_{-is}^{-i\infty} \frac{e^{-t}}{t}\, dt = -\int_s^{\infty} \frac{e^{it}}{t}\, dt,$$

whence

$$\boxed{\mathrm{ci}\, s = -\int_s^{\infty} \frac{\cos t}{t}\, dt,} \qquad (7.19\text{–}19)$$

and

$$\boxed{\mathrm{si}\, s = -\int_s^{\infty} \frac{\sin t}{t}\, dt,} \qquad (7.19\text{–}20)$$

since these functions are real for positive real values of s. Combining (7.19–20) and (7.19–18) we immediately find

$$\int_0^{\infty} \frac{\sin t}{t}\, dt = \tfrac{1}{2}\pi,$$

in accordance with (3.6–22).

7.19.8 – The sici-curve

The curve represented parametrically by

$$x(u) = \mathrm{ci}\, u, \qquad y(u) = \mathrm{si}\, u, \qquad (7.19\text{–}21)$$

where u is positive, has some remarkable properties. First we observe that

$$\frac{dx}{du} = \frac{\cos u}{u}, \quad \frac{dy}{du} = \frac{\sin u}{u} \qquad (7.19\text{–}22)$$

and it follows that the angle between the tangent and the positive x-axis is given by

$$\vartheta = u. \qquad (7.19\text{–}23)$$

If now s denotes the arc length, reckoned positively from the point $u = 1$ onwards in the direction of increasing values of the parameter u, we deduce at once from (7.19–22)

$$\frac{ds}{du} = \frac{1}{u}$$

hence

$$s = \log u. \tag{7.19–24}$$

Taking account of (7.19–23) we get for the curvature $\varkappa = d\vartheta/ds$ the simple expression

$$\varkappa = e^{s}. \tag{7.19–25}$$

The curve is a spiral which winds infinitely many times around the origin and possesses a horizontal asymptote, (fig. 7.19–4). It is sometimes called the *sici-curve*, because of its parametric representation.

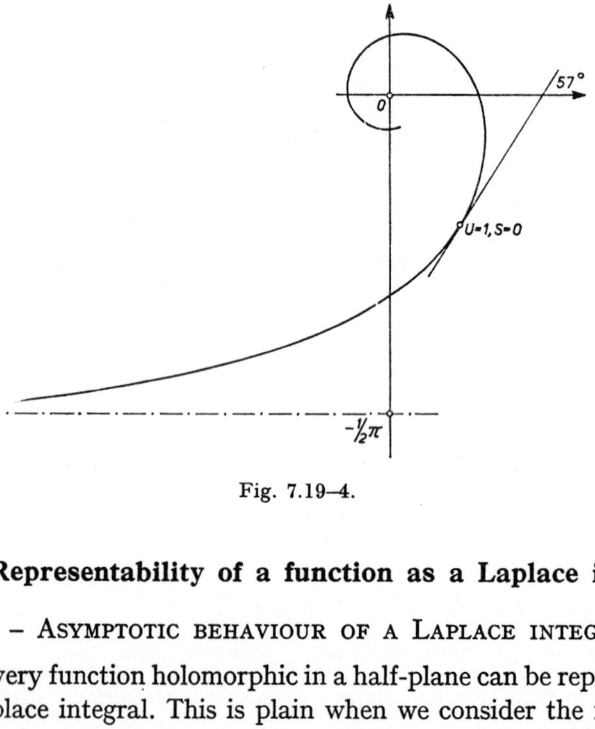

Fig. 7.19–4.

7.20 – Representability of a function as a Laplace integral

7.20.1 – Asymptotic behaviour of a Laplace integral

Not every function holomorphic in a half-plane can be represented as a Laplace integral. This is plain when we consider the function $\varphi(s) = 1$, for a necessary condition which must be satisfied by $\varphi(s)$ is that it tends to zero as $s \to \infty$ along the positive real axis. In fact, we have the theorem:

If a Laplace integral

$$\int_0^\infty e^{-st} a(t) dt \tag{7.20–1}$$

is convergent at $s = s_0$*, its value tends uniformly to zero as* $s \to \infty$ *in any angular area*

$$|\arg(s-s_0)| \leqq \vartheta < \tfrac{1}{2}\pi. \tag{7.20–2}$$

In section 7.14.3 we established the fact that the integral is uniformly convergent in the area (7.20–2). Now we may write

$$\int_0^\infty e^{-st}a(t)dt = \int_0^\delta e^{-st}a(t)dt + \int_\delta^\omega e^{-st}a(t)dt + \int_\omega^\infty e^{-st}a(t)dt.$$

Let ε be any positive number. First we can choose δ in such a fashion that

$$\left|\int_0^\delta e^{-st}a(t)dt\right| < \tfrac{1}{3}\varepsilon,$$

whenever $\operatorname{Re} s \geqq \operatorname{Re} s_0$. Secondly we can take ω so large that

$$\left|\int_\omega^\infty e^{-st}a(t)dt\right| < \tfrac{1}{3}\varepsilon$$

for all s in the area (7.20–2). Finally we can find a non-negative real number σ such that

$$\left|\int_\delta^\omega e^{-st}a(t)dt\right| \leqq e^{-\sigma\delta}\int_0^\omega |a(t)|dt < \tfrac{1}{3}\varepsilon$$

whenever $\operatorname{Re} s > \sigma$. Hence, for all s in the area (7.20–2) and $\operatorname{Re} s > \sigma$ we have

$$\left|\int_0^\infty e^{-st}a(t)dt\right| < \varepsilon,$$

the desired result.

7.20.2 – Extension of Cauchy's integral theorem

We wish to state a sufficient condition for the representability of a function $f(s)$ as a Laplace integral. First we need an extension of Cauchy's integral theorem.

Let $f(s)$ *be holomorphic throughout a half-plane* $\operatorname{Re} s > \alpha$ *and let*

$$|f(s)| < A|s|^{-\delta}, \qquad \delta > 0, \tag{7.20–3}$$

for all sufficiently large $|s|$*,* A *being a suitable constant. Then if* c *is a real number* $> \alpha$ *and* z *a complex number with* $\operatorname{Re} z > c$

$$f(z) = -\frac{1}{2\pi i}\int_{c-i\infty}^{c+i\infty}\frac{f(\zeta)}{\zeta - z}d\zeta, \tag{7.20–4}$$

the integral being a Cauchy principal value.

We consider a rectangle with vertices $c \pm i\omega$, $\omega \pm i\omega$, $\omega > 0$ (fig. 7.20–1). Let L denote the path obtained from the boundary of the rectangle by removing the left-hand side. If ω is sufficiently large,

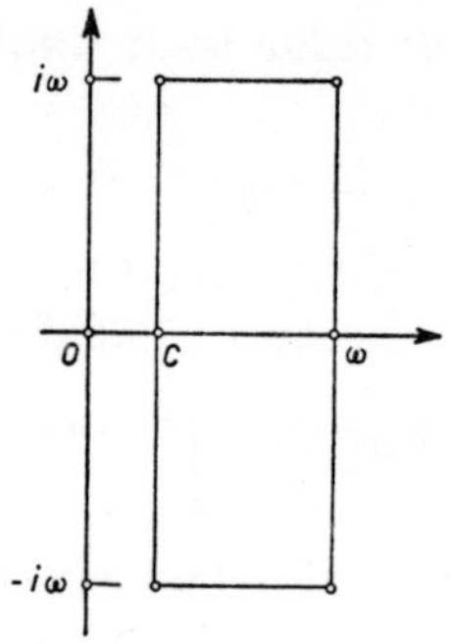

Fig. 7.20–1. Extension of Cauchy's integral theorem

the point z is inside the rectangle and by Cauchy's integral theorem we have

$$f(z) = -\frac{1}{2\pi i}\int_{c-i\omega}^{c+i\omega}\frac{f(\zeta)}{\zeta-z}\,d\zeta+\frac{1}{2\pi i}\int_L\frac{f(\zeta)}{\zeta-z}\,d\zeta.$$

Taking ω large enough we have on L

$$\frac{|f(\zeta)|}{|\zeta-z|}<\frac{A}{|\zeta|^{\delta}\,|\zeta-z|}=\frac{A}{|\zeta|^{1+\delta}\left|1-\dfrac{z}{\zeta}\right|}<\frac{2A}{\omega^{1+\delta}}$$

since we can make ω so large that $|z/\zeta| < \frac{1}{2}$. The length of L is $4\omega-2c$. Hence, by Darboux's theorem of section 2.4.3

$$\left|\int_L\frac{f(\zeta)}{\zeta-z}\,d\zeta\right|<\frac{2A}{\omega^{1+\delta}}\,(4\omega-2c)=\frac{2A}{\omega^{\delta}}\left(4-2\frac{c}{\omega}\right)$$

and thus the integral taken along L tends to zero as $\omega\to\infty$.

7.20.3 – Sufficient condition for the representability

Let $f(s)$ be holomorphic in the half-plane Re $s > \alpha$. *If $f(s)$ is of the form*

$$f(s)=\frac{B(s)}{s^{1+\delta}},\quad \delta>0, \tag{7.20–5}$$

$|B(s)|$ being bounded, then

$$f(s)=\int_0^\infty e^{-st}a(t)\,dt$$

for Re $s > c > \alpha$, *where*

$$a(t)=\frac{1}{2\pi i}\int_{c-i\infty}^{c+i\infty}e^{\zeta t}f(\zeta)\,d\zeta, \tag{7.20–6}$$

the integral being a Cauchy principal value.

Let $\zeta = c+iy$ on the path of integration in (7.20–6). We evidently have

$$\left|\int_{c-i\omega}^{c+i\omega} e^{\zeta t} f(\zeta) d\zeta\right| \leqq e^{ct} \int_{-\omega}^{\omega} \frac{B(\zeta)}{|c+iy|^{1+\delta}} dy < K e^{tc}$$

where K is a constant. Hence the integral

$$\int_0^\infty e^{-st} a(t) dt \int_{c-i\omega}^{c+i\omega} e^{t\zeta} f(\zeta) d\zeta$$

is convergent, whenever $\operatorname{Re} s > c$. In the equation

$$\int_0^T e^{-st} dt \int_{c-i\omega}^{c+i\omega} e^{\zeta t} f(\zeta) d\zeta = \int_{c-i\omega}^{c+i\omega} f(\zeta) d\zeta \int_0^T e^{-(s-\zeta)t} dt$$

we can, therefore, let $T \to \infty$ and we find

$$\int_0^\infty e^{-st} dt \int_{c-i\omega}^{c+i\omega} e^{\zeta t} f(\zeta) d\zeta = -\int_{c-i\omega}^{c+i\omega} \frac{f(\zeta)}{\zeta - s} d\zeta.$$

The function $f(s)$ certainly satisfies the conditions of the previous lemma. Hence we can let $\omega \to \infty$ and we obtain

$$\int_0^\infty e^{-st} dt \frac{1}{2\pi i} \int_{c-i\infty}^{c+i\infty} e^{\zeta t} f(\zeta) d\zeta = -\frac{1}{2\pi i} \int_{c-i\infty}^{c+i\infty} \frac{f(\zeta)}{\zeta - s} d\zeta = f(s).$$

7.20.4 – Pincherle's theorem

The condition imposed on $f(s)$ is rather severe. But it can be weakened.

Let $\varphi(s)$ be holomorphic in the half-plane $\operatorname{Re} s > \alpha \geqq 0$ *and of the form*

$$\varphi(s) = \frac{A}{s} + \frac{B(s)}{s^{1+\delta}}, \quad \delta > 0, \qquad (7.20\text{–}7)$$

where $|B(s)|$ is bounded, A being a constant. Then

$$\varphi(s) = \int_0^\infty e^{-st} a(t) dt, \quad \operatorname{Re} s > c > \alpha \geqq 0, \qquad (7.20\text{–}8)$$

with

$$a(t) = \frac{1}{2\pi i} \int_{c-i\infty}^{c+i\infty} e^{\zeta t} \varphi(\zeta) d\zeta,$$

the integral being a Cauchy principal value.

This theorem is due to Pincherle.

We can apply the previous theorem to the function

$$f(s) = \varphi(s) - \frac{A}{s}.$$

Then for $\operatorname{Re} s > c > \alpha$

$$f(s) = \int_0^\infty e^{-st} a_1(t) dt$$

where

$$a_1(t) = \frac{1}{2\pi i} \int_{c-i\infty}^{c+i\infty} e^{\zeta t} f(\zeta) d\zeta.$$

Adding the Dirichlet discontinuous factor (3.6–18), we get

$$a(t) = a_1(t) + A = \frac{1}{2\pi i} \int_{c-i\infty}^{c+i\infty} e^{\zeta t} \varphi(\zeta) d\zeta$$

provided that $t > 0$, while

$$\int_0^\infty e^{-st} a(t) dt = \int_0^\infty e^{-st} a_1(t) dt + \frac{A}{s} = f(s) + \frac{A}{s} = \varphi(s)$$

and the proof is complete.

7.20.5 – ILLUSTRATIVE EXAMPLE

The function

$$f(s) = e^{-\alpha\sqrt{s}}, \qquad \alpha > 0,$$

is holomorphic in the principal region $s + |s| \neq 0$. This function satisfies the condition of the theorem of section 7.20.3 with $\delta = 1$. We wish to evaluate the integral (7.20–6). By well-known arguments it can be found that the integral is the same as that evaluated along

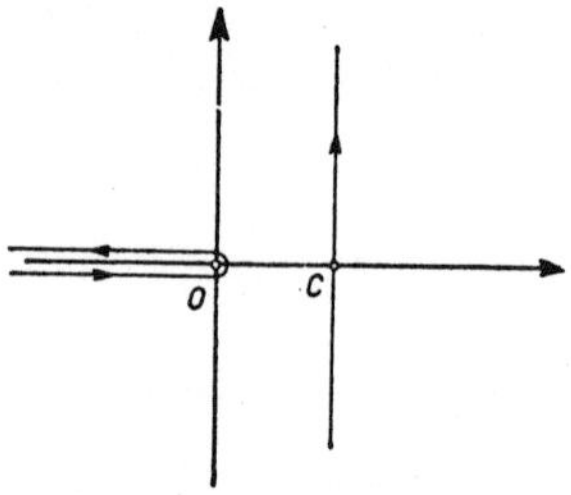

Fig. 7.20–2. Deformation of the path of integration parallel to the imaginary axis into a Hankel contour

a Hankel contour, (fig. 7.20–2). For the sake of brevity we omit the details. Hence

$$2\pi i a(t) = \int_\infty^0 \exp\,(ute^{-\pi i} - \alpha\sqrt{u}e^{-\frac{1}{2}\pi i}) e^{-\pi i} du$$

$$+ \int_0^\infty \exp\,(ute^{\pi i} - \alpha\sqrt{u}e^{\frac{1}{2}\pi i}) e^{\pi i} du$$

$$= \int_0^\infty e^{-ut}(e^{\alpha i\sqrt{u}} - e^{-\alpha i\sqrt{u}}) du = 2i \int_0^\infty e^{-ut} \sin \alpha\sqrt{u}\, du.$$

Replacing u by v^2 we arrive at the result

$$a(t) = \frac{2}{\pi} \int_0^\infty v e^{-v^2 t} \sin \alpha v \, dv.$$

Referring to (2.23–26) and (2.23–28) we have

$$\int_0^\infty e^{-(x+ia)^2} dx = \tfrac{1}{2}\sqrt{\pi}$$

whence, by equating real parts,

$$\int_0^\infty e^{-x^2} \cos 2ax \, dx = \tfrac{1}{2}\sqrt{\pi} e^{-a^2}.$$

Writing $v\sqrt{t}$ instead of x and putting $2a\sqrt{t} = \alpha$ we get

$$\int_0^\infty e^{-v^2 t} \cos \alpha v \, dv = \frac{\sqrt{\pi}}{2\sqrt{t}} e^{-\frac{\alpha^2}{4t}}.$$

Differentiation with respect to α yields

$$\int_0^\infty v e^{-v^2 t} \sin \alpha v \, dv = \frac{\alpha\sqrt{\pi}}{4\sqrt{t^3}} e^{-\frac{\alpha^2}{4t}}$$

and finally

$$a(t) = \frac{\alpha}{2\sqrt{\pi t^3}} e^{-\frac{\alpha^2}{4t}}, \qquad t > 0.$$

7.20.6 – Heaviside's expansion theorem

A case of frequent occurrence in engineering problems is that of

$$f(s) = \frac{P(s)}{Q(s)}$$

where $P(s)$, $Q(s)$ are polynomials, the degree of $Q(s)$ exceeding that of $P(s)$ at least by unity. The condition of the theorem of section 7.20.4 is obviously satisfied.

In section 3.4.2 we found that $f(s)$ can be decomposed into partial fractions of the type

$$c_{-k}(s-a)^{-k}, \qquad k = 1, \ldots, m,$$

where a is a zero of order m of $Q(s)$. In order to find $a(t)$ we have to evaluate integrals of the type

$$\frac{1}{2\pi i} \int_{c-i\infty}^{c+i\infty} \frac{e^{\zeta t}}{(\zeta-a)^k} d\zeta, \qquad \operatorname{Re} a < c, \qquad c > 0.$$

Now we observe that the residue of the integrand at $s = a$ is equal to

$$\frac{1}{(k-1)!} \frac{d^{k-1}}{ds^{k-1}} e^{st} \Big|_{s=a} = \frac{t^{k-1}}{(k-1)!} e^{at}.$$

By arguments which are almost the same as those of section **3.6.7** we readily find that this residue is the value of the above integral. We thus arrive at the result:

The function $a(t)$ *is a sum of functions of the type*

$$\frac{1}{(k-1)!}\, c_{-k}\, t^{k-1}\, e^{at}, \qquad k = 1, \ldots, m,$$

where in accordance with (3.4–7)

$$c_{-k} = \frac{1}{(m-k)!}\, \frac{d^{m-k}}{ds^{m-k}} \left\{ (s-a)^m \frac{P(s)}{Q(s)} \right\} \Bigg|_{s=a},$$

a being a zero of order m of $Q(s)$. It is to be understood that the sum is performed by taking for a all the zeros of $Q(s)$. This rule is known as *Heaviside's expansion theorem.*

CHAPTER 8

SUMMABILITY OF POWER SERIES OUTSIDE THE CIRCLE OF CONVERGENCE SUM FORMULAS - ASYMPTOTIC SERIES

8.1 – The principal star of a function

8.1.1 – RADIAL ANALYTIC CONTINUATION

A function $f(z)$ holomorphic in a region $\mathfrak{R}$ including the origin can be expanded in a power series

$$\sum_{\nu=0}^{\infty} a_\nu z^\nu \tag{8.1–1}$$

having a positive radius of convergence. The identity principle of section 2.11.2 asserts that there is only one function holomorphic throughout $\mathfrak{R}$ which coincides with the sum of the series (8.1–1) in a neighbourhood of the origin. As a consequence the properties of the function $f(z)$ are entirely determined by those of the series. The function $f(z)$ is called an *analytic continuation* of the series in the region $\mathfrak{R}$.

Now we consider the largest star-shaped region including the interior of the circle of convergence of the series (8.1–1) such that there exists a function which is holomorphic throughout this region and coincides with the sum of that series inside the circle of convergence. A region of this kind is characterized by the property: if P is a point of the region then all points of the segment OP belong to it. This region is called the *principal star* of the series (8.1–1) (or of the function whose expansion about O is given by that series).

Any half-ray issuing from O either belongs entirely to the principal star or there is a point a on it which does not lie in the star, whereas all points on the ray nearer to O are included in the star. A point a of this kind is called a *barrier-point*. It is a point of the boundary of the principal star.

Let $z \neq 0$ denote a point of the principal star or be a barrier-point. A function which is regular at all points between O and z and coincides with the sum of the series (8.1–1) in a neighbourhood of the origin is termed a *radial analytic continuation* of the series along the segment Oz.

It is not possible to continue the series radially beyond a barrier point. In fact, if we could find a function $\varphi(z)$ regular at the barrier point $z = a$ and at all points between O and a we could define a function $g(z)$ coinciding with $f(z)$ inside the principal star and coinciding with $\varphi(z)$ in the region where $\varphi(z)$ is holomorphic. It is understood, of course, that $\varphi(z)$ coincides with $f(z)$ in a neighbourhood of the origin. By taking a sufficiently small circle around a we could enlarge the principal star by a convex region, (fig. 8.1–1),

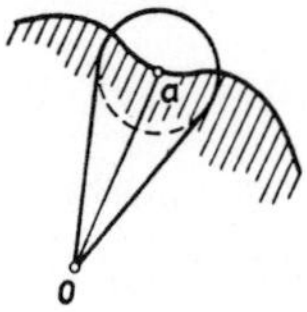

Fig. 8.1–1. Barrier point

(which overlaps the principal star) bounded by two tangents from O at the circle and a circular arc containing points that are not included in the star, contrary to the definition of the principal star.

8.1.2 – Example of a principal star

A simple example of a principal star is provided by the geometric series

$$\sum_{\nu=0}^{\infty} z^{\nu}, \tag{8.1–2}$$

this series being convergent for $|z| < 1$. The point $z = 1$ is a barrier-point. In fact, when $z \to 1-0$ along a line issuing from O the sum of the series tends to infinity. Every analytic continuation tends to infinity when $z \to 1$, for the function

$$f(z) = \frac{1}{1-z} \tag{8.1–3}$$

coincides with the sum of the series inside the circle of convergence. Hence the principal star is the entire z-plane cut along the half-ray on the real axis from 1 to $+\infty$, (fig. 8.1–2).

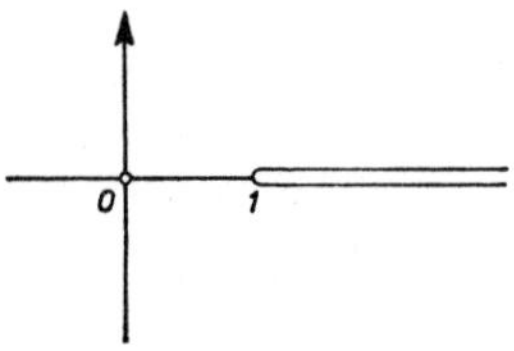

Fig. 8.1–2. Principal star of the geometric series

8.1.3 – BEHAVIOUR OF A SERIES AT A BARRIER-POINT

It should be noticed that at a barrier-point on the circumference of convergence the series need not be divergent. Thus, for instance, the series

$$\sum_{\nu=1}^{\infty} \frac{z^{\nu}}{\nu^2} \tag{8.1–4}$$

is convergent at $z = 1$. But the derivative is the series

$$\sum_{\nu=1}^{\infty} \frac{z^{\nu-1}}{\nu} \tag{8.1–5}$$

and this tends to infinity when $z \to 1$ from the inside of the circle of convergence. The series can be continued in the same star as the geometric series and its analytic continuation in the principal star can be represented by the function

$$\int_0^z \frac{1}{\zeta} \log \frac{1}{1-\zeta}\, d\zeta, \tag{8.1–6}$$

the path of integration being a rectilinear segment Oz where z is not a real number $\geqq 1$.

8.2 – Existence of barrier-points

8.2.1 – EXISTENCE OF AT LEAST ONE BARRIER-POINT

It is not possible to continue a power series beyond each point of the circumference of convergence, for we can prove:

The power series

$$\sum_{\nu=0}^{\infty} a_{\nu} z^{\nu} \tag{8.2–1}$$

has at least one barrier-point on its circumference of convergence.

Suppose the contrary is true. It means that there is no barrier-point at all on the circumference of convergence $|z| = R$, where R is assumed to be positive. Then we can find a function $f(z)$ holomorphic throughout a region including this circumference. At every point z_0 of the circumference the function $f(z)$ can be expanded as a power series in terms of powers of $z-z_0$, the radius of convergence being $R(z_0) > 0$. Thus the circumference $|z| = R$ can be covered by a system of open circular discs and by the well-known Heine-Borel theorem the line $|z| = R$ can be covered by a finite number of discs of this kind. The boundary of the region obtained by extending the region $|z| < R$ by the interiors of these discs does not come arbitrarily near to the line $|z| = R$. Hence we can find a region $|z| < R'$

with $R' > R$, where $f(z)$ is holomorphic. As a consequence, according to section 2.16.1, the Taylor expansion of $f(z)$ about the origin has a radius of convergence exceeding R, contrary to the assumption made about the series (8.2–1). This proves the assertion.

8.2.2 – The Pringsheim-Vivanti theorem

An interesting consequence of the previous result is the *Pringsheim-Vivanti theorem*:

If the radius of convergence of the series (8.1–1) *is unity and if all coefficients are real non-negative numbers, then* $z = 1$ *is a barrier-point.*

Suppose that $z = 1$ is not a barrier-point. Let $f(z)$ denote the sum of the series (8.1–1). It is evident that the series

$$\sum_{\nu=0}^{\infty} \frac{1}{\nu!} f^{(\nu)}(\tfrac{1}{2})(z-\tfrac{1}{2})^{\nu} \tag{8.2–2}$$

is convergent for $|z-\frac{1}{2}| < R$, where R is a number exceeding $\frac{1}{2}$. Since all the coefficients of the series are non-negative we evidently have

$$|f^{(n)}(\tfrac{1}{2}e^{i\theta})| \leqq f^{(n)}(\tfrac{1}{2}), \qquad n = 0, 1, 2, \ldots.$$

It follows that the series

$$\sum_{\nu=0}^{\infty} \frac{1}{\nu!} f^{(\nu)}(\tfrac{1}{2}e^{i\theta})(z-\tfrac{1}{2}e^{i\theta})^{\nu} \tag{8.2–3}$$

is convergent throughout a region $|z-\frac{1}{2}e^{i\theta}| < R'$, where $R' \geqq R > \frac{1}{2}$. Hence there is no barrier-point on $|z| = 1$, contrary to the assertion of the previous theorem.

8.2.3 – Natural boundary

There can be given examples of power series having each point on their circumference of convergence as barrier-point. Let us consider the series

$$\sum_{\nu=0}^{\infty} z^{2^{\nu}}. \tag{8.2–4}$$

The radius of convergence is 1. We see at once that the sum $f(z)$ of this series satisfies the functional equation

$$f(z) = z + f(z^2). \tag{8.2–5}$$

It follows that

$$f(z) = \sum_{\nu=1}^{m-1} z^{2\nu} + f(z^{2^m}),$$

where m is an arbitrary positive integer. The series (8.2–4) is divergent for $z = 1$. As a consequence all points

$$z = e^{i\theta}$$

with

$$\theta = \frac{2k\pi}{2^m}, \qquad k = 1, 2, \ldots, 2^{m-1},$$

m being an arbitrary positive integer, are barrier-points. Thus we establish the existence of a set of barrier-points which is everywhere dense on the circumference of convergence and it follows that it is not possible to continue the series beyond any point on this circumference. In fact, a series can only be continued beyond a point which possesses a neighbourhood free from barrier-points.

An arc consisting merely of barrier-points is called a *natural boundary.* We may state:

The circumference of convergence of the series (8.2–4) *is a natural boundary.*

The principal star of this series is the interior of the circle $|z| = 1$.

8.2.4 – Lambert's series

An alternative example is provided by *Lambert's series*

$$\sum_{\nu=1}^{\infty} \frac{z^\nu}{1-z^\nu}. \tag{8.2–6}$$

This series is uniformly convergent throughout any disc $|z| \leqq r < 1$. In fact, $|1-z|^n \geqq 1-r^n \geqq 1-r$, whenever $0 \leqq r \leqq 1$. Hence

$$\left|\frac{z^n}{1-z^n}\right| \leqq \frac{r^n}{1-r}.$$

By virtue of Weierstrass's theorem of section 2.20.3 the series represents a holomorphic function in the region $|z| < 1$.

We may write

$$\frac{z^n}{1-z^n} = \sum_{\mu=1}^{\infty} z^{\mu n}, \qquad n = 1, 2, \ldots, \tag{8.2–7}$$

and the Weierstrass double-series theorem of section 2.20.4 asserts that we can find the expansion of the function (8.2–6) in terms of powers of z by adding the series on the right of (8.2–7) term-by-term. It is easily seen that a term involving z^k occurs from (8.2–7) when and only when n is a divisor of k. Hence if τ_k denotes the number of (positive) divisors of k, 1 and k included, we may write

$$\sum_{\nu=1}^{\infty} \frac{z^\nu}{1-z^\nu} = \sum_{\nu=1}^{\infty} \tau_\nu z^\nu, \qquad |z| < 1. \tag{8.2–8}$$

The equality (8.2–6) makes it plausible that the point

$$z = e^{2\pi i p/q}, \tag{8.2–9}$$

where q is any integer > 1 and p a positive integer prime to q, is a barrier-point of the series on the right-hand side of (8.2–8). In fact, infinitely many terms of (8.2–6) are infinite at this point. But it remains possible that these mutually cancel. The following reasoning, however, makes it clear that this situation does not occur.

Let $f(z)$ denote the sum of the series (8.2–6) for $|z| < 1$. We may write

$$f(z) = f(z^q) + g(z)$$

where $g(z)$ involves all terms on the right of (8.2–6) corresponding to values of ν which are not divisible by q. Let

$$z = re^{2\pi i p/q}, \quad 0 < r < 1, \tag{8.2–10}$$

and consider the expression

$$(1-r)f(z). \tag{8.2–11}$$

Since $z^q = r^q$ we have

$$(1-r)f(z^q) = (1-r)f(r^q) = \frac{1-r}{1-r^q}\sum_{\mu=1}^{\infty}\frac{1-r^q}{1-r^{\mu q}}r^{\mu q}$$

$$= \frac{1}{\sum_{\nu=0}^{q-1} r^\nu}\sum_{\mu=1}^{\infty}\frac{r^{\mu q}}{\sum_{\nu=0}^{\mu-1} r^{\nu q}} > \frac{1}{q}\sum_{\mu=1}^{\infty}\frac{r^{\mu q}}{\mu} = \frac{1}{q}\log\frac{1}{1-r^q} \to \infty$$

as $r \to 1$. On the other hand, if n is not divisible by q,

$$|1-z^n|^2 = |1-r^n e^{2\pi i n p/q}|^2$$

$$= (1-r^n)^2 + 2r^n\left(1-\cos\frac{2\pi n p}{q}\right) > 4r^n \sin^2\frac{\pi n p}{q}.$$

Now we can find an integer λ_n such that

$$np = \lambda_n q + t$$

with $0 < t < q$, whence

$$|1-z^n|^2 > 4r^n \sin^2\frac{\pi t}{q} \geq 4r^n \sin^2\frac{\pi}{q}$$

and we deduce

$$|(1-r)g(z)| \leq \frac{1-r}{2\sin\frac{\pi}{q}}\sum_{\nu=0}^{\infty} r^{\frac{1}{2}\nu} = \frac{1-r}{2(1-\sqrt{r})\sin\frac{\pi}{q}} = \frac{1+\sqrt{r}}{2\sin\frac{\pi}{q}} \leq \frac{1}{\sin\frac{\pi}{q}}.$$

Thus we see that even the expression (8.2–11) tends to ∞ as $r \to 1$ and, therefore, the point (8.2–10) is a barrier-point. All points (8.2–10) with $r = 1$ constitute a set which is everywhere dense on $|z| = 1$, and we may state:

The circumference of convergence of the series

$$\sum_{\nu=1}^{\infty} \tau_\nu z^\nu$$

where τ_n *denotes the number of positive divisors of the number* n *is a natural boundary.*

8.3 – The Borel summability of a power series

8.3.1 – The Borel sum

The ordinary definition of the sum of a power series

$$\sum_{\nu=0}^{\infty} a_\nu z^\nu \tag{8.3–1}$$

has no meaning for any point z outside the circle of convergence. It is possible, however, to give an alternative definition which associates uniquely defined values to certain points z outside the circle and yields the same values as the ordinary definition when applied to the case that z is within the circle of convergence. We desire to consider in more detail an interesting method due to E. Borel which is closely related to the theory of radial analytic continuation.

To a given series (8.3–1) we associate a series

$$\boxed{\sum_{\nu=0}^{\infty} a_\nu \frac{(zu)^\nu}{\nu!},} \tag{8.3–2}$$

u being real. Let $a(zu)$ denote the sum of the series, assuming that this sum exists for a certain number of z and all positive values of u. Proceeding in a formal way we can evaluate the integral

$$\boxed{\int_0^\infty e^{-u} a(zu)\, du} \tag{8.3–3}$$

and we find

$$\sum_{\nu=0}^{\infty} a_\nu \frac{z^\nu}{\nu!} \int_0^\infty e^{-u} u^\nu \, du = \sum_{\nu=0}^{\infty} a_\nu z^\nu .$$

Accordingly, the integral (8.3–3) may be considered as the sum of the series (8.3–1) for all those values of z for which the integral has a meaning. At these points z the series (8.3–1) is called B_1*-summable* and the value (8.3–3) is referred to as its B_1*-sum* or *Borel-sum.* In many cases (8.3–3) has also a meaning at certain points outside the circle of convergence of (8.3–1).

8.3.2 – Illustrative example

An instructive example is provided by the geometric series. To the series

$$\sum_{\nu=0}^{\infty} z^{\nu}$$

we associate the series

$$a(zu) = \sum_{\nu=0}^{\infty} \frac{(zu)^{\nu}}{\nu!} = e^{zu},$$

valid for every positive value of u and every point in the complex plane. The integral

$$\int_0^{\infty} e^{-u}\, a(zu)du = \int_0^{\infty} e^{-(1-z)u}\, du = \frac{1}{1-z}$$

converges whenever $\mathrm{Re}\, z < 1$. Hence the geometric series is B_1-summable throughout the half-plane $\mathrm{Re}\, z < 1$, (fig. 8.3–1). More

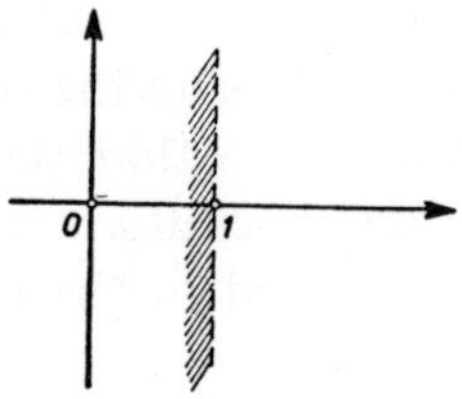

Fig. 8.3–1. The half plane Re $z < 1$.

generally, the series

$$\sum_{\nu=0}^{\infty} \frac{z^{\nu}}{z_1^{\nu+1}}, \qquad z_1 \neq 0,$$

is B_1-summable in the half-plane Re $(z/z_1) < 1$, for in this region the integral

$$\frac{1}{z_1}\int_0^{\infty} e^{zu/z_1} e^{-u}\, du = \frac{1}{z_1 - z}$$

is convergent. We may also say that this integral is convergent if z and the origin lie on the same side of the line L_1 through z_1 perpendicular to the line Oz_1.

If we consider the power series expansion in terms of powers of z of the function

$$f(z) = \sum_{\mu=1}^{m} \frac{b_{\mu}}{z_{\mu} - z}, \qquad z_{\mu} \neq 0, \quad \mu = 1, \ldots, m \qquad (8.3\text{–}4)$$

then the series is B_1-summable at a point z, when z and O lie on the same side of all lines $L_1, \ldots, L_m$, L_{μ} being the line through z_{μ} perpendicular to Oz_{μ}, $\mu = 1, \ldots, m$. The region consisting of all these points z is the interior of a convex polygon, (fig. 8.3–2), which may reduce to an angle, a strip or a half-plane. This is the *Borel*

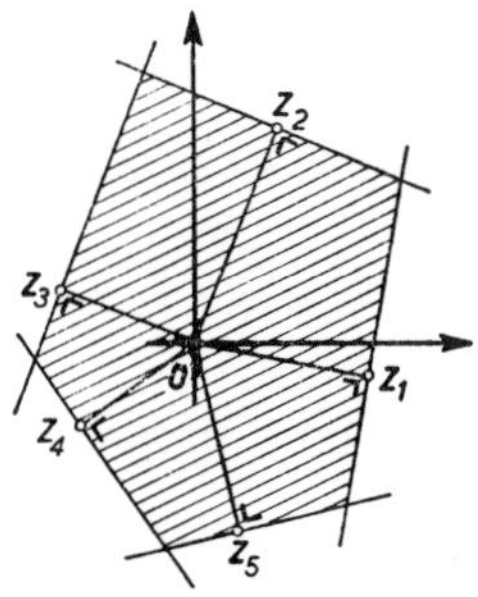

Fig. 8.3–2. The Borel polygon

polygon of the series representing $f(z)$ in a neighbourhood of the origin.

8.3.3 – The Borel polygon

Cauchy's integral formula, which is a generalization of (8.3–4), suggests that there may be a corresponding result for any function regular at the origin. Let $f(z)$ be regular at O and let $\mathfrak{P}$ denote the principal star of the power series (8.3–1) representing $f(z)$ in a neighbourhood of O. We consider the set $\mathfrak{B}_1$ of all points P such that the interior of the circle on OP as diameter is included in $\mathfrak{P}$, (fig. 8.3–3). This set is star-shaped and a subset of $\mathfrak{P}$. In the case of

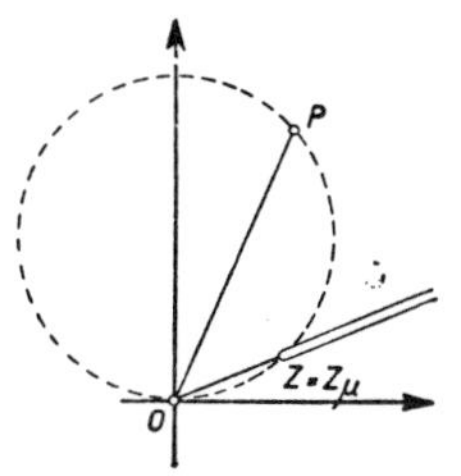

Fig. 8.3–3. Definition of the set $\mathfrak{B}_1$

a finite number of barrier-points it is a polygon of the type defined in section 8.3.2.

Borel proved that the integral (8.3–3) is convergent throughout the interior of $\mathfrak{B}_1$ and Phragmén completed this result by showing that the integral does not converge at every point inside the complementary set of $\mathfrak{B}_1$. The set $\mathfrak{B}_1$ is called the *Borel polygon of summability* of the series (8.3–1). Its boundary does not necessarily consist of linear segments of lines. Thus, for instance, when the circumference of convergence is a natural boundary, $\mathfrak{B}_1$ coincides with the closure of the circle of convergence.

8.3.4 – Summability along a line segment

We proceed to establish these facts more rigorously. The starting-point will be the following theorem:

Let (8.3–1) *be a power series which may or may not have a circle of convergence. Suppose that*

(i) *there is a value $z_0 \neq 0$ of z such that the associated series*

$$\sum_{\nu=0}^{\infty} a_\nu \frac{(z_0 u)^\nu}{\nu!} \tag{8.3–5}$$

is convergent for all positive values of u,

(ii) *the integral*

$$\int_0^\infty e^{-u}\, a(z_0 u) du, \tag{8.3–6}$$

where $a(z_0 u)$ denotes the sum of the series (8.3–5), *is convergent.*

Then the integral (8.3–3) *is also convergent at every point of the segment Oz_0.*

Otherwise stated: If the series (8.3–1) is B_1-summable at $z = z_0$, then it is also B_1-summable at $z = \vartheta z_0$, with $0 \leqq \vartheta \leqq 1$.

Since the case $\vartheta = 0$ is trivial, we consider only the values of ϑ satisfying $0 < \vartheta \leqq 1$. By hypothesis the integral

$$\int_0^\infty e^{-u}\, a(zu) du = \int_0^\infty e^{-u}\, a(\vartheta z_0 u) du \tag{8.3–7}$$

is convergent for $\vartheta = 1$. If we put $t = \vartheta u$, $s = \vartheta^{-1}$, the integral becomes

$$s \int_0^\infty e^{-st}\, a(z_0 t) dt. \tag{8.3–8}$$

This integral is a Laplace integral, being convergent for $s = 1$. Hence, on account of the theorem of section **7.15.1** it is also convergent for $s > 1$ i.e., (8.3–7) is convergent for $0 < \vartheta \leqq 1$.

The integral (8.3–8) is also defined for complex values of s and represents in the region $\operatorname{Re} s > 1$ a holomorphic function $\varphi(s)$. If we put $s = z_0/z$ we may consider $\varphi(s)$ as a function $h(z)$ holomorphic in the region

$$\operatorname{Re} \frac{z_0}{z} > 1. \tag{8.3–9}$$

The region (8.3–9) is the interior of a circle on Oz_0 as diameter, (fig. 8.3–4), for the expression on the left of (8.3–9) denotes the length of the projection of the segment Oz_0 upon the line Oz. Hence:

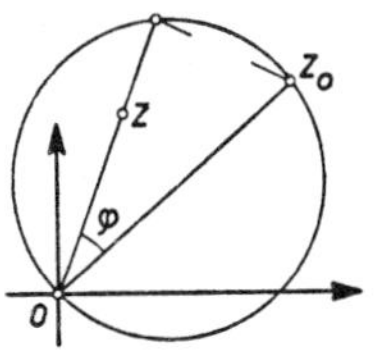

Fig. 8.3–4. The region Re $(z_0/z) > 1$

If the series (8.3–1) *is B_1-summable at $z = z_0$, then it is B_1-summable at $z = \vartheta z_0$, $0 \leqq \vartheta \leqq 1$, and its B_1-sum for these values of z is given by a function which is holomorphic inside a circle on Oz_0 as diameter.*

8.3.5 – Radial analytic continuation

Let us now assume that the series (8.3–1) has a finite (positive) radius R of convergence. Then the series

$$\sum_{\nu=0}^{\infty} a_\nu \frac{z^\nu}{\nu!}$$

represents an integral function, since

$$\limsup_{n\to\infty} \sqrt[n]{\frac{|a_n|}{n!}} = \frac{1}{R} \lim_{n\to\infty} \frac{1}{\sqrt[n]{n!}} = \frac{1}{R} \lim_{n\to\infty} \frac{n!}{(n+1)!} = 0.$$

Assuming that z is within the circle of convergence we have

$$\int_0^\infty \left(\sum_{\nu=0}^{\infty} a_\nu \frac{z^\nu u^\nu}{\nu!}\right) e^{-u}\, du = \sum_{\nu=0}^{\infty} a_\nu z^\nu \int_0^\infty \frac{e^{-u} u^\nu}{\nu!}\, du = \sum_{\nu=0}^{\infty} a_\nu z^\nu .$$

In fact, the series (8.3–2) is uniformly convergent as regards u in the interval $0 < \varepsilon \leqq u \leqq \omega$ and hence we may reverse the order of integration and summation. This will be proved in more detail in section 8.4.4. Thus we arrive at the result:

When the integral

$$\int_0^\infty e^{-u} \left(\sum_{\nu=0}^{\infty} a_\nu \frac{z^\nu u^\nu}{\nu!}\right) du \qquad (8.3\text{–}10)$$

is convergent at $z = z_0$, it represents a holomorphic function inside the circle on Oz_0 as diameter and it provides an analytic continuation of the power series (8.3–1) *along the segment Oz_0. At every point of this segment the series is B_1-summable.*

8.3.6 – Summability inside the Borel polygon

Let z_0 be any point of the principal star of the series (8.3–1) such that the region Re $(z/z_0) < 1$ is included in the star. The set of all these points constitutes the Borel polygon $\mathfrak{B}_1$.

It is easy to see that the integral (8.3–6) cannot be convergent at a point z_0 outside $\mathfrak{B}_1$, for then the circle on Oz_0 as diameter contains at least one barrier-point in its interior.

The analytic continuation of the series (8.3–1) be denoted by $f(z)$. We wish to prove that at every point in the interior of $\mathfrak{B}_1$ the integral

$$\int_0^\infty e^{-u} f(zu)du \tag{8.3–11}$$

is convergent. The argument is taken from the observation that the function $1/(1-z)$ can be represented as

$$\frac{1}{1-z} = \int_0^\infty e^{-u}\, e^{zu}\, du, \qquad \text{Re}\, z < 1. \tag{8.3–12}$$

Let P, representing the number z, denote an inner point of $\mathfrak{B}_1$. We describe a circle C on OP as diameter. Since P is in the principal star the function $f(z)$ is also regular at a point P' beyond P on the line OP sufficiently near to P and we may describe a slightly larger contour C' intersecting the line OP at P' and still included in the star. A contour of this kind may be constructed as follows. If Q is a point on the circle C we enlarge the segment OQ by a small segment $QQ' = PP' = \eta$ beyond OQ. We then find an arc that may be completed to a closed curve by a semi-circle of radius η around O, (fig. 8.3–5). Let ζ denote

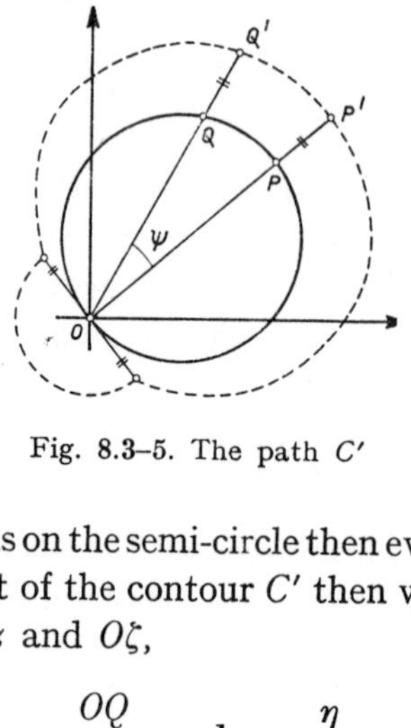

Fig. 8.3–5. The path C'

a point on C'. When ζ is on the semi-circle then evidently Re $(z/\zeta) \leq 0$. If ζ is on the first part of the contour C' then we have, if ψ denotes the angle between Oz and $O\zeta$,

$$\text{Re}\frac{z}{\zeta} = \frac{|z|}{|\zeta|}\cos\psi = \frac{OQ}{OQ'} = \frac{OQ}{OQ+\eta} = 1 - \frac{\eta}{OQ+\eta} \leq 1 - \frac{\eta}{OP+\eta} = 1-\delta,$$

where δ is a positive number. Hence we have along C'

$$\operatorname{Re}\frac{z}{\zeta} < 1. \tag{8.3–13}$$

Since $f(z)$ is regular at each point of C' we have on account of (8.3–12) and Cauchy's integral formula

$$f(z) = \frac{1}{2\pi i}\int_{C'} \frac{f(\zeta)}{\zeta - z}\, d\zeta = \frac{1}{2\pi i}\int_{C'} \frac{f(\zeta)}{\zeta}\, d\zeta \int_0^\infty e^{-u}\, e^{zu/\zeta}\, du,$$

the last integral being convergent by virtue of (8.3–13). In section 8.4.6 we shall prove that the reversal of the order of integrations is justified. And so we conclude that

$$f(z) = \int_0^\infty e^{-u}\, du\, \frac{1}{2\pi i}\int_{C'} \frac{f(\zeta)}{\zeta}\, e^{zu/\zeta}\, d\zeta = \int_0^\infty e^{-u}\, du\, \frac{1}{2\pi i}\int_{C'} \sum_{\nu=0}^{\infty} \frac{f(\zeta)}{\zeta^{\nu+1}} \frac{z^\nu u^\nu}{\nu!}\, d\zeta.$$

But we may contract C' inside the circle of convergence of the series (8.3–1). Because the series occurring in the second integral of the last member is uniformly convergent on C' we may reverse the order of integration and summation and we finally have

$$f(z) = \int_0^\infty e^{-u}\, du \sum_{\nu=0}^{\infty} \frac{z^\nu u^\nu}{\nu!} \frac{1}{2\pi i}\int_{C'} \frac{f(\zeta)}{\zeta^{\nu+1}}\, d\zeta = \int_0^\infty e^{-u}\, du \sum_{\nu=0}^{\infty} a_\nu \frac{(zu)^\nu}{\nu!}.$$

Thus we see that the series (8.3–1) is B_1-summable at each point inside $\mathfrak{B}_1$, its B_1-sum being $f(z)$.

8.4 – The Mittag-Leffler summability of a power series

8.4.1 – Introduction

An important argument in establishing Borel's result concerning the summability of a power series is the fact that the function $1/(1-z)$ can be represented by an infinite integral (8.3–12). Mittag-Leffler observed that there is a more general representation, viz.,

$$\boxed{\frac{1}{1-z} = \int_0^\infty e^{-u}\, E_\alpha(zu^\alpha)\, du,} \tag{8.4–1}$$

valid throughout any region $\operatorname{Re} z^{1/\alpha} < 1$, where $E_\alpha(z)$ is the function introduced in section 6.13.1. In this section we restrict the considerations to the most important case $\alpha \leqq 2$.

The region of convergence is bounded by the curve

$$r \cos^\alpha \frac{\theta}{\alpha} = 1, \qquad -\tfrac{1}{2}\alpha\pi < \theta < \tfrac{1}{2}\alpha\pi,$$

and it includes the origin. When $\alpha < 1$ it has some resemblence to a hyperbola, when $\alpha = 1$ it is a straight line and when $\alpha = 2$ it is a parabola, (fig. 8.4–1).

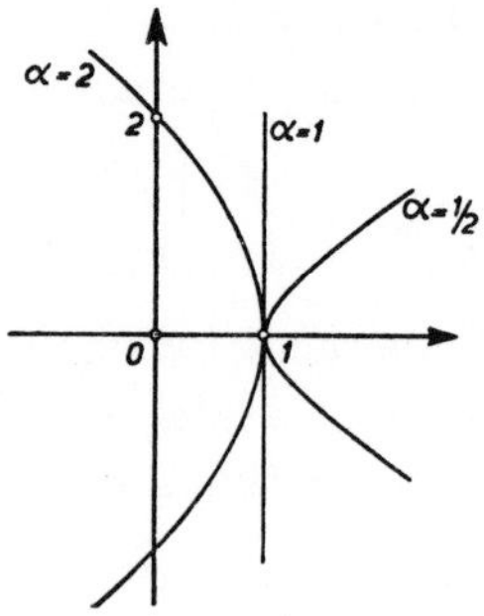

Fig. 8.4–1. Regions of convergence for the integral (8.4–1)

The region of convergence tends to the principal star of the geometric series $\sum_{\nu=0}^{\infty} z^\nu$ if α tends to zero.

8.4.2 – The Mittag-Leffler sum

It is natural to extend Borel's method in the following way. Consider the series

$$\boxed{\sum_{\nu=0}^{\infty} a_\nu \frac{(zu^\alpha)^\nu}{\Gamma(1+\alpha\nu)}.} \tag{8.4–2}$$

If this series is convergent for all positive values of u when z is a suitably chosen number and if also the integral

$$\boxed{\int_0^\infty e^{-u}\, a(zu^\alpha)du} \tag{8.4–3}$$

is convergent, $a(zu^\alpha)$ being the sum of the series (8.4–2), then the value of (8.4–3) is called the *Mittag-Leffler sum* or the *B_α-sum* of the series (8.3–1) at the given point z. For $\alpha = 1$ it reduces to the Borel-sum considered in the previous section.

8.4.3 – Summability along a line segment

The following theorem is an easy extension of the theorem of section 8.3.4.

Let (8.3–1) *be a power series which may or may not have a circle of convergence. Suppose that*

(i) *there is a value of* $z_0 \neq 0$ *such that the associated series*

$$\sum_{\nu=0}^{\infty} a_\nu \frac{(z_0 u^\alpha)^\nu}{\Gamma(1+\alpha\nu)} \tag{8.4–4}$$

is convergent for all positive values of u,

(ii) *the integral*

$$\int_0^\infty e^{-u} a(z_0 u^\alpha) du \tag{8.4–5}$$

where $a(z_0 u^\alpha)$ *denotes the sum of the series* (8.4–4) *is convergent.*

Then the integral

$$\int_0^\infty e^{-u} a(zu^\alpha) du \tag{8.4–6}$$

is also convergent at every point z *of the segment* Oz_0.

Let $z = \vartheta z_0$, $0 < \vartheta \leqq 1$, the case $\vartheta = 0$ being of no interest. The integral

$$\int_0^\infty e^{-u} a(zu^\alpha) du = \int_0^\infty e^{-u} a(\vartheta z_0 u^\alpha) du \tag{8.4–7}$$

is convergent for $\vartheta = 1$, by hypothesis. Upon putting $t^\alpha = \vartheta u^\alpha$, $s = \vartheta^{-1/\alpha}$ the integral (8.4–7) can be written as a Laplace-integral

$$s \int_0^\infty e^{-st} a(z_0 t^\alpha) dt, \tag{8.4–8}$$

this integral being convergent for $s = 1$ and hence also for $s \geqq 1$. This proves the assertion.

If s is considered as a complex variable then the integral (8.4–8) represents a holomorphic function $\varphi(s)$ in the region $\operatorname{Re} s > 1$. If we write

$$s = \left(\frac{z_0}{z}\right)^{1/\alpha}$$

the function $\varphi(s)$ may be considered as a function $h(z)$ holomorphic throughout the set

$$\operatorname{Re} \left(\frac{z_0}{z}\right)^{1/\alpha} > 1. \tag{8.4–9}$$

When $z = \vartheta z_0$, $0 \leqq \vartheta \leqq 1$, this function coincides with the integral (8.4–6).

The set (8.4–9) consists of many parts. We consider only the region defined by (8.4–9) and the additional inequality

$$-\tfrac{1}{2}\alpha\pi < \arg \frac{z_0}{z} < \tfrac{1}{2}\alpha\pi$$

where α is assumed to be a number satisfying $0 < \alpha \leqq 2$. This region is bounded by the curve

$$r = r_0 \cos^\alpha \frac{\psi}{\alpha}, \qquad -\tfrac{1}{2}\alpha\pi \leqq \psi \leqq \tfrac{1}{2}\alpha\pi, \tag{8.4–10}$$

where ψ is the angle between Oz and Oz_0, $r = |z|$, $r_0 = |z_0|$, (fig. 8.4–2). The segment Oz_0 will be called the diameter of the curve.

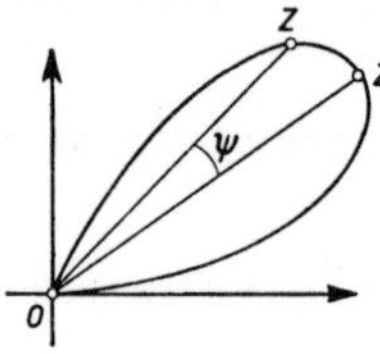

Fig. 8.4–2. The curve (8.4–10)

Summing up we have:

If the series (8.3–1) *is B_α-summable at $z = z_0$, it is B_α-summable at $z = \vartheta z_0$, $0 \leqq \vartheta \leqq 1$, and its B_α-sum for these values of z is given by a function which is holomorphic in the region*

$$\mathrm{Re}\left(\frac{z_0}{z}\right)^{1/\alpha} > 1, \qquad -\tfrac{1}{2}\alpha\pi < \arg\frac{z_0}{z} < \tfrac{1}{2}\alpha\pi, \tag{8.4–11}$$

including the inner points of the segment Oz_0.

8.4.4 – Radial analytic continuation

Next we suppose that the series (8.3–1) has a positive radius of convergence. Then the series

$$\sum_{\nu=0}^{\infty} a_\nu \frac{z^\nu}{\Gamma(1+\alpha\nu)} \tag{8.4–12}$$

is an integral function, since by virtue of (4.9–3)

$$\Gamma(1+\alpha n) = (\alpha n)^{\alpha n+\frac{1}{2}} \sqrt{2\pi}\, e^{\mu(\alpha n)-\alpha n},$$

where $\mu(\alpha n) \to 0$ as $n \to \infty$, and so

$$\limsup_{n\to\infty} \sqrt[n]{\frac{a_n}{\Gamma(1+\alpha n)}} = 0.$$

Now the series

$$\sum_{\nu=0}^{\infty} a_\nu \frac{(zu^\alpha)^\nu}{\Gamma(1+\alpha\nu)} \tag{8.4–13}$$

is uniformly convergent as regards u in the interval $0 \leqq u \leqq \omega$. Hence

$$\int_0^\omega e^{-u} \sum_{\nu=0}^{\infty} a_\nu \frac{(zu^\alpha)^\nu}{\Gamma(1+\alpha\nu)}\, du = \sum_{\nu=0}^{\infty} a_\nu z^\nu \int_0^\omega \frac{e^{-u} u^{\alpha\nu}}{\Gamma(1+\alpha\nu)}\, du.$$

But the series on the right is uniformly convergent as regards ω, for

$$\int_0^\omega e^{-u} \frac{u^{\alpha n}}{\Gamma(1+\alpha n)} du < \int_0^\infty e^{-u} \frac{u^{\alpha n}}{\Gamma(1+\alpha n)} du,$$

and we can, therefore, make $\omega \to \infty$, provided that z is in the circle of convergence. This leads to the result

$$\int_0^\infty e^{-u} \left(\sum_{\nu=0}^{\infty} a_\nu \frac{(zu^\alpha)^\nu}{\Gamma(1+\alpha\nu)} \right) du = \sum_{\nu=0}^{\infty} a_\nu z^\nu.$$

Thus we have established the theorem:

When the integral

$$\int_0^\infty e^{-u} \sum_{\nu=0}^{\infty} a_\nu \frac{(zu^\alpha)^\nu}{\Gamma(1+\alpha\nu)} du \qquad (8.4\text{–}14)$$

is convergent at $z = z_0$, *it represents a holomorphic function in thr region* (8.4–11) *and it provides an analytic continuation of the powee series* (8.3–1) *along the segment* Oz_0. *At every point of this segment the series is* B_α*-summable.*

Let z_0 denote any point of the principal star of the power series (8.3–1) such that the region (8.4–11) is included in the star. The set of all these points z_0 is a star-shaped domain which we denote by $\mathfrak{B}_\alpha$. It reduces to the Borel polygon for $\alpha = 1$.

It follows at once from this definition that the integral (8.4–14) does not converge outside $\mathfrak{B}_\alpha$, for in the contrary case we could find a region of the type (8.4–11) containing at least one barrier-point.

8.4.5 – The case of a geometric series

We consider in particular the geometric series. The corresponding integral (8.4–3) is

$$\int_0^\infty e^{-u} \sum_{\nu=0}^{\infty} \frac{(zu^\alpha)^\nu}{\Gamma(1+\alpha\nu)} du = \int_0^\infty e^{-u} E_\alpha(zu^\alpha) du. \qquad (8.4\text{–}15)$$

It follows from the asymptotic properties of $E_\alpha(z)$ established in section 6.13.3 that this integral is convergent whenever $\text{Re}\, z^{1/\alpha} < 1$ and hence it represents the function $1/(1-z)$ throughout this region. In fact, within the region $-\frac{1}{2}\alpha\pi \leqq \arg z \leqq \frac{1}{2}\alpha\pi$ the function $E_\alpha(z)$ behaves like $\exp z^{1/\alpha}$ for large values of $|z|$ and elsewhere it tends to zero. It is easy to see that the region of convergence is the interior of the domain $\mathfrak{B}_\alpha$ for the geometric series, (fig. 8.4–3).

This result can also be put in an alternative form which is interesting from the point of view of the Laplace integral. Assuming z real we can replace u by st, where $s^\alpha z = 1$ and s also real. An easy com-

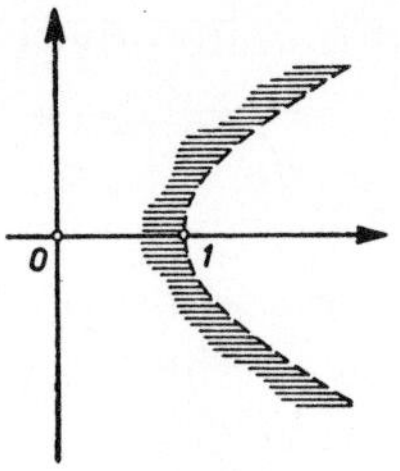

Fig. 8.4–3. The region of convergence for the integral (8.4–15)

putation yields

$$\frac{s^\alpha}{s^\alpha - 1} = s\int_0^\infty e^{-st} E_\alpha(t^\alpha)dt, \qquad \operatorname{Re} s > 1, \qquad (8.4\text{–}16)$$

both sides being holomorphic in the indicated region.

8.4.6 – Summability inside the domain $\mathfrak{B}_\alpha$

Now we are sufficiently prepared to complete the solution of the problem under consideration. Let $f(z)$ denote the analytic continuation of the power series (8.3–1) throughout its principal star. We wish to show that the integral

$$\int_0^\infty e^{-u} a(zu^\alpha)du \qquad (8.4\text{–}17)$$

is convergent throughout the interior of $\mathfrak{B}_\alpha$. Let P denote an inner point of $\mathfrak{B}_\alpha$. If ϱ denotes the distance from O to a point Q and ψ the angle between OP and OQ, the set of all points characterized by

$$\varrho = r\cos^\alpha \psi/\alpha, \qquad -\tfrac{1}{2}\alpha\pi \leqq \psi \leqq \tfrac{1}{2}\alpha\pi, \qquad (8.4\text{–}18)$$

is a curve encompassing a region included in the principal star and $f(z)$ is holomorphic in this region. Since there are points of $\mathfrak{B}_\alpha$ beyond P on the line OP in the interior, the function $f(z)$ is also regular on a slightly larger contour C' intersecting the line OP at P'. A contour of this kind may be constructed as follows. If Q is a point of the curve (8.4–18) we enlarge OQ by a small segment $QQ' = PP' = \eta$ beyond OQ. We then find an arc which may be completed to a closed loop by an arc of a circle of radius η about O, (fig. 8.4–4). If ζ is on the circular part then evidently $\operatorname{Re}(z/\zeta)^{1/\alpha} < 1$. If ζ is on the first part we have

$$\operatorname{Re}\left(\frac{z}{\zeta}\right)^{1/\alpha} = \frac{|z|^{1/\alpha}}{|\zeta|^{1/\alpha}}\cos\frac{\psi}{\alpha} = \left(\frac{OQ}{OQ'}\right)^{1/\alpha} = \left(\frac{OQ}{OQ+\eta}\right)^{1/\alpha}$$

$$= \left(1 - \frac{\eta}{OQ+\eta}\right)^{1/\alpha} \leqq \left(1 - \frac{\eta}{OP+\eta}\right)^{1/\alpha} = 1-\delta,$$

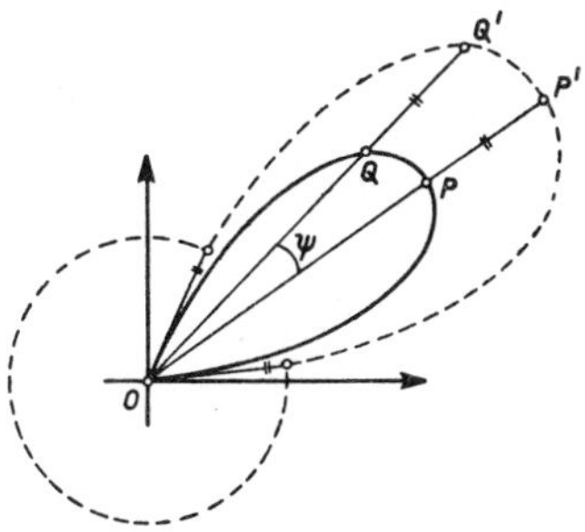

Fig. 8.4–4. The path C'

where δ is a positive number. Hence, everywhere on C'

$$\operatorname{Re}\left(\frac{z}{\zeta}\right)^{1/\alpha} < 1. \tag{8.4–19}$$

On account of the expression (8.4–15) for the function $1/(1-z)$ and by virtue of Cauchy's integral formula we get

$$f(z) = \frac{1}{2\pi i}\int_{C'} \frac{f(\zeta)}{\zeta - z}\, d\zeta = \frac{1}{2\pi i}\int_{C'} \frac{f(\zeta)}{\zeta}\, d\zeta \int_0^\infty \mathrm{e}^{-u} E_\alpha\left(\frac{zu^\alpha}{\zeta}\right) du,$$

the infinite integral being convergent by virtue of (8.4–19).

Reversing the order of integration we find

$$f(z) = \int_0^\infty e^{-u}\, du \frac{1}{2\pi i}\int_{C'} \frac{f(\zeta)}{\zeta} E_\alpha\left(\frac{zu^\alpha}{\zeta}\right) d\zeta.$$

But it is legitimate to contract the contour C' inside the circle of convergence of the series. We then have

$$\begin{aligned} f(z) &= \int_0^\infty \mathrm{e}^{-u}\, du \frac{1}{2\pi i}\int_{C'} \sum_{\nu=0}^\infty \frac{f(\zeta)}{\zeta^{\nu+1}} \frac{(zu^\alpha)^\nu}{\Gamma(1+\alpha\nu)}\, d\zeta \\ &= \int_0^\infty \mathrm{e}^{-u} \sum_{\nu=0}^\infty \frac{(zu^\alpha)^\nu}{\Gamma(1+\alpha\nu)}\, du \frac{1}{2\pi i}\int_{C'} \frac{f(\zeta)}{\zeta^{\nu+1}}\, d\zeta = \int_0^\infty \mathrm{e}^{-u} \sum_{\nu=0}^\infty a_\nu \frac{(zu^\alpha)^\nu}{\Gamma(1+\alpha\nu)}\, du. \end{aligned}$$

Thus we see that the series (8.3–1) is B_α-summable throughout the interior of $\mathfrak{B}_\alpha$, its B_α-sum being $f(z)$.

It remains to justify the reversal of the order of integration. The general theorem of section 2.20.6 is not applicable, for $f(z)/z$ is not necessarily regular at $z = 0$. We can proceed, however, in the following way. The starting point is the expression

$$\frac{1}{2\pi i}\int_{C'} f(\zeta)\left\{\frac{1}{\zeta - z} - \frac{1}{\zeta}\int_0^\infty \mathrm{e}^{-u} E_\alpha\left(\frac{zu^\alpha}{\zeta}\right) du\right\} d\zeta,$$

C' being the contour described above. We may write this as

$$f(z)-\frac{1}{2\pi i}\int_{C'}\frac{f(\zeta)}{\zeta}d\zeta\int_0^\omega e^{-u}E_\alpha\left(\frac{zu^\alpha}{\zeta}\right)du,$$

where C' now denotes a small circle around the origin. The last integral can be transformed into

$$\frac{1}{2\pi i}\int_0^\omega e^{-u}du\int_{C'}\frac{f(\zeta)}{\zeta}E_\alpha\left(\frac{zu^\alpha}{\zeta}\right)d\zeta$$

$$=\int_0^\omega e^{-u}du\sum_{\nu=0}^{\infty}\frac{1}{2\pi i}\int_{C'}\frac{f(\zeta)}{\zeta^{\nu+1}}\frac{(zu^\alpha)^\nu}{\Gamma(1+\alpha\nu)}d\zeta=\int_0^\omega e^{-u}\sum_{\nu=0}^{\infty}\frac{a_\nu(zu^\alpha)^\nu}{\Gamma(1+\alpha\nu)}du.$$

Hence, C' being again the original contour,

$$f(z)=\int_0^\omega e^{-u}a(zu^\alpha)du+\frac{1}{2\pi i}\int_{C'}f(\zeta)\left\{\frac{1}{\zeta-z}-\frac{1}{\zeta}\int_0^\omega e^{-u}E_\alpha\left(\frac{zu^\alpha}{\zeta}\right)du\right\}d\zeta,$$

where $a(zu^\alpha)$ is the sum of the series (8.4–2). Taking account of

$$\frac{1}{\zeta-z}=\frac{1}{\zeta}\int_0^\infty e^{-u}E_\alpha\left(\frac{zu^\alpha}{\zeta}\right)du$$

we find

$$f(z)=\int_0^\omega e^{-u}a(zu^\alpha)du+\frac{1}{2\pi i}\int_{C'}\left\{\int_\omega^\infty e^{-u}E_\alpha\left(\frac{zu^\alpha}{\zeta}\right)du\right\}\frac{f(\zeta)}{\zeta}d\zeta$$

and letting $\omega\to\infty$ we obtain the desired result.

8.5 – Plana's sum formula

8.5.1 – A general sum formula

We already encountered in section 3.7.2 the problem of summing a series of the form

$$\sum_{\nu=a}^{b}f(\nu) \tag{8.5–1}$$

in connection with Cauchy's residue theorem. It is our aim to study this problem again in more detail.

We assume that $f(z)$ is holomorphic throughout a region which includes a rectangle C with vertices $a\pm i\omega$, $b\pm i\omega$, $a<b$, a and b being integers. Let C_ϱ denote the rectangle indented at $z=a$ and $z=b$ by semi-circles of radius ϱ such that a and b are outside the contour, (fig. 8.5–1). On account of the considerations of section 3.7.3 we have

$$\sum_{\nu=a+1}^{b-1}f(\nu)=\frac{1}{2\pi i}\int_{C_\varrho}\pi\operatorname{ctn}\pi\zeta\, f(\zeta)d\zeta \tag{8.5–2}$$

C_ϱ being traversed in the counter-clockwise sense. Since $f(z)$ is assumed to be regular at $z = a$ we have in a small neighbourhood of $z = a$

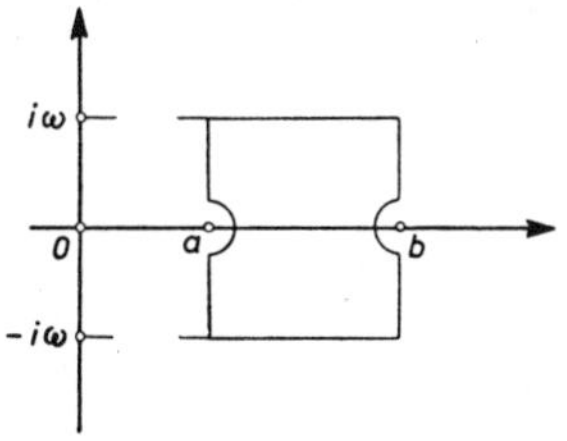

Fig. 8.5–1. Path of integration for the derivation of Plana's sum formula

$$\pi \operatorname{ctn} \pi z f(z) = \frac{f(a)}{z-a} + g(z),$$

$g(z)$ being regular at $z = a$. Integrating this along the semi-circular part with center a we get

$$i \int_{\frac{1}{2}\pi}^{-\frac{1}{2}\pi} f(a) d\theta + \chi_a(\varrho) = -\pi i f(a) + \chi_a(\varrho),$$

where $\chi_a(\varrho)$ tends to zero as $\varrho \to 0$. A similar result holds in the neighbourhood of the point b.

When C_ϱ^* denotes the path obtained from C_ϱ by deleting the semi-circular parts, we evidently have

$$\int_{C_\varrho} \pi \operatorname{ctn} \pi\zeta f(\zeta) d\zeta = \int_{C_\varrho^*} \pi \operatorname{ctn} \pi\zeta f(\zeta) d\zeta - \pi i f(a) - \pi i f(b) + \chi_a(\varrho) + \chi_b(\varrho). \tag{8.5–3}$$

Now we may define $\int_C$ as $\lim_{\varrho \to 0} \int_{C_\varrho^*}$. It is easy to show that this limit reduces to the integral in the ordinary sense, should the integrand be regular at $z = a$ and $z = b$.

Letting $\varrho \to 0$ we deduce from (8.5–2) and (8.5–3)

$$\sum_{\nu=a}^{b} f(\nu) = \tfrac{1}{2} f(a) + \tfrac{1}{2} f(b) + \frac{1}{2\pi i} \int_C \pi \operatorname{ctn} \pi\zeta \, f(\zeta) d\zeta. \tag{8.5–4}$$

As we shall see presently it will be convenient to treat the upper and the lower part of the rectangle C separately. By C' we denote the upper half of C and by C'' the lower half, both parts described from a to b, i.e., $C = -C' + C''$. We introduce a function $\psi(z)$ which is defined as

$$\psi(z) = \begin{cases} \operatorname{ctn} \pi z + i = \dfrac{2i}{1 - e^{-2\pi i z}}, & \text{when } \operatorname{Im} z > 0, \\[2ex] \operatorname{ctn} \pi z - i = \dfrac{2i}{e^{2\pi i z} - 1}, & \text{when } \operatorname{Im} z < 0. \end{cases} \tag{8.5–5}$$

By virtue of Cauchy's integral theorem the following equations hold:

$$\int_{C'} f(\zeta)d\zeta = \int_{C''} f(\zeta)d\zeta = \int_a^b f(t)dt. \qquad (8.5\text{–}6)$$

Hence we may replace (8.5–4) by

$$\sum_{\nu=a}^{b} f(\nu) = \tfrac{1}{2}f(a)+\tfrac{1}{2}f(b)+\int_a^b f(t)dt+\frac{1}{2i}\int_C \psi(\zeta)f(\zeta)d\zeta. \qquad (8.5\text{–}7)$$

This formula will be the starting-point for further developments.

8.5.2 – Plana's sum formula

Next we suppose that $f(z)$ satisfies the following conditions:
(i) $f(z)$ is holomorphic in a region including the strip

$$a \leqq x \leqq b, \text{ where } x = \operatorname{Re} z; \qquad (8.5\text{–}8)$$

(ii) when $y = \operatorname{Im} z$ tends to infinity then

$$e^{-2\pi|y|}f(x+iy) \to 0, \qquad (8.5\text{–}9)$$

uniformly in $a \leqq x \leqq b$.

It is readily seen that the contributions to the last integral occurring in (8.5–7) from the horizontal parts of C tend to zero as $\omega \to \infty$. An easy computation yields

$$\sum_{\nu=a}^{b} f(\nu) = \tfrac{1}{2}f(a)+\tfrac{1}{2}f(b)+\int_a^b f(t)dt+Q(b)-Q(a) \qquad (8.5\text{–}10)$$

where

$$\boxed{Q(x) = \frac{1}{i}\int_0^\infty \frac{f(x+iy)-f(x-iy)}{e^{2\pi y}-1}dy.} \qquad (8.5\text{–}11)$$

Assuming, in particular, that $Q(b) \to 0$, $f(b) \to 0$ as $b \to \infty$, and that the first integral on the right of (8.5–10) converges as $b \to \infty$ (it being understood that the conditions (i) and (ii) remain valid for every positive integral value of b), we obtain *Plana's sum formula*

$$\boxed{\sum_{\nu=a}^{\infty} f(\nu) = \tfrac{1}{2}f(a)+\int_a^\infty f(t)dt-Q(a).} \qquad (8.5\text{–}12)$$

8.5.3 – Application to the Riemann zeta function

We wish to illustrate Plana's sum formula in the following example. For the function $f(z)$ we take

$$f(z) = z^{-s} = \exp(-s \log z). \qquad (8.5\text{–}13)$$

Then

$$f(x+iy)=\exp\{-s\log(x+iy)\}=\exp\left\{-s\log\sqrt{x^2+y^2}-is\arctan\frac{y}{x}\right\}$$

$$=(x^2+y^2)^{-\frac{1}{2}s}\left\{\cos\left(s\operatorname{arc\,tan}\frac{y}{x}\right)-i\sin\left(s\arctan\frac{y}{x}\right)\right\},$$

whence

$$Q(x)=-2\int_0^\infty(x^2+y^2)^{-\frac{1}{2}s}\sin\left(s\arctan\frac{y}{x}\right)\frac{dy}{e^{2\pi y}-1}.$$

Now, assuming Re $s>1$,

$$\int_1^\infty f(t)dt=\int_1^\infty t^{-s}\,dt=\frac{1}{s-1}.$$

Hence $f(x)=x^{-s}\to 0$ as $x\to\infty$.

Anticipating the result $Q(x)\to 0$ as $x\to\infty$ we may apply Plana's sum formula by taking $a=1$, for the conditions (i) and (ii) are easily verified for every positive value of b.

We find the following expression for the Riemann zeta function, due to Jensen,

$$\boxed{\zeta(s)=\tfrac{1}{2}+\frac{1}{s-1}+2\int_0^\infty(1+y^2)^{-\frac{1}{2}s}\sin(s\arctan y)\frac{dy}{e^{2\pi y}-1}.}\qquad(8.5\text{–}14)$$

It remains to study the behaviour of $Q(x)$ when x tends to infinity. Assuming $x>0$, we have for all $y>0$

$$0<\arctan\frac{y}{x}<\tfrac{1}{2}\pi.$$

Now $|\sin(s\arctan y/x)|$ is bounded and the same is true for

$$\frac{\left|\sin\left(s\arctan\dfrac{y}{x}\right)\right|}{|s|\arctan\dfrac{y}{x}}.$$

By writing $\int_0^\infty=\int_0^1+\int_1^\infty$ we find, assuming $\sigma=\text{Re}\,s>0$,

$$|Q(x)|\leqq 2A\int_0^1(x^2+y^2)^{-\frac{1}{2}\sigma}\frac{|s|\arctan\dfrac{y}{x}}{e^{2\pi y}-1}dy+2B\int_1^\infty(x^2+y^2)^{-\frac{1}{2}\sigma}\frac{dy}{e^{2\pi y}-1}$$

$$<\frac{2}{x^\sigma}\left(A\int_0^1\frac{|s|\arctan\dfrac{y}{x}}{e^{2\pi y}-1}dy+B\int_1^\infty\frac{dy}{e^{2\pi y}-1}\right),$$

where A and B are suitably chosen constants (depending on s), the integrals being convergent. Thus we confirm that $Q(x) \to 0$ as $x \to +\infty$.

It is not difficult to show that the integral on the right of (8.5–14) is holomorphic throughout the entire s-plane. It may, therefore, serve to define $\zeta(s)$ everywhere except at $s = 1$.

On taking $s = 0$ we find at once

$$\zeta(0) = -\tfrac{1}{2}. \tag{8.5–15}$$

Further, taking account of (4.9–30)

$$\lim_{s\to 1}\left(\zeta(s) - \frac{1}{s-1}\right) = \tfrac{1}{2} + 2\int_0^\infty \frac{y}{1+y^2}\,\frac{dy}{e^{2\pi y}-1} = \gamma \tag{8.5–16}$$

because of

$$\sin \arctan y = \frac{y}{\sqrt{1+y^2}}.$$

Finally, differentiating with respect to s, making $s = 0$ and using (4.9–28)

$$\zeta'(0) = 2\int_0^\infty \frac{\arctan y}{e^{2\pi y}-1}\,dy - 1 = -\log\sqrt{2\pi}. \tag{8.5–17}$$

These results were obtained in a different way in the sections 7.9.3 and 7.9.4.

8.5.4 – Additional remarks

The formulas (4.9–28) and (4.9–30) used previously can also easily be deduced by means of the general sum formula (8.5–10).

Take first the function

$$f(z) = \log z = \log\sqrt{x^2+y^2} + i \arctan\frac{y}{x}.$$

Then

$$Q(x) = 2\int_0^\infty \frac{\arctan \dfrac{y}{x}}{e^{2\pi y}-1}\,dy$$

and evidently $Q(x) \to 0$ as $x \to \infty$. By taking $a = 1$, $b = n$ in (8.5–10) we get

$$\begin{aligned}\log n! &= \tfrac{1}{2}\log n + \int_1^n \log t\,dt + Q(n) - Q(1)\\ &= (n+\tfrac{1}{2})\log n - n + 1 - Q(1) + Q(n).\end{aligned}$$

By Stirling's theorem of section 4.7.4

$$\log n! = (n+\tfrac{1}{2})\log n - n + \log\sqrt{2\pi} + \mu(n),$$

where $\mu(n)$ tends to zero as $n \to \infty$. And so

$$1-Q(1) = 1-2\int_0^\infty \frac{\arctan y}{e^{2\pi y}-1}\,dy = \log \sqrt{2\pi}.$$

Secondly we take

$$f(z) = \frac{1}{z} = \frac{x}{x^2+y^2} - \frac{iy}{x^2+y^2}$$

whence

$$Q(x) = -2\int_0^\infty \frac{y}{x^2+y^2}\,\frac{dy}{e^{2\pi y}-1}.$$

Since $Q(x) \to 0$ as $x \to \infty$, we easily find

$$\gamma = \lim_{n\to\infty}\left(1+\frac{1}{2}+\ldots+\frac{1}{n}-\log n\right) = \tfrac{1}{2}+2\int_0^\infty \frac{y}{1+y^2}\,\frac{dy}{e^{2\pi y}-1},$$

the desired result.

8.6 – The Euler-Maclaurin sum formula

8.6.1 – Statement and proof of the formula

Let us introduce the function

$$q(x, y) = \frac{1}{2i}\{f(x+iy)-f(x-iy)\}. \tag{8.6–1}$$

The integral (8.5–11) representing $Q(x)$ can be written as

$$Q(x) = 2\int_0^\infty \frac{q(x, y)}{e^{2\pi y}-1}\,dy. \tag{8.6–2}$$

We can expand $q(x, y)$ in a series of Maclaurin in terms of powers of y. Observing that

$$q^{(2k)}(x, 0) = 0$$

and

$$q^{(2k+1)}(x, y) = \tfrac{1}{2}(-1)^k\{f^{(2k+1)}(x+iy)+f^{(2k+1)}(x-iy)\},$$

the differentiation of $q(x, y)$ being understood with respect to y, we readily find

$$q(x, y) = \sum_{\nu=1}^{n} \frac{(-1)^{\nu-1}y^{2\nu-1}}{(2\nu-1)!}\,f^{(2\nu-1)}(x)+q_{2n+1}(x, y), \tag{8.6–3}$$

the remainder being

$$q_{2n+1}(x, y)$$
$$= \frac{(-1)^n y^{2n+1}}{2(2n)!}\int_0^1 (1-u)^{2n}\{f^{(2n+1)}(x+iyu)+f^{(2n+1)}(x-iyu)\}\,du. \tag{8.6–4}$$

Recalling the expression (4.8–38) for Bernoulli's numbers

$$\frac{B_{2k}}{2k} = 2\int_0^\infty \frac{y^{2k-1}}{e^{2\pi y}-1}\,dy$$

we get

$$Q(x) = \sum_{\nu=1}^{n} (-1)^{\nu-1} \frac{B_{2\nu}}{(2\nu)!} f^{(2\nu-1)}(x) + R_n(x) \tag{8.6–5}$$

with

$$R_n(x) = 2\int_0^\infty \frac{q_{2n+1}(x, y)}{e^{2\pi y}-1}\,dy. \tag{8.6–6}$$

Inserting this into the general sum formula (8.5–10) and assuming that the conditions (i) and (ii) of section 8.5.2 are satisfied, we obtain the famous *Euler-Maclaurin sum formula*

$$\begin{gathered}\sum_{\nu=a}^{b} f(\nu) = \tfrac{1}{2}f(a) + \tfrac{1}{2}f(b) + \int_a^b f(t)\,dt \\ + \sum_{\nu=1}^{n} (-1)^{\nu-1} \frac{B_{2\nu}}{(2\nu)!} \{f^{(2\nu-1)}(b) - f^{(2\nu-1)}(a)\} + R_n(b) - R_n(a).\end{gathered} \tag{8.6–7}$$

This formula is all-important in analysis, in particular in number theory. In subsequent sections we shall discuss some illustrative examples.

8.6.2 – Application to the Euler constant

First we consider the function

$$f(z) = \frac{1}{z}.$$

Since $f^{(k)}(z) = (-1)^k k! z^{-k-1}$, we find taking $a = 1$

$$\begin{aligned}\sum_{\nu=1}^{b} \frac{1}{\nu} &= \frac{1}{2} + \frac{1}{2b} + \log b \\ &+ \sum_{\nu=1}^{n} (-1)^{\nu} \frac{B_{2\nu}}{2\nu} \frac{1}{b^{2\nu}} - \sum_{\nu=1}^{n} (-1)^{\nu} \frac{B_{2\nu}}{2\nu} + R_n(b) - R_n(1).\end{aligned} \tag{8.6–8}$$

As we shall see presently $R_n(b) \to 0$ as $b \to \infty$. Then we deduce from (8.6–8)

$$\gamma = \lim_{b\to\infty} \left(\sum_{\nu=1}^{b} \frac{1}{\nu} - \log b \right) = \tfrac{1}{2} - \sum_{\nu=1}^{n} (-1)^{\nu} \frac{B_{2\nu}}{2\nu} - R_n(1). \tag{8.6–9}$$

Hence (8.6–8) may be written in the form

$$\gamma = \sum_{\nu=1}^{b} \frac{1}{\nu} - \log b - \frac{1}{2b} - \sum_{\nu=1}^{n} (-1)^{\nu} \frac{B_{2\nu}}{2\nu} \frac{1}{b^{2\nu}} - R_n(b). \tag{8.6–10}$$

For $b = 1$ this expression reduces to (8.6–9).

In the case under consideration it is an easy matter to find an estimate for $|R_n(x)|$. In fact

$$|f^{(2n+1)}(x+iy)| = \frac{(2n+1)!}{(x^2+y^2)^{n+1}} < \frac{(2n+1)!}{x^{2n+2}},$$

provided that $y > 0$. Hence

$$|q_{2n+1}(x, y)| < (2n+1)\frac{y^{2n+1}}{x^{2n+2}}\int_0^1 (1-u)^{2n}\,du = \frac{y^{2n+1}}{x^{2n+2}},$$

and so

$$|R_n(x)| < \frac{B_{2n+2}}{2n+2}\,\frac{1}{x^{2n+2}}.$$

Thus we see that $R_n(x) \to 0$ as $x \to \infty$. The real part of z^{-2n-2} is essentially positive whenever $x > 0$, for $\arg z^{-2n-2} = (\arg z)/(2n+2)$. This leads to the conclusion that the sign of the integrand in (8.6–4) is that of $(-1)^{2n+1} = -1$ and we may, therefore, write

$$R_n(x) = (-1)^{n+1}\theta\,\frac{B_{2n+2}}{2n+2}\,\frac{1}{x^{2n+2}}, \qquad 0 < \theta < 1. \tag{8.6–11}$$

Inserting (8.6–11) into (8.6–10) we obtain the following expression for the Euler constant

$$\gamma = \sum_{\nu=1}^{b}\frac{1}{\nu} - \log b - \frac{1}{2b} + \sum_{\nu=1}^{n}(-1)^{\nu-1}\frac{B_{2\nu}}{2\nu}\,\frac{1}{b^{2\nu}} + (-1)^n\theta\,\frac{B_{2n+2}}{2n+2}\,\frac{1}{b^{2n+2}}. \tag{8.6–12}$$

In particular, taking $b = 1$,

$$\gamma = \frac{1}{2} + \frac{B_2}{2} - \frac{B_4}{4} + \ldots + (-1)^{n-1}\frac{B_{2n}}{2n} + (-1)^n\theta\,\frac{B_{2n+2}}{2n+2}. \tag{8.6–13}$$

8.6.3 – Value of B_{2n} for large values of n

The series on the right of (8.6–12) or (8.6–13) are not convergent as $n \to \infty$, since the general term does not tend to zero. In fact, in view of (7.7–8) we have

$$\frac{B_{2n}}{(2n)!} = \frac{2}{(2\pi)^{2n}}\,\zeta(2n). \tag{8.6–14}$$

Hence

$$B_{2n} > \frac{1}{2\pi}\,\frac{2}{2\pi}\cdots\frac{2n}{2\pi} \tag{8.6–15}$$

and the number of factors exceeding two on the right of (8.6–15) tends to infinity as $n \to \infty$. Hence also $B_{2n}/2n$ tends to infinity.

The magnitude of B_{2n} for large values of n can be estimated on applying Stirling's formula (4.7–21) taking account of

$$\lim_{n\to\infty} \zeta(n) = 1. \tag{8.6–16}$$

This latter statement follows at once from

$$1 < \zeta(n) = 1+\frac{1}{2^n}+\frac{1}{3^n}+\ldots < 1+\int_0^\infty \frac{dx}{(1+x)^n} = 1+\frac{1}{n-1},\ n > 1.$$

An easy calculation yields from (8.6–14)

$$\boxed{\lim_{n\to\infty} \frac{B_{2n}}{4\sqrt{\pi n}\left(\dfrac{n}{e\pi}\right)^{2n}} = 1.} \tag{8.6–17}$$

8.6.4 – Semi-convergent series

It is well-known that the alternating series

$$\sum_{\nu=0}^{\infty} (-1)^\nu c_\nu = \sum_{\nu=0}^{n} (-1)^\nu c_\nu + r_n \tag{8.6–18}$$

is convergent when the numbers $c_0, c_1, \ldots$ are all positive and decrease monotonously to zero. The remainder r_n can be written as

$$\begin{aligned}(-1)^{n+1} r_n &= c_{n+1}-(c_{n+2}-c_{n+3})-(c_{n+4}-c_{n+5})-\ldots\\ &= (c_{n+1}-c_{n+2})+(c_{n+3}-c_{n+4})+\ldots.\end{aligned}$$

Hence

$$0 < (-1)^{n+1} r_n < c_{n+1}.$$

We can look upon this result as follows. If we approximate the sum of the series (8.6–18) by means of a partial sum of terms, *the error turns out to be alternating in sign, its sign being that of the first omitted term and its value being numerically less than that term.*

The last property holds also for the divergent series (8.6–12) and (8.6–13). Series of this kind are called semi-convergent. More precisely: A divergent series (8.6–18) where $c_0, c_1, \ldots$ are positive, is called *semi-convergent to a number* c if

$$r_n = c - \sum_{\nu=0}^{n} (-1)^\nu c_\nu$$

has the sign of $(-1)^{n+1}$ and is numerically less than c_{n+1}. It should be noticed that the number c is not uniquely determined by the series. In many cases a semi-convergent series is a very useful tool in numerical computations.

8.7 – Stirling's series

8.7.1 – Expansion of Binet's function

We wish to apply the Euler-Maclaurin formula to the function

$$f(z) = \log (z+c) \tag{8.7–1}$$

where c is a real number > -1. Since

$$f^{(k)}(z) = (-1)^{k-1}\frac{(k-1)!}{(z+c)^k}, \qquad k > 0,$$

we readily find, b being a positive integer,

$$\begin{aligned}\sum_{\nu=1}^{b} \log (\nu+c) &= \tfrac{1}{2}\log (1+c) + \tfrac{1}{2}\log (b+c) - (1+c)\log (1+c)\\ &\quad + (b+c)\log (b+c) + (1+c) - (b+c)\\ &\quad + \sum_{\nu=1}^{n} \frac{(-1)^{\nu-1}B_{2\nu}}{(2\nu-1)2\nu}\left(\frac{1}{(b+c)^{2\nu-1}} - \frac{1}{(1+c)^{2\nu-1}}\right) + R_n(b) - R_n(1).\end{aligned}$$

Observing that

$$\log \Gamma(b+c+1) = \sum_{\nu=1}^{b} \log (\nu+c) + \log \Gamma(1+c)$$

and putting $s = b+c$, we get (8.7–2)

$$\log \Gamma(s+1) = (s+\tfrac{1}{2})\log s - s + C(c) + \sum_{\nu=1}^{n} \frac{(-1)^{\nu-1}B_{2\nu}}{(2\nu-1)2\nu}\,\frac{1}{s^{2\nu-1}} + R_n(b),$$

where $C(c)$ includes all terms not involving b, i.e.,

$$\begin{aligned}C(c) &= \log \Gamma(1+c) - (c+\tfrac{1}{2})\log (1+c)\\ &\quad + (1+c) - \sum_{\nu=1}^{n} \frac{(-1)^{\nu-1}B_{2\nu}}{(2\nu-1)2\nu}\,\frac{1}{(1+c)^{2\nu-1}} - R_n(1).\end{aligned} \tag{8.7–3}$$

By arguments similar to those used in section 8.6.3 we have

$$R_n(x) = \frac{(-1)^n\theta\, B_{2n+2}}{(2n+1)(2n+2)}\,\frac{1}{(x+c)^{2n+1}}, \qquad 0 < \theta < 1, \quad x > 0.$$

Hence, letting $b \to \infty$

$$\log \Gamma(s+1) - (s+\tfrac{1}{2})\log s + s \to C(c), \quad \text{as } s \to \infty. \tag{8.7–4}$$

From Stirling's theorem (section 4.9.2) we deduce

$$C(c) = \log \sqrt{2\pi}.$$

Thus we obtain the following expansion for Binet's function

$$\boxed{\mu(s) = \sum_{\nu=1}^{n} \frac{(-1)^{\nu-1}B_{2\nu}}{(2\nu-1)2\nu}\,\frac{1}{s^{2\nu-1}} + (-1)^n\theta\,\frac{B_{2n+2}}{(2n+1)(2n+2)}\,\frac{1}{s^{2n+1}}} \tag{8.7–5}$$

where s is assumed to be positive and θ a number between 0 and 1. The series on the right is known as *Stirling's series*.

Taking $s = 1$ we find

$$\log\sqrt{2\pi} = 1 - \frac{B_2}{1\cdot 2} + \frac{B_4}{3\cdot 4} + \ldots + (-1)^n \frac{B_{2n}}{(2n-1)2n} + (-1)^{n+1}\theta\frac{B_{2n+2}}{(2n+1)(2n+2)}, \qquad (8.7\text{–}6)$$

the series on the right being semi-convergent to $\log\sqrt{2\pi}$.

8.7.2 – Alternative method

An alternative method for obtaining Stirling's series starts from Binet's first integral (4.9–21) for the function $\mu(z)$. We recall the expansion (4.9–23), viz.,

$$\left(\frac{1}{e^t-1} - \frac{1}{t} + \frac{1}{2}\right)\frac{1}{t} = 2\sum_{\lambda=1}^{\infty}\frac{1}{t^2+4\lambda^2\pi^2}. \qquad (8.7\text{–}7)$$

Now, assuming $u > 0$, $v > 0$,

$$\frac{1}{u+v} = \frac{1}{v} - \frac{u}{v^2} + \ldots + (-1)^{n-1}\frac{u^{n-1}}{v^n} + (-1)^n\vartheta\frac{u^n}{v^{n+1}} \qquad (8.7\text{–}8)$$

where

$$\vartheta = \frac{1}{1+u/v}$$

is between 0 and 1. Taking $u = t^2$, $v = 4\lambda^2\pi^2$ we may write the right-hand side of (8.7–7) as

$$\sum_{\nu=1}^{n}\sum_{\lambda=1}^{\infty}\frac{2(-1)^{\nu-1}t^{2\nu-2}}{(2\lambda\pi)^{2\nu}} + \sum_{\lambda=1}^{\infty}\frac{2(-1)^n\vartheta(\lambda,t)t^{2n}}{(2\lambda\pi)^{2n+2}}$$
$$= \sum_{\nu=1}^{n}\frac{2(-1)^{\nu-1}t^{2\nu-2}}{(2\pi)^{2\nu}}\zeta(2\nu) + \frac{2(-1)^n\theta(t)t^{2n}}{(2\lambda\pi)^{2n+2}}\zeta(2n+2),$$

where $\theta(t)$ is also between 0 and 1.

With reference to (7.7–8) this result can be put into the form

$$\sum_{\nu=1}^{n}\frac{(-1)^{\nu-1}B_{2\nu}}{(2\nu)!}t^{2\nu-2} + (-1)^n\theta(t)\frac{B_{2n+2}}{(2n+2)!}t^{2n}.$$

Multiplying by e^{-st} and integrating from 0 to ∞, we again have

$$\mu(s) = \sum_{\nu=1}^{n}\frac{(-1)^{\nu-1}B_{2\nu}}{(2\nu-1)2\nu}\frac{1}{s^{2\nu-1}} + R_n(s) \qquad (8.7\text{–}9)$$

with

$$R_n(s) = (-1)^n \frac{B_{2n+2}}{(2n+2)!} \int_0^\infty e^{-st}\theta(t)t^{2n}\,dt$$

and

$$|R_n(s)| < \frac{B_{2n+2}}{(2n+2)!} \int_0^\infty e^{-st}\,t^{2n}\,dt = \frac{B_{2n+2}}{(2n+1)(2n+2)} \frac{1}{s^{2n+1}},$$

in accordance with (8.7–5).

8.8 – The Bernoullian polynomials

8.8.1 – Definition

The Euler-Maclaurin sum formula has been derived under rather severe restrictions imposed on the function $f(z)$, which could easily be verified, however, in the examples given before. It is our aim to obtain the same formula under weaker assumptions. This will be made possible by using certain polynomials which shall be defined first.

From (2.17–19) we deduce the expansion

$$\frac{t}{e^t-1} = 1-\tfrac{1}{2}t + \sum_{\nu=1}^{\infty} \frac{(-1)^{\nu-1}B_{2\nu}}{(2\nu)!} t^{2\nu}. \tag{8.8–1}$$

Now we consider the more general expansion

$$\boxed{\frac{te^{xt}}{e^t - 1} = 1+ \sum_{\nu=1}^{\infty} \frac{B_\nu(x)}{\nu!} t^\nu,} \tag{8.8–2}$$

the series on the right of (8.8–1) and (8.8–2) being convergent whenever $|t| < 2\pi$. The expansion (8.8–2) reduces to (8.8–1) for $x = 0$. It defines the functions

$$B_1(x), B_2(x), \ldots,$$

of the real variable x uniquely.

Taking $x = 1$ we get

$$\frac{te^t}{e^t-1} = \frac{-t}{e^{-t}-1} = 1+\tfrac{1}{2}t+ \sum_{\nu=1}^{\infty} \frac{(-1)^{\nu-1}B_{2\nu}}{(2\nu)!} t^{2\nu}. \tag{8.8–3}$$

Hence

$$B_{2n}(0) = B_{2n}(1) = (-1)^{n-1}B_{2n}, \qquad n \geqq 1, \tag{8.8–4}$$

$$B_{2n+1}(0) = B_{2n+1}(1) = 0, \qquad n \geqq 1, \tag{8.8–5}$$

whereas

$$B_1(0) = -\tfrac{1}{2}, \qquad B_1(1) = \tfrac{1}{2}. \tag{8.8–6}$$

Writing (8.8–2) as

$$1+\sum_{\nu=1}^{\infty}\frac{B_\nu(x)}{\nu!}t^\nu=\left(1+\sum_{\nu=1}^{\infty}\frac{B_\nu(0)}{\nu!}t^\nu\right)\sum_{\nu=0}^{\infty}\frac{x^\nu t^\nu}{\nu!}$$

and equating coefficients, we find

$$\boxed{B_n(x)=x^n+\binom{n}{1}B_1(0)x^{n-1}+\binom{n}{2}B_2(0)x^{n-2}+\ldots+B_n(0),} \qquad (8.8\text{–}7)$$

which may be written symbolically as

$$B_n(x) = (B+x)^n, \qquad (8.8\text{–}8)$$

agreeing on

$$B^k x^{n-k} = B_k(0)x^{n-k}.$$

For $x = 1$ we find recurrence formulas for the Bernoullian numbers.

It is plain that (8.8–2) can be written symbolically as

$$\frac{te^{xt}}{e^t-1}=e^{(B+x)t}. \qquad (8.8\text{–}9)$$

From (8.8–7) follows that the functions $B_n(x)$ are polynomials of degree n. They are called *Bernoullian polynomials*.

8.8.2 – Functional relations

The polynomials $B_n(x)$ have some remarkable properties which are easy consequences of their definition by means of the generating function on the left of (8.8–2).

The identity

$$\frac{te^{(x+1)t}}{e^t-1}-\frac{te^{xt}}{e^t-1}=te^{xt}, \qquad (8.8\text{–}10)$$

or symbolically

$$e^{(B+x+1)t}-e^{(B+x)t}=te^{xt},$$

implies the fundamental relation

$$\boxed{B_n(x+1)-B_n(x)=nx^{n-1},} \qquad n \geqq 1. \qquad (8.8\text{–}11)$$

Differentiating (8.8–2) with respect to x we find

$$t+\sum_{\nu=1}^{n}\frac{B_\nu(x)}{\nu!}t^{\nu+1}=\frac{t^2e^{xt}}{e^t-1}=\sum_{\nu=1}^{\infty}\frac{B'_\nu(x)}{\nu!}t^\nu$$

and equating coefficients

$$\boxed{B'_n(x) = nB_{n-1}(x),} \qquad n \geqq 1, \qquad (8.8\text{–}12)$$

where we have to interpret $B_0(x)$ as being identically equal to 1. Hence

$$\int_0^1 B_n(x)dx = \frac{1}{n+1}\int_0^1 B'_{n+1}(x)dx = \frac{B_{n+1}(1)-B_{n+1}(0)}{n+1}$$

and so, taking account of (8.8–4) and (8.8–5),

$$\boxed{\int_0^1 B_n(x)dx = 0,} \qquad n \geqq 1. \qquad (8.8\text{–}13)$$

Finally, observing that

$$\frac{te^{xt}+te^{(1-x)t}}{e^t-1} = t\frac{\cosh (x-\frac{1}{2})t}{\sinh \frac{1}{2}t},$$

$$\frac{te^{xt}-te^{(1-x)t}}{e^t-1} = t\frac{\sinh (x-\frac{1}{2})t}{\sinh \frac{1}{2}t}$$

are even and odd functions of t respectively, we have

$$\boxed{B_{2n-1}(x) = -B_{2n-1}(1-x), \quad B_{2n}(x) = B_{2n}(1-x).} \qquad (8.8\text{–}14)$$

In particular,

$$B_1(\tfrac{1}{2}) = B_3(\tfrac{1}{2}) = \ldots = 0. \qquad (8.8\text{–}15)$$

8.9 – The associate periodic functions

8.9.1 – Definition

In many cases it is convenient to introduce certain periodic functions which coincide with the Bernoullian polynomials in the interval $0 \leqq x < 1$ up to a multiplicative constant. More precisely:

By the associate periodic functions are understood the functions

$$\mathsf{P}_n(x) = \frac{B_n(x)}{n!} \qquad (8.9\text{–}1)$$

for $0 \leqq x < 1$ *and with period* 1.

It follows that the functions $\mathsf{P}_n(x)$ are continuous for all x if $n > 1$, whereas $\mathsf{P}_1(x)$ has a jump -1 for every integral value of x. Evidently

$$\mathsf{P}_1(x) = x-[x]-\tfrac{1}{2} \qquad (8.9\text{–}2)$$

is the same function as considered in section 4.9.1.

According to (8.8–12) the function $\mathsf{P}_n(x)$ satisfies the relation

$$\boxed{\mathsf{P}'_n(x) = \mathsf{P}_{n-1}(x)} \qquad (8.9\text{–}3)$$

except for $n = 1$ when x is an integer.

8.9.2 – Alternative proof of the Euler-Maclaurin sum formula

Let $f(x)$ denote a real or complex function of the real variable x. We assume the existence and continuity for all derivatives which occur in the sequel for $x \geqq a$, where a is any integer.

We are already in possession of the Euler sum formula (7.9–5) having the remainder

$$\int_a^b \mathsf{P}_1(u)\, f'(u)du. \tag{8.9–4}$$

In view of (8.9–3) we have

$$\{\mathsf{P}_k(u)\, f^{(k-1)}(u)\}' = \mathsf{P}_{k-1}(u)\, f^{(k-1)}(u) + \mathsf{P}_k(u)\, f^{(k)}(u). \tag{8.9–5}$$

Hence, when $k \geqq 2$,

$$\int_a^b \mathsf{P}_{k-1}(u) f^{(k-1)}(u)du = \mathsf{P}_k(b) f^{(k-1)}(b) - \mathsf{P}_k(a) f^{(k-1)}(a) - \int_a^b \mathsf{P}_k(u)\, f^{(k)}(u)du$$

$$= \mathsf{P}_k(0)\{f^{(k-1)}(b) - f^{(k-1)}(a)\} - \int_a^b \mathsf{P}_k(u) f^{(k)}(u)du. \tag{8.9–6}$$

Multiplying the first and the last member by $(-1)^k$, we get from (7.9–5), taking account of (8.8–4), by adding successively the expressions corresponding to $k = 1, 2, \ldots, n$,

$$\sum_{\nu=a}^{b} f(\nu) = \tfrac{1}{2}f(a) + \tfrac{1}{2}f(b) + \int_a^b f(u)du + \sum_{\nu=1}^{n} \frac{(-1)^{\nu-1} B_{2\nu}}{(2\nu)!} \{f^{(2\nu-1)}(b) - f^{(2\nu-1)}(a)\} + R_n \tag{8.9–7}$$

with

$$R_n = \int_a^b \mathsf{P}_{2n+1}(u)\, f^{(2n+1)}(u)du. \tag{8.9–8}$$

This is again the Euler-Maclaurin sum formula with an alternative expression for the remainder.

8.9.3 – The general Stirling theorem

In a similar way we can also derive a general expression for Binet's function $\mu(z)$, starting from (4.9–7). Upon integration by parts we get

$$\int_0^\infty \frac{\mathsf{P}_k(u)}{(z+u)^k} du = -\frac{\mathsf{P}_{k+1}(0)}{z^k} + k\int_0^\infty \frac{\mathsf{P}_{k+1}(u)}{(z+u)^{k+1}} du.$$

Hence, taking successively $k = 1, 2, \ldots$ we find after $2n$ steps

$$\boxed{\mu(z) = \sum_{\nu=1}^{n} \frac{(-1)^{\nu-1} B_{2\nu}}{(2\nu-1)2\nu} \frac{1}{z^{2\nu-1}} - (2n)!\int_0^\infty \frac{\mathsf{P}_{2n+1}(u)}{(z+u)^{2n+1}} du,} \tag{8.9–9}$$

in accordance with the expressions found previously, but now extended to the case of complex values of z. As in section 4.9.2 we have, putting $z = re^{i\theta}$,

$$\left|\int_0^\infty \frac{\mathsf{P}_{2n+1}(u)}{(z+u)^{2n+1}}\,du\right| \leqq \sec^{2n+1}\tfrac{1}{2}\theta \int_0^\infty \frac{|\mathsf{P}_{2n+1}(u)|}{(r+u)^{2n+1}}\,du.$$

Hence the last term of (8.9–8) is $O(|z|^{-2n-1})$ as $z \to \infty$, provided that arg z does not come arbitrarily near to $\pm\pi$. This is Stirling's theorem in its most general form.

8.9.4 – Fourier expansions of the associate functions

On applying the residue theorem it is not difficult to obtain Fourier expansions of the associate functions. We consider the function

$$z^{-n}\frac{e^{sz}}{e^z-1}, \qquad 0 \leqq s \leqq 1, \tag{8.9–10}$$

where n is an integer > 0. Its poles are at $z = 0, \pm 2\pi i, \pm 4\pi i, \ldots.$ Evidently $\mathsf{P}_n(s)$ is the residue of the function at the origin. The function $e^{sz}/(e^z-1)$ is bounded on the perimeter of a rectangle C_r, whose vertices are $\pm r \pm (2r+1)\pi i$, r being a positive integer. It follows that the integral

$$\frac{1}{2\pi i}\int_{C_r} \zeta^{-n}\frac{e^{s\zeta}}{e^{\zeta}-1}\,d\zeta \tag{8.9–11}$$

tends to zero as $r \to \infty$. The sum of the residues of the function (8.9–10) at $z = 2m\pi i$ and $z = -2m\pi i$, $m > 0$, is

$$\begin{aligned}&(2m\pi i)^{-n}e^{(s-1)2m\pi i}+(-2m\pi i)^{-n}e^{-(s-1)2m\pi i}\\ &= (2m\pi)^{-n}i^{-n}e^{2m\pi is}+(-2m\pi)^{-n}i^{-n}e^{-2m\pi is}.\end{aligned}$$

Hence, replacing s by x,

$$\boxed{\mathsf{P}_{2n+1}(x) = (-1)^{n+1}\,2\sum_{\nu=1}^{\infty}\frac{\sin 2\nu\pi x}{(2\nu\pi)^{2n+1}}} \tag{8.9–12}$$

and

$$\boxed{\mathsf{P}_{2n}(x) = (-1)^{n+1}\,2\sum_{\nu=1}^{\infty}\frac{\cos 2\nu\pi x}{(2\nu\pi)^{2n}}}\,. \tag{8.9–13}$$

These formulas have been established under the assumption $n > 0$. But (8.9–12) is still valid for $n = 0$. In fact, this result may be verified from (2.16–16) by putting $\pi-\varphi = \pi x$. It should be noticed that, in accordance with the general theory of Fourier series, the sum of the series is $\frac{1}{2}\mathsf{P}_1(x+0)+\frac{1}{2}\mathsf{P}_1(x-0)$ at an integral value of x.

By formal differentiation of the Fourier series (8.9–12) we obtain the relation (8.9–13).

Finally we wish to make an interesting application of (8.9–12). Inserting $x = \frac{1}{4}$ and taking account of (3.7–28), we readily find

$$(2n+1)(-1)^n E_{2n} = 4^{2n+1} B_{2n+1}(\tfrac{1}{4}),$$

and so, by virtue of (8.8–7), (8.8–4), (8.8–5) and (8.8–6),

$$\boxed{(2n+1)(-1)^{n+1} E_{2n}=1-2\binom{2n+1}{2}+\sum_{\nu=1}^{n}(-1)^{\nu-1}4^{2\nu}\binom{2n+1}{2\nu}B_{2\nu}.}$$

Thus it turns out to be possible to express the Euler numbers in terms of the Bernoulli numbers.

8.10 – Asymptotic expansions

8.10.1 – Poincaré's definition

Let $f(s)$ denote a single valued function defined in any angular area $|s| > R$, $\alpha \leqq \arg s \leqq \beta$, R being a positive constant. A series

$$\sum_{\nu=0}^{\infty} a_\nu s^{-\lambda_\nu} \tag{8.10–1}$$

where $\lambda_0, \lambda_1, \ldots$ are real numbers with the property

$$\lambda_0 < \lambda_1 < \ldots \to +\infty \tag{8.10–2}$$

is called an *asymptotic expansion* of $f(s)$, if for every fixed n the expression

$$s^{\lambda_n}\Big(f(s)-\sum_{\nu=0}^{n} a_\nu s^{-\lambda_\nu}\Big) \tag{8.10–3}$$

tends to zero as $|s| \to \infty$, $\arg s$ satisfying the condition mentioned above. This is Poincaré's definition.

It is customary to write

$$f(s) \sim \sum_{\nu=0}^{\infty} a_\nu s^{-\lambda_\nu}. \tag{8.10–4}$$

The series (8.10–1) may or may not be convergent.

A classical example of an asymptotic expansion is afforded by Binet's function $\mu(s)$. According to section 8.9.3 we have

$$\mu(s) \sim \sum_{\nu=1}^{\infty} (-1)^{\nu-1} \frac{B_{2\nu}}{(2\nu-1)2\nu} s^{-(2\nu-1)}, \tag{8.10–5}$$

valid whenever $|\arg s| \leqq \vartheta < \pi$.

Since $f(s)-\sum_{\nu=0}^{n} a_\nu s^{-\lambda_\nu}$ is $o(|s|^{-\lambda_n})$, a divergent asymptotic series is often more suited for numerical computation than a convergent series.

8.10.2 – Asymptotic expansion of log Γ (s)

It may happen that, even though the function $f(s)$ does not possess an asymptotic expansion of any type, we can find a function $g(s)$ and a function $h(s)$ such that

$$\frac{f(s)-g(s)}{h(s)} \sim \sum_{\nu=0}^{\infty} a_\nu s^{-\lambda_\nu}. \tag{8.10–6}$$

In this case we formally write

$$f(s) \sim g(s)+h(s) \sum_{\nu=0}^{\infty} a_\nu s^{-\lambda_\nu}. \tag{8.10–7}$$

Thus we may write for the logarithm of the gamma function

(8.10–8)

$$\log \Gamma(s) \sim (s-\tfrac{1}{2}) \log s - s + \tfrac{1}{2} \log 2\pi + \sum_{\nu=1}^{\infty} (-1)^{\nu-1} \frac{B_{2\nu}}{(2\nu-1)2\nu} s^{-(2\nu-1)}.$$

8.10.3 – Uniqueness

If a function $f(s)$ possesses an asymptotic expansion of a given type, then the coefficients a_n, $n = 0, 1, \ldots$, are uniquely determined. In fact, for a given value of n we have

$$s^{\lambda_n}(f(s)-a_0 s^{-\lambda_0}-a_1 s^{-\lambda_1}-\ldots-a_n s^{-\lambda_n}) \to 0$$

as $s \to \infty$ along a certain half-ray issuing from the origin. And so

$$s^{\lambda_n}(f(s)-a_0 s^{-\lambda_0}-\ldots-a_{n-1} s^{-\lambda_{n-1}}) \to a_n. \tag{8.10–9}$$

On taking successively $n = 0, 1, 2, \ldots$ the truth of the statement follows. In particular,

$$s^{\lambda_0} f(s) \to a_0.$$

On the other hand two different functions may possess the same asymptotic expansion. The functions $f(s)$ and $f(s)+e^{-s}$ have the same asymptotic expansion in an angular area included in the right half of the s-plane, for then $e^{-s} s^{\lambda n} \to 0$ as $s \to \infty$.

8.10.4 – Asymptotic expansion of Mittag-Leffler's function

For the sake of illustration we wish to discuss an asymptotic expansion of Mittag-Leffler's function $E_\alpha(s)$ introduced in section 6.13.1. We consider only the case $0 < \alpha < 2$. The special case $\alpha = 1$ is of little interest, for then the function coincides with e^s and possesses the expansion

$$E_1(s) \sim 0+0\cdot s^{-1}+0\cdot s^{-2}+\ldots, \qquad (8.10\text{–}10)$$

valid in the range $|\arg s| \geqq \vartheta > \frac{1}{2}\pi$ whereas

$$E_1(s) \sim e^s+0\cdot s^{-1}+0\cdot s^{-2}+\ldots \qquad (8.10\text{–}11)$$

in the range $|\arg s| \leqq \frac{1}{2}\pi$.

The function $E_\alpha(s)$ is intimately related to the integral (6.13–6), viz.,

$$E(s) = \frac{1}{2\pi i}\int_{L(1,\varphi)} \frac{e^t\, t^{\alpha-1}}{t^\alpha - s}\, dt,$$

the path of integration being the same as considered in section 6.13.2. It is assumed, of course, that $t^\alpha \neq s$ on the path of integration.

Now we may write

$$E(s) = \frac{-1}{2\pi i}\int_{L(1,\varphi)} \left(\frac{1}{s}+\frac{t^\alpha}{s^2}+\ldots+\frac{t^{(n-1)\alpha}}{s^n}-\frac{t^{n\alpha}}{s^n(t^\alpha - s)}\right) t^{\alpha-1} e^t\, dt.$$

By virtue of (6.13–3) we have, assuming $\alpha \neq 1$,

$$E(s) = \sum_{\nu=1}^{n} \frac{-s^{-\nu}}{\Gamma(1-\alpha\nu)} + R_n(s) \qquad (8.10\text{–}12)$$

where

$$R_n(s) = \frac{s^{-n}}{2\pi i}\int_{L(1,\varphi)} \frac{t^{(n+1)\alpha-1}\, e^t}{t^\alpha - s}\, dt, \qquad (8.10\text{–}13)$$

the integral on the right being convergent, since $|\arg t| > \frac{1}{2}\pi$ on the rectilinear parts of the path of integration. It is easily seen that

$$s^n R_n(s) \to 0$$

as $|s| \to \infty$, provided $|\arg s \pm \alpha\varphi| \geqq \delta > 0$. Hence, according to the results of section 6.13.3:

$$E_\alpha(s) \sim -\sum_{\nu=1}^{\infty} \frac{s^{-\nu}}{\Gamma(1-\alpha\nu)}, \qquad 0 < \alpha < 2, \quad \alpha \neq 1 \qquad (8.10\text{–}14)$$

provided that $\frac{1}{2}\alpha\pi < \vartheta \leqq |\arg s| \leqq \pi$. We take φ such that $\frac{1}{2}\alpha\pi < \alpha\varphi < \vartheta$. Again

$$E_\alpha(s) \sim \frac{1}{\alpha} e^{s^{1/\alpha}} - \sum_{\nu=1}^{\infty} \frac{s^{-\nu}}{\Gamma(1-\alpha\nu)}, \quad 0 < \alpha < 2, \quad \alpha \neq 1 \qquad (8.10\text{–}15)$$

provided that $|\arg s| \leqq \frac{1}{2}\alpha\pi$.

The series on the right of (8.10–14) is divergent, since $E_\alpha(s)$ is an integral function and hence $s = \infty$ is a singular point of the function.

8.10.5 – Integration of an asymptotic expansion

We wish to remark that an asymptotic series of a function can be integrated term-by-term in the following sense:

If $f(s)$ possesses the asymptotic expansion (8.10–1) *valid in the area $|s| > R > 0$, $\alpha \leqq \arg s \leqq \beta$, where $\lambda_0 > 1$, then*

$$\int_s^\infty f(t)\,dt \sim \sum_{\nu=0}^{\infty} \frac{-a_\nu}{1-\lambda_\nu} s^{1-\lambda_\nu} \qquad (8.10\text{–}16)$$

where the path of integration is a half-ray issuing from s and included in the angular area $\alpha \leqq \arg s \leqq \beta$, provided, of course, that the integral on the left of (8.10–16) exists.

By hypothesis we have

$$|f(s) - \sum_{\nu=0}^{n} a_\nu s^{-\lambda_\nu}| < \varepsilon |s|^{-\lambda_n},$$

when $|s|$ is sufficiently large, $\alpha \leqq \arg s \leqq \beta$, ε being an arbitrary positive number. Hence

$$\left| \int_s^\infty f(t)dt - \sum_{\nu=0}^{n} \frac{-a_\nu}{1-\lambda_\nu} s^{1-\lambda_\nu} \right| < \int_{|s|}^\infty \varepsilon t^{-\lambda_n} dt = \varepsilon \frac{-|s|^{1-\lambda_n}}{1-\lambda_n},$$

that is

$$|s|^{\lambda_n - 1} \left| \int_s^\infty f(t)dt - \sum_{\nu=0}^{n} \frac{-a_\nu}{1-\lambda_\nu} s^{1-\lambda_\nu} \right| < \frac{\varepsilon}{1-\lambda_n}.$$

This proves the assertion.

8.10.6 – Asymptotic expansion in the vicinity of the origin

By putting $t = 1/s$ in (8.10–1) we obtain the following definition of an asymptotic expansion of a function $f(t)$ as $t \to 0$.

Let $f(t)$ be single valued in an angular sector $0 < |t| < R$, $\alpha \leqq \arg t \leqq \beta$. A series

$$\sum_{\nu=0}^{\infty} a_\nu t^{\lambda_\nu} \qquad (8.10\text{–}17)$$

where $\lambda_0, \lambda_1, \ldots$ are numbers with the same property as mentioned in section 8.10.1 is called an asymptotic expansion of $f(t)$ as $t \to 0$ if for every fixed n the expression

$$t^{-\lambda_n}\left(f(t)-\sum_{\nu=0}^{n} a_\nu t^{\lambda_\nu}\right) \tag{8.10–18}$$

tends to zero as $t \to 0$, arg t remaining in the range mentioned above. In this case we also write

$$f(t) \sim \sum_{\nu=0}^{\infty} a_\nu t^{\lambda_\nu}. \tag{8.10–19}$$

8.11 – Asymptotic expansion of Laplace integrals

8.11.1 – Statement of the main theorem

Let $a(t)$ denote a function of the real positive variable possessing an asymptotic expansion

$$a(t) \sim \sum_{\nu=0}^{\infty} a_\nu t^{\lambda_\nu} \tag{8.11–1}$$

as $t \to 0$, where $-1 < \lambda_0 < \lambda_1 < \ldots \to \infty$. *Assuming that the Laplace integral*

$$\varphi(s) = \int_0^\infty e^{-st} a(t)\,dt \tag{8.11–2}$$

has a half-plane of simple convergence, then $\varphi(s)$ *possesses the asymptotic expansion*

$$\varphi(s) \sim \sum_{\nu=0}^{\infty} a_\nu \Gamma(\lambda_\nu+1) s^{-(\lambda_\nu+1)} \tag{8.11–3}$$

as $s \to \infty$ *in the angular area* $|\arg s| \leqq \vartheta < \frac{1}{2}\pi$.

The theorem states that the expansion (8.11–3) is obtained from (8.11–1) by term-by-term integration. For the proof of this important theorem we need some lemmas which we will state first.

8.11.2 – A first lemma

Let α *denote a positive number which exceeds the abscissa of simple convergence* σ_c *of the Laplace-integral* (8.11–2). *Then*

$$\int_0^\omega a(t)dt = o(e^{\alpha\omega}) \tag{8.11–4}$$

as $\omega \to \infty$.

If the abscissa of simple convergence is negative the integral

$$\int_0^\infty a(t)\,dt$$

exists and so the integral on the left of (8.11–4) is bounded. In this case the truth of the assertion is evident. It remains to consider the case $\sigma_c \geqq 0$. By virtue of (7.15–1) we have

$$\sigma_c = \limsup_{\omega \to \infty} \frac{\log \left| \int_0^\omega a(t)dt \right|}{\omega}$$

that is

$$\left| \int_0^\omega a(t)dt \right| < e^{(\sigma_c+\varepsilon)\omega},$$

ε being an arbitrary positive number and ω being sufficiently large. Since by hypothesis $\alpha > \sigma_c$ we can take ε in such a way that $\sigma_c+\varepsilon < \alpha$. Hence

$$\left| \int_0^\omega a(t)dt \right| < e^{\alpha\omega} e^{(\sigma_c+\varepsilon-\alpha)\omega} < \delta e^{\alpha\omega}$$

where δ is arbitrarily small and ω sufficiently large. This completes the proof of the assertion.

8.11.3 – A second lemma

For all values of s satisfying $\operatorname{Re} s > \max(0, \sigma_c)$ *we have*

$$\int_0^\infty e^{-st} a(t)dt = s\int_0^\infty e^{-st} \int_0^t a(u)du\, dt. \tag{8.11–5}$$

Let s be real and $s > \max(0, \sigma_c)$. Upon integrating by parts we get

$$\int_0^\omega e^{-st} a(t)dt = e^{-s\omega} \int_0^\omega a(t)dt + s\int_0^\omega e^{-st} \int_0^t a(u)du\, dt. \tag{8.11–6}$$

Now we take a number α such that $\sigma_c < \alpha < s$. By virtue of (8.11–4) the first term on the right tends to zero as $\omega \to \infty$ and we thus obtain (8.11–5) for real values of s. Referring to the theorem of section 7.16.1 and the identity principle we deduce the validity of the assertion in the general case of complex values of s.

8.11.4 – A third lemma

The function

$$\psi(s) = \int_1^\infty e^{-st} a(t)dt \tag{8.11–7}$$

is $O(e^{-\operatorname{Re} s})$ *as* $s \to \infty$ *in the angular area*

$$|\arg s| \leqq \vartheta < \tfrac{1}{2}\pi. \tag{8.11–8}$$

Consider the function $a^*(t)$ defined as follows

$$a^*(t) = \begin{cases} 0 \text{ when } 0 < t \leqq 1, \\ a(t) \text{ when } t > 1. \end{cases}$$

Then

$$\int_0^\infty e^{-st} a^*(t)dt = \int_1^\infty e^{-st} a(t)dt = \psi(s) \qquad (8.11\text{–}9)$$

and so, taking account of (8.11–5),

$$\psi(s) = s\int_0^\infty e^{-st}\int_0^t a^*(u)du\,dt = s\int_1^\infty e^{-st}\int_1^t a(u)du\,dt$$

whenever $\operatorname{Re} s > \max\,(0, \sigma_c)$. By virtue of the lemma of section 8.11.2

$$\int_1^t a(u)du = o(e^{\alpha t}), \qquad \alpha > \max\,(0, \sigma_c), \qquad t \to \infty$$

whence

$$\left|\int_1^t a(u)du\right| < Ce^{\alpha t}, \qquad t \geqq 1,$$

C being a suitable constant. As a consequence we have

$$|\psi(s)| \leqq |s|C\int_1^\infty e^{-(\operatorname{Re} s-\alpha)t}dt = \frac{C|s|}{\operatorname{Re} s-\alpha}\, e^{-(\operatorname{Re} s-\alpha)},$$

provided that $|s|$ is sufficiently large. Assuming $\operatorname{Re} s \geqq 2\alpha$ then in the angular area (8.11–8) the following inequality is valid:

$$\frac{|s|}{\operatorname{Re} s-\alpha} \leqq \frac{|s|}{\frac{1}{2}\operatorname{Re} s} \leqq 2\sec\vartheta$$

and so

$$|\psi(s)| \leqq 2\sec\vartheta \cdot Ce^{\alpha} e^{-\operatorname{Re} s}.$$

This proves the assertion.

8.11.5 – The fundamental lemma

After these preliminaries we can establish the following fundamental lemma:

Let

$$a(t)t^{-\beta} \to 0, \qquad \beta > -1 \qquad (8.11\text{–}10)$$

as $t \to 0$, $t > 0$. *If* $\varphi(s)$ *denotes the integral* (8.11–2) *then*

$$\varphi(s)s^{\beta+1} \to 0 \qquad (8.11\text{–}11)$$

as $s \to \infty$ *in any angular area* (8.11–8).

We may write

$$\int_0^\infty e^{-st} a(t)dt = \int_0^1 e^{-st} a(t)dt + \int_1^\infty e^{-st} a(t)dt.$$

The previous lemma asserts

$$\int_1^\infty e^{-st} a(t)\,dt = O(e^{-\operatorname{Re} s}).$$

In the angular area (8.11–8) we have

$$\frac{|s|}{\mathrm{Re}\, s} \leqq \sec \vartheta$$

and from

$$e^{-\mathrm{Re}\, s}|s|^{\beta+1} \leqq e^{-\mathrm{Re}\, s}(\sec \vartheta \cdot \mathrm{Re}\, s)^{\beta+1} \to 0,$$

as Re s increases indefinitely, we deduce

$$s^{\beta+1} \int_1^{\infty} e^{-st} a(t) dt \to 0$$

as $s \to \infty$ in the angular area mentioned above.

By hypothesis we may put

$$a(t) = \varepsilon(t) t^{\beta}$$

where $\varepsilon(t) \to 0$ as $t \to 0$. Hence

$$\chi(s) = \int_0^1 e^{-st} a(t) dt = \int_0^1 e^{-st} t^{\beta} \varepsilon(t) t dt = \int_0^{\delta} e^{-st} \varepsilon(t) t^{\beta} dt + \int_{\delta}^1 e^{-st} \varepsilon(t) t^{\beta} dt,$$

where δ denotes a number between 0 and 1. If ε is an arbitrary positive number we can take δ in such a way that $|\varepsilon(t)| \leqq \varepsilon$, whenever $0 < t \leqq \delta$. Assuming Re $s > 0$ and taking account of (7.17–11) we have

$$\left|\int_0^{\delta} e^{-st} \varepsilon(t) t^{\beta} dt\right| \leqq \varepsilon \int_0^{\infty} e^{-t\,\mathrm{Re}\, s} t^{\beta} dt = \varepsilon \frac{\Gamma(\beta+1)}{(\mathrm{Re}\, s)^{\beta+1}}.$$

Again

$$\left|\int_{\delta}^1 e^{-st} \varepsilon(t) t^{\beta} dt\right| \leqq e^{-\delta\,\mathrm{Re}\, s} \int_{\delta}^1 |\varepsilon(t)| t^{\beta} dt = A e^{-\delta\,\mathrm{Re}\, s},$$

A being a constant. Hence

$$|\chi(s) s^{\beta+1}| \leqq \varepsilon \Gamma(\beta+1) \left(\frac{|s|}{\mathrm{Re}\, s}\right)^{\beta+1} + A e^{-\delta\,\mathrm{Re}\, s}|s|^{\beta+1}$$

$$\leqq \varepsilon \Gamma(\beta+1) \sec^{\beta+1} \vartheta + A e^{-\delta\,\mathrm{Re}\, s}(\sec \vartheta \cdot \mathrm{Re}\, s)^{\beta+1}.$$

This completes the proof of the assertion.

8.11.6 – Proof of the main theorem

Now the proof of the theorem stated in section 8.11.1 can be given in a few lines. By hypothesis we have

$$\left(a(t) - \sum_{\nu=0}^{n} a_{\nu} t^{\lambda_{\nu}}\right) t^{-\lambda_n} \to 0 \qquad (8.11\text{–}12)$$

as $t \to 0$. Replacing in the fundamental lemma of section 8.11.5 $a(t)$ by the expression between brackets on the left of (8.11–12) and β by λ_n we get

$$s^{\lambda_n+1}\left(\int_0^\infty e^{-st}a(t)dt - \sum_{\nu=0}^{n} a_\nu \int_0^\infty e^{-st}t^{\lambda_\nu}dt\right) \to 0$$

as $s \to \infty$ in the described manner. Taking account of (7.17–11) the assertion follows.

8.11.7 – Differentiation of an asymptotic expansion

The function represented by (8.11–2) is holomorphic throughout the half-plane of simple convergence (7.16.1) of the integral. In this case *an asymptotic expansion of the derivative is obtained by term-by-term differentiation of* (8.11–2). In fact, according to (7.16–2) we have

$$\varphi'(s) = -\int_0^\infty e^{-st}\, t\, a(t)dt. \tag{8.11–13}$$

On the other hand it follows from (8.11–1) that

$$t a(t) \sim \sum_{\nu=0}^{\infty} a_\nu t^{\lambda_\nu+1}$$

as $t \to 0$. Hence, by virtue of the theorem of section 8.11.1

$$\varphi'(s) \sim -\sum_{\nu=0}^{\infty} a_\nu \Gamma(\lambda_\nu+2)s^{-(\lambda_\nu+2)} = -\sum_{\nu=0}^{\infty} a_\nu(\lambda_\nu+1)\,\Gamma(\lambda_\nu+1)s^{-(\lambda_\nu+2)},$$

the desired result.

In general it does not follow that the formally derived asymptotic series of $f(s)$ represents $f'(s)$ asymptotically. A counter-example is the following. The function $f(s) = e^{-s}\sin\exp s$ possesses the asymptotic series $\sum_{\nu=0}^{\infty} 0 \cdot s^{-\nu}$ for positive real values of s. But $f'(s) = -e^{-s}\sin\exp s + \cos\exp s$ does not tend to any limit as $s \to \infty$ along the positive real axis.

8.12 – Illustrative examples

8.12.1 – Elementary example

A trivial example of an asymptotic expansion of a Laplace integral is provided by the function

$$\frac{1}{s+1} = \int_0^\infty e^{-st}e^{-t}dt. \tag{8.12–1}$$

Since

$$e^{-t} = \sum_{\nu=0}^{\infty} \frac{(-1)^\nu}{\nu!}t^\nu,$$

we have

$$\frac{1}{s+1} \sim \sum_{\nu=0}^{\infty} (-1)^{\nu} s^{-(\nu+1)}, \tag{8.12–2}$$

valid in the area $|\arg s| \leqq \vartheta < \frac{1}{2}\pi$. Actually the expansion holds in a larger area, since the series on the right is convergent for $|s| > 1$.

8.12.2 – Expansion of Binet's function

A more interesting example is provided by Binet's function $\mu(s)$ represented by the integral (7.17–6). According to (8.8–1) we have

$$\left(\frac{1}{e^t-1} - \frac{1}{t} + \frac{1}{2}\right)\frac{1}{t} = \sum_{\nu=1}^{\infty} (-1)^{\nu-1} \frac{B_{2\nu}}{(2\nu)!} t^{2\nu-2},$$

the series being convergent for $|t| < 2\pi$. Hence

$$\mu(s) \sim \sum_{\nu=1}^{\infty} (-1)^{\nu-1} \frac{B_{2\nu}}{(2\nu)!} (2\nu-2)!\, s^{-(2\nu-1)}. \tag{8.12–3}$$

This is the same series as obtained in section 8.9.3. Until now we can only state the validity for $|\arg s| \leqq \vartheta < \frac{1}{2}\pi$.

Upon formal differentiation we get

$$\mu'(s) \sim \sum_{\nu=1}^{\infty} (-1)^{\nu} \frac{B_{2\nu}}{2\nu} s^{-2\nu}$$

and so we obtain an expansion of the function $\Psi(s)$ of section 4.8.1

$$\Psi(s) \sim \log s - \frac{1}{2s} + \sum_{\nu=1}^{\infty} (-1)^{\nu} \frac{B_{2\nu}}{2\nu} s^{-2\nu}, \quad |\arg s| \leqq \vartheta < \tfrac{1}{2}\pi, \tag{8.12–4}$$

this result being in accordance with (8.6–13) when $s = 1$.

8.12.3 – Expansion of the incomplete gamma function

The expansion

$$(1+t)^{z-1} = \sum_{\nu=0}^{\infty} \binom{z-1}{\nu} t^{\nu} \tag{8.12–5}$$

where

$$\binom{z-1}{n} = \frac{(z-1)(z-2)\ldots(z-n)}{n!},$$

z being a complex number, enables us to obtain an asymptotic expansion of the incomplete gamma function $Q(s, z)$, for we may represent this function by the integral (7.19–8). Hence

$$Q(s, z) \sim e^{-s} s^{z} \sum_{\nu=0}^{\infty} \binom{z-1}{\nu} \nu!\, s^{-(\nu+1)}, \qquad |\arg s| \leqq \vartheta < \tfrac{1}{2}\pi. \tag{8.12–6}$$

Many interesting functions may be derived from $Q(s, z)$ by taking special values of z. We wish to discuss amply the case $z = 0$.

In section 7.19.6 we encountered the infinitely many valued function Ei s and it is readily seen that one of the branches of $-\mathrm{Ei}\,(-s)$ coincides with $Q(s, 0)$. Hence this branch possesses the asymptotic expansion

$$\boxed{-\mathrm{Ei}\,(-s) \sim \frac{e^{-s}}{s} \sum_{\nu=0}^{\infty} (-1)^{\nu} \nu!\, s^{-\nu},} \qquad |\arg s| \leqq \vartheta < \tfrac{1}{2}\pi. \quad (8.12\text{–}7)$$

8.12.4 – The modified exponential integral

In many cases it is more convenient to introduce another function coinciding with $-Q(-s, 0)$ up to an additive constant. The function $Q(s, z)$ has only been defined in the region $s \neq 0$, $-\pi < \arg s < \pi$. Hence $Q(-s, 0)$ is not unambiguously defined, unless we agree on the argument of $-s$. This may be done in the following way. By the symbol $s e^{\varepsilon\pi i}$, where $\varepsilon = \pm 1$, we denote a number whose argument is $\arg s + \varepsilon\pi$, such that this argument has also its principal value. As a consequence $\varepsilon = +1$, when $\arg s \leqq 0$, and $\varepsilon = -1$, when $\arg s > 0$.

Now we may introduce the single valued function

$$\overline{\mathrm{Ei}}\, s = -Q(s\, e^{\varepsilon\pi i}, 0) - \varepsilon\pi i. \qquad (8.12\text{–}8)$$

From (7.19–7) we easily find

$$\boxed{\overline{\mathrm{Ei}}\, s = \gamma + \log s + \sum_{\nu=1}^{\infty} \frac{s^{\nu}}{\nu!\,\nu},} \qquad s + |s| \neq 0, \qquad (8.12\text{–}9)$$

taking account of $\log (s e^{\varepsilon\pi i}) = \log s + \varepsilon\pi i$. It is plain that one branch of Ei s coincides with $\overline{\mathrm{Ei}}\, s + \pi i$. Moreover, $\overline{\mathrm{Ei}}\, s$ has a meaning when s is real and positive.

8.12.5 – Asymptotic expansion of $\overline{\mathrm{Ei}}\, s$

We proceed to derive an asymptotic expansion of the function introduced previously. Our first task consists in finding a representation of $\overline{\mathrm{Ei}}\, s$ as a Laplace integral. By a reasoning similar to that of section 7.19.7 we see that the function $Q(s, 0)$ can be represented by

$$\int_s^{\infty} \frac{e^{-t}}{t}\, dt$$

where the path of integration avoids the origin and consists of an arc connecting s with any point s^*, followed by a half-ray issuing from s^* and making an angle with the positive real axis which does not exceed numerically $\frac{1}{2}\pi$, (fig. 8.12–1). Now we replace this path by a half ray along a line through s and the origin.

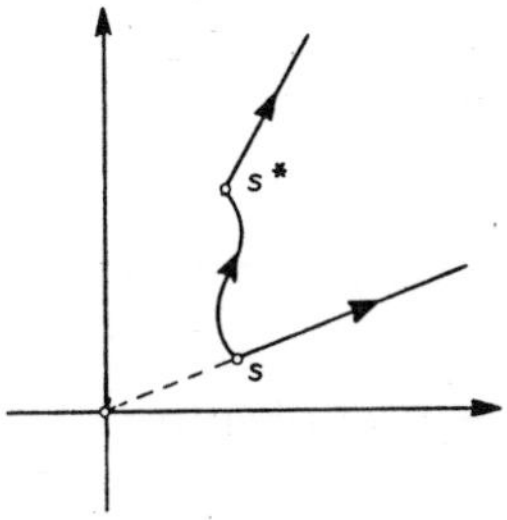

Fig. 8.12–1. Modification of the path of integration for $Q(s, 0)$

It may happen that then the origin is on the path, viz. in the cases $\arg s > \frac{1}{2}\pi$ or $\arg s < -\frac{1}{2}\pi$. It will be sufficient to consider the first case more closely. If the path of integration is the half-ray

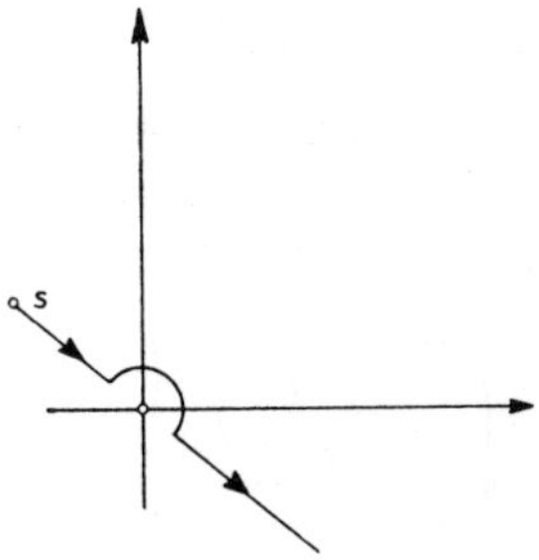

Fig. 8.12–2. Path of integration for $Q(s, 0)$ when $\arg s > \frac{1}{2}\pi$

issuing from s and indented at the origin by a small semi-circle of radius ϱ, (fig. 8.12–2), we evidently have

$$Q(s, 0) = \int_{s}^{\varrho s/|s|} \frac{e^{-t}}{t} dt + \int_{-\varrho s/|s|}^{\infty} \frac{e^{-t}}{t} dt + i \int_{\arg s}^{\arg s - \pi} e^{-\varrho e^{i\theta}} d\theta,$$

whence, letting $\varrho \to 0$,

$$Q(s, 0) = \int_{s}^{\infty} \frac{e^{-t}}{t} dt - \pi i,$$

where the integral is taken on a linear path and is to be understood as a Cauchy-principal value.

Similarly we have, (fig. 8.12–3),

$$Q(s, 0) = \int_{s}^{\infty} \frac{e^{-t}}{t} dt + \pi i, \qquad \text{when } \arg s < -\tfrac{1}{2}\pi.$$

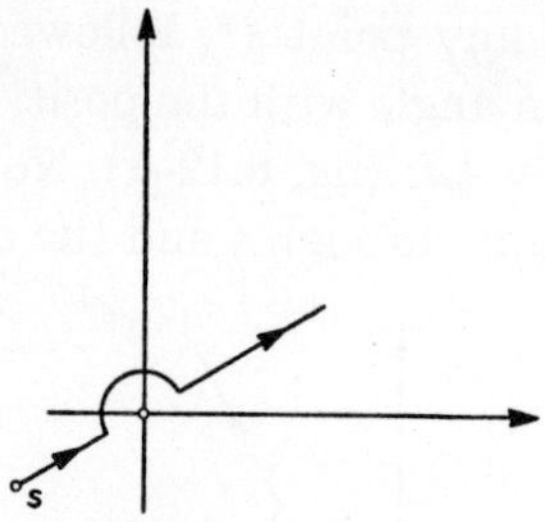

Fig. 8.12–3. Path of integration for $Q(s, 0)$ when $\arg s < -\frac{1}{2}\pi$

We may combine these results into

$$Q(s\,\mathrm{e}^{\varepsilon\pi i}, 0) = \int_{-s}^{\infty} \frac{\mathrm{e}^{-t}}{t}\,dt - \varepsilon\pi i \tag{8.12–10}$$

provided that $\mathrm{Re}\, s > 0$. And so

$$\overline{\mathrm{Ei}}\, s = -\int_{-s}^{\infty} \frac{\mathrm{e}^{-t}}{t}\,dt. \tag{8.12–11}$$

The path of integration is represented by $t = -s+su$, $u > 0$. Inserting this into (8.12–11) and replacing afterwards u by t we obtain the desired expression for $\overline{\mathrm{Ei}}\, s$, viz.

$$\boxed{\overline{\mathrm{Ei}}\, s = \mathrm{e}^{s} \int_{0}^{\infty} \mathrm{e}^{-st} \frac{1}{1-t}\,dt,} \qquad \mathrm{Re}\, s > 0, \tag{8.12–12}$$

the integral being a Cauchy principal value.

In the general theory of Laplace integrals we assumed that the function $a(t)$ is bounded in any finite interval $0 < t_1 \leqq t \leqq t_2$. It is, however, easily shown that the results are also valid, when $t_0 > 0$ is a point of infinity, provided that

$$\lim_{\delta\to 0} \left(\int_{a}^{t_0-\delta} |a(t)|\,dt + \int_{t_0+\delta}^{b} |a(t)|\,dt \right), \qquad a < t_0 < b$$

exists, in other words, that the Cauchy principal value $\int_{a}^{b} |a(t)|\,dt$ has a meaning at $t = t_0$. In our example this condition is satisfied at $t_0 = 1$. Hence, we may infer that

$$\boxed{\overline{\mathrm{Ei}}\, s \sim \frac{\mathrm{e}^{s}}{s} \sum_{\nu=0}^{\infty} \nu!\, s^{-\nu},} \qquad |\arg s| \leqq \vartheta < \tfrac{1}{2}\pi. \tag{8.12–13}$$

8.12.6 – Asymptotic expansions of the cosine integral and the sine integral

Let now Ei is denote the branch of the exponential integral coinciding with $-Q(-is, 0)$. Then

$$\mathrm{Ei}\, is = -\int_{-is}^{\infty} \frac{e^{-t}}{t}\, dt, \qquad \mathrm{Re}\, s > 0,$$

the path of integration being a half-ray issuing from $-is$ and rep-

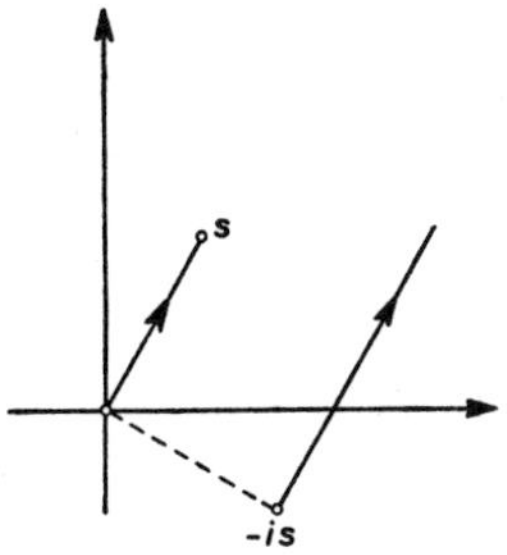

Fig. 8.12–4. Path of integration for Ei is

resented by $t = -is+us$, where u is positive, (fig. 8.12–4). Hence, replacing afterwards u by t

$$\mathrm{Ei}\, i s = -e^{is} \int_0^{\infty} e^{-st} \frac{1}{t-i}\, dt,$$

which may be written as

$$\mathrm{Ei}\, i s = -(\cos s + i \sin s)\{A(s)+iB(s)\} \tag{8.12–14}$$

where

$$A(s) = \int_0^{\infty} e^{-st} \frac{t}{1+t^2}\, dt, \qquad B(s) = \int_0^{\infty} e^{-st} \frac{1}{1+t^2}\, dt. \tag{8.12–15}$$

Taking account of (7.19–16) we may infer that

$$\mathrm{ci}\, s = -A(s) \cos s + B(s) \sin s \tag{8.12–16}$$

and

$$\mathrm{si}\, s = -A(s) \sin s - B(s) \cos s, \tag{8.12–17}$$

since the functions occurring in these equations are real for positive real values of s. In (8.12–16) a single valued branch of ci s is to be taken.

From (8.12–15) we easily obtain the following asymptotic expansion for the integral cosine and the integral sine:

(8.12–18)

$$\operatorname{ci} s \sim \frac{\cos s}{s} \sum_{\nu=0}^{\infty} (-1)^{\nu+1} (2\nu+1)!\, s^{-(2\nu+1)} + \frac{\sin s}{s} \sum_{\nu=0}^{\infty} (-1)^{\nu} (2\nu)!\, s^{-2\nu}$$

and

(8.12–19)

$$\operatorname{si} s \sim \frac{\sin s}{s} \sum_{\nu=0}^{\infty} (-1)^{\nu+1} (2\nu+1)!\, s^{-(2\nu+1)} + \frac{\cos s}{s} \sum_{\nu=0}^{\infty} (-1)^{\nu+1} (2\nu)!\, s^{-2\nu},$$

where $|\arg s| \leqq \vartheta < \frac{1}{2}\pi$. Roughly speaking the function ci s behaves like $\sin s/s$ and si s like $-\cos s/s$ for large values of $|s|$.

8.12.7 – The sum of the squares of ci s and si s

Finally we wish to discuss the function

$$f(s) = \operatorname{ci}^2 s + \operatorname{si}^2 s. \qquad (8.12\text{–}20)$$

By virtue of (7.19–19), (7.19–20), (8.12–16) and (8.12–17) we have

$$f'(s) = \frac{2(\cos s \operatorname{ci} s + \sin s \operatorname{si} s)}{s} = -\frac{2A(s)}{s}.$$

On the other hand we have according to (8.12–15) and (8.11–5)

$$2A(s) = \int_0^{\infty} e^{-st} \frac{d}{dt} \log (1+t^2) dt = s \int_0^{\infty} e^{-st} \log (1+t^2) dt,$$

and hence $-2A(s)/s$ is also the derivative of

$$\int_0^{\infty} e^{-st} \frac{\log (1+t^2)}{t} dt,$$

as may be deduced utilizing (7.16–2). We may even conclude that $f(s)$ and the last integral coincide, since according to section 7.20.1 a Laplace integral tends to zero as $s \to \infty$ in the angular area $\arg s \leqq \vartheta < \frac{1}{2}\pi$, while $f(s)$ tends to zero like s^{-2}, as follows from (8.12–18) and (8.12–19). Thus we arrive at the interesting formula

$$\operatorname{ci}^2 s + \operatorname{si}^2 s = \int_0^{\infty} e^{-st} \frac{\log (1+t^2)}{t} dt, \qquad \operatorname{Re} s > 0. \qquad (8.12\text{–}21)$$

It is not difficult to obtain also an asymptotic expansion for the function on the left.

8.13 – Rotation of the path of integration

8.13.1 – A LEMMA

Hitherto we only considered Laplace integrals evaluated along the positive real axis. Sometimes it is convenient to take as a path of integration another half-ray issuing from O, (fig. 8.13–1). We shall prove the following theorem.

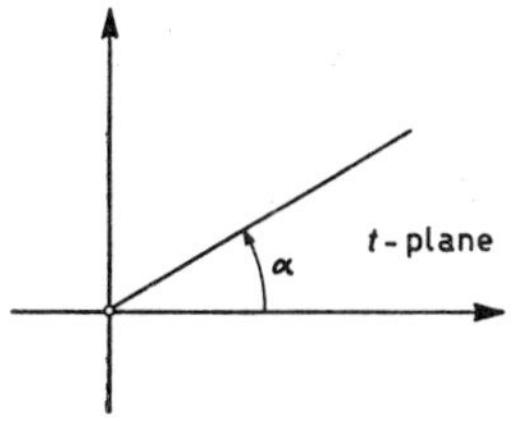

Fig. 8.13–1. Rotation of the path of integration in the t-plane

If along the ray $\arg t = \alpha$ *the function* $a(t)$ *satisfies the conditions* (i) *and* (ii) *of section* 7.14.1, *while*

$$a(t) = O(e^{\varrho |t|}), \qquad \varrho > 0, \qquad \text{as } t \to \infty, \tag{8.13–1}$$

then the integral

$$\int_0^{\infty e^{i\alpha}} e^{-st} a(t) dt \tag{8.13–2}$$

taken along the path $\arg t = \alpha$ *is convergent in the half-plane*

$$\operatorname{Re}(s e^{i\alpha}) > \varrho, \tag{8.13–3}$$

that is a half-plane bounded by a line perpendicular to the ray $\arg s = -\alpha$, while $|s| > \varrho$, (fig. 8.13–1). In fact, by putting $t = ue^{i\alpha}$,

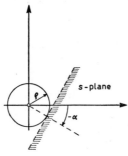

Fig. 8.13–2. The half-plane of convergence corresponding to a rotated path of integration

u being real and positive, the integral (8.13–2) may be written as

$$e^{i\alpha} \int_0^{\infty} a(ue^{i\alpha}) e^{-su e^{i\alpha}} du \tag{8.13–4}$$

and since $|a(t)| < A e^{\varrho|t|}$ when $|t|$ is sufficiently large, A being a suitably chosen constant, the integral (8.13–4) turns out to be convergent whenever Re $(s e^{i\alpha}) > \varrho$. The remark that the integral represents a function holomorphic throughout this half-plane, deserves mention.

8.13.2 – Rotation of the path of integration

In many important cases the function $a(t)$ satisfies the following conditions:

(i) It is holomorphic throughout an angular region, (fig. 8.13–3),

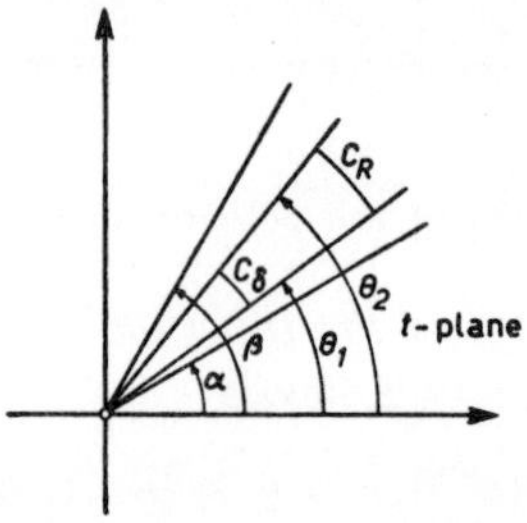

Fig. 8.13–3. Angular region (8.13–3) in the t-plane

$$\alpha < \arg t < \beta, \qquad |t| > 0, \qquad \text{where } \beta - \alpha < \pi. \tag{8.13–5}$$

(ii) Along any line $\arg t = \vartheta$, $\alpha < \vartheta < \beta$, the integral

$$\int_{\delta}^{\infty e^{i\vartheta}} |a(t)| dt$$

tends to a (finite) limit as $\delta \to 0$.

(iii) For sufficiently large $|t|$ the inequality

$$|a(t)| < A e^{\varrho|t|}, \qquad \varrho \geqq 0 \tag{8.13–6}$$

holds, provided that t is in the region (8.13–5).

(iv) There is a real number $\lambda > -1$ such that $|a(t)t^{-\lambda}|$ remains bounded as $t \to 0$ within the region (8.13–5).

These conditions imply the following theorem:

There exists a function $f(s)$ which is represented by (8.13–2) *along every half-ray* $\arg t = \vartheta$, $\alpha < \vartheta < \beta$ *and is holomorphic in the region* Re $s\, e^{i\vartheta} > \varrho$, $\alpha < \vartheta < \beta$, (fig. 8.13–4).

First we consider the integral

$$\int_{C_\delta} e^{-st} a(t) dt \tag{8.13–7}$$

along the circular arc $C_\delta : t = \delta e^{i\theta}$, $\alpha < \theta_1 \leqq \theta \leqq \theta_2 < \beta$, δ being a small positive number. By hypothesis $a(t) = b(t)t^\lambda$ where $b(t)$

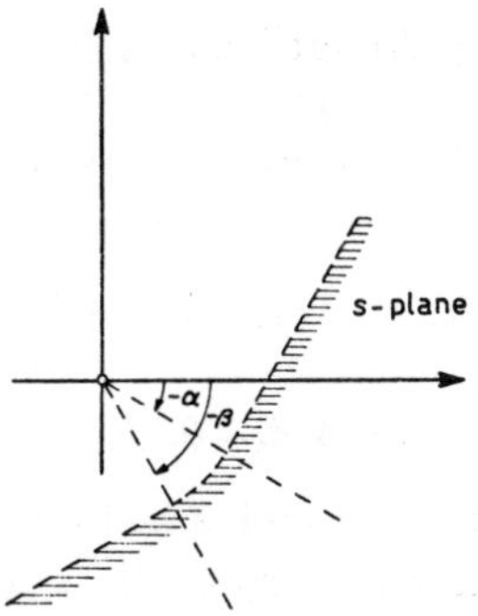

Fig. 8.13–4. Region of convergence corresponding to the region (8.13–5)

is bounded as $t \to 0$ within the region (8.13–5). If t stands for $\delta e^{i\theta}$ the integral takes the form

$$i\delta^{1+\lambda}\int_{\theta_1}^{\theta_2} e^{-st}b(t)\,e^{i\theta(1+\lambda)}\,d\theta$$

and tends to zero as $\delta \to 0$.

Now we consider the integral (8.13–7) taken along a contour C consisting of the segments $\arg t = \theta_1$, $\arg t = \theta_2$, $|t| \leqq R$, and the circular arc C_R. By virtue of Cauchy's integral theorem and the result stated above we have

$$\int_0^{Re^{i\theta_1}} e^{-st}a(t)dt - \int_0^{Re^{i\theta_2}} e^{-st}a(t)dt = \int_{C_R} e^{-st}a(t)dt. \qquad (8.13\text{–}8)$$

Since $\beta-\alpha < \pi$ the two half-planes Re $(se^{i\theta_1}) > \varrho$ and Re $(se^{i\theta_2})$

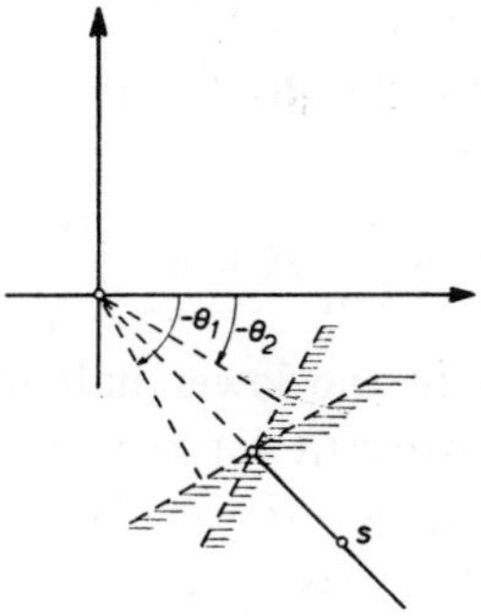

Fig. 8.13–5. Overlapping of two half-planes of convergence

$> \varrho$ have a region in common, (fig. 8.13–5). In particular the points

$$\arg s = -\tfrac{1}{2}(\theta_1+\theta_2), \qquad |s| \cos \tfrac{1}{2}(\theta_1-\theta_2) > \varrho \qquad (8.13\text{–}9)$$

are included in both half-planes. Let s be a point of this kind. For every t on C_R we have Re $st = |s|\, R \cos \{\theta-\tfrac{1}{2}(\theta_1+\theta_2)\} \geqq |s|R$

$\cos \frac{1}{2}(\theta_2-\theta_1)$. Assuming $|R|$ sufficiently large the condition (8.13–6) asserts

$$|a(R)| < A e^{\varrho R}.$$

Hence

$$\left|\int_{C_R} e^{-st} a(t)dt\right| \leq A(\theta_2-\theta_1)Re^{-|s|R\cos\frac{1}{2}(\theta_2-\theta_1)+\varrho R}$$

$$= A(\theta_2-\theta_1)Re^{-R\{|s|\cos\frac{1}{2}(\theta_2-\theta_1)-\varrho\}}$$

and because we can take $|s|$ in such a fashion that $|s| \cos \frac{1}{2}(\theta_2-\theta_1)>\varrho$ this last expression tends to zero as $R \to \infty$. And so the equation (8.13–8) leads to the conclusion

$$\int_0^{\infty e^{i\theta_1}} e^{-st} a(t)dt = \int_0^{\infty e^{i\theta_2}} e^{-st} a(t)dt \qquad (8.13\text{–}10)$$

on the half-ray (8.13–9) when $|s|$ exceeds a certain number. Both sides of (8.13–10) represent holomorphic functions as s varies. As a consequence they coincide throughout the region common to both half-planes mentioned above. This completes the proof of the theorem.

8.13.3 – Applications

An interesting application of the method of rotating the path of integration will be discussed now. The starting point will be the function $Q(s, 0)$ represented as a Laplace integral (7.19–8) with $z = 0$,

$$Q(s, 0) = e^{-s}\int_0^\infty e^{-st}\frac{1}{1+t}dt, \qquad \operatorname{Re} s > 0.$$

We take as path of integration the positive imaginary axis and we obtain the function

$$ie^{-s}\int_0^\infty e^{-ist}\frac{1}{1+it}dt = e^{-s}\int_0^\infty e^{-ist}\frac{t+i}{1+t^2}dt \qquad (8.13\text{–}11)$$

coinciding with $Q(s, 0)$ in the lower half of the complex s-plane. The integral is still convergent for real positive values of s and is continuous. Replacing i by $-i$ we obtain

$$e^{-s}\int_0^\infty e^{ist}\frac{t-i}{1+t^2}dt \qquad (8.13\text{–}12)$$

representing $Q(s, 0)$ throughout the upper part of the s-plane. For real positive values of s the integrals (8.13–11) and (8.13–12) coincide. Equating real and imaginary parts we readily find

$$\int_0^\infty \frac{\cos st}{1+t^2}dt = \int_0^\infty \frac{t \sin st}{1+t^2}dt \qquad (8.13\text{–}13)$$

in addition with

$$\int_0^\infty \frac{t \cos st + \sin st}{1+t^2}\,dt = e^s Q(s, 0) = -e^s \operatorname{Ei}(-s). \qquad (8.13\text{–}14)$$

On the other hand, s being still positive, taking account of (8.12–8) and (8.13–11),

$$Q(se^{-\pi i}, 0) = -\overline{\operatorname{Ei}}\, s - \pi i = e^s \int_0^\infty e^{-ist} \frac{t-i}{1+t^2}\,dt$$

$$= e^s \int_0^\infty \frac{(t \cos st - \sin st) - i(\cos st + t \sin st)}{1+t^2}\,dt$$

where $Q(se^{-\pi i}, 0)$ is defined by continuity.

Equating real and imaginary parts we get

$$\int_0^\infty \frac{t \cos st - \sin st}{1+t^2}\,dt = -e^{-s}\, \overline{\operatorname{Ei}}\, s \qquad (8.13\text{–}15)$$

and

$$\int_0^\infty \frac{\cos st + t \sin st}{1+t^2}\,dt = \pi e^{-s}. \qquad (8.13\text{–}16)$$

Combining (8.13–16) and (8.13–13) we may infer that

$$\int_0^\infty \frac{\cos st}{1+t^2}\,dt = \int_0^\infty \frac{t \sin st}{1+t^2}\,dt = \tfrac{1}{2}\pi e^{-s}, \qquad s > 0, \qquad (8.13\text{–}17)$$

in accordance with (3.6–6) and (3.6–8). The equations (8.13–14) and (8.13–15) yield

$$\boxed{\int_0^\infty \frac{t \cos st}{1+t^2}\,dt = -\tfrac{1}{2}e^{-s}\, \overline{\operatorname{Ei}}\, s - \tfrac{1}{2}e^s \operatorname{Ei}(-s)} \qquad (8.13\text{–}18)$$

and

$$\boxed{\int_0^\infty \frac{\sin st}{1+t^2}\,dt = \tfrac{1}{2}e^{-s}\, \overline{\operatorname{Ei}}\, s - \tfrac{1}{2}e^s \operatorname{Ei}(-s),} \qquad (8.13\text{–}19)$$

where s is assumed to be positive.

8.13.4 – Extension of the theorem of 8.11.1

We proceed to state a general theorem about asymptotic expansions which is an extension of the theorem of section 8.11.1.

Suppose that $a(t)$ satisfies the conditions (i), (ii) and (iii) of section 8.13.2. Let

$$a(t) \sim \sum_{\nu=0}^{\infty} a_\nu t^{\lambda_\nu}, \qquad -1 < \lambda_0 < \lambda_1 < \ldots \to \infty \qquad (8.13\text{–}20)$$

as $t \to 0$ along every line $\arg t = \vartheta$, $\alpha < \vartheta < \beta$. Then, evidently also (iv) is satisfied and the integral (8.13–2) represents a function $f(s)$ holomorphic throughout the region $\alpha - \frac{1}{2}\pi < \arg s < \beta + \frac{1}{2}\pi$. Now we assert that *the function* $f(s)$ *possesses an asymptotic expansion*

$$f(s) \sim \sum_{\nu=0}^{\infty} a_\nu \Gamma(1+\lambda_\nu) s^{-(1+\lambda_\nu)} \tag{8.13–21}$$

as $|s| \to \infty$, *provided that* $\alpha - \frac{1}{2}\pi + \delta \leqq \arg s \leqq \beta + \frac{1}{2}\pi - \delta$, δ *being any positive number.*

In the half-plane $\operatorname{Re}(s\mathrm{e}^{i\vartheta}) > \varrho$ we have

$$\int_0^{\infty \mathrm{e}^{i\vartheta}} \mathrm{e}^{-st} a(t)\,dt = \mathrm{e}^{i\vartheta} \int_0^{\infty} \mathrm{e}^{-s\mathrm{e}^{i\vartheta}|t|} a(|t|\mathrm{e}^{i\vartheta})\,d|t|.$$

By virtue of (8.13–20) we may write

$$a(|t|\mathrm{e}^{i\vartheta}) \sim \sum_{\nu=0}^{\infty} a_\nu |t|^{\lambda_\nu} \mathrm{e}^{i\lambda_\nu \vartheta}.$$

Next we apply the theorem of section 8.11.1. This yields

$$f(s) \sim \mathrm{e}^{i\vartheta} \sum_{\nu=0}^{\infty} a_\nu \mathrm{e}^{i\lambda_\nu \vartheta} \Gamma(1+\lambda_\nu)(s\mathrm{e}^{i\vartheta})^{-(1+\lambda_\nu)} = \sum_{\nu=0}^{\infty} a_\nu \Gamma(1+\lambda_\nu) s^{-(1+\lambda_\nu)},$$

the desired result.

Taking account of the above theorem we easily see that the expansions discussed in the previous section are certainly valid in the range $|\arg s| \leqq \vartheta < \pi$. Because they are power series they cannot hold for all values of $\arg s$, unless the function is regular at $s = \infty$. An example of this kind is provided by (8.12–2) the series being convergent whenever $|s| > 1$.

8.13.5 – The error function

In this section we wish to discuss an important function. In the expression (7.19–1) for $P(s, z)$ we take $z = \frac{1}{2}$ and replace s by s^2. We thus obtain the function

$$P(s^2, \tfrac{1}{2}) = \int_0^{s^2} \mathrm{e}^{-t} t^{-\frac{1}{2}}\,dt = 2\int_0^{s} \mathrm{e}^{-t^2}\,dt, \tag{8.13–22}$$

this function being holomorphic throughout the entire s-plane.

Letting $s \to \infty$ along a half-ray which makes an angle with the positive real axis being numerically less than $\frac{1}{4}\pi$ we readily find

$$P(\infty, \tfrac{1}{2}) = 2\int_0^{\infty} \mathrm{e}^{-t^2}\,dt = \Gamma(\tfrac{1}{2}) = \sqrt{\pi}. \tag{8.13–23}$$

Now we introduce the function

$$\boxed{\operatorname{erf} s = \frac{2}{\sqrt{\pi}} \int_0^s e^{-t^2}\, dt,} \tag{8.13–24}$$

the so-called (Gaussian) *error function.*

Expanding the integrand as a power series we readily obtain

$$\boxed{\operatorname{erf} s = \frac{2}{\sqrt{\pi}} \sum_{\nu=0}^{\infty} \frac{(-1)^\nu}{\nu!} \frac{s^{2\nu+1}}{2\nu+1}.} \tag{8.13–25}$$

Besides (8.11–24) we also consider the *complementary error function*

$$\boxed{\operatorname{erfc} s = 1 - \operatorname{erf} s} \tag{8.13–26}$$

and it is plain that this function may be represented by

$$\operatorname{erfc} s = \frac{2}{\sqrt{\pi}} \int_s^\infty e^{-t^2}\, dt, \tag{8.13–27}$$

the path of integration being a half-ray issuing from s and extending to the right. It is not difficult to show that it coincides with $Q(s^2, \frac{1}{2})\pi^{-\frac{1}{2}}$ for Re $s > 0$. This remark leads to the assertion that an asymptotic expansion of erf s is found from (8.12–6) by inserting $z = \frac{1}{2}$ and replacing s by s^2. Observing that

$$\binom{-\frac{1}{2}}{n} = (-1)^n \frac{1 \cdot 3 \cdot \ldots \cdot (2n-1)}{2^n n!} = (-1)^n \frac{(2n)!}{2^{2n}(n!)^2}$$

we readily find

$$\operatorname{erfc} s \sim \frac{e^{-s^2}}{\sqrt{\pi}} \sum_{\nu=0}^{\infty} (-1)^\nu \frac{(2\nu)!}{4^\nu \nu!} s^{-(2\nu+1)}. \tag{8.13–28}$$

We proceed to prove this result in a straight-forward manner. First we represent erfc s as a Laplace integral. On the path of integration we have $t = u+s$, $u > 0$. Hence

$$\int_s^\infty e^{-t^2}\, dt = \int_0^\infty e^{-(u+s)^2}\, du = e^{-s^2} \int_0^\infty e^{-2us} e^{-u^2}\, du,$$

whence, replacing $2u$ by t, assuming now $t > 0$,

$$\operatorname{erfc} s = \frac{e^{-s^2}}{\sqrt{\pi}} \int_0^\infty e^{-st} e^{-\frac{1}{4}t^2}\, dt. \tag{8.13–29}$$

The function $e^{-\frac{1}{4}t^2}$ satisfies the conditions of section 8.13.4 whenever $|\arg t| \leqq \vartheta < \frac{1}{4}\pi$. Observing that

$$\Gamma(n+\tfrac{1}{2}) = \frac{1}{4^n} \frac{(2n)!}{n!} \sqrt{\pi}$$

and taking account of (8.13–26), we finally have

$$\operatorname{erf} s \sim 1-\frac{1}{\pi}\frac{e^{-s^2}}{s}\sum_{\nu=0}^{\infty}(-1)^{\nu}\Gamma(\nu+\tfrac{1}{2})s^{-2\nu}, \tag{8.13–30}$$

where $|\arg s| \leqq \vartheta < \frac{3}{4}\pi$. It is easy to deduce (8.13–28) from this result.

8.13.6 – Fresnel's integrals

In Fresnel's theory of diffraction of light-waves the integrals

$$\mathrm{C}(s) = \int_0^s \cos \tfrac{1}{2}\pi u^2\, du, \qquad \mathrm{S}(s) = \int_0^s \sin \tfrac{1}{2}\pi u^2\, du \tag{8.13–31}$$

play an important part. They represent functions which are holomorphic throughout the entire s-plane.

It is interesting to note that they can be expressed in terms of the Gaussian error function. In fact, we have

$$\mathrm{C}(s)-i\mathrm{S}(s) = \int_0^s e^{-\frac{1}{2}\pi i u^2}\, du = \int_0^s e^{-(u\sqrt{\frac{1}{2}\pi i})^2}\, du = \frac{2}{\sqrt{2\pi i}}\int_0^{s\sqrt{\frac{1}{2}\pi i}} e^{-t^2}\, dt$$

and so

$$\mathrm{C}(s)-i\mathrm{S}(s) = \frac{1}{\sqrt{2i}}\operatorname{erf} s\sqrt{\tfrac{1}{2}\pi i}.$$

A similar expression is obtained by replacing i by $-i$. Combining these results we get

$$\mathrm{C}(s) = \frac{1}{2}\frac{1}{\sqrt{-2i}}\operatorname{erf} s\sqrt{-\tfrac{1}{2}\pi i}+\frac{1}{2}\frac{1}{\sqrt{2i}}\operatorname{erf} s\sqrt{\tfrac{1}{2}\pi i} \tag{8.13–32}$$

and

$$\mathrm{S}(s) = \frac{1}{2i}\frac{1}{\sqrt{-2i}}\operatorname{erf} s\sqrt{-\tfrac{1}{2}\pi i}-\frac{1}{2i}\frac{1}{\sqrt{2i}}\operatorname{erf} s\sqrt{\tfrac{1}{2}\pi i}. \tag{8.13–33}$$

In these equations it is to be understood that $\arg\sqrt{i} = \frac{1}{4}\pi$ and $\arg\sqrt{-i} = -\frac{1}{4}\pi$. It is now an easy matter to derive asymptotic expansions for the Fresnel integrals.

For large positive values of s the function $\operatorname{erf} s$ behaves like $1-e^{-s^2}/s\sqrt{\pi}$. Hence the function $\mathrm{C}(s)$ behaves like $\frac{1}{2}+\sin\frac{1}{2}\pi s^2/\pi s$ and the function $\mathrm{S}(s)$ behaves like $\frac{1}{2}-\cos\frac{1}{2}\pi s^2/\pi s$.

Finally we wish to remark that the curve represented parametrically by

$$x(s) = \sqrt{\pi}\,\mathrm{C}\left(\frac{s}{\sqrt{\pi}}\right), \qquad y(s) = \sqrt{\pi}\,\mathrm{S}\left(\frac{s}{\sqrt{\pi}}\right) \tag{8.13–34}$$

is Cornu's spiral which we considered at the end of section 3.6.13.

8.14 – The method of steepest descents

8.14.1 – Description of the method

The method of steepest descents has been invented by Debye to evaluate approximatively integrals of the type

$$\int_C e^{sf(\zeta)} g(\zeta) d\zeta \tag{8.14–1}$$

for large positive values of the parameter s. The same method can also be used to obtain asymptotic expansions.

The functions $f(z)$ and $g(z)$ are assumed to be holomorphic throughout a certain region; the path C is within this region.

It is plain that the integral (8.14–1) is large when the real part of $f(z)$ is large. Hence the integral will be largest when the path C passes through regions where $\operatorname{Re} f(z)$ is large. There will be advantage in choosing the path so that the largest values of $\operatorname{Re} f(z)$ are concentrated in the shortest possible arc on it.

As we know from section 2.14.1 the function $u(x, y) = \operatorname{Re} f(z)$ can never have an absolute maximum inside a region. But we may look at the stationary points, i.e., the points z_0 where $f'(z_0) = 0$, i.e.,

$$u_x(x_0, y_0) = 0, \qquad u_y(x_0, y_0) = 0.$$

In a 3-dimensional space in which the (x, y)-plane is embedded as a horizontal plane we can consider the set of points whose height above this plane is given by $u(x, y)$. These points constitute a surface and the points where $u_x = u_y = 0$ are the so-called *saddle-points*.

We make the additional assumption that at a saddle-point $f''(z)$ is different from zero. We can show that through any saddle-point it will be possible to draw two curves such that $u(x, y)$ is constant along them. In sectors between these curves $u(x, y)$ will be alternatively greater and less than at the saddle-point itself. In fact, in a sufficiently small neighbourhood of a saddle-point we have

$$\begin{aligned} u(x,y) = {} & u(x_0, y_0) + (x-x_0)^2 u_{xx}(x_0, y_0) + \\ & + 2(x-x_0)(y-y_0) u_{xy}(x_0, y_0) + (y-y_0)^2 u_{yy}(x_0, y_0) + \ldots \end{aligned} \tag{8.14–2}$$

The curve $u(x, y) = u(x_0, y_0)$ presents an ordinary double-point at $z = z_0$, for, taking account of (1.4–1),

$$u_{xy}^2 - u_{xx} u_{yy} = u_{xy}^2 + u_{xx}^2 > 0. \tag{8.14–3}$$

Hence two branches of this curve pass through (x_0, y_0). Moreover, for sufficiently small values of $|x-x_0|$ and $|y-y_0|$ the sign of $u(x, y) - u(x_0, y_0)$ is determined by the quadratic form on the right of (8.14–2) and because of (8.14–3) it takes positive as well as negative values. The sectors where $u(x, y)$ is greater than $u(x_0, y_0)$ might be called "hills", two others "valleys", (fig. 8.14–1).

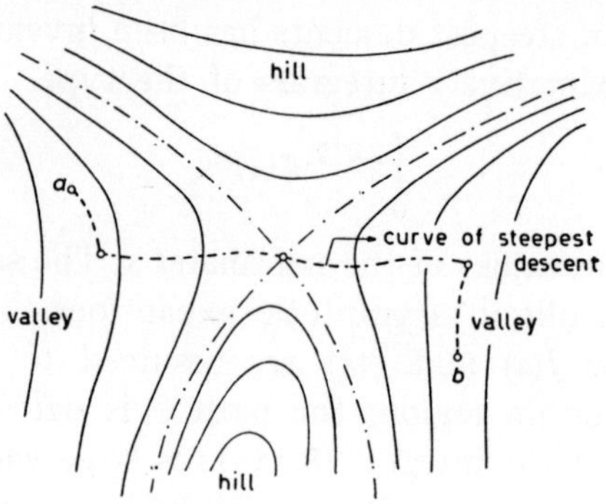

Fig. 8.14–1. Saddle-point

If we wish to keep large values of $u(x, y)$ in as short a stretch of the path as possible we must avoid the hills and keep as far as possible the valleys. If the end-points of C lie in the same valley the path must never go outside this valley; but if they are in different valleys the path must be deformed into a path that goes through a saddle-point. In the latter case the integral will be much greater than in the former and, therefore, most interest attaches to the case where the end-points are in different valleys.

It will be convenient to replace C by another path which is a *curve of steepest descent*, without affecting seriously the value of the integral. Let us consider a curve on the surface under consideration, the curve being referred to a parameter p. The height of a point of this curve above the (x, y)-plane is $u\{x(p), y(p)\}$ and its slope is measured by

$$\frac{d}{dp} u\{x(p), y(p)\} = u_x \frac{dx}{dp} + u_y \frac{dy}{dp}. \qquad (8.14\text{–}4)$$

If, in particular, p denotes the arc length along the projection of the curve upon the (x, y) plane, we may write

$$\cos\theta = \frac{dx}{dp}, \qquad \sin\theta = \frac{dy}{dp}.$$

Hence the slope (8.14–4) is equal to

$$u_x \cos\theta + u_y \sin\theta.$$

This is numerically maximal for variations of θ, provided that

$$-u_x \sin\theta + u_y \cos\theta = -v_y \sin\theta - v_x \cos\theta = -\frac{dv}{dp} = 0,$$

where $v = \operatorname{Im} f(z)$. We have taken account of the Cauchy-Riemann equations (1.3–7). Hence v is constant along the path, this path being of steepest descent. There will be one in each valley. In general the end-points of the path of integration C are not on curves of steepest descent, but can be joined to them by curves within the valleys.

Along a line of steepest descent we have

$$f(z) = f(z_0) - t \tag{8.14–5}$$

z_0 being a saddle-point and t a positive real number. Introducing t as a parameter along the curve we may approximate the integral (8.14–1) by a Laplace-integral

$$\int_a^b e^{-st} g\{z(t)\} \frac{dz}{dt}\, dt. \tag{8.14–6}$$

Under suitable conditions we may find an asymptotic expansion approximating the given integral (8.14–1) for large values of s.

8.14.2 – Asymptotic expansion of the gamma function

In general the method of steepest descents is a tedious one and so elementary illustrative examples are rather scarce. Fortunately the gamma function affords an example which is very well suited for our purpose.

Assuming s real and positive we have

$$\Gamma(s) = \frac{1}{s}\Gamma(s+1) = \frac{1}{s}\int_0^\infty e^{-x} x^s\, dx = s^s \int_0^\infty e^{-xs} x^s\, dx$$

or

$$\Gamma(s) = s^s \int_0^\infty e^{(-x+\log x)s}\, dx, \tag{8.14–7}$$

this result holding also for complex values of s. Thus we transformed the integral for the gamma-function into the form (8.14–1).

It is apparent that $x = 1$ is a saddle-point and in this case the path of integration is already a curve of steepest descent. In fact, $f(z) = -z + \log z$ is real for real positive values of z.

The points $x > 1$ and $0 < x < 1$ are in different valleys. Now $f(x)$ increases steadily from $-\infty$ to 0 as x increases from 0 to 1 and then decreases steadily from 0 to $-\infty$ as x increases from 1 to $+\infty$. It is therefore natural to consider the parts of the integral taken from 0 to 1 and from 1 to ∞ separately.

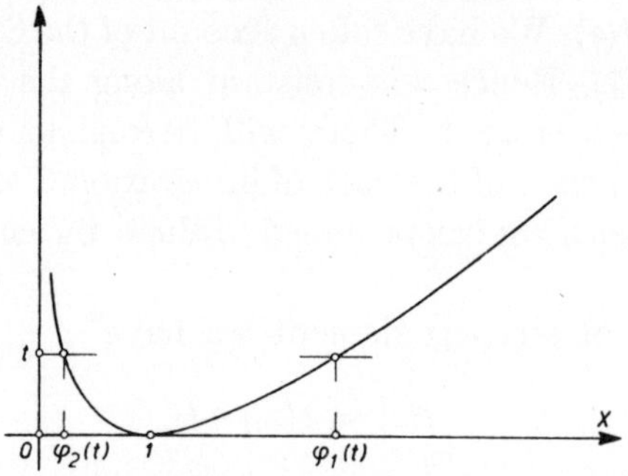

Fig. 8.14–2. Graph of the function $x-1-\log x$

In accordance with (8.14–5) we put

$$t = x-1 - \log x. \qquad (8.14\text{–}8)$$

This equation for x admits of two real solutions $\varphi_1(t)$ and $\varphi_2(t)$ provided that t is positive, the first being > 1 and the second between 0 and 1, (fig. 8.14–2).

Writing $\int_0^\infty = \int_0^1 + \int_1^\infty$ and performing the substitution $x = \varphi_2(t)$, $x = \varphi_1(t)$ respectively, we readily find

$$\Gamma(s) = s^s e^{-s} \int_0^\infty e^{-st} \left(\frac{d\varphi_1}{dt} - \frac{d\varphi_2}{dt}\right) dt. \qquad (8.14\text{–}9)$$

Our next aim will be to derive an asymptotic expansion of the integral on the right. First we observe that $x = 1$ is a zero of order 2 of the function on the right of (8.14–8). Hence there are two branches in a neighbourhood of $t = 0$ which can according to section 3.12.5 be expressed as power series in terms of $t^{1/2}$.

In order to facilitate the computation we put $\frac{1}{2}\tau^2 = t$ and so we have to seek a power series in terms of τ satisfying the equation

$$\tfrac{1}{2}\tau^2 = x-1 - \log x. \qquad (8.14\text{–}10)$$

There are various methods to solve an equation of this kind. Often the Lagrange series considered in section 3.13.3 can be applied. But in general it is difficult to get many terms of the series which represents a solution.

In our example a simple trick will make things quite easy. Differentiation of both members of (8.14–10) with regard to τ yields

$$\tau = \frac{dx}{d\tau}\left(1 - \frac{1}{x}\right)$$

and so

$$x\tau = \frac{dx}{d\tau}(x-1). \tag{8.14–11}$$

Now we put

$$x = 1+a_1\tau+a_2\tau^2+\ldots$$

and we easily deduce the following recursive relations for the coefficients

$$a_1^2 = 1, \quad ka_1a_k+(k-1)a_2a_{k-1}+\ldots+a_ka_1 = a_{k-1}, \quad k = 2, 3, \ldots. \tag{8.14–12}$$

Starting from $a_1 = 1$ we can successively find as much coefficients as we want. The solutions of (8.14–8) are evidently

$$\varphi_1(t) = 1+a_1(2t)^{\frac{1}{2}}+a_2(2t)+a_3(2t)^{3/2}+\ldots$$

and

$$\varphi_2(t) = 1-a_1(2t)^{\frac{1}{2}}+a_2(2t)-a_3(2t)^{3/2}+\ldots$$

whence

$$\varphi_1(t)-\varphi_2(t) = \sum_{\nu=0}^{\infty} 2a_{2\nu+1}(2t)^{\frac{1}{2}(2\nu+1)}$$

and so

$$\frac{d\varphi_1}{dt}-\frac{d\varphi_2}{dt} = \sum_{\nu=0}^{\infty} 2^{\nu}(2\nu+1)\sqrt{2}\,a_{2\nu+1}t^{\frac{1}{2}(2\nu-1)}. \tag{8.14–13}$$

Now we apply the theorem of section 8.13.4. We readily find

$$\Gamma(s) \sim e^{-s}s^{s-\frac{1}{2}}\sqrt{2}\sum_{\nu=0}^{\infty} 2^{\nu}(2\nu+1)\,\Gamma(\nu+\tfrac{1}{2})a_{2\nu+1}s^{-\nu}$$

or

$$\Gamma(s) \sim e^{-s}s^{s-\frac{1}{2}}\sqrt{2\pi}\sum_{\nu=0}^{\infty}(2\nu+1)(2\nu-1)\ldots 3\cdot 1\,a_{2\nu+1}s^{-\nu} \tag{8.14–14}$$

where $a_1 = 1$ and the other coefficients are found from (8.14–12). This expansion is valid in the range $-\pi+\delta \leqq \arg s \leqq \pi-\delta$, δ being any positive number.

To conclude with we shall give the numerical values of the first terms. An easy computation yields

$$a_1 = 1, \quad a_2 = \tfrac{1}{3}, \quad a_3 = \frac{1}{2^2\cdot 3^2}, \quad a_4 = \frac{-1}{2\cdot 3^3\cdot 5}, \quad a_5 = \frac{1}{2^5\cdot 3^3\cdot 5},$$

$$a_6 = \frac{1}{2\cdot 3^5\cdot 5\cdot 7}, \quad a_7 = \frac{-139}{2^7\cdot 3^5\cdot 5^2\cdot 7},$$

$$a_8 = \frac{1}{2^3\cdot 3^6\cdot 5\cdot 7}, \quad a_9 = \frac{-571}{2^{11}\cdot 3^8\cdot 5^2\cdot 7}, \text{ etc.}$$

Hence

$$\boxed{\Gamma(s)\sim e^{-s}s^{s-\frac{1}{2}}\sqrt{2\pi}\left(1+\frac{1}{12}s^{-1}+\frac{1}{288}s^{-2}-\frac{139}{51840}s^{-3}-\frac{571}{2488320}s^{-4}+\ldots\right).} \tag{8.14–15}$$

INDEX

Abel,
  method of summation by parts of —, 25
  — sum, 28
  theorem of —, 25
abscissa,
  — of absolute convergence, 351, 392
  — of simple convergence, 353, 393
absolutely convergent, 18, 176, 351
accumulation point, 7
addition theorem,
  — of the jacobian functions, 296
  — of the pe function, 249
  — of the zeta function, 252
algebraic form of complex number, 1
amplitude, 286
a-point of a function, 340
Appell's function, 364
arc, smooth —, 41
argument, of a complex number, 2
  principal —, 2
  — principle, 155
associate periodic functions, 451
associated, 231
A-summability, 27

Bernoulli's numbers, 87
Bernoullian polynomials, 449
Bessel's function, 174
Binet,
  — 's first representation, 216
  — 's function, 212
  — 's second representation, 217
binomial series, 83
bisection formula of the pe function, 259
Borel-Caratheodory theorem, 335
Borel polygon, 427
Borel's theorem, 330, 341
Borel sum, 425
boundary point, 9
bounded set, 9
branch, 36
Brouncker, series of —, 82
Bürmann's series, 163

Cahen's theorem, 354
canonical product, 186
Casorati-Weierstrass theorem, 114
Cauchy,
  — Hadamard theorem, 21
  — Liouville theorem, 72
  — 's inequality, 89
  — 's integral formula, 64
  — 's integral theorem, 58
  series of —, 81
  — 's theorem about the integral of the logarithmic derivative, 146
  — 's theorem of residues, 122
  — principal value, 127
chain, 41
  closed —, 41
  homologous —s, 43
chordal distance, 6
closure, 9
circle of convergence, 19
circles, Jensen —, 150
circular function, 31
circumference of convergence, 19
cluster point, 119
coefficients, Euler-Fourier —, 108
complementary,
  formula of —, arguments, 191
  — modulus *k*, 283, 292
complex,
  algebraic form of a — number, 1
  conjugate —, 2
  extended — plane, 3
  — plane, 1
  polar form of a — number, 1
  — sphere, 3
conformal mapping, 5
congruent points, 238
conjugate function, 13
connected set, 9
connectivity of a region, 45
constant, Euler —, 189
continuous, function, 7
  chordally —, 7
  uniformly —, 9
contour, 10
  regular —, 42
convergence, 19
  abscis of absolute —, 351, 392
  abscis of simple —, 353,393
  circle of —, 19
  circumference of —, 19
  exponent of —, 308
  radius of —, 19
  region of —, 19
convergent,
  — sequence of functions, 15
  uniformly —, 15, 17, 178

— series, 16
absolutely —, 18, 176, 351
— infinite product, 175
conversion factor, 264
— formulas of the theta functions, 264
Cornu's spiral, 139
cosine,
principal inverse —, 39
principal inverse hyperbolic —, 40
covering theorem, 9
curve,
closed regular —, 42
continuous —, 10
Jordan —, 10
piecewise smooth —, 41
regular —, 41
cycle, 41

Darboux, theorem of, 54
decomposition,
— into partial fractions, 120
— of meromorphic functions, 217
Prym's —, 201
degree, exponential —, 312
derivative,
— of holomorphic function, 10, 12
logarithmic —, 145
diagram, Lindelöf-Phragmén —, 349
differentiable, 10
digamma function, 204
Dirichlet series,
general —, 350
ordinary —, 350
discontinuous factor, theorem of the —, 129
discriminant of pe function, 248
distance, 41
chordal —, 6
divergent,
— infinite product, 175
— sequence of functions, 15
double-periodicity of pe function, 228
duplication formula,
— of Legendre, 193
— of pe function, 250
— of sigma function, 257

elliptic
— function, 239
— integral, 241, 286
— of Jacobi
—s of Weierstrass, 241
equation,
functional —, 35, 190
functional — of the zeta function, 366
Kepler's —, 167
essential singularity, 114

Euler,
— constant, 189
formulas of —, 30, 193
—'s formula for the logarithm, 98
— Fourier coefficients, 108
— integral of the second kind, 133, 195
— integral of the first kind, 135, 204,
— numbers, 86
excentric anomaly, 167
exceptional, 340
expansion, Laurent's —, 204
exponent of convergence, 308
exponential,
— degree, 312
— function, 29
extended complex plane, 3
exterior region, 10

function,
Appell's —, 364
Binet's —, 212
Bessel's —, 174
chordally continuous —, 7
circular —, 31
conjugate —, 13
continuous —, 7
derivative —, 12
digamma —, 204
doubly-periodic —, 237
elliptic —, 239
entire, see integral, p.24
exponential —, 29
gamma —, 188
generalized zeta —, 364
harmonic —, 13
holomorphic —, 12
hyperbolic —, 31
integral —, 24
inverse —, 159
Lindelöf-Phragmén —, 348
locally bounded —, 61
meromorphic —, 120
Mittag-Leffler's —, 345
multiply valued —, 36
pe — of Weierstrass, 228
psi —, 204
rational —, 120
regular —, 112
sigma — of Weierstrass, 230
simply periodic —, 236
theta —, 109
theta — of Jacobi, 263
zeta — of Riemann, 350
zeta — of Weierstrass, 228
Factorization of an integral function, 181
Fagnano,
—'s point, 302

—'s theorem, 302
field, 239
finite order, 318
formula,
  bisection — of the pe function, 259
  Cauchy's —, 64
  conversion —s of the theta functions, 264
  duplication — of Legendre, 193
  duplication — of the pe function, 250
  duplication — of the sigma function, 257
  — of the fourth powers, 270
  Euler's—,s 30, 193
  Gauss's —, 190
  — of complementary arguments, 191
  — of Schwarz, 79
  Gauss's multiplication —, 194
  Jensen's —, 152
  Mittag-Leffler's —, 224
  Poisson's integral —, 79
  Poisson-Jensen —, 154
  Poisson's summation —, 109
  Rodrigues's —, 173
  Wallis's —, 187
Fourier series, 107
fundamental,
  — identity of circular functions, 31
  — period-parallelogram, 238
  — set of poles, 240
  — theorem of algebra, 62, 72, 155
functional equation,
  — of a theta function, 109
  — of the exponential function, 30
  — of the logarithm, 35, 190
  — of the zeta function, 366

Gamma function, 188
Gauss,
  —'s formula, 190
  —'s multiplication formula, 194
  —'s sum, 139
genus, 312
  infinite —, 312
general Dirichlet series, 350
generalized zeta function, 364
Goursat's lemma 57
Gudermann's series, 215

Hadamard,
  —'s factorization theorem, 333
  —'s first theorem, 330
  —'s second theorem, 332
  —'s three circles theorem, 75
Hankel's integral, 202
harmonic function, 13
Heine-Borel theorem, 9
holomorphic function, 12
homologous,
  — chains, 43
  — zero, 43
Hurwitz, theorem of —, 156, 382
hyperbolic function, 31

identity,
  Parceval's —, 90
  — principle, 71
inequality,
  Cauchy's —, 89
  Jordan's —, 125
infinite,
  convergent — product, 175
  divergent — product, 175
  — genus, 312
  — order, 319
  — product, 175
  — series, 16
integral,
  Euler — of the first kind, 135, 204
  Euler — of the second kind, 133, 195
  factorization of an — function, 181
  Hankel's —, 202
  Laplace —, 173
  Legendre's complete elliptic — of the first kind, 283
  Legendre's complete elliptic — of the second kind, 301
  Legendre's elliptic — of the first kind, 286
  Legendre's elliptic — of the second kind 301
  line —, 45
  Raabe's —, 208
  Schläfli's —, 173
  uniformly convergent —, 17
  — function, 24,
  Weierstrass's elliptic, —, 281
integration by parts, 52
interior point, 9
  — region, 10
invariance of a region, 158
invariants of pe function, 247
inverse function, 159
irreducible set of points, 238
isolated,
  — point, 8
  — set, 231
  — singularity, 113, 114

Jacobi,
  elliptic functions of —, 241, 286

imaginary transformation of —, 270
theta functions of —, 263
Jensen,
— circles, 150
—'s formula, 152
—'s series, 206
—'s theorem, 151
Jordan,
— curve, 10
—'s inequality, 125
—'s lemma, 126
—'s theorem, 10

Kepler's equation, 167
klothoids, 139

Lagrange's series, 165
Laguerre,
—'s first theorem, 313
—'s second theorem, 314
Landau's proof of Hadamard's factorization theorem, 337
Laplace,
equation of —, 13
—'s integral, 173
lattice-points, 227
Laurent's series, 105
—'s expension, 104
Legendre,
—'s complete elliptic integral of the first kind, 283
—'s complete elliptic integral of the second kind, 301
—'s elliptic integral of the first kind, 286
—'s elliptic integral of the second kind, 301
—'s polynomials, 168
—'s relation, 252, 304
duplication formula of —, 193
Leibniz's series, 83
lemma,
— of Goursat, 57
Schwarz's —, 98
Jordan's —, 126
length of a regular curve, 54
limes, 20
— inferior, 20
— superior, 20
limit of a sequence (of functions), 15
Lindelöf-Phragmén,
— diagram, 349
— function, 348
line integral, 46
locally bounded function, 61
logarithm, principal —, 36
logarithmic, derivative, 145
Liouville's theorem, 239
Lucas's theorem, 148

mapping of a region, 158
maximum modulus theorem, 74
meromorphic, — function, 120
— part, 120
Mittag-Leffler,
general — problem, 231
—'s formula, 224
—'s function, 345
— sum, 432
modulus, 283, 292
complementary —, 283, 292
of a complex number, 2
monogenity, 11
Morera, theorem of, 69
multiple point, 10
multiplication formula of Gauss, 194
multiplicator, 283
multiply,
— connected region, 44
— valued function, 36

Neighbourhood, 6
normal family of holomorphic functions, 100
numbers,
Bernoulli —, 87
Euler —, 86

Open set, 9
order,
— of a function, 319
— of a sum, 321
— of a zero, 69
— of an elliptic function, 240
— of multiplicity, 114
finite —, 318
infinite —, 319
oriented curve, 41
orthogonality, relation of —, 170

Parseval's identity, 90
path of integration, 48
Pe function,
addition theorem of —, 249
bisection formula of —, 259
duplication formula of —, 250
— of Weierstrass, 228
period-parallelogram, 238
fundamental —, 238
periodic function, 235
periodicity-factor of sigma function, 253

Phragmén's theorem, **342**
Picard's theorem, **24, 339**
Plana's sum formula, **438**
Poincaré's first theorem, **316**
—'s second theorem, **317**
point, Fagnano's —, 302
Poisson,
—'s integral formula, 79
—'s summation formula, **109**
— Jensen formula, 154
polar form of complex number, **1**
pole, 114
polynomial, Legendre's —, **168**
power,
— series, 17
— with variable exponent, **37**
— with variable basis, **37**
formula of fourth —s, **270**
preliminary addition theorems, **297**
primary factors of Weierstrass, **181**
primitive period. 236
principal,
argument, 2
— inverse cosine, 38
— inverse sine, 39
— inverse tangent, 39
— inverse hyperbolic cosine, 40
— inverse hyperbolic sine, 40
— inverse hyperbolic tangent, 40
— logarithm, 36
— region, 8
Cauchy's — value, 127
product,
canonical —, 186
infinite —, 175
Prym's decomposition, 201
psi function, 204

Quasi-periodicity, 251
Quotients, sigma —, 257

Raabe's integral, 208
radius of convergence, 19
rank, 186
rational function, 120
region, 9
exterior —, 10
— of convergence, 19
interior —, 10
invariance of a —, 158
mapping of a region, 158
multiply connected —, 44
simply connected —, 44
regular,
— contour, 42
— curve, 41
— function, 112
— point, 112
relation,
— of orthogonality, 170
Legendre's —, 252, **304**
removable singularity, **66**
representation, **66**
Binet's first —, **216**
Binet's second —, **217**
residue, 116
Riemann,
theorem of —, **65**
zeta function of —, **350**
Rodrigues's formula, **173**
Rouché's theorem, **155**

Schläfli's integral, **173**
Schwarz,
—'s formula, 79
—'s lemma, 98
sequence of functions, **16**
series,
— of Brouncker, 82
— of Cauchy, 81
— of Fourier, 107
— of functions, 16
— of Laurent, 105
— of Leibniz, 83
— of Taylor, 81
Bürmann's —, **163**
general Dirichlet —, **350**
Gudermann —, **215**
Jensen's —, 206
Lagrange's —, **165**
ordinary Dirichlet —, **350**
power —, 17
Teixeira's —, **164**
set,
bounded —, 9
connected —, 9
fundamental — of poles, 240
irreducible — of points, 238
isolated —, 231
open —, 9
sigma,
— functions of Weierstrass, 230, 252
duplication formula of — function, 257
— quotients, 257
simply connected region, 44
sine,
principal inverse —, 39
principal inverse hyperbolic —, 40
singularity,
essential —, 114
isolated —, 113
smooth arc, 41